CARDIOVASCULAR DYNAMICS

ROBERT F. RUSHMER, M.D.

PROFESSOR OF PHYSIOLOGY AND BIOPHYSICS,
UNIVERSITY OF WASHINGTON MEDICAL SCHOOL

SECOND EDITION, *Illustrated*

W. B. SAUNDERS COMPANY

PHILADELPHIA AND LONDON   1961

THIS BOOK IS DEDICATED TO

DIXIE, DON, ANN AND BETSY

They also served

Preface

CARDIOVASCULAR DYNAMICS is an extensive revision, enlargement and reorganization of a book originally published under the title Cardiac Diagnosis: A Physiologic Approach. The components of the cardiovascular system are presented in terms of their structure, function and control under normal conditions, followed by consideration of the changes induced by common disease states. This text was designed for students of the cardiovascular system in the broadest sense—from first year medical students to experienced cardiologists. It is specifically intended for use in vertical teaching, i.e., as a supplemental text for courses in Physiology, Physical Diagnosis, and Clinical Cardiology.

Chapters 1 and 2 are devoted to the basic principles of the function of the cardiovascular system, and Chapters 3 and 4 indicate the mechanisms by which the heart and peripheral circulation are controlled. In Section II of Chapter 4 are presented some disease states which affect peripheral blood flow, an arrangement setting a pattern for the remainder of the book. For example, in Chapter 6 discussion of the control of systemic arterial pressure is followed by an exploration of mechanisms responsible for "high blood pressure." The cardiovascular response to arising, discussed in Chapter 7, forms a foundation for orthostatic hypotension and fainting reactions. The normal cardiovascular adaptations to exercise (Chapter 8) are a basis for understanding the limitations in exercise tolerance from various types of heart disease. Consideration of the factors affecting the coronary blood flow and its control introduces the problems of myocardial ischemia in Chapter 9. Comprehension of the function of the heart valves and the production of heart sounds and murmurs (Chapter 10) is fundamental to an appreciation of the effects of valvular disease (Chapter 12). The control of the distribution of the blood and of the total blood volume is used as an unusual introduction to congestive heart failure in Chapter 16. Common methods of cardiovascular diagnosis, including estimation of cardiac output, pressure recording, electrocardiography, auscultation and evaluation of the size and configuration of the heart are presented in Chapters 3, 5, 10, 11 and 13 respectively. By judicious selection, classroom assignments can be restricted to physiology, physical diagnosis or clinical cardiology. The most important forms of cardiovascular disease are included among the examples employed to elucidate the nature of abnormal cardiovascular function. However, the text is not intended as a handbook for the practice of cardiology since it was not considered appropriate to detail all forms of cardiovascular disease.

The illustrations are distinctive in respect to both their nature and their utilization. Important ideas in each chapter

v

have been illustrated in order to facilitate discussion and aid visualization of concepts. The figures are intended to explain ideas rather than offer evidence for arguments. Realism in the schematic drawings has been retained as much as possible to provide visual images of physiologic and pathologic mechanisms in situ rather than abstractions. The legend for each figure is self-explanatory and the illustrations are thus rendered independent of the text. Cross references are made to figures rather than text pages in the belief that it is more efficient to refresh the memory by studying pictures than by re-reading the text.

Graphs and tables have been avoided for two reasons: (a) their interpretation is often difficult and tedious and (b) it seems more important to understand why certain phenomena occur rather than how much specific variables are altered under experimental conditions. Graphs tend to suggest cause-and-effect relations which may not exist. When experimental records are reproduced, a schematic representation of the experimental method is included in most instances.

References have been cited to defend a position or to provide sources of additional information which I feel may interest the reader. By definition, the references cited in classic contributions are likely to be outmoded. For this reason, priority has been given to recent papers because they provide a much more convenient point of departure for further reading. This decision unfortunately results in failure to ascribe due credit to many investigators who have contributed to our fund of knowledge.

At the risk of appearing excessively biased, I have tried to avoid exhaustive presentations of conflicting viewpoints. If a single hypothesis appeared adequate to explain a particular phenomenon, alternative explanations have not necessarily been included. Attention has been directed to many deficiencies in current knowledge which can be corrected only by further investigations.

ROBERT F. RUSHMER, M.D.

Acknowledgements

A BOOK OF THIS SORT represents a small sample of facts and concepts selectively extracted from a vast store of material on the subject. The final content of this manuscript has been greatly influenced by a series of investigations accomplished in association with a closely knit research team representing several fields of interest, including Messrs. Richard M. Ellis and Donald Baker, electronics engineers; John A. Hendron, Jr. and Alden A. Nash, x-ray technicians; Dean Franklin, Robert Moss, Joseph Klink, Nolan Watson, William Schlagel, Raymond Smith and Donald Harding, electronics technicians; Drs. Dean K. Crystal, Clyde Wagner, Allan W. Lobb, Earl Lasher and Bliss L. Finlayson, surgeons; and Wayne Quinton, instrumentation engineer. The ingenuity, persistence and technical competence of this group were indispensable to the successful completion of the studies summarized in this text. The various research projects were supported in part by grants from the National Heart Institute of the National Institutes of Health, United States Public Health Service; the Washington State Heart Association and the American Heart Association; and the Washington State Fund for Biology and Medicine.

I am indebted to a number of colleagues for reviewing and criticizing certain portions of the manuscript, including Drs. T. C. Ruch, Allan C. Young, H. D. Patton, Richard Blandau and Russell Weiser. My close association with Dr. Robert A. Tidwell and other members of the Cardiac Clinics and staff of the Children's Orthopedic Hospital has been invaluable. Dr. Allen M. Scher summarized his recent investigations in Chapter 10. Miss Carol Ann Burns carried the heavy secretarial load and I gratefully acknowledge her interest, cooperation and patience in the preparation of the manuscript. Mrs. Maryeva Terry contributed greatly through her expert editorial revisions and suggestions concerning the planning of the format. I gratefully acknowledge the wholehearted cooperation of the W. B. Saunders Company in the production of the book.

Most of the illustrations from the first edition were designed and executed by the author although many were refined and labeled by Miss Jessie Phillips, Miss Virginia Brooks and Mrs. Mary Jane Owens. The relatively small number of signed drawings is no indication of the extent of their contribution to the illustrations in the book. Seventy-five new illustrations were prepared by Mrs. Helen Halsey from rough sketches. Half-tone drawings of congenital malformations of the heart in Chapter 19 were executed by Miss Phillips for a series of three motion picture films, directed by the author, produced by Mr. Ralph Pearson and sponsored by Dr. and Mrs. Maimon Samuels.

Photographic reproductions were prepared by Mr. John Newby and Mr. Roy Hayashi.

Several of the original illustrations in this book first appeared in articles by the author and his associates in the following journals: *American Journal of Physiology* (Fig. 20, Chapter 1; Fig. 11, Chapter 8); *Circulation* (Figs. 9, 10, 14, Chapter 2; Fig. 1, Chapter 6; Figs. 12, 13, Chapter 8); *Circulation Research* (Fig. 5, Chapter 2; Figs. 7, 14, Chapter 3; Fig. 5, Chapter 6; Figs. 2, 3, Chapter 8); *Handbook of Physiology, Section II, Vol. I* (Figs. 15, 16, Chapter 3; Figs. 10, 11, Chapter 7); *IRE Transactions on Medical Electronics* (Fig. 8, Chapter 4); *Journal of Pediatrics* (Fig. 21, Chapter 14); *Physiological Reviews* (Figs. 6, 7, 10, Chapter 8). I wish to express my appreciation to the publishers of these journals for permission to reproduce the illustrations.

ROBERT F. RUSHMER, M.D.

Contents

Chapter 14. EMBRYOLOGIC DEVELOPMENT AND CONGENITAL MALFORMATIONS OF THE HEART................. 390

Chapter 15. THE CARDIAC RESERVE AND COMPENSATED HEART DISEASE... 435

Chapter 1

PROPERTIES OF THE VASCULAR SYSTEM

The vital processes in living cells involve the utilization of oxygen and metabolic fuels and simultaneous elimination of metabolic waste products. Unicellular organisms such as amoebae live in large expanses of water with which they exchange these substances continuously, primarily by the process of diffusion.

Diffusion is the movement of particles from regions of high concentration into regions of lower concentration. If a drop of dye is placed in a beaker of motionless water, the molecules of dye will gradually disperse until finally they are uniformly distributed throughout the water (Fig. 1A). This dispersion results from the ran-

THE PROCESS OF DIFFUSION

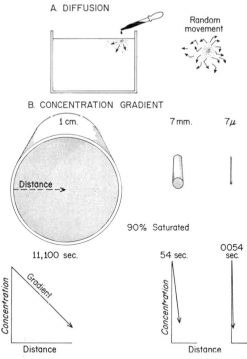

A. DIFFUSION

Random movement

B. CONCENTRATION GRADIENT

1 cm.   7 mm.   7μ

Distance →

90% Saturated

11,100 sec.   54 sec.   0054 sec.

Concentration / Gradient / Distance

Concentration / Distance

FIGURE 1.   *A*, Substances dissolved or suspended in a continuous fluid medium tend to become uniformly dispersed as the particles move from regions of higher concentration to regions of lower concentration by Brownian movement.

B, The rate of diffusion is determined by the steepness of the concentration gradient. In small volumes, as in body cells, diffusion can occur extremely rapidly because the concentration gradients are very steep.

dom movement of molecules (Brownian movement) such that at any moment more molecules are moving away from the source of dye th n are moving toward it. If dye, salt, sugar and urea are placed in four different regions of the water-filled beaker, they will all achieve uniform distribution by movement of each molecular species from the region of its high concentration into regions of its lower concentration.

By random movement, a molecule of water could theoretically pass from a man's head to his toe unassisted by circulation or flow currents, but this would require more than 100 years. The same molecule could cover a distance of 1.5 μ in approximately 0.003 second. In any particular continuous fluid phase the rate at which a substance diffuses depends primarily upon the steepness of the concentration gradient.

A cylinder of tissue 1 cm. in diameter, suddenly placed in an atmosphere of 100 per cent oxygen, would become 90 per cent saturated with oxygen after 11,100 seconds (about three hours). If the diameter of the cylinder were only 0.7 mm., the same degree of saturation would occur in 54 seconds (Fig. 1B). A single cell 7 μ in diameter would be saturated in .0054 second.[1] Note that as the distance of diffusion from the surface to the center of the tissue is reduced the concentration gradient becomes very steep and diffusion occurs very rapidly. In general, a single cell, bathed in an expanse of nutrient fluid, can survive by diffusion alone (Fig. 2A). As the cell utilizes oxygen, its concentration drops in the protoplasm and other molecules of oxygen diffuse toward the cell from regions of higher concentration outside.

In addition, many different types of cells have the ability to engulf particles (phagocytosis) or to imbibe droplets of fluid in the form of vesicles which may move toward the center of the cell. This process of vesicle formation has long been

NUTRITION OF CELLS

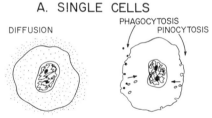

A. SINGLE CELLS

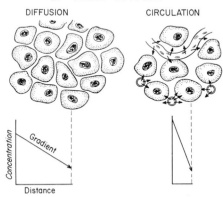

FIGURE 2.   A, Single cells may be nourished by diffusion alone. Many cells display active imbibition of solid particles (phagocytosis) and of droplets of fluid (pinocytosis) by envelopment or vesicle formation.

B, Small cell masses can also be nourished by diffusion alone. The concentration gradients are flattened and transport is slow. In large cell masses, steep concentration gradients are maintained by circulation of nutrient fluids or blood into the immediate vicinity of the individual cells in each tissue.

known to occur in amoebae and has been called pinocytosis, i.e., "drinking" by cells. Infolding of the cell membrane produces a tiny pouch which envelops a droplet of extracellular fluid (Fig. 2A). This process is receiving greatly increased attention since electron micrographs of many different mammalian cells show circular rings which appear to be vesicles. Indeed, this process has been proposed as a mechanism for active transport of materials across the capillary endothelium (see below).

As cells group together to form more complex organisms, the distance of diffusion to the center of the mass increases and the shallow diffusion gradient limits the rate of transfer of various substances (Fig. 2B). Such organisms must either subsist on low levels of metabolism or develop a circulatory system.

In a large complex mass of cells, like the mammalian body, rapid diffusion along steep concentration gradients is achieved by providing a continuous flow of blood in the vicinity of all cells. The streams of blood must be contained within channels which retard diffusion only minimally. These requirements are satisfied by hundreds of millions of thin-walled capillaries distributed profusely throughout every portion of the body. The capillary density (number of capillaries/volume of tissue) reflects the tissue's requirements for blood flow. With the specialization of cells and tissues into complex organisms, blood flow must not only supply metabolic needs but also serve other functions such as dissipation of heat, movement, secretion, absorption and excretion.

In mammalian forms, blood with high concentrations of oxygen and nutritive substances and with low concentrations of carbon dioxide and metabolites is brought into the vicinity of each cell in the body. In skeletal muscle, for example, each capillary serves tissue with a volume only about twelve times its own. Thus, the diffusion distances are very small and the concentration gradients are extremely steep so long as the capillary blood flow is not interrupted (Fig. 3). When capillary flow ceases, the concentration gradients immediately begin to flatten and diffusion slows as the various substances approach uniform dispersion through the fluids. If the utilization of oxygen and metabolic fuels increases, their concentrations in the region of the cells are reduced and the steeper concentration gradients accelerate diffusion. Faster capillary flow is then required to maintain maximally steep diffusion gradients.

Blood pumped by the heart is distributed to the billions of capillaries by a diffuse arborization of the arterial tree with a single artery giving off branches which divide and subdivide to produce a complicated ramification. In the same way, blood leaving the capillaries returns to the heart by way of venous channels which have similar ramifications. The functional properties of the circulatory system reflects this architectural arrangement.

THE SYSTEMIC CIRCULATION

Visualization of the systemic circulation can be simplified by means of a schematic drawing in which all the capillaries are arranged in parallel (Fig. 4), and all arterial branches having the same caliber are arranged one above the other. Similarly, the corresponding branches of the venous system are vertically oriented. In this way it is possible to demonstrate the effects of the branching arterial and venous systems on the pressure and flow of blood in corresponding segments of the circulatory tree.

Volume Flow Through Various Segments of the Circulatory System

The anatomic complexity of the peripheral circulatory distribution tends to obscure some very basic principles which are obvious in a single tube. For example, if fluid flows into the single straight tube at the bottom of Figure 4 at a rate of 5 liters per minute, the same quantity of fluid must flow out of the tube. Similarly, 5 liters must flow past each of the vertical lines (A, B, C, D, E) during each minute. The only possible exception to this rule would result from a shift of fluid from one segment to another. Such a redistribution of fluid would produce transient and relatively insignificant differences in the flow past the various regions of the tube. A schematic representation such as Figure 4 shows the general applicability of this rule in the systemic circulation, namely: the quantity of blood flowing past each vertical line is exactly equal to

DIFFUSION OF SUBSTANCES BETWEEN BLOOD AND TISSUES

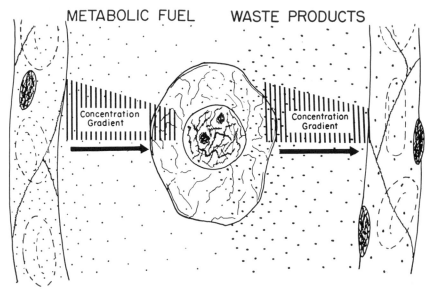

FIGURE 3.   Metabolic fuels and waste products are transferred between the blood and tissue cells by diffusion. The rate of transfer depends upon the concentration gradient for each substance and the distance of diffusion.

VOLUME FLOW THROUGH THE SYSTEMIC CIRCULATION

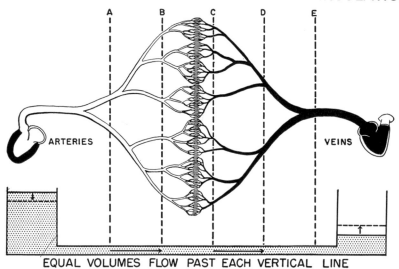

FIGURE 4.   Arborization of the systemic circulatory system is schematically represented with all vessels of the same caliber arranged vertically. This simplified illustration emphasizes the fact that the volume of fluid flowing past each vertical line in a unit time must be equal to the quantity entering and leaving the system, just as in a single tube.

the quantity pumped into the system, and the quantity leaving the system, per unit time except for slight and transient differences due to redistribution of the fluid volumes within the system. It is true that the flow may be greater through one parallel channel than through another, but the total flow through all corresponding segments must be essentially identical. This very simple principle is neglected in many discussions of circulatory dynamics.

Cross-sectional Area of the Circulatory System (Fig. 5)

When an artery or vein bifurcates, the cross-sectional area of its branches exceeds that of the parent vessel. The number of vessels formed by this branching is so great that the estimated cross-sectional area of the capillaries is approximately 625 sq. cm. in a 13 kg. dog with an aortic area of only 0.8 sq. cm.[2] Since the volumes of blood flowing through corresponding segments of the system are equal, changes in cross-sectional area affect the velocity of blood flow.

Velocity of Blood Flow (Fig. 5)

Just as water in a rushing stream slows down when it enters a broad pool, so the velocity of flow is reduced in regions of the

THE RELATION BETWEEN CROSS-SECTIONAL AREA AND THE VELOCITY OF FLOW IN THE SYSTEMIC CIRCULATION

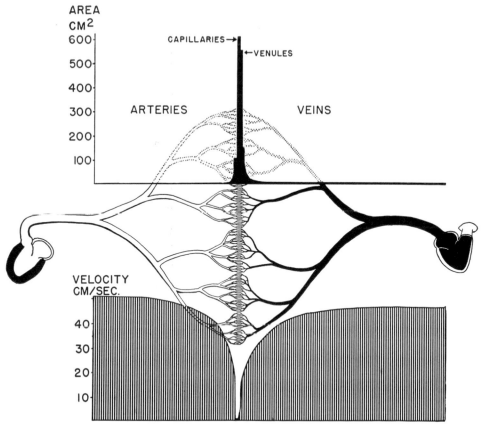

FIGURE 5. Cross-sectional areas of various segments of the systemic circulation computed for a 13 kg. dog. Note the tremendous area in the arterioles, capillaries and venules. The velocity of blood flow is inversely proportional to the cross-sectional area so that blood flows through the capillaries at about 0.07 cm. per second (see reference 2).

FACTORS INFLUENCING THE PRESSURE DROP IN FLUIDS FLOWING THROUGH TUBES (POISEUILLE'S LAW)

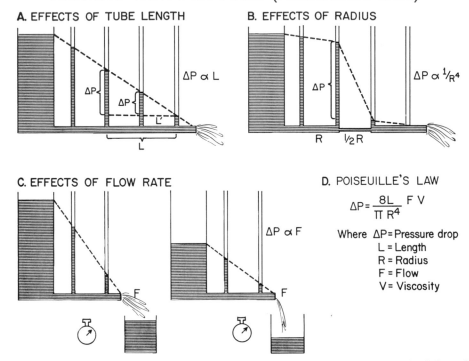

A. EFFECTS OF TUBE LENGTH

$\Delta P \propto L$

B. EFFECTS OF RADIUS

$\Delta P \propto \frac{1}{R^4}$

C. EFFECTS OF FLOW RATE

$\Delta P \propto F$

D. POISEUILLE'S LAW

$$\Delta P = \frac{8L}{\pi R^4} F V$$

Where ΔP = Pressure drop
L = Length
R = Radius
F = Flow
V = Viscosity

FIGURE 6.   *A*, The drop in pressure (ΔP) during laminar flow of a homogeneous fluid through a rigid tube of constant caliber is directly proportional to the length of the tube.

B, Under the same conditions, the pressure drop is also inversely proportional to the reciprocal of the radius to the fourth power ($1/R^4$) and directly proportional to the volume flow (F) through the tube and to the viscosity (V) of the fluid. The relationships between these factors are included in the formula which is an expression of Poiseuille's law.

circulation with large cross-sectional areas. In the aorta, blood travels at a velocity of 40 to 50 cm. per second and in the capillaries it moves at about 0.07 cm. per second.[2] Slow flow in the peripheral capillaries provides time for the exchange of materials across the capillary walls. After passing into the veins, the blood again accelerates as the cross-sectional area progressively decreases. However, the caliber of the veins exceeds that of corresponding arteries, so the velocity of venous blood only approaches and does not equal that of the arterial blood. It is obviously necessary to distinguish between volume flow and velocity of blood flow. The volume flow of blood through a particular tube depends upon the pres-sure gradient, the resistance to flow and the physical characteristics of blood.

Resistance to Blood Flow in the Circulation (Fig. 6

Fluid flows through tubes in response to a gradient in pressure. The progressive reduction in the pressure of fluid passing through a tube of constant bore repre-sents the energy which is lost as heat due to friction, i.e., heat lost in the collisions of the moving molecules composing the fluid. The difference between the pres-sures at the two ends of a tube is a meas-ure of the frictional loss of energy or of the resistance to the flow of fluid. For ex-ample, consider a laminar flow of water through the horizontal tubes in Figure 6.

The pressure gradient is indicated by the height of the columns of water in the vertical tubes. In a tube of constant bore, the pressure drop is directly proportional to the length of the tube. Thus, if the length of the tube is doubled, the magnitude of the pressure drop is also doubled. During passage of a homogeneous fluid through the segment labeled R, the pressure drop is given as 1 cm. of water. During passage through the next segment, where the radius is only $\frac{1}{2} R$, the pressure drop is 16 cm. of water. The frictional resistance, as indicated by the pressure gradient, is proportional to $1/R^4$ (the reciprocal of the fourth power of the radius) so that reducing radius by one-half increases the pressure drop sixteenfold. The pressure drop is also directly proportional to the rate of flow. Finally, the pressure drop along a tube is directly proportional to the viscosity of the fluid. The interrelationships of these factors have been combined in a formula (Fig. 6) which

summarizes Poiseuille's law for streamlined flow of viscous fluids through rigid tubes.

Poiseuille's law cannot be quantitatively applied to the circulatory system for several reasons: (a) Blood vessels are not rigid; they stretch in response to an increase in pressure. Elevated internal pressure may produce an increase in both radius and length. For this reason, the pressure and the dimensions of the tube are not independently variable. (b) Plasma is a truly viscous fluid, but whole blood is not. If plasma is perfused through an ordinary rigid tube, even the smallest differential pressure will produce some flow. On the contrary, when whole blood is perfused through the vascular system of an animal's extremity, no flow is produced until the pressure gradient from arteries to veins reaches 10 mm. Hg (even more in the presence of vasoconstriction). (c) Blood is not a homogeneous fluid since it contains large numbers of cellular ele-

LAMINAR FLOW OF FLUIDS

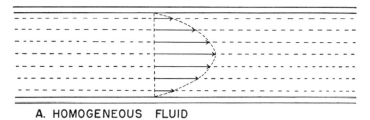

A. HOMOGENEOUS FLUID

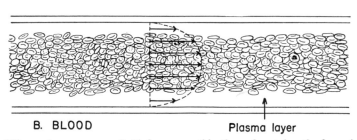

B. BLOOD   Plasma layer

FIGURE 7.   When a homogeneous fluid flows smoothly through a tube, the layer immediately in contact with the wall does not move, while the inner layers flow at progressively faster velocities toward the center of the stream. When the velocity of flow is increased beyond some critical level, turbulence develops. The flow of blood is laminar in most portions of the circulatory tree. The blood cells assemble in the center of the stream and move more or less *en masse.*

ments which affect its flow through the vascular system. In most portions of the circulatory tree the flow is laminar, but the presence of cells slows the flow in the center of the stream (Fig. 7).

Pressure Gradients in the Circulatory Tree

While Poiseuille's law is not entirely applicable to the circulatory system, the factors illustrated in Figure 6 apply in a qualitative sense. As the arterial blood pressure and the length of the vessels tend to remain relatively fixed and the viscosity of the blood has limited variability, the caliber of the vessels unquestionably plays a predominant role in determining

PRESSURES AND VOLUMES OF BLOOD IN THE SYSTEMIC CIRCULATION

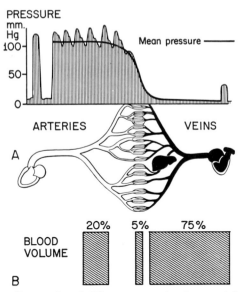

FIGURE 8. *A*, The pressures in the arterial system are elevated and pulsatile. The mean arterial pressure declines very gradually as blood flows through the main branches of the arterial tree. In the small vessels, the pressure head diminishes rapidly and the fluctuations are damped out because of the high resistance to flow. In the major veins, the pressure gradient is again very shallow.

B, The volume of blood in the arteries is relatively fixed at about 20 per cent of the total. The veins contain about 75 per cent of the systemic blood volume but can alter their capacity over a wide range.

both the pressure gradients and the flow through various segments of the circulatory system (Fig. 8). The blood flows through the major arterial trunks with little frictional loss, as indicated by the very slight gradients in the mean arterial pressure. As the arteries divide and subdivide, the caliber of the vessels diminishes and the pressure gradients become correspondingly steeper, particularly in the arterioles and capillaries. Similarly, the confluence of veins is associated with a reduction in resistance as blood flows from the capillaries toward the heart. In the larger veins blood flows briskly in response to very shallow pressure gradients. The marked increase in resistance in the small vessels produces a precipitous fall in pressure which forms a functional line of demarcation between the arterial and the venous portions of the systemic circulation (Fig. 8).

The volumes of blood contained within various segments of the systemic circulation are illustrated at the bottom of Figure 8. At any moment, the capillaries contain only about 5 per cent of the blood, the arterial system holds only about 20 per cent and the remaining 75 per cent of the blood is accommodated by the capacious venous system.

FUNCTIONS OF SYSTEMIC ARTERIES

The systemic arteries serve as a pressure reservoir by means of the elastic properties of the walls (Fig. 9*A*). The contracting left ventricle rapidly ejects blood into the aorta, which becomes distended as the arterial pressure rises. When the ventricle relaxes, the inflow ceases but the wall tension in the arteries continues to drive blood through the peripheral capillaries. The arterial pressure falls progressively until the next ventricular contraction. By this mechanism the systemic arterial pressure fluctuates above and below a mean pressure of about 90 mm. Hg and never falls to zero. The completely intermittent flow into the arteries is converted into a slightly fluctuating but continuous flow through the systemic capillaries.

In addition to its function as a pressure reservoir, the systemic arterial system serves as a series of low resistance conduits (Fig. 9B). In the arteries of the arm, the fluctuations of the arterial pressure obscure the pressure drop required to propel the blood from the axilla to the wrist. However, direct measurements demonstrate that the mean arterial pressure at the wrist is only 2 or 3 mm. Hg lower than that in the axillary artery. Thus, a negligible proportion of the systemic arterial pressure is dissipated in propelling blood out to the peripheral arterial branches.

The pressure in an elastic tube is an expression of the tension exerted by its walls. Increased internal pressure can be attained by four mechanisms: (a) increased distention by accumulation of fluid, (b) active contraction of the walls without a change in contained volume, (c) external compression and (d) the hydrostatic effects of continuous columns of blood.

The pressure-volume relations of *isolated* segments of the arterial system are schematically presented in Figure 10A. If the arteries displayed purely elastic properties, the arterial pressure would be determined solely by the volume of blood contained within them. In other words, so long as the mean arterial pressure remained constant, the mean volume of blood within the arterial system would also be constant. According to the distensibility curve in Figure 10A, pulse pressure should always be greater if the arterial pressure were increased while the stroke volume remained the same. The distensibility of the aorta varies widely in different individuals (Fig. 10B). Further, the pressure-volume relationships in *isolated* arteries may not strictly apply to conditions in the intact animal or man because the caliber of arteries *in situ* may be actively reduced by contraction of the walls in response to an increase in arterial pressure[3] and by topically applied epinephrine.[4]

The actual amount and significance of active constriction of the arteries is not

FUNCTIONS OF SYSTEMIC ARTERIES

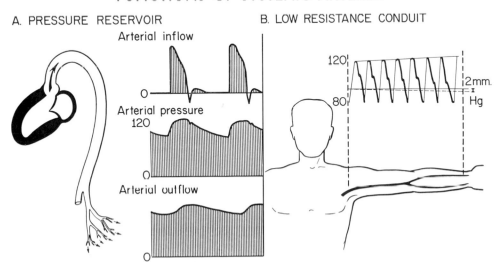

A. PRESSURE RESERVOIR

B. LOW RESISTANCE CONDUIT

FIGURE 9. *A*, The elastic walls of the arterial system serve as a pressure reservoir which converts the intermittent inflow from the ventricle into a fairly constant outflow through the systemic capillaries.

B, The fluctuating systemic arterial pressures tend to obscure the fact that very shallow pressure gradients propel the normal blood flow along the main arterial trunks. For example, the drop in mean arterial pressure from the axilla to the wrist is in the order of 2 to 3 mm. Hg.

PRESSURE-VOLUME RELATIONS IN ISOLATED ARTERIES

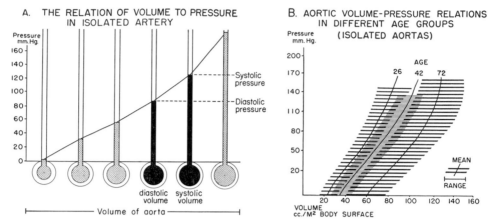

FIGURE 10.   *A,* The relation between volume and pressure in an isolated artery is illustrated sche-matically to emphasize the fact that as long as the distensibility of the wall remains constant, volume should always be the same at a particular pressure level.

B, The pressure-volume relations (distensibility) vary widely in different individuals in the same age group, although the curve tends to shift toward larger volume and less distensibility as subjects grow older. (From Remington *et al.: Amer. J. Physiol.,* 153:298–308, 1948.)

known. The arterial system contains only about 20 per cent of the total blood in the systemic circulation (see Fig. 8). Even if contraction reduced the volume of the arterial system by 30 per cent, only 250 to 300 cc. of blood would be displaced. In general, this system is considered to have a relatively constant volume so long as the arterial pressure remains fixed.

Relatively small increments of volume change in the arteries produce large changes in pressure. For example, the arterial pulse wave at rest represents a large pressure fluctuation induced by the sudden injection of some 80 cc. of blood into the central end of the arterial system. In contrast, a similar quantity of blood leaves the venous system at approximately equivalent rates during each cardiac cycle, but the venous pressure varies only a few millimeters of mercury during each cycle. This fact points up the principal differences between the relatively fixed-capacity arterial pressure reservoir and the variable-capacity, low pressure, ve-nous volume reservoir.

The walls of the large arteries and veins are so thick and tough that their bursting

pressure ranges in the thousands of milli-meters of mercury. Interposed between the arteries and veins lie the capillaries which have exceedingly small diameters and very thin walls. Thin walls and small caliber are required in capillaries for the rapid diffusion of substances between the blood and tissues. The mean internal pressure in arteries is normally about 100 mm. Hg. The delicate capillary walls sup-port pressure amounting to 20 to 30 mm. Hg at heart level and more than 100 mm. Hg in the lower extremities during stand-ing. At first sight, it is difficult to visualize how the fragile capillaries can support such very high internal pressures. The ex-planation lies in the very small caliber of these vessels.

The Relation Between Pressure, Wall Tension and Caliber of Vessels

This relationship is graphically illus-trated by a partially inflated rubber balloon.[5] During inflation, the mid-portion of the balloon expands while the distal portion remains undistended (Fig. 11). The portion of the balloon with a large radius is very tense and resists indentation, indicating that the walls are under high tension. The pressure is equal throughout the inside of the balloon and yet in the undistended region the walls are relatively flaccid and can be easily compressed.[5] This commonplace example illustrates the law of Laplace ($T = P \times R$), which states that the tension in the wall of a hollow cylinder is directly proportional to the product of the tube's radius and the pressure being supported by the wall. Burton,[6] applying this law to the vascular system, pointed out that an aorta with a radius of 1.3 cm. supports a pressure of 100 mm. Hg with a wall tension of 170,000 dynes per centimeter of length (Fig. 11). In contrast, capillaries with a radius of 4μ support a pressure of some 30 mm. Hg with a wall tension of only 16 dynes per centimeter of length. In other words, the pressure in the aorta is about three or four times as great as that in the capillaries while the radius is some

THE RELATION BETWEEN PRESSURE, WALL TENSION AND RADIUS IN HOLLOW ORGANS

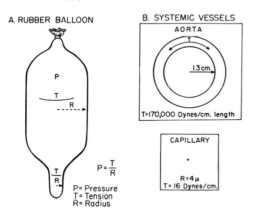

A. RUBBER BALLOON

B. SYSTEMIC VESSELS

AORTA

1.3 cm.

T=170,000 Dynes/cm. length

CAPILLARY

R=4μ
T= 16 Dynes/cm.

$P = \dfrac{T}{R}$

P= Pressure
T= Tension
R= Radius

FIGURE 11.   *A,* In a partially expanded balloon, internal pressure is constant throughout, but the wall tension is very much greater in the distended portion than in the undistended tip because of the difference in radius. As the radius increases, the wall tension must also increase to support a given pressure.

B, Because of the tremendous differences in radius, the wall tension is approximately 10,000 times as great in the aorta as in a capillary, even though they support similar pressures.

three thousand times as great. Therefore, the wall tension in the aorta is about ten thousand times as great as that in the capillaries. The breaking strength of lens paper or Kleenex is over three thousand times as great as the tension in the walls of capillaries at heart level. In tubes of very small caliber, no great strength is required to support a high internal pressure. By the same token, the capillary walls can be very thin so that the distance of diffusion from the central portion of the capillary blood to the outside can be very short. These physical attributes of the capillaries are essential to their function.

THE STRUCTURE AND FUNCTION OF CAPILLARIES

A major portion of the pressure drop between the arteries and veins occurs at the points of controlled resistance at the entrance to the capillary channels (see Fig. 8). In addition, a fairly steep pressure gradient along the capillaries is required to maintain flow because of their small caliber. The velocity of blood flow is less in the capillaries than elsewhere because of their tremendous total cross-sectional area (Fig. 5). For the same reason, the total surface area of capillary walls is very extensive, particularly in relation to the quantity of blood within each capillary vessel and the total volume of the capillary beds, about 5 per cent of the total blood volume. All the blood in the capillaries comes very close to the extravascular tissue spaces, a condition essential for the rapid transfer of substances by diffusion.

Ions and small molecules diffuse across the capillary walls at a surprising rate. Flexner and his associates[7], [8] studied this problem with radioactive tracers and concluded that 60 per cent of the sodium in plasma was exchanged for extravascular sodium in one minute. Similarly, 64 per cent of the chloride in plasma and 140 per cent of the water were calculated to be exchanged each minute.[7]

STRUCTURE AND PERMEABILITY OF CAPILLARIES

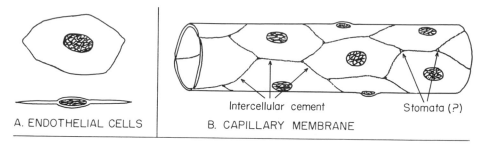

A. ENDOTHELIAL CELLS

Intercellular cement

Stomata (?)

B. CAPILLARY MEMBRANE

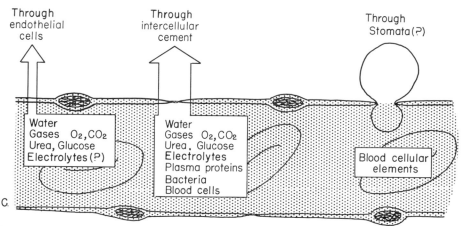

Through endothelial cells

Through intercellular cement

Through Stomata(?)

Water
Gases O_2, CO_2
Urea, Glucose
Electrolytes(?)

Water
Gases O_2, CO_2
Urea, Glucose
Electrolytes
Plasma proteins
Bacteria
Blood cells

Blood cellular elements

C.

FIGURE 12.   Capillaries are formed of endothelial cells joined at their edges by "intercellular cement" to form tubes. It seems likely that water, gases, small organic molecules and possibly certain electrolytes can pass through the endothelial cells. Most of the capillary exchange probably occurs through the intercellular cement (see text). It has been postulated that blood cellular elements pass through orifices between endothelial cells, called stomata.

Using more quantitative techniques, Pappenheimer et al[9] obtained evidence that the amount of water and lipid-insoluble molecules transferred is some two hundred times greater than the values calculated by Flexner and his group. They found that the area of the capillary walls available for diffusion of a molecule the size of water is less than 0.2 per cent of the total wall surface. Ultramicroscopic holes or "pores" in the capillary wall with uniform diameters of 30 Angstrom units (A) account very well for the diffusion rates of fat-insoluble molecules ranging in size from that of sodium chloride to that of hemoglobin. The data could also be explained by a range of pore dimensions

with a mean of 24 A and a standard deviation of 12 A. The total area of the "pores" is so small that they may be localized to the spaces between adjacent endothelial cells. Renkin[10] presented evidence that lipid-soluble substances may diffuse through the capillary endothelium so that capillary exchange of oxygen and carbon dioxide may utilize the entire capillary wall.

The Structure of Capillary Walls

Typical capillaries are generally regarded as thin-walled tubes of endothelial cells. The endothelial cells resemble fried eggs in shape and are only about 1μ thick except at the nucleus (Fig. 12). These flat cells are joined at their edges by a substance called "intercellular cement,"[11] which is visualized as composed of long chain molecules bridging the slit between adjacent cells. Interstices between these molecules are considered responsible for the sieve-like properties of capillary walls and may correspond to the "pores" described above. The endothelial tube is believed to be lined with a layer of colloid adsorbed upon its inner surface. Surrounding the capillary tube is another membrane consisting of cells (pericytes) resembling fibroblasts intermingled with reticular fibers which completely surround the vessel.[11-14] Between the capillary wall and the perivascular membrane is the "perivascular space," which is occupied by a fluid which flows freely within it (Fig. 13). The perivascular membrane forms a line of demarcation between the fluid in the perivascular space and the gelatinous matrix in the interstitial spaces. The so-called "tissue fluid" is largely bound in a gel structure resembling the familiar gelatin desserts. According to Chambers and Zweifach,[11] the presence of a relatively stiff layer of

material against the outer surface of the capillary endothelium is evident when a leukocyte passes outward through the capillary wall. The extruded portion of the cell never moves directly away from the wall, but spreads over the outer surface of the endothelium and remains for some time pressed closely between it and the pericapillary sheath. The cell finally works its way through the interstices of the sheath to move more freely in the less resistant regions of the connective tissue matrix.

The pericapillary sheath appears to give mechanical support to capillaries. Hyaluronidase applied to the frog mesentery abruptly produced microscopic petechial hemorrhages when liquefaction of the gels extended to the capillaries, softening the supporting connective tissue sheath.[11] It has long been recognized that increased "permeability" of capillaries may occur without increased fragility (characterized by the rupture of capillaries with the formation of petechial hemorrhages). It has been suggested that the capillary endothelium is responsible for permeability while the condition of the perivascular membrane determines the degree of capillary fragility.

Although this anatomic relationship has been demonstrated primarily in connective tissues, most of the body capillaries are distributed to the vicinity of the cells by way of the connective tissue stroma of the various organs. Thus, the anatomic relationships illustrated in Figure 13 may obtain widely throughout the body, although this has not been clearly shown. Electron microscopy has demonstrated very distinctive differences in the structure of capillaries in various specialized tissues of the body (see Fig. 17).

Little is known about the functional significance of the endocapillary layer, the perivascular membrane or the interstitial gel, so the postulated mechanisms are generally described in terms of the char-

THE RELATION OF CAPILLARIES TO TISSUE SPACES

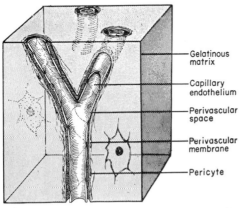

Gelatinous matrix

Capillary endothelium

Perivascular space

Perivascular membrane

Pericyte

FIGURE 13.   In many tissues the capillaries lie within a space containing free fluid (perivascular space), surrounded by another membrane (perivascular membrane) which separates the perivascular fluid from the interstitial gel.

OSMOTIC PRESSURES IN BODY FLUIDS

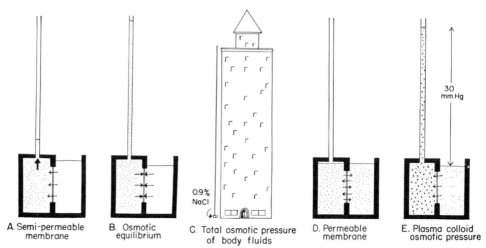

A. Semi-permeable membrane   B. Osmotic equilibrium   C. Total osmotic pressure of body fluids   D. Permeable membrane   E. Plasma colloid osmotic pressure

FIGURE 14.   *A*, When two solutions of different osmotic concentrations are separated by an appropriate semi-permeable membrane, fluid moves from the region of lower concentration through the membrane to dilute the solution with higher concentration.

B, Osmotic equilibrium is reached when the hydrostatic pressure in the vertical fluid column precisely balances the osmotic pressure exerted by the more concentrated solution.

C, The total osmotic pressure of any of the body fluids is about 7.9 atmospheres when equilibrated with pure water. This pressure is equivalent to the vertical column of 0.9 per cent saline solution extending to the top of a 20-story building.

D, If solutions of different osmotic concentration are separated by permeable membranes, no osmotic pressure is present at equilibrium because both the water and solutes diffuse to produce equal osmotic concentrations throughout the fluid phase. For this reason the tremendous potential osmotic pressure of body fluid (*C*) serves merely to maintain osmotic equilibrium throughout the fluid compartments of the body.

E, Since the capillary walls are highly permeable to solutes other than plasma proteins, the osmotic pressure of the plasma is determined by the difference in concentration of the proteins and amounts to only about 25 to 30 mm. Hg.

acteristics of the capillary membrane alone.

Water Balance at the Capillaries

Since water molecules move back and forth so rapidly between blood and tissues and since the pressure inside the capillaries is greater than extravascular pressure, why does water remain in the blood stream rather than pour out into the tissues? The fluid exchange across capillary walls was described by Starling[15] as follows:

In Lecture II, I called your attention to the fact that the non-diffusible constituents of the blood serum, chiefly proteins, were capable of exercising an osmotic pressure or osmotic attraction for water, which amounted to about 4 mm. Hg for every 1 per cent protein in the serum. Blood plasma with 6 to 8 per cent proteins

would therefore exert an osmotic pressure of 25 to 30 mm. Hg as compared with an isotonic salt solution. The importance of these results lies in the fact that, although the osmotic pressure of the proteins of the plasma is so insignificant when contrasted with that of its saline constituents, it is of an order of magnitude comparable to that of the capillary blood pressure [see Figure 14]; and whereas capillary pressure is the chief determining factor in the production of interstitial fluid, the osmotic difference of pressure dependent on the greater concentration of the fluid within as compared with that without the blood vessels might be sufficient to determine absorption. In fact the osmotic attraction of the serum, or plasma, for the extravascular fluid will be proportional to the forces expended in the production of the latter, so that at any given time there may be a balance between the hydrostatic pressure of the blood in the capillaries and the osmotic attraction of the blood for the surrounding fluids. With increased capillary pressure there must be increased transudation. The blood will become more concentrated until equilibrium is established at a somewhat higher point, when there is a more dilute fluid in the tissue spaces and therefore a higher absorbing force to balance the increased capillary pressure. With diminished capillary pressure there will be an osmotic absorption of salt solution from the extravascular fluid; this becomes richer in proteins, and the process will come to an end when the difference between its protein osmotic pressure and that of the intravascular plasma is equal to the diminished capillary pressure.

According to this hypothesis, the filtration or reabsorption of fluid across the capillary walls depends upon the net effect of four interdependent forces: (*a*) capillary pressure, (*b*) tissue pressure, (*c*) osmotic pressure of the plasma and (*d*) osmotic pressure of the tissue fluids. For sake of convenience, the difference between capillary pressure and tissue pressure will be called *effective capillary pressure* or *filtration pressure*. The difference between plasma and tissue osmotic pressure will be termed *effective plasma osmotic pressure*. The maximal effective plasma osmotic pressure ranges around 30 mm. Hg in regions where the capillaries are virtually impermeable to proteins. The average effective capillary pressure is in this

range at heart level. Starling's hypothesis calls for a fairly complete balance of filtration and reabsorption in relatively impermeable capillaries at heart level when the mean capillary pressure approximates effective colloid osmotic pressure (Fig. 15). Under these conditions, no filtrate or lymph would be formed.

Capillary Permeability in Different Regions

The effective plasma osmotic pressure is markedly reduced in capillaries with greater permeability to protein. Judged from the protein concentration of lymph from different regions, capillary permeability is not uniform throughout the body (Fig. 16). For example, lymph actively flowing from skin and connective tissues generally contains less than 1 per cent protein. Lymph from heart, lungs, intestines and kidney usually contains protein in concentrations between 3 and 4 per cent. Liver lymph carries as much as 6 per cent protein when the plasma concentration is only about 7 per cent,

FACTORS DETERMINING FLUID EXCHANGE IN CAPILLARIES

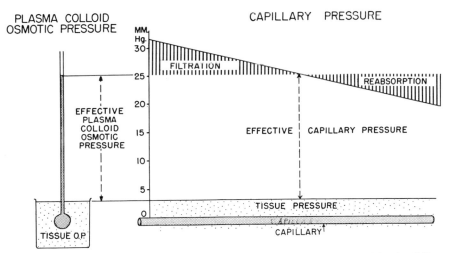

FIGURE 15.   The effective colloid osmotic pressure of the plasma is determined by the difference in protein concentration in tissues and in the plasma. The effective capillary pressure is the difference between capillary pressure and tissue pressure. The pressure gradient in capillaries under a specific set of conditions may produce filtration at the arteriolar end of the capillary and reabsorption in the venular end of the capillary with no net fluid exchange. Such complete fluid balance is the exception rather than the rule.

RELATIVE PERMEABILITY OF CAPILLARIES IN VARIOUS TISSUES

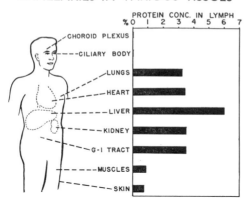

FIGURE 16. Under normal conditions, the choroid plexus, ciliary body and renal glomeruli are essentially impermeable to protein. Capillaries in most of the viscera are relatively permeable, judging from the protein content of lymph. In muscle and skin, the capillaries are but slightly permeable to proteins.

suggesting an effective colloid osmotic pressure of about 4 mm. Hg in the liver sinusoids. In tissues where protein escapes from capillaries in concentrations of 3 per cent or more, lymph flows continuously. However, lymph is not universally accepted as an example of tissue fluid.

Capillary Structure in Various Tissues. The traditional view that capillaries uniformly consist of simple endothelial tubes throughout the body has been exploded by electron microscopy. Consistent differences in capillaries and pericapillary investments in different tissues have been reported by various investigators. For example, the capillaries of the skin (Fig. 17A) are found to consist of endothelial cells joined very firmly at the edges with no evidence of sieve-like intercellular cement[11] or pores of the dimensions computed by Pappenheimer *et al.*[9] The endothelial tube has no obvious perforations and is apparently enclosed completely by a basement membrane.[16] Pericapillary cells enclose the capillary, but the cytoplasm of these cells does not appear to provide a complete investment of the en-

tire capillary surface. Perivascular spaces are not generally observed in fixed normal tissues by either the light or the electron microscope, although they are consistently observed in living connective tissues. Perhaps the perivascular fluid is absorbed completely by the dehydration processes used in the preparation of tissues for microscopic examination.

The capillaries in skeletal muscle and in the heart closely resemble those found in the skin with respect to the structure of the endothelial cells, their attachments and the basement membrane. However, the external investment by pericapillary cells or pericytes is not so consistent.

A great deal of attention has been directed to numerous small vesicles about 200 to 600 Angstrom units (A) in diameter (Fig. 17B) which appear in all endothelial cells. These vesicles tend to be concentrated along the inner and outer endothelial cell borders. The absence of demonstrable "pores" within or between the endothelial cells, coupled with the presence of these vesicles, has led many electron microscopists to adopt the concept that such vesicles form on one surface of an endothelial cell, engulfing a droplet of fluid, and transport this droplet across the cell to be released on the opposite side of the capillary wall.

The concept of active transport of solutions across capillary walls by vesicles (pinocytosis) rests primarily upon the thorough demonstration of phagocytosis and pinocytosis in unicellular animals (see Fig. 2A) and the appearance of vesicular structures in electron micrographs of endothelial cells. Alksne[16] studied the passage of colloidal particles of mercuric sulfide across dermal capillaries; the particles appeared to pass within vesicular structures in the endothelial cytoplasm rather than between the endothelial cells. The validity of this concept and its physiologic significance have not yet been generally accepted pending more conclusive evidence. Capillaries without obvious fenestrations or perforations have been seen in the skin, cardiac muscle, the lung and the central nervous system. Vesicles are even visible in the endothelial cells of capillaries having large perforations through which blood plasma apparently can pass without serious obstruction.

Capillaries in many tissues are reported to have easily visualized openings within or between the processes of the endothelial cells. For example, liver sinusoids contain large intercellular gaps of several thousand Angstrom units in diameter. Apparently these sinusoids can restrain blood cells, but can exert no selective action on the outflow of plasma. Vesicles are prominent in both the endothelial

VARIATIONS IN CAPILLARY STRUCTURE

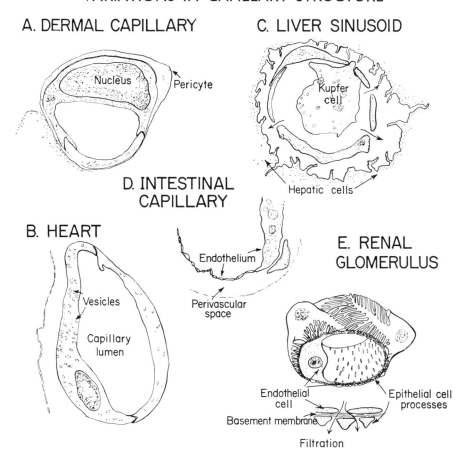

A. DERMAL CAPILLARY

C. LIVER SINUSOID

D. INTESTINAL CAPILLARY

B. HEART

E. RENAL GLOMERULUS

FIGURE 17. Schematic diagrams of electron micrographs indicate the extent to which capillaries display different characteristics in various tissues.

A, Dermal capillaries appear to be formed by endothelial cells joined at their edges without visible spaces between (after Alksne[16]). Such capillaries may be enveloped by pericytes.

B, Capillaries in the heart also consist of continuous membranes of endothelial cells. Capillary endothelial cells characteristically contain large numbers of vesicles which have been implicated by some investigators in active transport of substances across the capillary membrane (Bennett *et al.*[19]).

C, Liver sinusoids are discontinuous membranes with larges spaces between cells through which cellular elements can pass freely (after Hampton[18]).

D, Intestinal capillaries may exhibit very thin regions in endothelial cells which may not be a continuous barrier between the capillary lumen and perivascular space (after Bennett *et al.*[19]).

E, The renal glomerulus is a complex structure composed of endothelial cells, basement membrane and epithelial cells through which filtration occurs (after Yamada[20]).

FACTORS INFLUENCING FLUID BALANCE AT THE CAPILLARIES

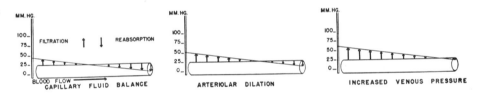

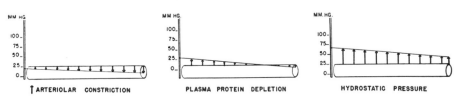

FIGURE 18.   Filtration and reabsorption of fluid are balanced only when the effective plasma osmotic pressure precisely equals the mean effective capillary pressure. Dilatation of arterioles causes a steeper capillary pressure gradient with little change in venous pressure. Increased venous pressure and hydrostatic pressure in dependent parts elevates the pressures along the whole length of the capillary. Plasma protein depletion and increased capillary permeability reduce the tendency for reabsorption and foster excess filtration. Net reabsorption of fluid is aided by arteriolar constriction or by elevating the capillaries above heart level. (From Sodeman, W. A.: Pathologic Physiology: Mechanisms of Disease. Philadelphia, W. B. Saunders Co., 1956.)

cells and Kupffer's cells (Fig. 17C). Thus, the hepatic cells are bathed with blood plasma and the liver lymph has a protein concentration like that of plasma (see Fig. 16).

Endothelial cells in the capillaries of the intestine of the mouse[19] are perforated by numerous fenestrations (300 to 600 A) which are bridged or covered by material like that composing basement membranes (Fig. 17D). This material could serve as a molecular sieve, straining particles and colloids out of the fluids passing through the capillary wall.

Yamada[20] has presented a composite drawing illustrating schematically the structure of glomerular capillaries of the kidney (Fig. 17E). Represented are two epithelial cells with their complex trabeculae and interdigitating pedicles completely investing the capillary. Between these pedicles are narrow filtration slits. The inner surface of the capillary is lined by endothelial cells with numerous fenes-

trations, which are out of register with the filtration slits. A continous layer of basement membrane is sandwiched between the epithelial and endothelial layers. Fluid filtered from the glomerular capillary may pass through the fenestrations as illustrated in the lower diagram. The basement membrane apparently restrains the plasma proteins within the capillary lumen.

A morphologic classification of capillaries based on the presence or absence of endothelial fenestrations, pericapillary investment and basement membranes has been proposed by Bennett et al.,[19] but Luft and Hechter's[21] observations indicate a need for caution in basing morphologic and functional interpretations on electron micrographs of capillaries. When bovine adrenal glands were fixed one or two hours after the death of the animal, the capillary endothelium consistently exhibited fenestrations, but when adrenal glands prepared in a similar fashion were perfused with warm, oxygenated bovine blood for an hour or so, the capillaries were intact—no fenestrations could be seen. Thus, the structure of capillaries may be labile and may change under different conditions including the preparation of material for examination

The filtrates from plasma which pass into the tissue spaces are either reabsorbed into the blood or returned to the circulation by the lymphatic system.

Variations in Capillary Pressure

Most of the confirmatory evidence for Starling's hypothesis has been derived from experiments with capillaries at or near heart levels in small animals.[22] Clearly, filtration is most likely to predominate in regions where marked elevation in capillary pressure is not balanced by a corresponding increase in extravascular pressure.

Since fluid flows from regions of high pressure to regions of lower pressure, the pressure in peripheral veins establishes the minimal capillary pressure in each capillary network. Similarly, the filling pressure of the right ventricle establishes the lower end of the shallow gradient in venous pressure (Fig. 8). Thus, the capillary pressure is affected by changes in either local venous pressure or the diastolic pressure in the right ventricle.

Some factors which affect capillary fluid balance are illustrated schematically in Figure 18. When a man stands up, the long hydrostatic columns of blood tend to produce great increases in capillary pressure without corresponding increases in effective osmotic pressure of the blood. This problem will be considered in Chap. 7.

THE LYMPHATIC SYSTEM

Lymphatic collecting vessels tend to travel in close anatomic relation to the veins and have a similar function, i.e., the return of blood elements from the tissues to the venous reservoirs near the heart (Fig. 19). Further, the lymphatic and venous systems both have superficial and deep distributions. On the surface of the body, the superficial lymphatic collecting vessels usually accompany the superficial veins just beneath the skin. They also lie just beneath the mucous membrane throughout the whole length of the digestive, respiratory and genitourinary tracts. These networks of collecting lymphatics drain lymphatic capillaries abundantly distributed in the submucosa and in the dermis of the skin, forming a continuous network throughout all the internal and external linings of the body except the cornea of the eye.

The *deep* lymphatic vessels intertwine and anastomose around the veins which accompany the deep arteries in their regional distribution to the organs of the body (Fig. 19). Arteries, veins and deep lymphatics tend to share the same sheaths and are distributed to the same tissues and organs.

The lymphatic system has two transport functions: (a) the return of capillary filtrate to the circulation and (b) the removal of foreign particles and exudates from tissue spaces and serous cavities. Since the lymphatic capillary networks are distributed through the interstitial spaces along with the blood capillaries, the terminal vessels of the two systems must lie very near each other (Fig. 19). Most commonly, the lymphatic capillaries are believed to end blindly in interstitial spaces at varying distances from the capillaries of the blood vascular system. There is also evidence that lymphatic capillaries may develop along the perivascular spaces where growth appears to be less impeded. Lymphatic vessels which terminate within the pericapillary spaces are ideally located for the transportation of filtrate from the capillary beds. Lymphatics lying free within the interstitial spaces may remove foreign particles and

THE LYMPHATIC SYSTEM
LYMPHATIC SYSTEM PARALLELS THE VEINS

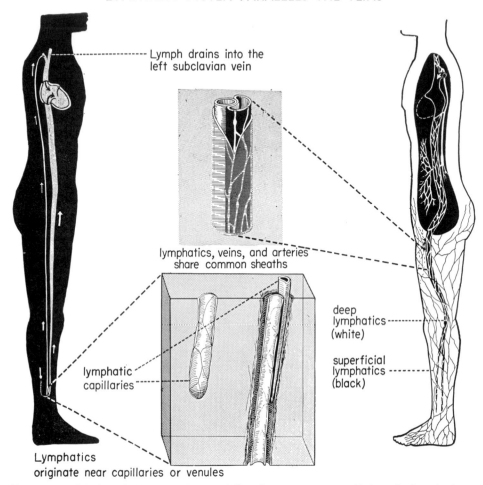

FIGURE 19.   The lymphatic system is essentially a "paravenous system" since the lymphatic capillaries lie in close association with the capillaries and veins of the blood vascular system; the collecting lymphatics tend to accompany veins and arteries and drain into the central veins. Like the veins, the lymphatic system consists of both deep and superficial distributions of vessels and carries constituents of the blood back to the region of the heart.

inflammatory exudates. Under certain conditions, apertures have been observed in lymphatic capillaries surrounded by inflammatory exudate.[23] When the tissues are clear of free fluid the lymphatic capillaries have continuous unbroken endothelial membranes.

There are many gaps in our knowledge of lymphatic function. The forces driving a fluid laden with protein and cellular elements through the continuous wall of a lymphatic capillary have not been clearly elucidated. This problem is most acute in the skin of a dependent extremity where vascular pressures are very high and the tissue pressures very low. The exact mechanisms elevating lymph from dependent extremities to the level of the subclavian vein are not universally agreed upon, although a number of possibilities exist. The lymphatic collecting vessels are intimately associated with the veins and are subject to the same muscular and abdomino-thoracic pumping actions (see Chap. 7). Confined within the same sheath as arteries and veins, the lymphatics would tend to be compressed by changes in the caliber of these vessels. Even the arterial pulse may act as an accessory pump, displacing lymph upward with each wave of distention. Irisawa[24] showed that both leg movements and weight bearing elevate lymphatic pressure propelling the lymph toward the heart (Fig. 20). Finally, there is some evidence that certain lymphatics have independent contractility which theoretically could propel lymph by a peristaltic type of action. The lymphatic pressure in the thoracic duct must exceed the pressure in the subclavian veins into which it empties.

THE VENOUS SYSTEM

The veins not only act as conduits to channel blood from the capillaries to the heart, but they also adjust their total capacity to accommodate variations in total blood volume. The pressure at the point of outflow from a system of tubes establishes the lower end of the pressure gradient which promotes flow through the tubes. The point of outflow from the systemic veins is the right ventricle during each diastole. If the pressure in the right atrium fell below the pressure outside the wall of this vessel, the filling pressure of the right ventricle would be zero. Actually, the pressure within the right atrium and ventricle remains within a narrow range at very low levels in spite of changes in the total blood volume or the distribution of blood in the circulation. For example, the average normal adult can walk into a blood bank, give up 500 cc. of blood and, after a few minutes, walk out again.

The maintenance of a fairly constant right atrial and right ventricular pressure under varying conditions requires adjustments in the capacity of various portions of the venous system. Measurements on *isolated* segments of veins reveal smaller pressure increments with increasing volume than occur in arteries. The greater venous distensibility represents only part of the adaptability of the venous system. The variable capacity of the venous system is also vested in specialized venous reservoirs and in alterations in the caliber of venous channels through venoconstriction.

CHANGES IN LYMPHATIC PRESSURE

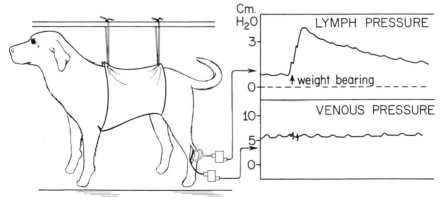

FIGURE 20.   In dogs suspended in a sling, spontaneous leg movements or weight bearing produced changes in lymphatic pressure. This observation suggests that external compression of lymph channels plays an important role in the transport of lymph. (After Irisawa.[24])

THE PRESSURE-VOLUME RELATIONS IN VEINS

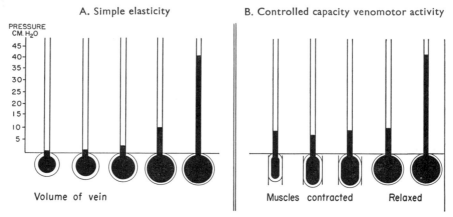

FIGURE 21.   *A,* The relation between the pressure and the volume of isolated veins differs from that of isolated arteries (see Fig. 10). The veins accommodate relatively large volumes of fluid with very slight increase in pressure until the limits of elasticity are approached. With very great distention, the pressure rises to very high levels.

B, By virtue of controlled capacity, the volume of blood contained within veins may be varied without corresponding changes in pressure (see text). The capacity of the venous system can be varied by active contraction of veins and venous reservoirs or by external compression, i.e., through contraction of surrounding skeletal muscle. In this schematic drawing the adaptability in venous capacity is illustrated as though the control resulted solely from external compression.

Reservoirs of Blood

A large portion of the venous vascular bed has variable capacity under neural control. Franklin[25] stated: "In the body, the musculature of the veins controls a large part of the venous system and associated blood depots, and hence the venous return and heart minute volume." By virtue of a sphincter-like action of the hepatic vein near its entrance into the inferior vena cava, the blood content of the liver can be increased or diminished. Evidence has been presented that widespread constriction can occur over the distribution of the hepatic veins.[26] The tremendous enlargement of the liver accompanying right ventricular failure is a striking example of the variable capacity of this organ. At the same time, impedance to outflow from the hepatic veins would also tend to foster accumulation of blood within the capacious splanchnic veins. Further, the mesenteric veins are among the most reactive and muscular in the body and there is evidence that they

can be constricted and relaxed by neural mechanisms to accommodate varying amounts of blood.[25] It has long been recognized that the spleen acts as a depot from which blood may be expressed in times of stress. This function is not well developed in the human spleen since it contains only some 200 to 250 cc. The subpapillary plexus of the skin has a potential role as a blood depot, but this function is intimately related to dissipation of heat. In other words, this blood is rarely released into the general circulation at the expense of temperature regulation. The pulmonary veins are generally believed to have less distensibility than the systemic veins, but very likely play a role in cushioning transient differences in the output of the right and left ventricles. Although measuring the capacity of internal organs is very difficult, there is some evidence that the capacity of the venous channels may also be controlled by "venomotor" activity.[27, 28] Variations in venous "tone" would contribute to adjustment in the capacity of the circulation in response to alteration in blood volume.[29] The fixed pressure-volume relations of isolated veins (Fig. 21*A*) do not apply to the intact circulation. Instead, adaptability in the capacity of veins provides a mechanism by which the volume of the venous system can change within rather wide limits without corresponding changes in venous pressure (Fig. 21*B*). The functional significance of this feature lies in the control of central venous pressure and will be discussed in Chapter 7 and Chapter 16.

PULMONARY CIRCULATION

The systemic and pulmonary vascular beds are connected in series to form a continuous circuit. Although these two vascular systems are superficially similar, the following important differences between them should be kept in mind. (*a*) The systemic circulation is a high-resistance circuit with a large difference in pressure between the arteries and veins, while the pulmonary circuit normally offers very slight resistance to flow. (*b*) The pulmonary vessels supply only one type of tissue (alveolar membranes), so the requirements for vasomotor control are not as great as those in the systemic circulation. (*c*) The volume of blood in the pulmonary system is neither so great nor so variable as that in the systemic circulation. (*d*) Since the lungs immediately enclose the heart, hydrostatic columns are fairly short even from the most distant portions of the pulmonary parenchyma. (*e*) The pulmonary circulation is confined within the thoracic cage, so extravascular conditions are fairly uniform throughout.

Anatomy of the Pulmonary Circulation

The ramifications of the pulmonary arterial system closely parallel the arborization of the bronchial system. The main-stem bronchi give off lateral branches which divide and subdivide like the branches of a tree. At the tip of each

terminal branch is a bronchiole which divides into two respiratory bronchioles. In turn, these divide into two branches, each of which gives off three alveolar ducts. The alveolar ducts are connected through a variable number of atria to a tuft of alveolar sacs (air cells). Gaseous interchange between the air and blood may occur in all divisions beyond the bronchioles.

Structurally, the main pulmonary arteries closely resemble the aorta. The walls of the main arteries and their branches remain essentially the same down to the intrapulmonary branches with outside diameters of about 1 mm., except that the amount of smooth muscle in the wall progressively increases in the smaller branches.[30] Muscular arteries ranging in diameter from 1 to 0.1 mm. have a prominent media of circularly arranged smooth muscle between the internal and external elastic laminae. The walls of arterial branches less than 0.1 mm. in diameter consist essentially of poorly supported endothelial tubes which abruptly break up into a profusely anas-

CAPILLARIES SUPPLYING RESPIRATORY MEMBRANES

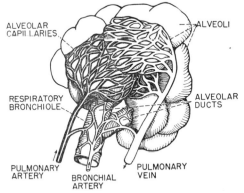

FIGURE 22.   The terminal branches of the pulmonary artery enter directly into widely anastomotic alveolar capillary networks which are not equipped with true muscular arterioles or precapillary sphincters. In the respiratory bronchioles, the pulmonary and bronchial arterial branches serve the same capillary networks. These common capillary beds drain into the pulmonary veins.

PRESSURES IN THE PULMONARY VASCULAR SYSTEM

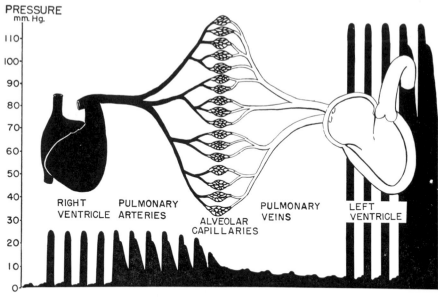

FIGURE 23.   Since the pulmonary arterial system offers slight resistance to blood flow, the pressure difference between pulmonary artery and left atrium amounts to only 4 to 6 mm. Hg. This low-pressure head drives the same volume of blood through the pulmonary circuit as flows through the systemic circulation with a gradient of some 90 mm. Hg.

tomatic capillary network. Thus, the pulmonary circulation does not contain any vessels corresponding to the muscular arterioles in the systemic circulation. The alveolar capillaries are the principal structural element in the walls of the respiratory membranes (Fig. 22). The capillary network is so dense that in many alveoli the space between capillaries is less than their diameter.[31]

Resistance to Blood Flow Through the Pulmonary Circuit

For several reasons the normal intravascular pressures do not fall abruptly in the small vessels of the lung (Fig. 23): (a) There are no high-resistance muscular arterioles in the terminal ramifications of the vascular tree. (b) The pulmonary capillaries are extremely voluminous, diffusely anastomotic and of relatively large caliber. (c) The pulmonary vessels are passively distended in response to increased pulmonary blood flow. (d) There is a large reserve capacity in the lung which

is not fully utilized except under conditions of stress. For example, an entire lung with all its capillary bed can be removed without increasing the pulmonary arterial pressure. (e) Finally, all vessels in the pulmonary vascular tree have a somewhat larger caliber than corresponding vessels in the systemic circulation. The net effect is a total pulmonary resistance to flow only about one-eighth of that in the systemic circulation.

During systole, the right ventricular pressure rises to about 22 mm. Hg. The pulmonary arterial pressures average about 22/8 mm. Hg with a mean arterial pressure of about 13 mm. Hg.[32] The pressure at the point of outflow from the pulmonary circuit (the left ventricular diastolic pressure) is about 7 mm. Hg (Fig. 23). Thus, a pressure gradient of only about 6 mm. Hg will force through the pulmonary circuit the same quantity of blood which passes through the systemic circuit under a gradient of 90 mm. Hg. Furthermore, the pulmonary arterial pressure may remain unchanged or diminish slightly when the cardiac output increases threefold. One case has been described in which a pressure gradient of 4 mm. Hg propelled 15 liters of blood per minute through the pulmonary circuit.[33] The small pressure gradient between the pulmonary artery and the left atrium is the basis for the statement that the pulmonary circuit has an exceedingly slight resistance to flow.

Vasomotor Effects on Pulmonary Resistance. It is generally believed that the changes in pulmonary resistance associated with increased pulmonary blood flow result largely or entirely from passive distention of these vessels.[31, 34] Evidence demonstrating active vasomotor responses in the lungs has been quite unimpressive (see Figs. 13 and 15, Chap. 4). However, pulmonary arterial hypertension is frequently associated with congenital and rheumatic valvular heart disease and may be greatly alleviated by appropriate therapy. Such evidence indicates that active vasoconstriction in the pulmonary arterial system contributes to the increased pulmonary resistance.[35, 36] Inhalation of gases with low oxygen tension produces increased resistance to blood flow. If the low oxygen tension is confined to one lung, blood flow through this region is diminished, diverting blood into the unaffected region.[37-39] If the observation that no arterioles exist in the pulmonary vascular tree is anatomically correct, changes in pulmonary resistance are accomplished by variations in caliber of the arterial branches, which are well supplied with innervated smooth muscle.

Functions of the Pulmonary Circulation

The pulmonary circuit simultaneously performs three functions: (a) gaseous exchange of oxygen and carbon dioxide between the alveolar air and blood, (b) storage of blood in a variable volume reservoir and (c) blockade of foreign particles, thrombi and other types of emboli circulating in the systemic venous blood.

Gas Exchange: The Principal Function of the Lungs. Blood passing through the alveolar capillaries of the lungs is effectively spread into a layer about 10μ thick and 100 sq. m. in area. The alveolar air is separated from the blood by only two layers of tissue, the endothelial cells and a delicate alveolar membrane. Some investigators deny the existence of an alveolar membrane between the endothelial barrier and the alveolar spaces. The oxygen tension is lower and the carbon dioxide tension is greater in blood entering the alveolar capillaries than in the alveolar air. Blood traverses the alveolar capillaries in about 1 second. Propelled by their diffusion gradients, oxygen and carbon dioxide are exchanged so rapidly that blood leaving the alveolar capillaries is normally in virtual equilibrium with the alveolar air (Fig. 24A). The action of carbonic anhydrase in the erythrocytes and rapid dissociation of carbon dioxide from reduced hemoglobin as it is converted to oxyhemoglobin facilitate exchange of carbon dioxide. The gaseous exchange is sufficiently rapid only when the diffusion distances are extremely small. Thus, very thin layers of fluid accumulating between the alveolar air and the blood can seriously retard respiratory exchange.

Oxygen and carbon dioxide cannot be exchanged when the blood flows through collapsed alveoli because it does not come in contact with alveolar air. Thus, blood passing through non-aerated alveoli would retain the character of venous blood. However, resistance to flow increases markedly in atelectatic lung tissue, automatically shunting blood from non-aerated portions into the inflated regions of the lung.

Reservoir Function of the Lungs. Since the pulmonary vessels constitute a low-pressure, distensible system, any slight increase in outflow pressure at the left ventricle or relative increase in input from

FUNCTIONS OF THE LUNGS

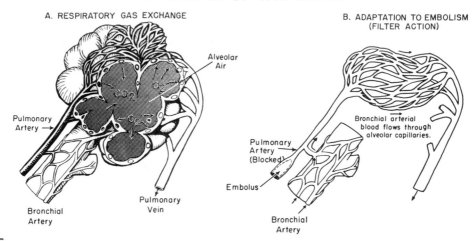

A. RESPIRATORY GAS EXCHANGE

B. ADAPTATION TO EMBOLISM
(FILTER ACTION)

FIGURE 24. *A*, Gas exchange, the principal function of the lungs, occurs because of the higher concentration of oxygen and lower concentration of carbon dioxide in the alveolar air than in the venous blood arriving at the pulmonary capillaries.

B, Embolic obstruction of pulmonary arteries does not produce necrosis of pulmonary parenchyma because bronchial arterial blood is diverted through dilated channels into the alveolar capillaries. Because of this dual blood supply, the lungs can serve as filters for emboli without self-destruction.

the right ventricle will cause considerable quantities of blood to accumulate within the lungs. Presumably, engorgement of the lungs will cause elevated pressure throughout the pulmonary circuit because the pressure gradient is so shallow. However, it seems likely that considerable distention may occur with little elevation in pressure. For example, there is evidence that considerable quantities of blood are displaced into the heart and lungs after reclining.[40, 41] In summarizing such data, Sjöstrand[42] reported that an average of more than 600 ml. of blood was shifted from the lower extremities to the rest of the body after five standing subjects reclined. He concluded that more than half of this volume was accommodated in the lungs.

As much as 25 per cent of the blood in the thorax (heart and lungs) may be shifted to the legs. This reserve volume in the pulmonary circuit appears to be distributed diffusely through the lungs, where it is held "on tap" until drawn from in order to effect the rapid readjustment of the circulation required for larger

cardiac output. Reserve blood in the lungs has been compared with water dammed up behind a sluice gate where it compensates for occasional variations in supply and output. On this basis, the lungs have an important reservoir function. This distensible vascular network may also serve to cushion transient differences in right and left ventricular output, e.g., at the onset of violent exercise.

Filter Action of the Lungs. If foreign bodies, thrombi, air bubbles or fat particles enter the systemic arterial system, they generally occlude a terminal artery within some organ. This reduces or eliminates circulation to the tissues supplied by that arterial branch, and the tissue cells frequently die. If it occurs in a vital organ such as the brain or heart, this is a serious event. Fortunately, most of the emboli enter the blood stream on the venous side of the circulation and lodge in the lungs. By virtue of a double circulation, the pulmonary vascular tree is particularly adapted to filtering out these circulating vascular plugs without self-destruction.

In parallel with the pulmonary arterial system, the bronchial arteries transmit oxygenated blood throughout the walls of the bronchial tree as far peripherally as the bronchioles.[31] Anastomotic connections between pulmonary and bronchial arteries are not believed to occur normally.[43] However, anastomoses of small caliber exist in the walls of the bronchioles and alveolar ducts, where they share common capillary beds (Fig. 24B). The venous drainage from the bronchial arterial system is by way of the pulmonary vein except in the first two or three divisions of the bronchial tree. Obstruction or occlusion of a branch of the pulmonary artery does not affect the blood supply to the bronchial system.[44] Dilatation of channels in the common capillary networks provides a mechanism for diverting oxygenated blood through the alveolar membranes when pulmonary arterial flow is arrested or reduced (Fig. 24B). Thus, lung tissue is rarely destroyed by obstruction of the pulmonary blood supply. The diffuse anastomotic connections between adjacent alveoli provide additional protection against occlusion of small peripheral branches of the pulmonary arterial system. The affected lung tissue survives while the embolus is resorbed or recanalized, after which the tissue resumes its activity. There is every reason to believe that this sequence of events occurs repeatedly during any person's lifetime without producing symptoms unless the embolus is very large or is located in a critical position.

SUMMARY

The systemic circulation consists of three functional divisions, the arterial pressure reservoir, the venous volume reservoir and the capillary networks. The precipitous drop of pressure due to high resistance to flow through the arterioles, capillaries and venules forms the functional region of demarcation between the arterial and venous systems. So long as the pressure difference between arteries and veins remains constant, the blood flow through the capillaries is determined by the resistance to flow through the minute vessels. The quantity of blood flowing per unit time through the arteries, capillaries and veins must be identical except for insignificant differences in flow involved in shifting blood from one region to another. The central arterial and venous pressures tend to remain fixed within relatively narrow ranges regardless of the total amount of blood flowing through the system per unit time (cardiac output). The average volume of blood in the arterial system tends to remain fairly constant so long as the mean arterial blood pressure is unchanged. In contrast, the central venous pressure tends to remain relatively constant in spite of variations in the total quantity and distribution of blood through adjustments in the capacity of venous reservoirs. Cardiovascular response to disease cannot be fully understood without consideration of the mechanisms by which the normal circulatory system adjusts to various conditions including changes in body posture, changes in regional blood flow and cardiac output.

REFERENCES

1. HILL, A. V. The diffusion of oxygen and lactic acid through tissues. *Proc. Roy. Soc.*, B104:39–96, 1928.
2. GREEN, H. D. Circulation: physical principles. Pp. 208–232 in *Medical Physics*, Vol. 1, O. Glasser, Ed. Chicago, Year Book Publishers, 1944.
3. WIGGERS, C. J., and WÉGRIA, R. Active changes in size and distensibility of the aorta during acute hypertension. *Amer. J. Physiol.*, 124:603–611, 1938.
4. HEYMANS, C., and VAN DEN HEUVAL-HEYMANS, G. New aspects of blood pressure regulation. *Circulation*, 4:581–586, 1951.
5. WOLF, A. V. Demonstrations concerning pressure-tension relations in various organs. *Science*, 115:243–244, 1952.
6. BURTON, A. C. On the physical equilibrium of small blood vessels. *Amer. J. Physiol.*, 164:319–329, 1951.
7. COWIE, D. B., FLEXNER, L. B., and WILDE, W. S. Capillary permeability, rate of transcapillary exchange of chloride in the guinea

pig as determined with radiochloride. *Amer. J. Physiol.*, 158:231–236, 1949.

8. FLEXNER, L. B., COWIE, D. B., and VOSBURGH, G. J. Studies on capillary permeability with tracer substances. *Cold Spr. Harb. Symp. Quant. Biol.*, 13:88–98, 1948.

9. PAPPENHEIMER, J. R., RENKIN, E. M., and BORRERO, L. M. Filtration, diffusion and molecular sieving through peripheral capillary membranes. A contribution to the pore theory of capillary permeability. *Amer. J. Physiol.*, 167:13–46, 1951.

10. RENKIN, E. M. Capillary permeability to lipid-soluble molecules. *Amer. J. Physiol.*, 168:538–545, 1952.

11. CHAMBERS, R., and ZWEIFACH, B. W. Intercellular cement and capillary permeability. *Physiol. Rev.*, 27:436–463, 1947.

12. CLARK, E. R., and CLARK, E. L. Observations on living mammalian lymphatic capillaries—their relation to the blood vessels. *Amer. J. Anat.*, 60:253–298, 1937.

13. PFUHL, W. Physiologische Anatomie der Blutkapillaren. *Z. Zellforsch.*, 20:390–416, 1934.

14. ZWEIFACH, B. W. The structure and reactions of the small blood vessels in Amphibia. *Amer. J. Anat.*, 60:473–514, 1937.

15. STARLING, E. H. *The Fluids of the Body.* Chicago, W. T. Keener & Co. 1909, 186 pp.

16. ALKSNE, J. F. The passage of colloidal particles across the dermal capillary wall under the influence of histamine. *Quart. J. Exp. Physiol.*, 44:51–66, 1959.

17. MOORE, D. H., and RUSKA, H. The fine structure of capillaries and small arteries, *J. Biophys. Biochem. Cytol.*, 3:457–462, 1957.

18. HAMPTON, J. C. An electron microscope study of the hepatic uptake and excretion of submicroscopic particles injected into the blood stream and into the bile duct. *Acta anat.*, 32:262–291, 1958.

19. BENNETT, H. S., LUFT, J. H., and HAMPTON, J. C. Morphological classification of vertebrate blood capillaries. *Amer. J. Physiol.*, 196:381–390, 1959.

20. YAMADA, E. The fine structure of the renal glomerulus of the mouse. *J. Biophys. Biochem. Cytol.*, 1:551–566, 1955.

21. LUFT, J., and HECHTER, O. An electron microscopic correlation of structure with function in the isolated perfused cow adrenal, preliminary observations. *J. Biophys. Biochem. Cytol.*, 3:615–620, 1957.

22. LANDIS, E. M. Capillary permeability and factors affecting composition of capillary filtrate. *Ann. N. Y. Acad. Sci.*, 46:713–731, 1946.

23. CLARK, E. R., and CLARK, E. L. Further observations on living lymphatic vessels in the transparent chamber in the rabbit's ear —their relation to the tissue spaces. *Amer. J. Anat.*, 52:273–305, 1933.

24. IRISAWA, A., and RUSHMER, R. F. Rela-

tionship between lymphatic and venous pressure in leg of dog. *Amer. J. Physiol.*, 196:495–498, 1959.

25. FRANKLIN, K. J. *A Monograph on Veins.* Springfield, Illinois, Charles C Thomas, 1937.

26. THOMAS, W. D., and ESSEX, H. E. Observations on the hepatic venous circulation with special reference to the sphincteric mechanism. *Amer. J. Physiol.*, 158:303–310, 1949.

27. ALEXANDER, R. S. Venomotor participation in vascular reflexes. *Fed. Proc.*, 13:2, 1954.

28. DUGGAN, J. J., LOVE, V. L., and LYONS, R. H. A study of reflex venomotor reactions in man. *Circulation*, 7:869–873, 1953.

29. LANDIS, E. M., and HORTENSTINE, J. C. Functional significance of venous blood pressure. *Physiol. Rev.*, 30:1–32, 1950.

30. BRENNER, O. Pathology of the vessels of the pulmonary circulation. *Arch. Int. Med.*, 56:211–237, 1935.

31. MILLER, W. S. *The Lung*, 2nd ed. Springfield, Illinois, Charles C Thomas, 1947, 222 pp.

32. COURNAND, A. Some aspects of the pulmonary circulation in normal man and in chronic cardiopulmonary diseases. *Circulation*, 2:641–657, 1952.

33. HICKAM, J. B. Atrial septal defect. A study of intracardiac shunts, ventricular outputs, and pulmonary pressure gradients. *Amer. Heart J.* 38:801–812, 1949.

34. HAMILTON, W. F. Pressure relations in the pulmonary circuit. *Amer. Ass. Advancement of Science Publ. No. 13*, pp. 324–331, 1940.

35. BAYLISS, R. I. S. Effect of lung disease on the heart and circulation. *Brit. Med. Bull.*, 8:354–357, 1952.

36. HALMÓGYI, D., FELKAI, B., IVÁNYI, J., TÉNYI, M., ZSÓTÉR, T., and SZÜCS, Z. The role of the nervous system in the maintenance of pulmonary arterial hypertension in heart failure. *Brit. Heart J.*, 15:15–24, 1953.

37. ATWELL, R. J., HICKAM, J. B., PRYOR, W. W., and PAGE, E. P. Reduction of blood flow through the hypoxic lung. *Amer. J. Physiol.*, 166:37–44, 1951.

38. PETERS, R. M., and ROOS, A. Effect of unilateral nitrogen breathing on pulmonary blood flow in dogs. *Fed. Proc.*, 11:122, 1952.

39. WESTCOTT, R. N., FOWLER, N. O., SCOTT, R. C., HAUENSTEIN, V. D., and McGUIRE, J. Anoxia and human pulmonary vascular resistance. *J. Clin. Invest.*, 30:957–970, 1951.

40. KJELLBERG, S. R., RUDHE, U., and SJÖSTRAND, T. The amount of hemoglobin and the blood volume in relation to the pulse rate and cardiac volume during rest. *Acta physiol. scand.*, 19:136–145, 1949.

41. KJELLBERG, S. R., RUDHE, U., and SJÖSTRAND, T.: The relationship between the pulmonary blood content, the heart volume and the filling rate of the left ventricle. *Acta physiol. scand.*, 24:49–60, 1952.

42. SJÖSTRAND, T.: Volume and distribution of

blood and their significance in regulating the circulation. *Physiol. Rev.*, 33:202–228, 1953.

43. SILVER, C. P. The radiological pattern of injected pulmonary and bronchial arteries. *Brit. J. Radiol.*, 25:617–624, 1952.

44. BERRY, J. L., and DALY, I. deB. The relation between pulmonary and bronchial vascular systems. *Proc. Roy. Soc.*, B109:319–336, 1931.

Chapter 2

FUNCTIONAL ANATOMY OF CARDIAC CONTRACTION

The energy released during ventricular systole represents the combined output of the various bundles of myocardial fibers. The contribution of each bundle depends not only on its contractile power, but also on its anatomic orientation within the cardiac walls. This chapter is devoted to describing the functional anatomy of cardiac contraction as a background which is essential for an understanding of cardiac adaptability and control.

The two fundamental requirements of the cardiovascular system are: (a) circulation of blood without interruption and (b) regulation of blood flow in response to the varying demands of the tissues. If the circulation is interrupted, even briefly, survival of the individual is jeopardized. If a patient loses his normal ability to increase the volume flow of blood in response to demand, he is restricted in the amount of physical activity and useful work he can perform. Extreme limitations in the ability to increase cardiac output produce bedridden patients. Fundamentally, the heart must continuously adapt its output to balance the flow through the billions of capillaries in the body.

CONCEPTS OF MUSCULAR CONTRACTION

The walls of the heart are composed of bundles and sheets of myocardial fibers intertwined in a very complex fashion (see Figs. 4 and 5). The pumping action

of the heart depends upon contraction of these myocardial fibers. The mechanisms by which muscle fibers convert chemical energy into mechanical work have been studied intensively and a multitude of theories have been evolved. It is not appropriate here to plunge deeply into this rather chaotic subject, but a superficial consideration indicates the great similarity of the contractile mechanisms of smooth muscle, myocardium and skeletal muscle. Szent-Gyorgyi[1] demonstrated that two substances, actin and myosin, can be extracted from muscle and purified. These purified substances will combine to form fibers of actomyosin, which will contract when they are immersed in a solution containing adenosine triphosphate (ATP). Further, it is possible to remove practically everything but myosin, actin and tropomyosin from muscle by soaking it for long periods in 50 per cent glycerol. This residual structure will still contract when supplied with ATP. Thus, the resting muscle has been visualized as containing actin, myosin and ATP in a dissociated state.[2] The actin and the myosin of skeletal muscle, myocardium and smooth muscle are interchangeable; actin from one may combine with myosin from another to produce contractile actomyosin. This was the picture of muscular contraction before the advent of the electron microscope.

Electron micrographs show that myofibrils are made up of still smaller fila-

30

ments, each about 50 to 100 A in diameter (Fig. 1). Huxley[3] has clearly demonstrated that there are two types of myofilaments, one being almost twice as thick as the other. These thick and thin filaments are linked together by an intricate system of cross bridges which project from the thick fibers at fairly regular intervals. He proposed a sliding model concept of muscular contraction, summarized schematically in Figure 1. This concept rapidly achieved wide acceptance because it was consistent with much other evidence and supported by crisp, detailed electron micrographs.[4] The two types of

myofilaments have been identified in association with the cross bands of muscle. The thin filaments extend in both directions from the Z band. The dark A band is occupied by the thick filaments, which are partially overlapped by the thin filaments. The central light area (H zone) of the A band represents the region occupied only by the thicker filaments. Over a wide range of muscle lengths, the A bands remain of constant length during both contraction and stretching. The I bands shorten in relation to the shortening of the muscle. As the width of the I band diminishes, the H zone shrinks just as

MUSCULAR CONTRACTION

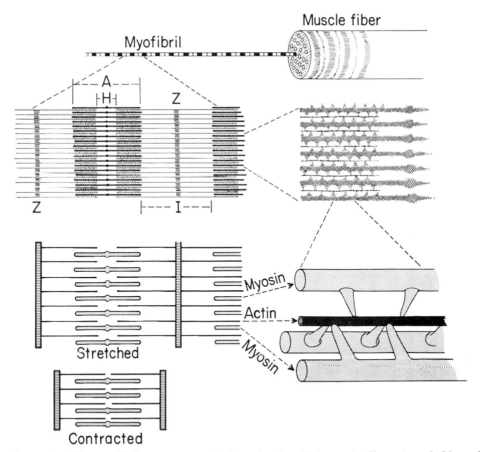

FIGURE 1.   The myofibrils are composed of overlapping thick myosin filaments and thin actin filaments. The amount of overlap is diminished during stretching and increased during contraction. Many cross bridges are observed at regular intervals between the actin and myosin filaments. These cross bridges have been visualized as forming linkages at specific sites on the actin fibers and drawing them onward during contraction. (After Huxley.[4])

ANATOMIC AND FUNCTIONAL SIMILARITY BETWEEN DIFFERENT TYPES OF MUSCLE

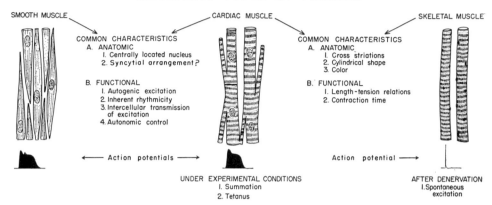

FIGURE 2.   Properties common to visceral smooth muscle and myocardium are listed between schematic drawings of these fibers. Functional characteristics shared by myocardium and skeletal muscle are similarly indicated between drawings. These different types of fibers are distinguished by their controlling mechanisms, the fundamental contractile process being very similar in each type. As far as control is concerned, myocardium is more closely related to visceral smooth muscle than to skeletal muscle. Schematic representations of action potentials from three types of muscle are indicated at the bottom of respective drawings. Smooth muscle has a rapid depolarization which is sustained for an extended period and may have multiple superimposed spikes (after Bozler[5, 6]). Myocardium tends to remain depolarized for a period approximately equal to the duration of contraction. In contrast, skeletal muscle rapidly recovers its polarization after excitation and responds to repetitive stimulation to produce sustained contractions. Under experimental conditions summation and tetanus can be produced in myocardial fibers, even though such a response is usually considered typical of skeletal muscle. Denervated skeletal muscle exhibits spontaneous autogenic excitation (fibrillation), which is the typical form of excitation in myocardium and visceral smooth muscle.

though these two sets of filaments slide past each other. Actually the tips of filaments may meet and deform at extreme degrees of shortening, and the expected new sets of bands appear at the points of contact.

Ample evidence indicates that the thin filaments are indeed actin and the thick filaments are myosin. The nature of the cross bridges is not known, but they have been assigned an important role in a theory proposed by Huxley.[4] According to this scheme, the cross bridges oscillate, and are able to form attachments at specific sites on the thin actin filaments and draw them a short distance. Although this description has not been widely accepted, it serves as an example of a concept by which muscular contraction could be explained in terms of current knowledge of the ultrastructure and chemical composition of muscle. Much more definitive in-

formation will be required to resolve this problem, but the rapid progress in recent years is most encouraging.

The Relation of Myocardium to Other Types of Muscle

Since the contractile mechanisms are similar in the various kinds of muscle, the principal functional differences arise from dffierences in the mechanisms for excitation and control. Because myocardium superficially resembles skeletal muscle in its cross striation, color, and in the speed, vigor and duration of its contraction, the common tendency is to assume that cardiac muscle is only slightly different from skeletal muscle. On the contrary, myocardium more closely resembles visceral smooth muscle with respect to its functional characteristics and control (Fig. 2). Bozler[5, 6] has classified smooth muscle into two main divisions, (a) multiunit smooth muscle and (*b*) visceral smooth muscle. Multiunit smooth muscle, in the peripheral vascular system and the bladder, is directly innervated by motor nerves originating in the autonomic nervous system, and resembles skeletal muscle in many aspects of its excitation and control.

In contrast, visceral smooth muscle, in the ureter, uterus and gastrointestinal tract, is not directly innervated by motor nerves (Fig. 2). Waves of excitation originate in the muscle fibers and are conducted throughout the contiguous cells. Although protoplasmic continuity between adjacent cells cannot be demonstrated, a mass of visceral smooth muscle functions like a syncytium, so that excitation originating at one site may spread to all other portions. In the ureter, pacemaker activity is well developed at a point near the hilus of the kidney. Waves of excitation originate at this point at fairly regular intervals and proceed in an orderly fashion down the length of the tube. Thus, the electrical activity of visceral smooth muscle is similar to that of the myocardium but very different from that of skeletal muscle (Fig. 2). Visceral smooth muscle is controlled by the autonomic nervous system principally through the release of hormonal substances rather than through direct motor innervation. Thus, visceral smooth muscle is closely related to myocardium so far as its excitation and control are concerned. If the completeness of contraction or relaxation can vary in smooth muscle, there is no *a priori* reason for discarding this possibility in the myocardium.

The similarity of the basic contractile mechanisms is emphasized by the fact that apparent differences among the various types of muscle can be largely eliminated under specific conditions. For example, tetanus can be produced in papillary muscle from a mammalian heart maintained at 27° C. and electrically stimulated at a rapid rate.[7] A skeletal muscle deprived of its motor nerve supply exhibits fibrillation due to myogenic impulses which spread along the individual fibers to produce asynchronous contractions. This phenomenon can be directly observed on the surface of the tongue after degeneration of its motor nerves.

ANATOMIC COMPONENTS OF THE HEART

Four rings of dense connective tissue are joined to form a single fibrous "skeleton" of the heart. The atria, ventricles, valves and arterial trunks are all firmly attached to this skeleton (Fig. 3). The two atria resemble a thin-walled, shallow cup of myocardium divided by a partition down the center. Each atrium has an atrial appendage, the functional significance of which is completely unknown. The margins of the atrial shell are fastened to the superior surface of the mitral and tricuspid valve rings.

The aorta and the pulmonary artery originate at the superior surface of the corresponding semilunar valve rings. Thus, the atrial chambers and the arterial trunks are anchored to the superior surface of the fibrous skeleton. The inflow and outflow channels of each ventricle lie side by side. The atrioventricular (A-V) valves are fastened to the inferior surface of the mitral and tricuspid valve rings with the fibrous connective tissue at the root of each valve leaflet merging with that of the corresponding valvular ring. Chordae tendineae, extending from the inferior margins of each leaflet of the A-V valves, are fastened directly to the internal surface of the ventricular walls and to papillary muscles projecting from the endocardial surface of the ventricular chambers.

The right and left ventricles are fastened to the entire circumference of the fibrous skeleton of the heart. The upper margin of the interventricular septum is attached along the line of fusion between the mitral and tricuspid valve rings. The

ANATOMIC COMPONENTS OF THE HEART

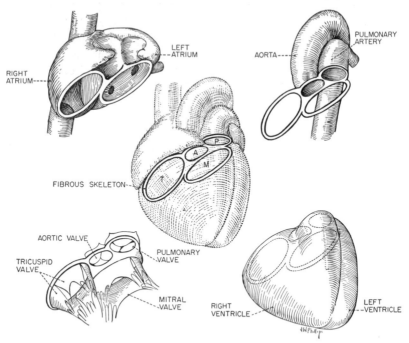

FIGURE 3.   The fibrous skeleton of the heart consists of four valve rings joined together. To these dense connective tissue annuli fibrosi are fastened the two major arterial trunks and all four cardiac chambers. The atria and arterial trunks are attached to the superior surface of this fibrous skeleton and the ventricles and atrioventricular valve leaflets are fastened to its inferior aspect.

membranous portion of the septum is fused at the junction of the pulmonary and aortic valve rings.

The Anatomy of the Ventricular Walls

The ventricles serve as the major source of energy for the circulation of blood and are composed of sheets of myocardial fibers encircling the ventricular chambers in a complex fashion[8-10] reminiscent of the windings of a turban. The various muscular layers in the ventricles are so tightly bound together that they are very difficult to dissect into individual components. According to Robb and Robb,[10] the ventricular walls are composed of four different muscles: the superficial sinospiral and bulbospiral muscles, and the deep sinospiral and bulbospiral muscles (Fig. 4). The superficial layers originate from the fibrous skeleton of the heart, spiral down toward the apex, enter the vortex and

then spiral in the opposite direction back to their insertion on the fibrous skeleton. The deep sinospiral and bulbospiral muscles also originate at the connective tissue of the valve rings and descend varying distances toward the apex. They then encircle the ventricular chambers before ascending to their insertions on the fibrous skeleton. Whether a muscle bundle is called "sinospiral" or "bulbospiral" depends solely upon the valve ring at which it originates. This division is purely arbitrary and appears to complicate the picture unnecessarily.

From a functional point of view, the ventricular musculature can be divided into two groups of myocardial bundles,[11] the spiral muscles and the deep constrictor muscles, as illustrated schematically in Figure 5. A block of tissue cut from the mid-portion of the right or left ventricular wall contains myocardial fibers primarily oriented in three general directions. The inner and outer layers are spiral muscle which follow oblique courses approximately 90 degrees apart since they spiral in opposite directions. As the spiral muscle bundles contract, the oblique traction by the outer layer is counteracted by tension developed in the opposite direction by the inner layer. The combined effect of their contraction is a shortening of the chambers along their longitudinal axes rather than a rotation of the ventricles. Because of the swirling, intertwining and

ANATOMY OF THE VENTRICULAR WALLS

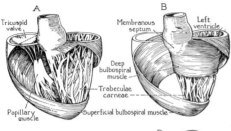

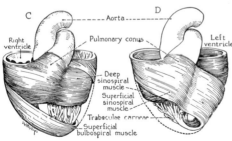

FIGURE 4. *A*, The superficial bulbospiral muscle bundles arise principally from the mitral ring and form the external investment for portions of the left and right ventricles as they spiral toward the apex. Emerging from the vortex on the inside of the chambers, these muscle bundles spiral back toward the valve rings either as trabeculae carneae or as papillary muscles which are joined to the valves through chordae tendineae.

B, The deep bulbospiral muscle fibers encircle the basilar portions of the left ventricle.

C, The deep sinospiral muscle encircles both the right and the left ventricular chambers.

D, The superficial sinospiral muscle is a counterpart of the superficial bulbospiral muscle. The anatomic distinction between the superficial sinospiral and bulbospiral muscles is arbitrary and functionally unimportant. (After Robb and Robb: *Amer. Heart J.*, 23:455–467, 1942.)

overlapping of the superficial bundles along their course down toward the apex and back toward the base, the spiral layers are thin near the base and thick near the apex where they constitute the full thickness of the wall.

The deep myocardial bundles lying between the external and internal spiral layers encircle the basilar two-thirds of the ventricular chambers. These layers have been labeled the "constrictor" muscle because their shortening acts to reduce the diameter of the chambers like the clenching of a fist. The left ventricle and the interventricular septum contain a large mass of deep constrictor fibers while

FUNCTIONAL COMPONENTS OF VENTRICULAR MUSCULATURE

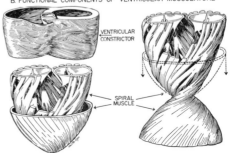

FIGURE 5. The muscular architecture of the ventricles.

A, Blocks of tissue removed from the walls of the ventricles are composed of three layers of muscle. The myocardial fibers in these layers are oriented roughly in the three general directions indicated by the arrows.

B, From a functional point of view, the ventricles are formed of two sets of myocardial bundles: (*a*) the internal and external layers of spiral muscle, which enclose (*b*) the ventricular constrictor muscles. The internal and external investments of the ventricular chambers are composed of the same muscle bundles, which are strongly twisted at the vortex and spiral in opposite directions from the apex toward the base.

the right ventricle contains a relatively thin layer of these fibers.

Because the mass of the constrictor fibers in the left ventricular wall is very large, its contraction produces primarily a reduction in the chamber's diameter with a smaller degree of shortening along the longitudinal axis. In the right ventricular wall, on the other hand, the predominance of spiral muscle produces much ventricular shortening with relatively little movement of the free wall toward the septum. Such shortening of the right ventricular chamber should tend to draw the tricuspid valve ring toward the apex of the heart. These predictions have been confirmed by cinefluorographic studies of ventricular contraction (see reference 11).

The Functional Anatomy of Heart Valves

The heart valves are so simple and effective that the best available man-made substitutes are gross caricatures by comparison. Not only do they open and close rapidly and seal completely against high pressures with minimal obstruction to flow, but their delicate-appearing cusps may endure the ravages of repetitive closure for more than 100 years.

Semilunar Valves. The aortic and pulmonary valves are similar, each consisting of three symmetrical valve cusps. Two cusps of equal size could close tightly, but would not open completely without considerable elastic stretch. Three cusps can theoretically open to the full dimensions of the valve ring and yet produce a perfect seal when closed. Behind the aortic valve cusps are three outpouchings, the sinuses of Valsalva, which help prevent obstruction of the coronary ostia. If a valve leaflet came in contact with the coronary orifice, shutting off the flow of blood from the aorta, coronary pressure would fall rapidly as blood left the coronary arterial system, and the valve cusp would be sealed against the coronary

ostium by a high differential pressure. This unfortunate accident is presumably prevented by the presence of adequate space behind the open valve cusps.

Atrioventricular Valves. The tricuspid and mitral valves are larger and much more complicated than the semilunar valves. The anatomic distinction between the mitral valve and the tricuspid valve is largely artificial since both valves consist fundamentally of two large opposing cusps and small intermediary cusps at each end. However, the chordae tendineae of the tricuspid valve usually insert on three fairly distinct groups of papillary muscles, while only two principal papillary muscles serve the mitral valve. The anatomy of the papillary muscles is subject to considerable individual variability, some being deeply notched, grooved or separated into multiple heads. Since the structure and function of the mitral and tricuspid valves are similar, only the former will be described in detail.

The Mitral Valve. The mitral valve is interposed between the low-pressure left atrium and the high-pressure left ventricle. The two valve cusps are unequal in size. The large anteromedial (aortic) cusp hangs down like a curtain between the mitral and aortic orifices, while the shorter posterolateral cusp originates from the lateral portions of the mitral ring. The combined surface area of the two valve cusps is nearly twice as great as the area of the mitral orifice which they must occlude. The mitral valve orifice is considerably smaller than the mitral ring because the valve cusps are joined at the commissures so the upper portion of the mitral valve resembles a funnel.

The chordae tendineae correspond to multiple guy lines extending from the papillary muscles into the structure of the valve cusps (see Fig. 6). It is important to recognize that the chordae tendineae from adjacent regions of the two valve cusps insert upon the same or adjacent papillary muscles (Fig. 6). Thus, tension exerted

ATRIOVENTRICULAR VALVES

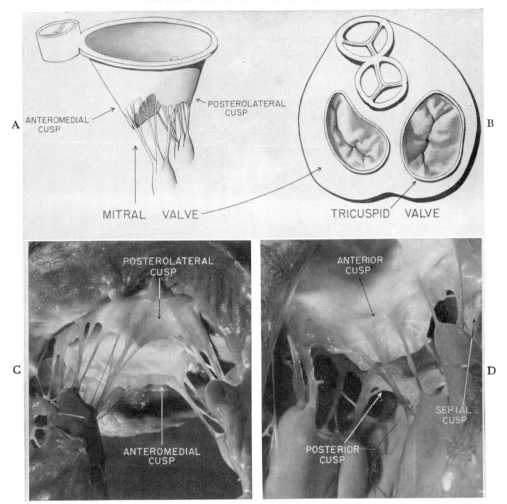

FIGURE 6.   *A,* The mitral valve is shaped like a funnel when open and is closed by the approximation of two broad, membranous cusps. The chordae tendineae originate from the tips of two sets of papillary muscles and prevent eversion of the valve cusps into the left atrium during ventricular systole. The major chordae merge into the edge of the short leaf, but may insert several millimeters back from the edge of the larger aortic leaf.

B, The mitral and tricuspid valves are similar in both structure and function. They both consist primarily of two broad, opposing valve cusps with smaller intermediate cusps situated at each end. The tricuspid valve has a somewhat larger intermediate cusp and a total of three separate papillary muscles. (After Spalteholz, W.: Hand Atlas of Human Anatomy. Philadelphia, J. B. Lippincott Co., 1933.)

C, In a normal heart specimen, the walls of the left ventricle were excised to illustrate the posterolateral aspect of the mitral valves, chordae tendineae and papillary muscles. Transillumination reveals that fibers of the chordae tendineae extend long distances within the valve cusps.

D, The three papillary muscles and corresponding valve cusps of the tricuspid valve were photographed as viewed from within the right ventricular cavity.

CONDUCTION SYSTEM OF THE HEART

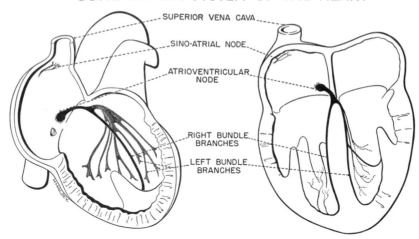

FIGURE 7.   The sino-atrial node is the normal pacemaker of the heart. No specialized conduction system has been described in the atria. The A-V node, common bundle and bundle branches conduct the wave of excitation from the atrium to the ventricular myocardium (see reference 12).

through the chordae tends to draw the two valve cusps together. If the papillary muscles begin their contraction early in ventricular systole, traction on the valve cusps should facilitate apposition of the valves.

COORDINATION OF THE HEART BEAT

To produce efficient pumping, the complex mass of myocardial bundles must contract more or less simultaneously. The effectiveness of the ventricles is lost if the individual myocardial bundles contract in a random fashion, e.g., in ventricular fibrillation. Coordinated contraction of the complex pattern of myocardial bundles stems from the syncytial arrangement of the myocardial fibers; excitation beginning at one site spreads to all other contiguous areas. Excitation of the thick ventricular walls is facilitated by a rapidly conducting system of Purkinje fibers. The conduction system is responsible for periodic initiation of excitation (pacemaker activity), a delay between atrial and ventricular contraction (A-V nodal delay) and the rapid spread of excitation to all portions of the ventricular walls so that their contraction is sufficiently simul-

taneous to produce effective pumping action. When the conduction system is operating normally, this stereotyped sequence of events is repeated during each successive cardiac cycle.

The Conduction System of the Heart

The sino-atrial (S-A) node is a small mass of specialized myocardial tissues embedded in the atrial wall near the entrance of the superior vena cava (Fig. 7). This node consists of an accumulation of modified myocardial cells. Shaped like an Indian war club, it has a fringe of delicate fibers merging with surrounding myocardial fibers. The S-A node is the normal pacemaker, spontaneously originating the spreading waves of excitation at a more rapid rate than any other part of the heart. If it were isolated from all neural and hormonal control, the S-A node would probably generate impulses at a rate in excess of 100 per minute. However, a large number of fibers from the parasympathetic and sympathetic nervous systems terminate in the vicinity[12] of the S-A node. Discharge of the vagal fibers releases acetylcholine, which tends to slow the rate of impulse formation, and the sympathetic fibers release epinephrine-like substances, which act to accelerate the frequency of impulse formation. Since the vagal influence generally predominates, the "normal" heart rate ranges between 60 and 100 impulses per minute.[13] The S-A node retains its position as pacemaker for the entire heart so long as it generates impulses at a faster rate than any other region of the myocardial syncytium and so long as the spreading wave of excitation is rapidly conducted from the atria into the ventricles.

The Sequence of Excitation

Apparently no conduction system serves the atria, so a wave of excitation originating in the S-A node spreads in all directions like the concentric wave produced by dropping a pebble into a pool of water. It travels at a rate of about 1 meter per second and reaches the most distant portions of the atrium in about 0.08 second. As it approaches the interatrial septum, the wave of excitation reaches another mass of specialized conducting tissue, the atrioventricular (A-V) node.

The A-V node is located near the posterior margin of the interatrial septum close to the entrance of the coronary sinus (Fig. 8). When the wave of excitation reaches the A-V node, it does not proceed directly to the ventricles, but is delayed there for intervals ranging around 0.08 to 0.12 second. It has been suggested that

this delay is due to slow conduction along delicate fibers connecting the atrial myocardium with A-V nodal tissue. During the A-V nodal delay, atrial contraction is largely completed. The A-V node is the bulbous end of a bundle of Purkinje fibers —the bundle of His—which passes forward along the right side of the interatrial septum before plunging downward across the A-V junction to the upper margin of the muscular interventricular septum. There the bundle divides into two branches—the right and left bundles— which descend on opposite sides of the interventricular septum. The bundle branches ramify into a network of Purkinje fibers which are distributed over the inner surface of the ventricular chambers.

After leaving the A-V node, the wave of excitation passes rapidly (4 to 5 meters per second) along the Purkinje fibers of the common bundle and the bundle branches.[12, 14] The endocardial surfaces of the ventricular chambers are excited early (see Fig. 15), and the endocardial layers (trabeculae carneae and papillary muscles) are first to contract. Thus, the wave of excitation probably penetrates the ventricular walls from the endocardial to the epicardial surface. The rapid spread of excitation through the ventricles produces more or less simultaneous contraction of the ventricular musculature. It is apparent that waves of excitation origi-

SEQUENCE OF CARDIAC EXCITATION

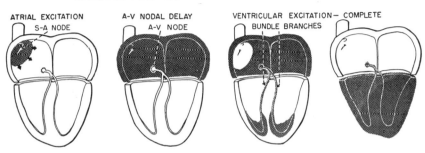

FIGURE 8. Excitation of the heart is normally initiated by an impulse which is generated by the S-A node and which spreads rapidly in all directions through the atrial musculature. After a slight delay at the A-V node, impulses are conducted by the Purkinje system into the ventricles where a wave of excitation spreads from the endocardial surfaces through the ventricular musculature.

ROENTGENOGRAPHIC ANATOMY OF DOG HEART

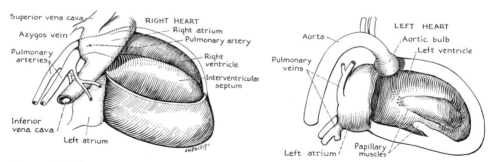

FIGURE 9. The anatomic relations of the cardiac chambers and arterial trunks in the dog as viewed from the right side for comparison with angiocardiograms presented in subsequent figures. The right atrium lies above the left atrium on the posterior aspect of the heart. The interventricular septum presents a convex surface to the right ventricular cavity. Thus, the right ventricular cavity has a crescentic transverse section and partially encircles the left ventricular cavity.

nating at abnormal sites or following devious pathways will interfere to some extent with the coordinated contraction of the various chamber walls. This problem will be considered in a subsequent section (Chapter 10). For the present, the discussion will be confined to normal cardiac cycles.

THE SEQUENCE OF EVENTS DURING THE CARDIAC CYCLE

So long as the heart receives excitation along the normal pathways and the heart rate remains constant, each successive cardiac cycle tends to follow the same pattern of contraction and relaxation. A clear picture of the mechanical events of the cardiac cycle is required for logical interpretation of many physiologic events, e.g., timing of heart murmurs and analysis of electrocardiograms or arterial and venous pulse contours.

The Cardiac Cycle: Cinefluorographic Angiocardiography

X-rays penetrating the body of a dog illuminate a fluorescent screen producing an image of the cardiac silhouette. Motion pictures of these images record changes in the size and shape of the heart. If a radiopaque substance such as Diodrast is rapidly injected into the jugular

vein, the course of the opacified blood can be followed through the heart and great vessels.[15] The changes in size and configuration of the individual cardiac chambers can be visualized as a two-dimensional projection or silhouette. For purposes of orientation the anatomic relations of the great vessels and cardiac chambers in the heart of the dog are indicated in Figure 9 as viewed from the right side. Note that the right ventricle does not extend to the apex of the heart in the dog. Further, the configuration of the ventricular chambers is not the same in dogs and in man. Although the fundamental principles of cardiac contraction in dogs probably resemble those in humans, caution must be exercised in applying the discussion which follows to cardiac function in man.

The typical sequence of events which occurs during filling and contraction of the right atrium and right ventricle of a dog is illustrated in Figure 10. Diodrast flowed along the superior vena cava during the eight frames in column *A* and entered the right atrium in the third frame of column *B* (*B*-3). In frame *B*-5, the tricuspid valves everted into the right atrium and blood gushed into the right ventricle (*B*-6). The variations in density of the right ventricular shadow in frames *B*-7 and *B*-8 represent the mixing of the incoming blood with the residual blood

CHANGES IN SIZE AND SHAPE OF THE RIGHT ATRIUM AND VENTRICLE

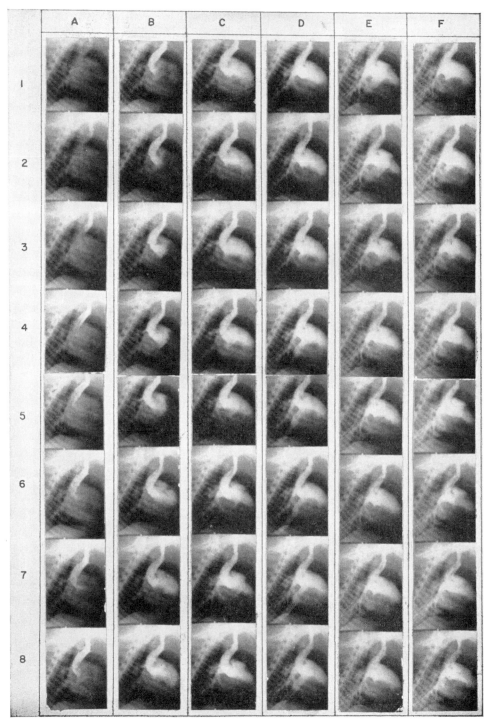

FIGURE 10. Successive frames from a cinefluorographic film exposed at 15 frames per second illustrate the filling and contraction of the right atrium and right ventricle during 3.2 seconds following the injection of contrast medium. Examine each column in succession from above downward to observe the sequence of events.

FILLING OF THE RIGHT VENTRICLE

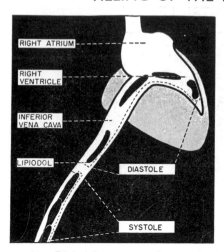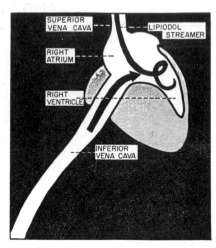

FIGURE 11. Lipiodol streamers, floating freely in the blood, move relatively slowly during one phase of the cardiac cycle, then suddenly accelerate and move without hesitation into the right ventricular cavity, presumably during the rapid filling phase of ventricular diastole (see text). Similar streamers of Lipiodol descending along the superior vena cava frequently display a swirling motion which may be due to the convergence of the two currents of blood flowing into the atrium.

remaining in the ventricle after the preceding systole. The next contraction began in frames *C*-5 and *C*-6, as indicated by the protrusion of the right atrial appendage associated with atrial systole. In frame *C*-6, the right ventricle began to contract and in the next three frames was reduced to a small triangular area with its base at the tricuspid valves. Between frames *C*-8 and *D*-1 (1/15 second), the right ventricle was filled and apparently remained unchanged in size until the succeeding contraction (*D*-8). During the remainder of this cycle, Diodrast passed through the right atrium and flowed into the inferior vena cava down to the level of the diaphragm against the oncoming stream of blood. The opacified blood in the inferior vena cava returned to the heart during the next filling period. The right ventricle did not distend noticeably during the latter part of diastole even when there was sufficient pressure to force Diodrast against the stream of blood into the inferior vena cava. Diastolic filling appears to be largely complete very early in the diastolic interval.

Filling of the Right Ventricle. Diastolic filling of the right ventricle can be studied by injecting Lipiodol into a systemic vein. Lipiodol is a radiopaque, viscous oil which is very cohesive and tends to flow along with the stream of blood as a long ribbon or as multiple globules, depending upon how it is injected. The course of one Lipiodol streamer ascending the inferior vena cava is indicated by serial tracings in Figure 11. The movement was relatively slow during systole. At the beginning of the rapid filling in early diastole the Lipiodol streamer accelerated rapidly, passing along the inferior vena cava, through the atrium and into the right ventricle. Thus, the blood which fills the right ventricle comes not only from the atrium, but also from a considerable distance down the inferior vena cava.

Blood streams from the superior and inferior venae cavae converge at the right atrium. Streamers of Lipiodol and Diodrast moving down the superior vena cava frequently exhibit a spiral flow as they enter the ventricle (Fig. 11). This is attributed to a swirling motion of the blood produced by the confluence of the two streams. These currents tend to mix the venous blood within the right ventricle.

Contraction of the Right Ventricle. Cinefluorographic films indicate that a longitudinal section of the right ventricular chamber is roughly triangular. It is bounded by a convex septal wall and the concave free wall, which enclose a crescent-shaped slit between them (Figs. 9 and 11). The action of the right ventricle resembles that of the old-fashioned bellows used to kindle fires. Since the sides of the bellows are large compared to the space between them, their very slight movement toward each other causes displacement of a large volume from within. In the right ventricular cavity, a relatively narrow space is confined between two broad surfaces so that the surface area of the chamber is very great in relation to the volume.[16, 17] Additional details concerning the events in ventricular contraction have been derived from cinefluorographic records showing metal markers installed on the internal and external surfaces of the ventricular walls. Figure 12 summarizes the results of such experiments on ten dogs. In this schematic diagram, movements of the markers during systole are indicated by the direction and length of arrows superimposed upon an outline of the ventricular chambers as they would appear during diastole. Note that the general direction of movement of the right ventricular wall is toward the apex of the right ventricle. The interventricular septum shortens very slightly along its longitudinal dimension but its central portion is not consistently displaced toward either the right or the left ventricular cavity. The free wall of the left ventricle tends to move simultaneously toward the interventricular septum and toward the apex of the heart. Markers on the endocardial surface of the free ventricular walls moved greater distances than corresponding markers on the epicardial surface. This is an expression of the difference in the degree of shortening of the inner and outer layers of myocardial fibers (see Chapter 3).

The apex remained remarkably stationary in all studies of this type. Rotation of the ventricles was slight or negligible. Contraction of the right ventricular wall apparently acts primarily to draw the A-V valve ring toward the apex. During left ventricular contraction the diameter of the cylindrical portion of the ventricular chamber was reduced and the long

MOVEMENTS OF SPECIFIC POINTS ON THE VENTRICULAR WALLS

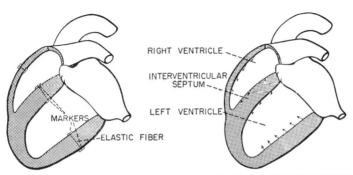

FIXATION OF METAL MARKERS   MOVEMENT OF METAL MARKERS

FIGURE 12.   Small metal rods connected by resilient elastic fibers were mounted on opposite sides of the ventricular walls and the positions of such markers during diastole and systole were noted on cinefluorographic films. The general direction and magnitude of the movements of the endocardial surfaces during systole are indicated by the arrows on the right.

COMPONENTS OF VENTRICULAR CONTRACTION

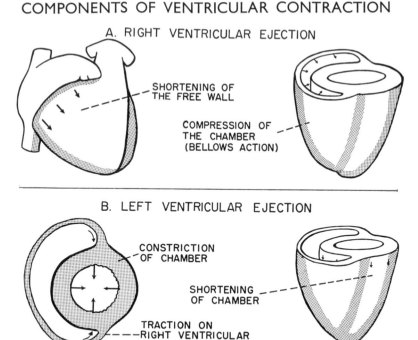

FIGURE 13.   *A*, Blood is ejected from the right ventricle by shortening of the free wall with downward displacement of the tricuspid valve ring and movement of the free wall toward the interventricular septum by myocardial shortening. Compression of the right ventricular cavity may be supplemented by traction exerted on the free wall by left ventricular contraction.

B, Left ventricular ejection is accomplished primarily by a reduction in the diameter of the chamber with some additional shortening of the longitudinal axis.

axis of the chamber shortened (Fig. 12). Since the interventricular septum did not shorten significantly, contraction of the right and left ventricular walls may cause the mitral and tricuspid valve rings to swing up and down from a fulcrum at their mutual attachments to the interventricular septum (see Fig. 3). In both ventricles the pins on opposite sides of the chamber remained widely separated at the end of each systole, indicating that large quantities of blood remain within the ventricle at the end of a systolic ejection (see also Figs. 10 and 14).

Blood is ejected from the right ventricle by three separate mechanisms occurring more or less simultaneously (Fig. 13): (*a*) Contraction of the spiral muscles (Fig. 5) draws the tricuspid valve ring toward the apex of the heart and shortens the longitudinal axis of the chamber. This shorten-

ing is the most obvious movement, but is much less effective than the bellows action in ejecting blood. (*b*) The free wall of the right ventricle moves toward the convex surface of the interventricular septum. This movement is very slight but extremely effective in ejecting blood. (*c*) Contraction of the deep circular fibers enclosing the left ventricular cavity must produce a greater curvature of the interventricular septum (Fig. 13), although the mid-portion (central axis) of this septum remains remarkably fixed in both position and length.[11] Since the free wall of the right ventricle is attached to the left ventricle along the interventricular groove, traction on this wall will also contribute to the bellows action on the right ventricular cavity. This effect is so slight that it cannot be readily demonstrated on cinefluorographic films. It has been clearly shown, however, that the free wall of the right ventricle can be almost completely destroyed by cauterization in dogs[18] or by coronary occlusion in man[19] without obvious effects on the circulatory efficiency. If right ventricular ejection can be maintained without contraction of the right ventricular myocardium, tension on the free wall of the chamber resulting from left ventricular contraction must be sufficient to account for the right ventricular output. This mechanism can be effective only if very slight movements of the free wall of the right ventricle toward the interventricular septum displace very large volumes of blood from the right ventricular cavity.

Clearly the configuration of the right ventricle is ideally suited to the ejection of large volumes of blood with minimal amounts of myocardial shortening. On the other hand, this architectural design is not conducive to the development of high intraventricular pressure.[16] If the normal right ventricle were suddenly required to provide the intraventricular pressures normally developed in the left ventricle, the right ventricular myocardium would have to develop tension many times as great as that in the left ventricle. Thus, we see that the right ventricle is specifically adapted to the task of pumping large or widely varying volumes of blood against a very low outflow pressure. Since the pulmonary vascular tree normally offers slight resistance to flow, the right ventricle normally ejects blood at relatively low pressure into the pulmonary artery (see Fig. 17). A sudden increase in pulmonary arterial pressure (massive pulmonary embolism) frequently leads to sudden death because the right ventricular myocardium cannot sustain the higher pressures needed to provide adequate flow through the lungs. If the pulmonary arterial pressure rises gradually, the right ventricle develops thick walls and a more cylindrical shape. In other words, the right ventricle adapts to

a chronic pressure load by assuming some of the characteristics of the normal left ventricle (see Fig. 7, Chap. 15).

Contraction of the Left Ventricle. The left ventricular cavity resembles a cylinder with a conoid segment at the apical end (Figs. 9 and 14). The cylindrical region is encircled by a strong cuff of deep fibers situated between thin layers of spiral muscle (see Fig. 5). The conoid segment is made up primarily of the intricately intertwined spiral muscle bundles as they enter and leave the vortex. Contraction of the left ventricle involves both a reduction in the diameter of the cylindrical portion and a shortening along the longitudinal axis of the chamber. Contraction of the deep constrictor muscle bundles acts to reduce the diameter of the chamber (see Fig. 13). This action accounts for most of the power and volume of the ejection, since the volume contained decreases with the square of the radius in a cylinder (Fig. 13B). Shortening of the longitudinal axis is less prominent and less effective in ejecting blood because the volume displacement is directly proportional to the change in length. Changes in the size and configuration of the left ventricular cavity can be visualized by cinefluorography (Fig. 14).

Shortening of the chamber involves movement of the mitral valve ring toward the apex of the heart (see Figs. 12, 13 and 14). During diastole, the A-V junction rapidly ascends toward the left atrium. Since the interventricular septum shortens very little (Fig. 12), the distance between the root of the aorta and the apex of the heart changes very little. This observation is consistent with Keith's conclusion[20] that the ventricular myocardium contracts toward a fulcrum or axis drawn between the apex of the heart and the roots of the arterial trunks.

In contrast to the right ventricle, the left ventricular cavity has a small surface area in relation to the contained volume by virtue of its cylindrical contour. The

LEFT VENTRICULAR CONTRACTION

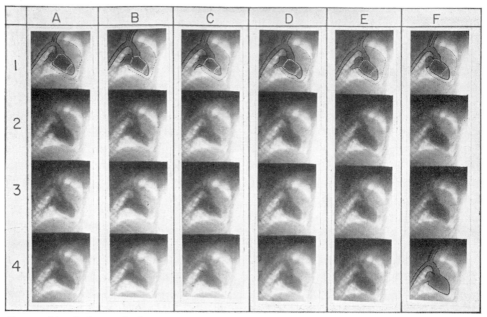

FIGURE 14.   Left ventricular contraction is illustrated by cinefluorographic angiocardiography in normal dogs. The diameter of the chamber is considerably reduced and its longitudinal axis is slightly shortened. Systole began in frame *A-3* and was completed in frame *C-1*. Diastolic filling appeared to be essentially complete in frame *D-3*, and little additional expansion could be noted during the remainder of the diastolic interval.

thick cuff of deep myocardial bundles is ideally situated to develop a very high internal pressure during contraction. Thus, the left ventricle is architecturally designed as a high-pressure pump, which is consistent with its role of supplying energy for the flow of blood through the high-pressure, high-resistance, systemic circulation (see Fig. 17). The normal left ventricle has less adaptability than the right ventricle in ejecting large volumes of blood. When the left ventricle is exposed to an excessive volume load for extended periods of time, e.g., in aortic insufficiency, the chambers often become tremendously dilated so that the surface area per unit volume is increased. In other words, the left ventricle assumes some of the characteristics of the right ventricle when large volumes must be ejected during each stroke.

Clearly, the anatomic and architectural features of the ventricular chambers reflect the type of work which each must perform. By the same token, the functional characteristics of the circulatory trees which they serve establish the nature of the load or the working conditions for each ventricular chamber.

Cyclic Changes in Ventricular Dimensions

Continuous measurements of the various ventricular dimensions provide an opportunity to synthesize a description of the changes in the volume and thus the changes in these chambers which are essential to their function as muscular pumps.

The internal diameters and internal length of the left ventricle have been measured by means of a magnetic steel stylus which moves in and out of a variable inductance coil with the movements of the walls (Fig. 15*A,C*). The external circumference and the length of the left and right ventricles have been measured by means of delicate rubber tubes filled with mercury which respond with an increase in electrical resistance as they are stretched (Fig. 15*B*). These records illustrate the following characteristics of the filling and emptying of the ventricles. At the beginning of the diastolic interval all dimensions of the ventricular chamber increase rapidly. This phase of rapid diastolic filling is very brief, and merges abruptly or gradually into the phase of slow filling which persists until atrial contraction ensues. When the ventricles are maximally distended (i.e., while the animal is resting quietly in the recumbent position, see Chapter 7), the dimensions reach a plateau at the end of the rapid filling phase and do not increase farther

during the remainder of diastole. Such an interval of unchanging ventricular volume is termed *the period of diastasis*. The diastolic interval normally ends with the onset of atrial contraction, which begins as the wave of excitation spreads over the atrium. Contraction of the atrial musculature reduces the capacity of the atrial chambers and displaces blood forward into the ventricles or backward into the great veins, depending on which course offers the least resistance.

The Isovolumetric Phase of Ventricular Systole. As the wave of excitation extends rapidly along the Purkinje system (Fig. 8) and spreads over the endocardial surface of the ventricles, the trabeculae carneae and the papillary muscles are excited and begin to contract. The shorten-

CYCLIC CHANGES IN LEFT VENTRICULAR DIMENSIONS

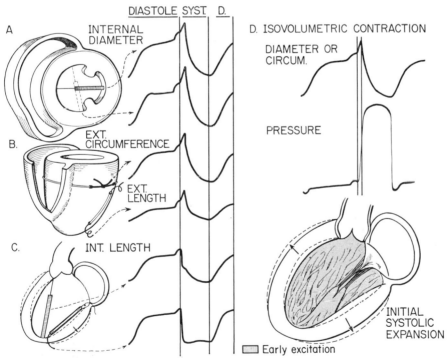

FIGURE 15. *A*, During ventricular diastole, all dimensions increase, rapidly at first and more gradually during the latter part of the filling interval. Atrial contraction adds a slight additional increment of blood. At the onset of ventricular systole, the internal diameters (A), external circumference and length (B) abruptly increase because the internal length (C) shortens during this interval which is called the isovolumetric contraction (D). The external length increases during this interval when the internal length is abruptly diminishing because of the outward bending of the thick-walled ventricle. (After Hawthorne, *Fed. Proc.*, 19:106, 1960.)

ing papillary muscles exert traction on the chordae tendineae, drawing the atrioventricular valves into apposition and the rising ventricular pressure seals them tight. The contracting papillary muscles draw the atrioventricular valve edges toward the apex,[21, 22] and the shortening endocardial layers draw the atrioventricular valve rings toward the apex of the heart. Since all four valves are closed, the contracting muscles elevate the pressure within the ventricle but do not change the volume they contain. Thus, the interval during which ventricular pressure rises to a level sufficient to open the semilunar valves has been called the period of isometric contraction. "Isometric contraction" refers to a condition in which a muscle develops tension without a change in its length. At the onset of systole, the length of the ventricles is abruptly shortened as the atrioventricular diaphragm rapidly descends. The other dimensions (diameter, circumference and external length) of the ventricle simultaneously expand. On this basis, this interval is more properly termed the period of isovolumetric contraction since all the myocardial fibers are changing length. The sudden lengthening of the circumferentially oriented constrictor muscles in the ventricle, just before they contract, may increase the effectiveness of their contraction.

Ventricular Systole. As the full thickness of the ventricular wall becomes excited, pressure in the ventricles exceeds corresponding arterial pressure and blood is very rapidly ejected from the ventricles. The rapidity of ventricular emptying is indicated by the reduction in the ventricular dimensions, rapid during early systole and slowing during the last part of systole. The various dimensional changes illustrated in Figure 15 are applicable to ventricular systole when the heart is normally well filled at the end of diastole. If the ventricular chambers are not well filled during diastole, the cir-

cumference is reduced at the onset of systole and systolic ejection is accomplished primarily by shortening of the longitudinal ventricular axis. This type of ejection occurs when cardiac size is below the normal range as a result of extremely fast heart rates, positive radial acceleration or exposure of the heart for experimental purposes (see Chap. 3).

Right Ventricular Inflow. The right atrium and the contiguous veins serve as a volume reservoir from which blood rapidly flows into the right ventricle during each diastolic filling interval. The function of this reservoir is illustrated more fully by tracings of sample records of dimensions, pressure and flow obtained during various studies on different dogs (Fig. 16). For example, the diameter of the superior vena cava, recorded by mutual inductance gauges,[23] has been observed to diminish during the atrial contraction, just as though it were invested with myocardium. In fact, there is some anatomical evidence that myocardial fibers extend along the veins leading to the heart. The right atrial pressure exhibits an abrupt increase during atrial contraction, a second increase during early ventricular systole as the A-V valves close, and a gradual rise during ventricular systole as the atrium fills. Atrial pressure drops precipitously during early diastole as blood gushes into the rapidly expanding ventricle. Flow through the inferior vena cava reaches its highest levels in early systole, presumably because of descent of the closed A-V valve during the isovolumetric period of ventricular systole (see Fig. 15D). A second peak in flow occurs during early diastole when ventricular filling is most rapid. In some instances, atrial contraction actually reverses the flow in the inferior vena cava. In general, the vena caval flow is higher when atrial pressure is diminished. A reciprocal relation is even more easily observed in some records of flow and circumference in the inferior vena cava; during rapid flow into the heart, the vena cava collapses somewhat and during slow flow the circumference tends to increase.[23] This is another way of saying that the inferior vena cava supplements the right atrial cavity as a volume reservoir just upstream from the right ventricular chamber. The wave forms of pressure, flow and dimensional changes in the atria and the large veins are extremely variable, so that the records shown here are only representative.

Left Ventricle Outflow. The record of aortic pressures rises very rapidly coincident with the peak ventricular ejection (Fig. 16B). During the latter part of systole, the pressure reaches a plateau and then begins to descend as the ventricular ejection slows. The closure of the aortic

valves is denoted by a sharp fluctuation commonly called the *dicrotic notch*. After the closure of the aortic valves, the pressure diminishes progressively as blood drains from the arterial system through the myriad arterioles and capillaries throughout the body. The extent to which the arterial pressure falls during diastole is determined by the rate of outflow from the arterial system and the duration of this outflow before the next ventricular systole supervenes. The variations in aortic circumference closely parallel the changes in arterial pressure, as would be expected in an elastic system.[24] However, slight differences in wave form, seen by many investigators, suggest that a wave of distention arrives before the wave of pressure. Although some investigators

PATTERNS OF INFLOW AND OUTFLOW

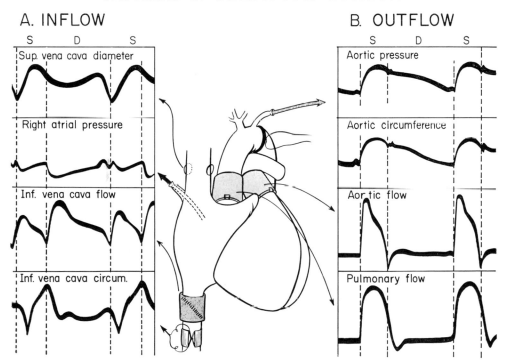

FIGURE 16. *A*, Changes in diameter of the superior vena cava, right atrial pressure, inferior vena caval flow and inferior vena caval circumference during the cardiac cycle demonstrated that the vena cava and right atrium serve as volume reservoirs (see text).

B, Changes in aortic pressure and aortic circumference are similar in wave form. The patterns of instantaneous flow in the aorta and pulmonary artery demonstrate that left ventricular ejection begins slightly later, reaches peak velocity earlier in systole and terminates earlier than right ventricular ejection.

MECHANICAL EFFECTS OF CARDIAC CONTRACTION

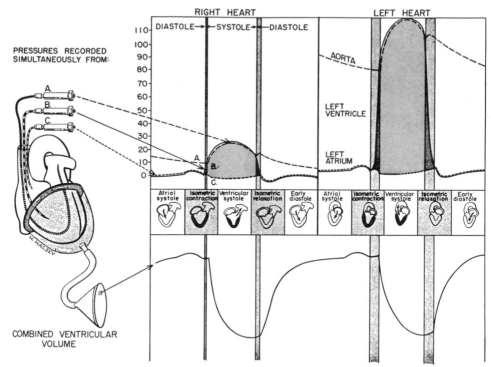

FIGURE 17. Simultaneous changes in atrial, ventricular and arterial pressures in the right and left ventricles are illustrated schematically along with fluctuations in combined ventricular volume to indicate the sequence of events during a single cardiac cycle (see text). The great difference in pressure developed by the two ventricles is consistent with the differences in their architecture (see Fig. 13).

have postulated that the smooth muscle in the aortic wall contracts during each successive cycle, one explanation for the earlier arrival of the distention is that changes in the length of the aorta may precede the changes in its circumference.[25] The abrupt descent of the base of the heart during isovolumetric contraction does in fact elongate the aorta before ventricular ejection begins.[25] When the left ventricle contracts, blood is ejected into the ascending aorta, rapidly at first and then gradually more slowly toward the end of systole. The typical flow pattern, recorded by means of an ultrasonic flowmeter, reveals a peak in both the velocity and the volume of flow early in the systolic interval (Fig. 16B). At the end of systole, the patterns become negative very briefly. This negativity represents the retrograde surge of blood responsible

for closure of the aortic valve. During diastole, the flow record oscillates slightly above and below zero. Simultaneous records of aortic and pulmonary flow demonstrate differences between left and right ventricular ejection. At the beginning of systole, the outflow from the right ventricle very slightly precedes the outflow from the left ventricle. The pulmonary flow reaches a peak much later than aortic flow. Right ventricular ejection continues well after cessation of the aortic flow. The retrograde surge in the pulmonary artery is much more sluggish and the fluctuations in flow during diastole are largely absent.

THE MECHANICAL EFFECTS OF CARDIAC CONTRACTION

Myocardial contraction produces a sequence of changes in the pressure and volume of blood in the ventricles which is traditionally described in terms of the atrial, ventricular and arterial pressures, and of the variations in the combined volume of both ventricles as measured by a cardiometer (Fig. 17).

During the later portion of diastole, the ventricular pressure equals the atrial pressure because the two chambers are connected through the wide A-V orifices and little or no blood is flowing between them. The wave of excitation spreading over the atrium is followed by atrial contraction. The contraction slightly increases both intra-atrial and intraventricular pressures because it suddenly compresses this portion of the venous volume reservoir. As the atrium contracts, blood may be displaced into the ventricular chambers or back into the large venous channels, depending upon which course offers the least resistance. The quantity of blood which enters the ventricle in response to atrial contraction is quite variable. Excitation of the ventricles begins as atrial contraction is being completed, and ventricular contraction begins about 0.075 second later.[26] Ventricular pressure rises to exceed arterial pressure during the period of isometric contraction, which lasts about 0.013 second in the right ventricle[27] and about 0.06 second in the left ventricle (Fig. 17).

During this period the ventricular volume is unchanged except for the movement of blood required to close and displace the valves. This period of isovolumetric contraction is characterized by a slight reduction in recorded ventricular volume and a slight increase in atrial pressure due to ballooning of the A-V valves. The atria relax and begin to refill during ventricular systole. Isovolumetric contraction of the ventricle ends when ventricular pressure exceeds the arterial pressure and is followed by rapid ejection of blood into the arterial system. Thus, the arterial pressure is elevated while the ventricular volume is abruptly diminished. The intraventricular and arterial pressures tend to level off and descend as the rate of ejection from the ventricles drops below the rate at which blood leaves the arterial system through the capillaries. The onset of ventricular relaxation is associated with a rapid drop in ventricular pressures below arterial pressure. The semilunar valves become approximated by a retrograde surge of blood in the root of the aorta, which produces the dicrotic notch in the arterial pressure wave. During isovolumetric relaxation, ventricular pressure rapidly drops below atrial pressure. The A-V valves swing open before a gush of blood from the atrium. The ventricles rapidly refill with blood from the thoracic veins and atria, as indicated by the abrupt upswing in the ventricular volume curve. The slope of the volume curve indicates that early filling of the ventricles is more rapid than ejection of blood by ventricular contraction. Ventricular filling is largely complete very soon after the onset of ventricular relaxation and, if the diastolic interval is sufficiently long, ventricular volume reaches a plateau during which no more blood enters from the atrium— the period of diastasis. The length of the diastolic interval is determined largely by the time required for the pacemaker to discharge the new wave of excitation which initiates another cardiac cycle.

REFERENCES

1. SZENT-GYORGYI, A. *The Nature of Life, a Study on Muscle.* New York, Academic Press, 1948.
2. SZENT-GYORGYI, A. *Chemistry of Muscular Contraction,* 2d ed. New York, Academic Press, 1951, 162 pp.
3. HUXLEY, H. E. The double array of filaments in cross-striated muscle. *J. Biophys. Biochem. Cytol.,* 3:631–648, 1957.
4. HUXLEY, H. E. The contraction of muscle. *Sci. Amer.,* 199:66–82, 1958.
5. BOZLER, E. An analysis of the properties of smooth muscle. *Cold Spr. Harb. Symp.,* 4:260–266, 1936.
6. BOZLER, E. Action potentials and conduction of excitation in muscle. *Biol. Symp.,* 3:95–110, 1941.

7. DiPALMA, J. R., and MASCATELLO, A. V. Excitability and refractory period of isolated heart muscle of the cat. *Amer. J. Physiol.*, 164:589–600, 1951.

8. FLETT, R. L. The musculature of the heart, with its application to physiology and a note on heart rupture. *J. Anat., Lond.*, 62:439–475, 1927–28.

9. MALL, F. P. On the muscular architecture of the ventricles of the human heart. *Amer. J. Anat.*, 11:211–266, 1911.

10. ROBB, J. S., and ROBB, R. C. The normal heart. *Amer. Heart J.*, 23:455–467, 1942.

11. RUSHMER, R. F., CRYSTAL, D. K., and WAGNER, C. The functional anatomy of ventricular contraction. *Circulat. Res.*, 1:162–170, 1953.

12. NONIDEZ, J. F. The structure and innervation of the conductive system of the heart of the dog and rhesus monkey, as seen with a silver impregnation technique. *Amer. Heart J.*, 26:577–597, 1943.

13. BOAS, E. P., and GOLDSCHMIDT, E. F. *The Heart Rate*. Springfield, Illinois, Charles C Thomas, 1932.

14. CURTIS, H. J., and TRAVIS, D. M. Conduction in Purkinje tissue of the ox heart. *Amer. J. Physiol.*, 165:173–178, 1951.

15. RUSHMER, R. F., and CRYSTAL, D. K. Changes in configuration of the ventricular chambers during the cardiac cycle. *Circulation*, 4:211–218, 1951.

16. RUSHMER, R. F., and THAL, N. The mechanics of ventricular contraction: a cinefluorographic study. *Circulation*, 4:219–228, 1951.

17. RUSHMER, R. F., and THAL, N. Factors influencing stroke volume: a cinefluorographic study of angiocardiography. *Amer. J. Physiol.*, 168:509–521, 1952.

18. KAGAN, A. Dynamic responses of the right ventricle following extensive damage by cauterization. *Circulation*, 5:816–823, 1952.

19. ZAUS, E. A., and KEARNS, W. M., JR. Massive infarction of the right ventricle and atrium. *Circulation*, 6:593–598, 1952.

20. KEITH, A. The functional anatomy of the heart. *Brit. Med. J.*, 1:361–363, 1918.

21. RUSHMER, R. F. Initial phase of ventricular systole: Asynchronous contraction. *Amer. J. Physiol.*, 184:188–194, 1956.

22. RUSHMER, R. F., FINLAYSON, B. L., and NASH, A. A. Movements of the mitral valve. *Circulat. Res.*, 4:337–342, 1956.

23. IRISAWA, H., GREER, A. P., and RUSHMER, R. F. Changes in dimensions of the venae cavae. *Amer. J. Physiol.*, 196:741–744, 1959.

24. RUSHMER, R. F. Pressure-circumference relations in the aorta. *Amer. J. Physiol.*, 183:545–549, 1955.

25. VAN CITTERS, R. L., and RUSHMER, R. F. Longitudinal and radial strain in pulse wave transmission. *Fed. Proc.*, 19:104, 1960.

26. WIGGERS, C. J., and KATZ, L. N. The contour of the ventricular volume curves under different conditions. *Amer. J. Physiol.*, 58:439–475, 1921–22.

27. COBLENTZ, B., HARVEY, R. M., FERRER, M. I., COURNAND, A., and RICHARD, D. W., JR. The relationship between electrical and mechanical events in the cardiac cycle of man. *Brit. Heart J.*, 11:1–22, 1949.

Chapter 3

THE CARDIAC OUTPUT

I. Factors Affecting Cardiac Output

An understanding of the principles governing cardiovascular responses in the normal person is a prerequisite for interpreting changes induced by disease. The five basic mechanisms by which cardiac output can be adjusted are indicated in Figure 1. The cardiac output is determined by the product of the heart rate and stroke volume. Stroke volume is determined by the diastolic volume of the

FACTORS AFFECTING STROKE VOLUME

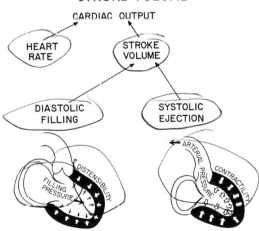

FIGURE 1. The cardiac output is influenced by at least five different factors which include changes in heart rate, and by four mechanisms which influence the stroke volume, namely (a) filling pressure, (b) ventricular distensibility, (c) arterial pressure and (d) contractility. Distensibility and contractility are terms which may in fact cover a number of additional independent factors.

ventricle minus the volume of blood in the ventricle at the end of systole. Diastolic filling is determined by the effective filling pressure and the resistance to distention offered by the ventricular wall. Systolic ejection is determined by the arterial blood pressure and the degree of myocardial shortening which can occur against that particular outflow pressure. The distensibility and contractility of the ventricular walls represent changes in the "physiologic condition" of the myocardium.

The following discussion will be devoted to a consideration of the control of the heart rate and the factors affecting contraction and distention of the cardiac chambers. Some mechanical and architectural features of the ventricles will receive attention because they also may affect the function of the heart as a pump.

CONTROL OF HEART RATE

Normally the heart rate is determined by the frequency with which the sino-atrial (S-A) node generates the impulses which spread over the atrium and ultimately activate the heart in the sequence illustrated in Figure 8, Chapter 2. Given suitable conditions, any myocardial fiber is capable of generating a conducted impulse, but the S-A node retains its role as a pacemaker of the heart (1) so long as it generates impulses more rapidly than any

53

other part of the heart and (2) so long as the conduction system functions normally (see Chap. 10). During the embryonic development of the heart, the ventricle forms first; initially it contracts very slowly and irregularly (see Fig. 1, Chap. 14). As the atrium develops, its faster inherent rate of impulse formation becomes manifest. The atrium takes over the pacemaker role and the embryonic heart rate quickens. The sinus venosus, the last portion of the heart to appear, has the highest rate of impulse formation and takes over the role of pacemaker. The S-A node is a vestigial remnant of the sinus venosus and is the pacemaker of the fully developed heart.

The Nature of Pacemaker Activity

The heart is not the only structure with an autogenic pacemaker. The ureter displays contraction waves that originate at a point near the pelvis of the kidney and descend at regular intervals toward the urinary bladder. The point where these conducted waves of excitation originate is a *pacemaker*, capable of spontaneously generating conducted impulses at regular intervals. The electrical potentials associated with this wave of excitation can be readily recorded. During the interval between the action potentials signaling waves of excitation, the recorded potentials along the ureter remain steady at a low level. At the site of the pacemaker, however, the cellular potentials rise progressively until they reach the threshold of excitability which sets off a conducted impulse (Fig. 2A). This gradual rise in potential between action potentials is called a *prepotential* and apparently represents a spontaneous phasic swing in the potential on the membranes of cells which establishes the rate at which contraction waves descend the ureter.[1] If the ureter is transected below the normal pacemaker, a new pacemaker site becomes established in the lower segment. This new pacemaker displays a prepotential but gener-

PACEMAKER ACTIVITY

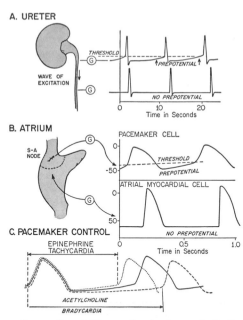

FIGURE 2.   *A*, Waves of excitation periodically pass down the ureter from a "pacemaker" site at which the membrane potentials of the cells spontaneously change (prepotentials) until threshold is reached to produce a propagated impulse spreading from cell to cell down the ureter.

B, Pacemaker cells in the sinus node normally exhibit spontaneous changes in membrane potentials (prepotentials) which lead to waves of excitation spreading centripetally from this site over the atrium.

C, Changes in heart rate induced by epinephrine or acetylcholine, acting at the pacemaker site, result from changes in the rate of membrane depolarization (slope of the prepotential) with very little alteration in the level of the threshold of excitability.

ates impulses at a slower rate than the normal site. The inherent rate of pacemaker activity is progressively slower at greater and greater distances below the pelvis of the kidney.

The correspondence between the pacemakers of the ureter and of the heart is obvious. The specialized myocardial fibers in the S-A node generate spontaneous swings in membrane potential, recorded as prepotentials within those myocardial cells which serve as pacemakers. When the membrane potential reaches the critical threshold level, a conducted impulse spreads in all directions over the atrial musculature. No prepotentials are visible in recordings from within other atrial myocardial cells.

The heart rate is normally adjusted through a change in the discharge rate of the S-A node. If the slope of the prepotential is altered, the interval required to reach the threshold level would change. West *et al.*[2] inserted very fine ultramicroelectrodes into individual S-A nodal cells which were apparently acting as pacemaker. When epinephrine was applied directly to the site, the rate of discharge was accelerated and prepotential slope became much steeper (Fig. 2C). In contrast, administration of acetylcholine produced slowing of the heart rate, associated with a much more gradual prepotential slope and a smaller action potential. Although changes in discharge rate could theoretically be achieved by alterations in threshold, this mechanism apparently is not as significant as the prepotential slope (Fig. 2C). Acetylcholine is the transmitter substance released from the parasympathetic nerves to the heart and norepinephrine is generally regarded as the transmitter substance released by sympathetic nerves distributed to the heart. Thus, the influences of these substances applied directly to pacemaker sites are believed to mimic the action of the sympathetic and parasympathetic nerves in the control of heart rate.

Autonomic Control of Heart Rate

In 1899, Hunt[3] concluded that the accelerator (sympathetic) nerves of the heart are almost always in tonic activity. The action potentials arriving at the region of sinus node are believed to trigger the release of an epinephrine-like substance at the nerve endings. This tonic activity can be identified in the medulla, particularly deep to the floor of the fourth ventricle.[4] This is the region where electrical stimulation produces large effects on both the heart rate and peripheral

vascular resistance. The term *cardioregulatory center* for such poorly localized sites is somewhat misleading, but is common usage. From the medullary centers, nerve fibers descend to the intermediolateral columns of the spinal cord (see Fig. 6, Chap. 4). The fibers course out to the sympathetic trunk through T_1, T_2, T_3, T_4 and sometimes T_5, and pass up to the stellate ganglion and to the heart through the cardiac nerves. Although the accelerator nerves cannot be dissociated from the other sympathetic nerves to the heart, the sympathetic accelerator fibers are more prominent on the right than on the left.[5]

The motor nucleus of the vagus nerve lies near the medullary sites where electrical stimulation produces tachycardia. However, the vagal nerve endings distributed to the S-A node produce a profound slowing of the heart by the mechanism illustrated in Figure 2C.

The actions of acetylcholine and the sympathetic transmitter substance are mutually antagonistic.[6] For example, if the vagus nerve is stimulated, the heart rate promptly slows. If sympathetic accelerator fibers are simultaneously stimulated at an appropriate frequency, the heart rate can be brought back to the control levels (Fig. 3A). Then if the vagal stimulation is discontinued so that the sympathetic stimulation is unopposed, the heart rate promptly accelerates. An acceleration of the heart rate alone is not a very effective mechanism for increasing cardiac output without additional mechanisms to maintain or to increase the stroke volume (Fig. 3B).

The heart rate can be precisely adjusted by balancing the retarding effects of vagal discharge against the accelerating effects of sympathetic stimulation. This is a form of reciprocal innervation at the effector organ, the S-A node. In addition, reciprocal innervation is also prominent in the central control over heart rate (i.e., at the medullary center). For

HEART RATE

A. AUTONOMIC BALANCE IN HEART RATE CONTROL

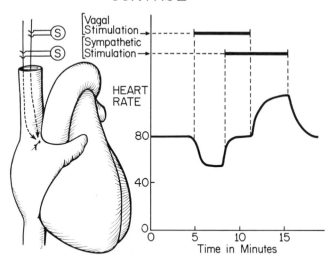

B. STROKE VOLUME DURING ARTIFICIAL TACHYCARDIA

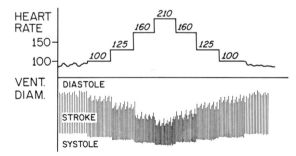

FIGURE 3.   *A*, Impulses descending the vagus nerve to the sinus node tend to produce slowing of the heart which can be precisely countered by activity of the sympathetic nerves to this site. Thus, the heart rate is regulated in terms of the balance between the sympathetic and vagal effects on the pacemaker.

B, An artificially induced tachycardia produces a progressive reduction in ventricular dimensions and in stroke deflection indicating that tachycardia alone is not an efficient mechanism for increasing cardiac output unless other mechanisms act to maintain or increase stroke volume.

example, the neural connections are so organized that activation of the motor nucleus of the vagus is associated with simultaneous inhibition of the medullary accelerator centers. The medullary centers of cardiac and peripheral vascular control are important in the control of blood pressure.[7] However, these control centers are influenced by nerves converg-ing from a wide variety of sites and sources.

Origins of Afferent Nerves Converging on the Cardioregulatory Centers

The vagus and sympathetic nerves con-duct impulses which result from a more or less continuous bombardment of the cardio-accelerator and cardio-inhibitor centers by afferent nerves from all over the body. The cardioregulatory centers are influenced by afferent fibers corresponding to those which play upon the vasomotor centers (Fig. 6, Chap. 4).

Impulses from the cerebral cortex impinge upon the cardio-accelerator and cardio-inhibitor centers, as evidenced by many common experiences. Excitement, anxiety, fear and depression[8, 9] affect the heart rate without any direct relation to metabolic activity. Cardio-acceleration occurs in anticipation of physical exertion before there is any significant increase in metabolism. An occasional individual can voluntarily alter his heart rate.[10] Clearly, the influence of higher centers on cardiovascular regulation cannot be ignored.

Stretch receptors in the carotid sinus and aortic arch exert a powerful influence on the cardioregulatory centers. A change in arterial blood pressure is reflected in a corresponding change in the frequency of impulses from the baroceptors (Fig. 4, Chap. 6) which in turn influences the rardioregulatory centers and the heart ahte. In general a drop in arterial blood pressure induces an acceleration of the ceart and vice versa.

Digital pressure on a hypersensitive carotid sinus promptly produces bradycardia, reduced peripheral resistance, a severe drop in arterial blood pressure and syncope.[11] Insertion of a needle into the brachial artery of subjects in the erect position frequently produces a very similar response.[12] Such syncopal reactions, termed *vago-vagal reactions*, may be produced by many conditions.[13, 14] Since sensory fibers from virtually all parts of the body influence heart rate and peripheral resistance, only a few of the more prominent examples can be mentioned.

Stimulation of internal organs may produce drastic cardiac inhibition. For example, stimulation of nerve endings in the upper portion of the respiratory tract may produce intense vagal depression of the heart rate. Thus, anesthetists must be extremely careful during intubation of the trachea because increased vagal activity may lead to cardiac standstill and death. Inhalation of irritant gases may intensely affect the heart rate. Phasic changes in heart rate (sinus arrhythmia) occur during normal respiratory cycles.

The gastrointestinal tract is supplied with afferent nerve fibers which travel along the vagus to the medulla. Nausea and vomiting are commonly associated with slowing of the heart whether they are due to digital stimulation of the pharynx or to ingestion of toxic substances. Visceral pain fibers are widely distributed and have a powerful slowing effect on heart rate. Painful stimulation of skeletal muscles may produce a similar autonomic response. Pressure on the eyeball may produce a profound slowing of the heart through the "oculocardiac reflex." In general, visceral afferent nerves, originating in nearly all tissues and organs except the skin, produce bradycardia. In contrast, somatic pain from the skin generally produces tachycardia along with some increase in arterial blood pressure. Additional details concerning the origins of nerve impulses which influence both heart rate and contractile properties of the heart are presented in Figure 11.

In 1906, Yandell Henderson[15] recorded the changing volume of mammalian ventricles by means of a cardiometer and noted that ventricular filling is largely completed during the first portion of diastole (see Figs. 15 and 17, Chap. 2). Further, an increase in heart rate encroached primarily on the slow filling phase of diastole ("diastasis"). He proposed the "law of uniform behavior" which implied that an increase in heart rate was the only requirement for an increase in cardiac output, since the stroke volume would not be seriously diminished unless the tachycardia was extreme. However, if a stepwise increase in heart rate is produced by stimulating electrodes in-

THE LENGTH-TENSION RELATIONSHIP OF MYOCARDIUM

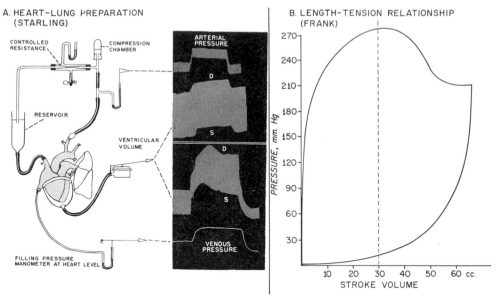

FIGURE 4.   *A*, The ventricles in a heart-lung preparation adapt to an increased work load (either increased arterial pressure or increased stroke volume) by an increase in diastolic distention. Such experiments led Starling and his associates to postulate that the energy released by the contracting myocardium was determined by the initial length of the myocardial fibers as indicated by the end diastolic ventricular volume. (After Patterson, Piper and Starling.[17])

B, The length-tension relationship of myocardium resembles that of skeletal muscle. Progressive stretch of relaxed myocardium is attended by a progressive increase in isometric contractile tension up to some level. This length-tension diagram, derived by Otto Frank from studies of frog myocardium, was employed by Starling to illustrate his concept of the "law of the heart" by applying values of pressure and stroke volume on the ordinate and abscissa which he regarded as representative of human subjects. The use of an isometric tension curve is not appropriate for illustrating changes which would occur with ejection of stroke volumes (see Fig. 6).

stalled upon the right atrium near the S-A node, a progressive reduction in the diastolic dimensions—and in stroke volume—is seen (Fig. 3*B*). An increase in heart rate accompanied by a diminution in stroke volume is not an efficient mechanism for increasing total cardiac output. Thus, it is important to consider the factors which influence the quantity of blood ejected during each systole (the stroke volume).

CONTROL OF STROKE VOLUME

The history of the basic concepts of cardiac function and control has been reviewed by Wiggers.[16] In 1895, Otto Frank recorded the isometric and iso-

tonic contractions of frog myocardium and established that, within limits, myocardium resembles skeletal muscle in developing greater tension as its resting length is increased (Fig. 4*B*). Patterson, Piper and Starling[17] used the heart-lung preparation (Fig. 4) to study the influence on cardiac function of variations in venous inflow, outflow resistance and heart rate.

Ventricular Responses in the Heart-Lung Preparation

In the heart-lung preparation, the quantity of blood entering the ventricles was increased by elevating the reservoir illustrated in Figure 4*A*. Experimentally induced elevation in "venous return" resulted in a higher venous pressure, a slight increase in arterial blood pressure and greater diastolic and systolic ventricular volumes. Records of this type have been interpreted as follows: (a) When the reservoir is elevated, the venous pressure rises and diastolic filling is increased. (b) The myocardial fibers fail to eject as much blood as entered during diastole, so an additional increment of blood remains within the ventricle. (c) The succeeding diastolic filling is even greater, but the volume ejected remains less than that which entered. (d) The diastolic filling exceeds the systolic ejection until the ventricles become distended to a point where the energy release by the myocardium is sufficiently increased to bring the inflow and outflow into balance. (e) The equilibrium between inflow and outflow is maintained with the ventricles at their new large diastolic and systolic size until the volume load is reduced. (f) As the reservoir is lowered, the energy released by the myocardium is excessive for the volume of inflow and the quantity ejected exceeds the volume which entered. For a few beats, outflow exceeds inflow until the systolic and diastolic ventricular volumes return to a lower level, actually smaller than during the control period in Figure 1.

The increased distention of the ventricles in response to a sudden increase in outflow pressure was explained as follows: The systolic increase in intraventricular pressure is not sufficient to eject all the blood that entered during the previous diastole (Fig. 1A). The succeeding diastolic filling remains the same, so an additional increment of blood remains within the ventricle. The systolic and diastolic volumes expand until the energy released by the lengthened myocardial fibers is sufficient to meet the greater requirements for intraventricular pressure during each cycle.

Starling's Law of the Heart

Starling and his associates[17] confirmed Frank's general conclusions except for one crucial point, namely, that an increased diastolic volume was usually, but not always, associated with a corresponding increase in filling pressure. They stated, "We thus find no constant connection between the diastolic tension and the succeeding contraction, though as a rule these two quantities will be altered together. But we do find a direct proportion between the diastolic volume of the heart (i.e., the length of its muscle fibres) and the energy set free in the following systole.

"The law of the heart is therefore the same as that of skeletal muscle, namely that the mechanical energy set free on passage from the resting to the contracted state depends on the area of 'chemically active surfaces,' i.e., on the length of the muscle fibres."[17]

According to these data, the normal response to either a greater volume load or a greater pressure load is an increase in both the diastolic and systolic ventricular volumes. A heart which becomes distended with a small or normal load is considered fatigued or depressed even though it may maintain a "normal" output while operating at this larger size. However, if the ventricles become distended beyond some critical size, the energy release becomes progressively less with added stretch on the myocardium and the heart "fails." The reduction of the contractile tension which occurs with excessive stretch in Frank's diagram (Fig. 4B) is a graphic illustration of this point. Under these conditions, increased diastolic distention with progressively higher venous pressure is attended by reduction in the contractile tension and in energy release. This is the most common definition of heart failure.

Wiggers and Katz[18] repeated these experiments using improved techniques.

Their results confirmed those of Starling and his associates that an increase in stroke volume was attended by an increase in diastolic volume (greater initial length of myocardial fibers). However, they concluded that "such changes were never dissociated from changes in initial intraventricular pressures." Apparently, Starling was not convinced by this evidence because in subsequent publications he restated his belief that diastolic volume may change without corresponding alterations in filling pressure.[19]

In the older concepts, variations in stroke volume are most frequently explained by a few fundamental rules which were generally held to apply so long as the functional condition of the myocardium remains within physiologic limits: (a) The *cardiac output* is determined by the venous return. (b) If the heart rate is constant, the *stroke volume* is determined by the venous return. (c) *Stroke volume* of the ventricles depends directly on the diastolic filling. (d) The *tension* of resting myocardial fibers depends upon their length. (e) *Diastolic filling* (and diastolic volume) of the ventricles is determined by effective filling pressure. (f) *The mechanical energy set free on passage from the resting to the contracted state depends on the length of the myocardial fibers.*

A number of these concepts were derived from Starling's experiments, and most of them have been erroneously cited at one time or another as "Starling's law of the heart." The concept that the diastolic volume is always determined by the effective filling pressure (e, above) is contrary to both the results and the conclusions of Starling and his associates. By the same token, belief in a constant relation between length and tension of resting myocardial fibers (d, above) cannot be attributed to these investigators.

Semantic confusion usually results from attempts to explain complicated reactions by oversimplification. There is often a basic fallacy in enunciating simple generalizations or laws designed to serve as universally applicable explanations of the behavior of complex biological systems. The concept that the energy release during myocardial contraction depends upon the length of the muscle fibers carries an implication that all other conditions remain unchanged. Included among the "other conditions" are the heart rate and the "physiologic condition" or "functional state" of the myocardium. A wide variety of factors influence the "physiologic condition" of the myocardium, including autonomic hormones, sympathetic nerves, chemical substances in the blood and the oxygen supply to the myocardium; there are probably others which are currently unrecognized. Starling's law can be unequivocally demonstrated as a dominant mechanism in a cardiac response only when all these factors are relatively fixed, a condition that is encountered rarely except in the experimental situation. In general, the Starling mechanism is consistently confirmed during experiments on isolated hearts or on hearts exposed by thoracotomy in animals under surgical anesthesia. Although the mechanism is unquestionably operative under all conditions, it can rarely be definitely identified as a dominant mechanism in cardiac control during spontaneous activity in intact animals and men.[20] A notable exception is the ventricular response to changes in position or to exposure to gravitational forces. During such events the Starling mechanism is clearly displayed (see Figs. 10 and 11, Chap. 7).

Applicability of Data from Anesthetized, Thoracotomized Animals. Within the limitations of the experimental methods, the validity of data obtained by such outstanding investigators as Frank, Starling and Wiggers is not questioned. However, deficiencies in the classic recording techniques must be recognized. Although changes in ventricular volume are recorded with reasonable accuracy by a cardiometer, it is the combined volume of the right and left ventricles which is measured. The cardiometer cannot be used to determine changes in volume of each ventricle individually. Since the right and left ventricles are very different in their anatomy, geometric configuration and function (Fig. 13, Chap. 2), changes in the volume of one chamber could easily obscure reactions in the other. Actually, the cyclic variations in the absolute volume of the individual cardiac chambers have never been directly measured in a beating heart. Even if it were possible to measure accurately and simultaneously all the significant variables in anesthetized, thoracotomized animals, application of these data to normal animals and to man would require some rather broad assumptions.

Effects of Anesthesia. Cardioregulatory influences from the higher centers of the central nervous system are undoubtedly depressed, distorted or eliminated by surgical anesthesia. Clearly, cerebral effects on cardiovascular control cannot be studied in anesthetized animals, whereas in normal individuals they may play important roles. Reflex mechanisms involving the lower levels of the nervous system are also depressed or distorted by anesthesia. Since the basic data which led to the traditional concepts of cardiac control were derived from controlled experiments, it is not surprising that the mechanical aspects of the cardiac response were emphasized with relatively little consideration of neural and hormonal influences.

Experimentally Applied Loads on the Heart. The circulatory system of an anesthetized dog is stable. In other words, nothing happens until some change is induced by the investigator. Experimentally induced loads on the heart are presumed to be equivalent to naturally occurring functional loads. For example, the cardiac output may be increased by rapid infusion of saline or blood from a reservoir,

a technique which need not be equivalent to the natural mechanisms for increasing stroke volume. An increase in ventricular filling pressure is virtually assured by this procedure. However, the increase in cardiac output when saline or blood substitutes are infused intravenously is a product of the relative anemia resulting from the dilution of the blood.[21, 22] Central venous pressures may be raised to very high levels by infusions of whole blood without an increase in cardiac output.

Effects of Thoractomy on the Heart. During the period when Starling was conducting his classic experiments, it was generally believed that the ventricles were almost completely evacuated by each systolic contraction under normal resting conditions. This concept persists in the general attitude that a small heart is a normal heart—indeed, the smaller the better. More recently, the presence of relatively large volumes of "residual" blood at the end of systole has been demonstrated in normal ventricles. The amount of residual blood in each ventricle, illustrated in Figures 10 and 14, Chapter 2, is typical of intact dogs.[24, 25] Equally convincing evidence of residual blood has been obtained in man.[26-28] Kjellberg et al.[29] demonstrated a close correlation between total blood volume and heart volume, and concluded that about 10 per cent of the blood volume is contained within the chambers of the heart.

Ferguson, Shadle and Gregg[30] observed gross differences between the performance of the heart in dogs with open and with closed chests. The average values for the left ventricular diastolic pressure, stroke work index and stroke volume index in dogs with closed chests were each more than four times that of animals with open chests and the cardiac index was twice as great. An important factor in the reduction of the stroke volume was the heart rate, which averaged three times greater in open chested animals (180 per

SHRINKAGE OF THE EXPOSED HEART

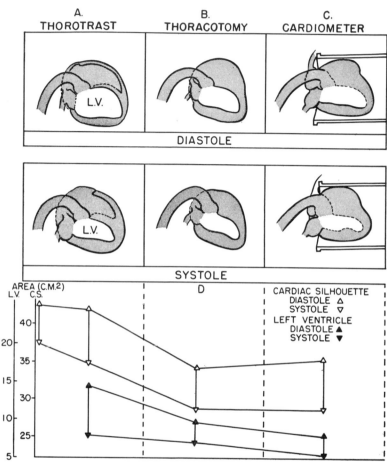

FIGURE 5.   *A,* Thorotrast was injected into a normal unanesthetized dog and its course through the heart was recorded cinefluorographically. The area of the cardiac silhouette and of the left ventricle during both systole and diastole are indicated in the graph, *D.*

B, After anesthesia and thoracotomy, the heart definitely became smaller.

C, The cardiac silhouette changed in configuration when the heart was placed in a loose-fitting cardiometer, but its area was not diminished. The left ventricular area was further reduced by this procedure. The left ventricle emptied almost completely at the end of systole, a situation which never was encountered among intact dogs.

minute) than in intact dogs (60 per minute).

Cinefluorographic studies have shown that the heart shrinks when an animal is anesthetized and thoractomized.[31] Films were taken of the hearts of normal dogs lying unrestrained on the table. Thorotrast (50 cc.) was then injected intravenously and another film obtained. The cardiac silhouette and heart chambers were then recorded cinefluorographically after each of the following procedures: (*a*) surgical anesthesia induced by intravenous Nembutal, (*b*) thoracotomy and (*c*) the application of a cardiometer. The area of the cardiac silhouette and of the left ventricular chambers consistently diminished (Fig. 5). After the thorax was opened the left ventricular chamber often appeared to empty almost completely during each systole. The heart remained very small for extended periods even after reinflation of the lungs and careful repair of the thoracotomy. In one or two days, the heart generally regained the control dimensions. The distention of the heart to the preoperative size appeared to be greatly accelerated by carefully removing as much air from the pleural space as possible. It seemed that small quantities of air within the thorax significantly affected the degree and persistence of the abnormally small heart size after thoracotomy. Thus, the original cardiometer experiments were probably conducted on hearts which were very much smaller than normal. Under these circumstances, it is not surprising that they would tend to become larger in response to an increased load. It seems possible that many of them could not have become smaller.

Loss of Myocardial Tension Due to Shortening

The graph illustrating an increase in contractile tension associated with elongation of the myocardial fibers (Fig. 4B) was derived by Frank and employed by Starling to illustrate the law of the heart. This relationship represents the changes in tension which occur during isometric contraction of myocardial strips. The heart cannot serve as a pump if the myocardial fibers contract isometrically because shortening of the fibers is required to eject the blood from the cardiac chambers. Using a condensor myograph, Lundin[32] studied the tension produced during myocardial contraction with and without shortening of the muscle and under many other conditions.

Isometric Contraction. When a strip of myocardium is stimulated to contract without being allowed to shorten, tension develops rapidly and is well sustained during the period of contraction. Lundin[32] found that tension developed during the contraction is related to the length of the fiber, as indicated in Figure 6, which corresponds to Frank's length-tension diagram. To obtain this graph, Lundin gradually stretched a bundle of myocardium until it just began to exert tension while relaxed. This was considered

EFFECTS OF SHORTENING ON MYOCARDIAL CONTRACTILE TENSION

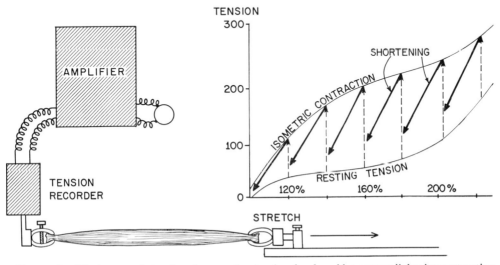

FIGURE 6. The increase in tension above resting tension developed by myocardial strips contracting under isometric conditions increased progressively from resting length to about 160 to 180 per cent of resting length, then diminished. If the myocardial strips shorten by 20 per cent during contraction, the contractile tension falls off sharply. (After Lundin.[32])

the resting length (100 per cent in Fig. 6). Additional stretch applied to the relaxed fiber progressively increased resting tension. Contraction of the myocardium at various degrees of stretch produced increased tension superimposed on the resting tension. The maximum tension produced by contraction occurred when the myocardium was about 180 per cent of the "resting length." Without myocardial shortening, no blood is pumped and no useful work is accomplished. The tension of contracting myocardial fibers during changes in length is vitally important, but has received little attention.

Myocardial Tension During Shortening. When a bundle of myocardium is allowed to shorten after the onset of contraction, the tension produced by isometric contraction falls precipitously (Fig. 6). This phenomenon has been related to high internal "viscosity" of myocardial fibers. "Viscosity" in this sense refers to the sharp rise in internal resistance or friction in a substance during sudden movement. For example, molasses will flow slowly in response to a small force, but a tremendous force is required to produce rapid acceleration. If a contracting muscle shortens abruptly, a portion of the energy of contraction is utilized to overcome the high resistance to a sudden change in length of the muscle fibers. Similar viscosity effects in skeletal muscle have been described by Gasser and Hill,[33] Buchthal et al.[34] and many others. The high viscosity of myocardium produces a fall in contraction tension as soon as shortening begins. The frictional energy loss due to internal viscosity accounts for increased heat production in muscles which shorten during contraction.

Rapid Stretch of Relaxed Myocardial Bundles. A very small force will gradually elongate relaxed myocardium to considerable lengths. On the other hand, the myocardium resists any rapid change in length because of internal viscosity. In other words, a rapid stretch is opposed by a prompt and significant rise in the tension of the fibers. In an intact heart, an abrupt inflow of blood would be opposed by this increased resistance to stretch while a slower inflow might induce greater distention with less filling pressure.

If viscosity in myocardial fibers is a prominent feature in the intact mammalian heart, a series of intriguing postulates can be evolved: Intraventricular pressure rises rapidly during the isometric period of contraction because the myocardial bundles need not shorten significantly. As soon as ventricular ejection begins, the myocardial fibers begin to shorten, and their tension falls off partly because of internal friction or "viscosity effects." The intraventricular pressure falls off correspondingly, and the rate of systolic ejection slows during the latter part of systole. Since viscosity is high in myocardial bundles, their tension drops to very low levels immediately after contraction stops, so that early diastolic filling meets little opposition. However, if the inflow is rapid, the ventricular myocardium is rapidly stretched so that tension is increased and further distention is resisted. If this is true, a rapid diastolic filling should stop abruptly in early diastole, while a slow inflow should produce progressive filling during the entire diastolic interval. Since the amount of energy lost through friction caused by myocardial viscosity depends upon the rate and extent of the change in fiber length, all of these factors involve either greater energy waste or less viscosity.

The efficiency of myocardial contraction would be materially improved by any mechanism which reduced the rate and extent of myocardial shortening. The contractile tension would be more effectively maintained, and the frictional energy loss would be diminished as the degree of myocardial shortening is lessened even though stroke volume and energy release remain constant.[25]

Relation of Diastolic Volume to the Degree of Myocardial Shortening. The degree of myocardial shortening can be reduced without changing the stroke volume if the diastolic distention of the ventricles is increased.[25] Consider a thin-walled elastic sphere with a radius of 10 cm., a circumference of 62.8 cm. and a volume of 4186 cc. If the radius and circumference were uniformly reduced by one-half (radius 5 cm. and circumference 31.4 cm.), the volume would be reduced to 523 cc. In other words, to reduce the circumference of a sphere by one-half,

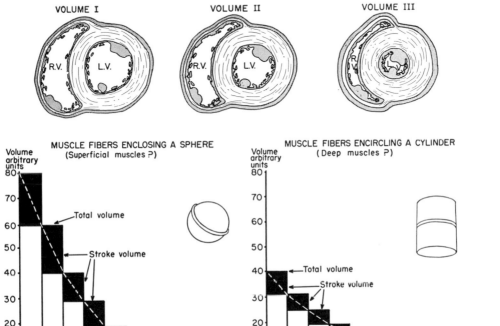

THE RELATION OF MYOCARDIAL LENGTH TO VENTRICULAR VOLUME

FIGURE 7.   The volume of blood ejected by a ventricle (stroke volume) depends upon two factors: (*a*) the diastolic volume and (*b*) the amount of myocardial shortening. Normally, the ventricles are well distended with blood during diastole (volume I) and eject only a portion of the blood within the chambers during systole (volume II). Similar volumes of blood could theoretically be ejected from less distended ventricles (such as volume II) by much more complete systolic emptying (volume III).

The superficial spiral muscles encircle a large volume which is roughly spherical in shape. Under these conditions, very slight degrees of myocardial shortening will eject very large volumes. The larger the initial volume, the greater the volume ejected for a particular degree of myocardial shortening as indicated by the black areas on the left.

The deep constrictor muscles encircle the cylindrical portion of the left ventrical chamber. The change in volume produced by a reduction in the circumference of a cylinder is much smaller (black areas on the right) than is produced by the same reduction in circumference of a sphere (black areas on the left). Furthermore, the circumference of the left ventricle is much smaller than the circumference of the entire heart. Thus, the superficial spiral layers of myocardial fibers have a much greater initial length and enclose a sphere, so very slight shortening ejects large volumes. The deep constrictor muscles describe circles of small circumference around a cylinder, so they must shorten a great deal more to eject the same volume.

nearly 90 per cent of its volume must be removed. Doubling the radius (20 cm.) would increase the volume to nearly 33,500 cc. Thus, a very slight reduction in circumference of a large sphere would eject a very much greater volume than the same reduction in circumference of a small sphere. The superficial spiral muscles tend to conform most closely to a spherical shape, and this analysis applies within limits to these myocardial fibers.

The deep constrictor muscles in the left ventricle are generally arranged circumferentially around a roughly cylindrical cavity. Here again, the reduction in volume produced by a reduction in circumference is much greater when the original circumference is large than when it is small. Thus, the degree of myocardial shortening required to eject a particular stroke volume is much less if the initial fiber length (diastolic volume) is great. Evidence has been presented that under normal conditions, ventricular contraction generally corresponds to a reduction in the chamber from volume I to volume II in Figure 7. Although the same stroke volume can be ejected by a change from volume II to volume III (Fig. 7), the relative degree of myocardial shortening would be much greater. When the diastolic volume is large, a relatively large stroke volume can be ejected with small degrees of myocardial shortening. As the degree of myocardial shortening decreases, the tension is more effectively maintained during ejection, the loss of energy due to viscosity or internal friction is diminished and the efficiency of the contractile mechanism is improved, i.e., more work is accomplished per unit of oxygen consumed.

Since the free wall of the right ventricle corresponds to a segment of a large sphere while the left ventricle resembles a cylinder, equal myocardial shortening in the two chambers would produce much larger stroke volumes from the right ventricle than from the left. The right and left ventricles must eject roughly equal quantities, so the degree of myocardial shortening cannot be equal in the two ventricles.

The Degree of Myocardial Shortening in Different Muscles of the Heart. The various myocardial bundles in the ventricles are oriented in different directions and describe circles of different diameters, so the degree of myocardial shortening must vary widely in different layers. In Figure 8B, the relative wall thickness and the radius of the left ventricular chamber at a particular size are represented by volume I. Volume II represents the same cross section with the ventricular volume reduced by half. In both cases it is obvious that the radius and circumference of the inner layer of myocardium (R_1 and C_1) are less than those of the outer layer (R_2, C_2). During contraction from volume I to volume II, the radius and circumference of the inner layer are reduced much more than those of the outer layers. This means that the inner layer of myocardium must shorten more than the outer layers. If this analysis is correct, the thickness of the ventricular walls should increase during systole and decrease during diastole. In the cinefluorographic angiocardiogram shown in Figure 14, Chapter 2, such an increase in wall thickness during systole can be readily visualized.

It is apparent that during any particular ventricular contraction, the inner layers of the deep constrictor muscles shorten to the greatest extent. Outer layers of the deep constrictor fibers shorten less and the superficial spiral muscles shorten the least. The relative degree of myocardial shortening in the inner lining of spiral muscle (trabeculae carneae) and papillary muscles cannot be assessed by this type of analysis. The difference in degrees of shortening by various myocardial layers is diminished when the diastolic and systolic volumes remain large; the maximum difference between the shortening of the superficial spiral muscle and that of the inner layer of deep constrictor fibers would occur when the left ventricle empties maximally (see volume III in Fig. 7).

Factors Opposing Complete Ventricular Emptying

Muscle fibers cannot shorten to an infinitely small length. The maximum degree of myocardial shortening probably ranges around 20 per cent of the resting length, but it is impossible to determine at what size of an intact ventricle the myocardial fibers are at resting length. If all the myocardial fibers constricted 20 per cent of their initial length, the inner layer of circumferential fibers would have attained this value and ceased contributing any tension, while the outer layers and particularly the spiral muscles might be

THE DEGREE OF MYOCARDIAL SHORTENING IN THE VENTRICULAR WALLS

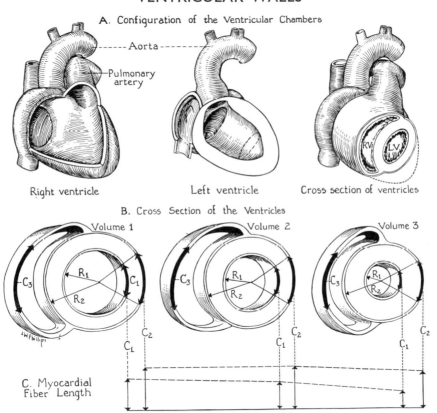

A. Configuration of the Ventricular Chambers

Right ventricle   Left ventricle   Cross section of ventricles

B. Cross Section of the Ventricles

C. Myocardial Fiber Length

FIGURE 8. The right ventricular cavity is enclosed by the convex interventricular septum and the concave free wall, which may be considered a segment of a very large sphere. Very slight shortening of the fibers in the free wall of the right ventricle (C_3) will eject very large volumes (see Fig. 7).

The left ventricle has been compared to a very thick-walled cylinder with a conoid segment at the apex (see Chap. 2). The circumferentially arranged deep constrictor fibers account for most of the wall thickness which encloses the cylindrical portion of the chamber. The deep constrictor fibers form a cuff of muscle which is so thick that the circles described by the inner layers have a much smaller radius (R_1) and circumference (C_1) than those described by the outer layers (R_2 and C_2). As the left ventricle contracts, the inner layers must shorten to a greater degree than the outer layers in ejecting a particular volume. On the basis of this analysis, during any normal systolic ejection the outer layers of the deep constrictor muscle must shorten to a lesser extent and the superficial spiral muscles shorten least of all. It is possible that no two layers of myocardial fibers shorten to exactly the same extent during ejection.

TENSION DEVELOPED BETWEEN MYOCARDIAL LAYERS
(INTERFASCICULAR TENSION)

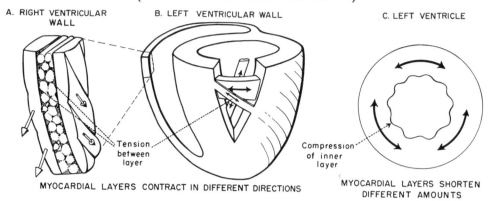

FIGURE 9.   *A*, Although the right ventricular wall is quite thin, it contains myocardial fibers oriented in three different directions. Simultaneous contraction of these fibers must create tension in the fibrous and myocardial connections between the different layers (interfasicicular tension).

B, The left ventricular wall is also composed of at least three layers of muscle, oriented primarily in three different directions (see Chap. 2). Interfascicular tension must develop in the connections between these layers during contraction.

C, The different layers of the thick-walled left ventricles must contract to different degrees in ejecting a particular volume of blood (see Fig. 8). This presumably causes tensions between layers of circularly arranged fibers, as well as compressing the inner layers.

able to contract still more. From this point on, further shortening by the outer layers would require an expenditure of energy in wrinkling and deforming the inner layers.

The trabeculae carneae represent preformed wrinkles and combine with the papillary muscles to occupy space in the ventricles. This permits more complete systolic ejection than would be possible if the inner walls of the ventricular chamber were smooth (see Fig. 7). Because of the space occupied by papillary muscles and trabeculae carneae, even the inner layers of circumferential fibers in the left ventricle can describe circles of reasonable diameter when the left ventricle is virtually emptied. This mechanism is less important in the right ventricle because of (*a*) its thin wall, (*b*) the very long fibers which enclose the cavity and (*c*) the large circles described by these fibers.

Interfascicular Tension. The myocardial bundles in the different muscle layers of the ventricular walls are oriented in different directions (Fig. 9). Furthermore,

the fibers must shorten to different degrees during their contraction. But these layers are bound tightly together. During ventricular contraction, the relative movements and displacements of these different muscle layers must stretch the connections between them. In other words, part of the tension developed by the contracting myocardial fibers must be expended in applying tension to the "interfascicular" connections. This "interfascicular tension" represents wasted energy so far as ventricular ejection is concerned because it actually opposes movements of the ventricular walls. However, as the ventricles relax, the potential energy stored as interfascicular tension is released, tending to restore the ventricular cavities toward their diastolic dimensions and facilitating rapid ventricular filling during early diastole. This mechanism leads to phenomena commonly termed *diastolic suction.*[35]

In some respects, the contractile energy which is stored as interfascicular tension has functional significance similar to that of myocardial viscosity. For example, the amount of energy stored as interfascicular tension probably increases as systolic ejection becomes more complete and decreases as the ventricles function at large diastolic and systolic dimensions. The ventricular volume at which the interfascicular tension is minimal has not been definitely established. As the ventricles relax, the interfascicular tension should tend to restore the ventricles to that particular ventricular volume. However, the effective filling pressure could distend the ventricles beyond the level of minimal interfascicular tension by distorting the interfascicular connections in the opposite direction. In all probability, the ventricular volume at which the interfascicular tension is minimal is reached at some point during diastole.

The Relation of Myocardial Viscosity and Interfascicular Tension to Starling's Law of the Heart. The basic principle that the energy released by contracting myocardial fibers is proportional to their initial length (diastolic volume) has generally been regarded as a fundamental property of the contractile mechanisms, which it probably is. In addition, the contractile energy wasted to overcome myocardial viscosity and create interfascicular tension is diminished when the ventricles function at large diastolic and systolic dimensions. Thus, not only is more energy released when the ventricles contract from larger ventricular volumes, but less is wasted, so the net useful energy is disproportionately greater.

Clearly, the ventricles function more efficiently at large diastolic and systolic dimensions because of three factors: (a) Starling's law of the heart, (b) myocardial viscosity, and (c) interfascicular tension. On the other hand, in accordance with the law of Laplace, myocardial fibers must develop higher tension to produce a particular level of intraventricular pressure when myocardial fibers describe circles with larger radii.

The Law of Laplace. According to the Laplace formula ($P = T/R$), the pressure (P) developed by a particular level of wall tension (T) is inversely proportional to the radius of the chamber. This law was invoked to explain the difference between the wall thicknesses of the aorta and the systemic capillaries when these widely different structures sustain pressures of the same magnitude (see Fig. 11, Chap. 1).

Applied to the contracting ventricle, the law of Laplace indicates that the myocardial tension required to sustain a particular level of intraventricular pressure diminishes as the radius of the chamber is reduced by ejection. In other words, this factor would tend to compensate to some extent for the loss of myocardial tension through myocardial viscosity and interfascicular tension. On the other hand, if the diastolic volume is increased, greater myocardial tension is needed to develop a particular level of intraventricular pressure. This factor may explain the development of hypertrophy rather than dilation when the left ventricle is exposed to chronic pressure loads.

During isometric contraction, intraventricular pressure rises abruptly until it exceeds the pressure in the corresponding arterial trunk. The intraventricular pressure is determined at any instant by the myocardial tension and the effective radius of the circles described by the myocardial fibers. As soon as intraventricular pressure exceeds the corresponding arterial pressure, blood is ejected from the chamber as the myocardial fibers begin to shorten. The myocardial tension falls because of myocardial viscosity. A portion of the myocardial tension is diverted to produce interfascicular tension. Thus, during the later part of systole, the rate of ejection slows although the intraventricular pressure remains high. Ejection of blood from the ventricles continues only so long as the myocardial fibers continue to sustain adequate tension while they are shortening. In other words, the volume of blood ejected during a ventricular contraction is determined by the amount of myocardial shortening which occurs before the net tension of the fibers drops below that required to maintain an interventricular pressure greater than that in the corresponding artery. The volume of blood ejected per stroke can be increased in at least two ways: (a) greater myocardial contractility and (b) greater diastolic distention.

In summary, the control of stroke volume has been explained largely on the basis of two fundamental concepts: (a) The diastolic volume of the ventricles is determined by the effective filling pressure, and (b) the energy released by the contracting myocardium is proportional to the initial length (diastolic volume) of the ventricular musculature (Starling's law of the heart). This mechanism is readily evident in the changes in ventricular volume and stroke volume during changes in posture (see Chap. 7). Under other conditions its influence is usually obscured by other mechanisms.

Under normal conditions the ventricles function at relatively large diastolic and systolic dimensions, so an increase in stroke volume can be attained by an increase in the degree of systolic emptying, by an increase in the extent of diastolic filling or by a combination of the two. The heart rate also plays an important role in the determination of the stroke volume, and also of the ventricular volume and cardiac output. If the heart rate, diastolic volume and systolic ejection are influenced by autonomic reflexes, cardiovascular responses can be promptly adjusted to varying circulatory demands through direct influence on the cardiac musculature as well as through peripheral vascular mechanisms. The factors which tend to produce an increase in heart rate also may act simultaneously to augment contractility, so that the effective filling pressure is maintained at relatively low

levels unless the cardiac output fails to meet the circulatory demands. In this case, diastolic filling may be further increased by an augmented filling pressure (increased central venous pressure).

The neural and humoral controlling mechanisms act by changing the functional characteristics of the myocardium.

Increased Myocardial Contractility

The contraction of the ventricles is greatly modified by many different factors including the heart rate, coronary blood supply, hormones (e.g., l-epinephrine and norepinephrine), autonomic nerves and probably others. The control of cardiac output depends in large measure upon mechanisms which modify the contractile properties of the myocardium. It is generally recognized that the administration of catechol amines increases the "vigor" of myocardial contraction. The intraventricular pressure rises more abruptly to greater heights, and the duration of the systole is shortened. Starling and his associates[17, 19] were fully aware that, even in the isolated heart, epinephrine acts to produce a more complete systolic ejection, greater stroke volume and greater energy release without an increase in diastolic distention. Indeed, the ventricular dimensions generally diminish under these conditions. The changes in ventricular activity induced by changes in the composition of perfusion fluids, by neurohormones or by stimulation of autonomic nerves have been attributed to changes in the "physiological state or condition of the myocardium." Changes in the "contractile properties" of the myocardium were commonly studied by administration of extracts of the adrenal medulla in the belief that the effects of such extracts simulated the action of the sympathetic nerves to the heart. Attention was directed particularly to the sympathetic nervous system and its effects, since acetylcholine and stimulation of vagal nerves to the heart have profound effects on heart rate but have little, if any, influence on the contractile properties of the myocardium[5] (see Fig. 11).

Effects of Epinephrine on Myocardium. The transmitter substance norepinephrine is released at the ends of the sympathetic nerves as the mechanism for inducing changes at the effector organ (myocardium, smooth muscle or glands). The adrenal gland, when stimulated by its sympathetic nerve supply, secretes a mixture containing about 80 per cent l-epinephrine and 20 per cent norepinephrine. Chromaffin tissue elsewhere in the body, particularly within the walls of the heart, also releases l-epinephrine. The direct effects of l-epinephrine on strips of myocardium are to increase the speed, vigor and power of myocardial contraction[32] and to produce acceleration of the heart by acting upon the pacemaker (Fig. 2). In dogs, the effects of norepinephrine on myocardial contraction are similar to those of l-epinephrine. In man, however, norepinephrine introduced into the blood stream is reported to have powerful vasoconstrictor effects on the peripheral vascular system but less effect on myocardial contraction.

Paradoxial Effects of Epinephrine on Heart Rate. When norepinephrine is injected intravenously in man and dogs, the more powerful contractile properties of the myocardium are noted but the heart rate slows. This paradoxical effect is seen because autonomic reflexes override the direct effects of the injected catechol amine on the pacemaker. The elevation of systemic arterial pressure augments the discharge rate of pressoreceptors in the carotid sinus and the aortic arch (see Chap. 6). This increased discharge inhibits the cardio-accelerator areas of the medulla and augments discharge of vagal fibers to the heart. The bradycardia accompanying elevation of the systolic ventricular pressure during infusions of "physiologic" concentrations of l-epinephrine and norepinephrine are illustrated in Figure 14.

During a wide variety of spontaneous cardiovascular adjustments, the characteristic response involves simultaneous increases in the heart rate, the systolic ventricular pressure and the mean arterial pressure. For example, tachycardia is associated with a similar increase in systolic ventricular pressure during exercise (see Fig. 14). This means that pressoreceptor reflexes must be overriden or suppressed during these spontaneous cardiovascular adjustments. The typical responses illustrated in Figure 14 also indicate that increased secretion of catechol amines by the adrenal gland probably does not dominate the normal spontaneous cardiovascular responses of intact animals and man.[36] The old concept that the actions of l-epinephrine and norepinephrine simulate the actions of a general sympathetic discharge is only partly true. These sympathomimetic drugs are not adequate experimental substitutes for studies of sympathetic control. Isoproterenol, a synthetic derivative of the naturally occurring catechol amines, produces tachycardia, increased cardiac "contractility," peripheral vasodilation and, often, reduced ventricular dimensions (see Fig. 14). The normal action of autonomic nerves is much more appropriately ascertained by direct observations on the results of stimulation than by administering hormones.

Effects of Sympathetic Cardiac Nerves. Stimulation of the left stellate ganglion and the sympathetic cardiac nerves to the heart induces profound changes in the contractile tensions developed during systole.[37, 38] The effects of the sympathetic nerves are more dramatically demonstrated by restricting the degree of myocardial shortening (see Fig. 6). Clamping of the aorta largely prevents

VENTRICULAR CONTRACTILE TENSION DURING SYMPATHETIC STIMULATION

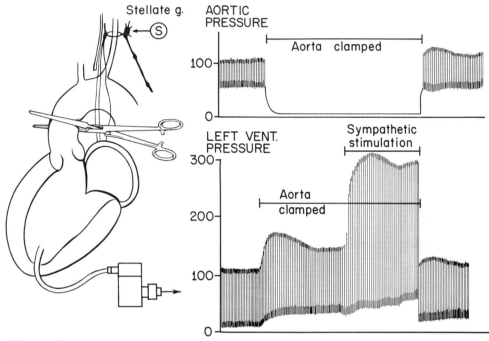

FIGURE 10.   Ventricular pressure is elevated during each systolic contraction by clamping the aorta so that the myocardium contracts more nearly isometrically. A very large additional increase in contractile tension can be produced by stimulating sympathetic cardiac nerves. This observation demonstrates a direct effect of the sympathetic nerve activity on myocardial contractile force, independent of any peripheral vascular effects of such stimulation.

ejection of blood, and the intraventricular pressure rises as aortic pressure rapidly drops toward zero. Ventricular systolic pressure is almost doubled when the ventricular contraction is rendered almost isometric (Fig. 10). If the sympathetic cardiac nerves on the left are stimulated when the ventricles are contracting almost isometrically, the ventricular pressure rises to extremely high levels, reaching 300 mm. Hg as in Figure 10 and up to 500 mm. Hg in other experiments. The cardiac sympathetic nerves on the left side profoundly affect the maximum tension which can be developed by the ventricular myocardium. The cardiac nerves on the right side generally produce a greater change in the heart rate and a smaller increase in contractile tension.

The sympathetic nerves to the heart on the right apparently converge on the S-A node to act on the pacemaker, while the left sympathetic nerves are more widely distributed to the atrial and ventricular myocardium (Fig. 11).

When stimulated, the parasympathetic nerves to the heart exert a powerful inhibitory effect on the heart rate. They do not, on the other hand, significantly affect the contractile properties of the ventricular myocardium if the bradycardia is prevented by direct stimulation of the atrial musculature to control the heart rate.[6] In fact, the parasympathetic nerves are apparently not distributed to the ventricular myocardium (see Fig. 11).

Although the sympathetic innervation of the heart apparently induces changes more closely resembling those observed during spontaneous cardiovascular responses, such conclusions can be based only on more direct comparisons than can be achieved in the anesthetized, thoractomized dog. Instead, the changes in cardiac performance must be studied continuously during various kinds of activity in healthy unanesthetized dogs. For this purpose it has been necessary to develop a completely new kind of physiologic instrumentation.

Techniques for Recording Cardiac Performance in Intact Dogs

Although it has not been possible to measure directly the absolute ventricular volume in intact animals, new techniques

have been devised[39-42] for continuously recording the circumference, diameter and length of the left ventricular chamber. The left ventricular pressure and the flow of blood through the aorta have also been measured in intact dogs, and records of all these parameters of ventricular function have been obtained during a wide range of activities for periods of days or weeks. These methods are described here briefly because they are recent developments which are not generally familiar; the data discussed in the remainder of this section have been obtained by these means.

Inductance and Resistance Gauges. *Left ventricular diameter* has been measured by variable inductance gauges installed with-

NEURAL CONTROL OF THE HEART

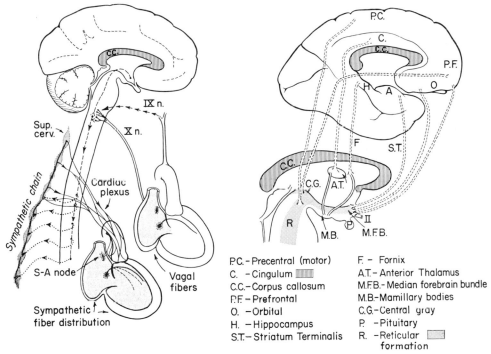

P.C. - Precentral (motor)	F. – Fornix
C. – Cingulum	A.T. - Anterior Thalamus
C.C.- Corpus callosum	M.F.B.- Median forebrain bundle
P.F. – Prefrontal	M.B.- Mamillary bodies
O. – Orbital	C.G.- Central gray
H. – Hippocampus	P. – Pituitary
S.T.- Striatum Terminalis	R. – Reticular formation

FIGURE 11. *A*, The vagus nerve endings are concentrated in the region of the sinus node and atrioventricular node and are more diffusely distributed over the atrium. They do not extend to the ventricular myocardium. Sympathetic fibers from T_1-T_5 are distributed to all parts of the atrium and ventricles. Impulses traveling along the vagus and sympathetic nerves to the heart come from the medulla or the diencephalon.

B, Neural pathways from many parts of the brain converge on the diencephalic region to influence autonomic outflow to the heart and other visceral structures.

in that chamber and connected to a recorder by wires on the outside. The gauge comprises a coil, anchored at one end to the free wall of the left ventricle, and a stylus, anchored to the mid-portion of the interventricular wall and free to move within the coil. The position of the stylus within the coil can be recorded to a fraction of a millimeter (see Fig. 12B).

Left ventricular length can also be determined with a variable inductance gauge. For this measurement the gauge is installed between the root of the aorta and the apex of the chamber.

Left ventricular circumference has been measured by a variable resistance gauge (a mercury-filled rubber tube) encircling the chamber; a wire from one end of the gauge passes into the right ventricular cavity to follow the contour of the interventricular septum. The absolute circumference of the gauge is determined from roentgenograms exposed perpendicular to the long axis of the ventricle (see Fig. 12C).

Sonocardiometry.[41, 42] Alternatively, a ventricular dimension may be measured in the intact dog with the sonocardiometer. With this instrument, the distance across the ventricular cavity is determined as the transit time of bursts of ultrasonic vibrations passing between barium titanate crystals installed on its walls (see Fig. 15C). These sound waves travel through blood and the ventricular walls at 1.5 mm./second, so that this transit time can be continuously recorded and calibrated as ventricular diameter.

Recording of Ventricular Pressure. *Effective left ventricular pressure* can be recorded by means of a small differential-transformer pressure gauge (see Fig. 15A). The pressure within the left ventricle is led to one side of the gauge through an indwelling catheter. The extracardiac pressure is transmitted from a balloon placed in the pleural space to the other side of the gauge through another cannula.

Recording of Aortic Flow. *Left Ventricular outflow* is continuously monitored by means of a plused ultrasonic flowmeter.[39, 40] Two small barium titanate crystals, serving as either transmitters or receivers of high-frequency sound (3 megacycles), are mounted at diametrically opposite positions in a bivalved plastic cylinder enclosing the root of the aorta (see Fig. 15B). The time required for a burst of sound to pass diagonally across the root of the aorta is the same in either direction when the blood is stationary. When the blood flows out of the ventricle, the sound travels faster downstream than upstream, and this difference in transit time is directly proportional to the mean velocity of blood flow in the aorta. Since the dimensions of the aorta were fixed by the rigid plastic cylinder, the mean velocity of flow could be directly calibrated in terms of instantaneous volume flow.

Stroke Work of Myocardial Fibers. Burch and Ray (see Fig. 12A) used typical records from Wiggers' experiments to plot ventricular pressure against ventricular volume, producing a loop which describes the function of the ventricular chambers. During diastole, the volume increased while the pressure dropped slightly. Isometric contraction produced a sudden rise in pressure with no change in volume. During ejection, the volume diminished while the pressure rose slightly. Isometric relaxation permitted the pressure to fall abruptly with little change in volume. If the pressure and volume of an individual ventricle were used to construct such a loop, the enclosed area would be a direct expression of the ventricular stroke work.

A plot of pressure against diameter produced a loop which was similar in contour to that obtained by Burch and Ray (Fig. 12B). If the diameter were directly proportional to the volume, the area of a pressure-diameter loop would indicate the stroke work of the entire left ventricle.

When the change in pressure is recorded on the vertical axis of a cathode ray oscilloscope and the variations in circumference on the horizontal axis, each cycle produces a similar loop (Fig. 12C). The area of such a loop does not indicate total ventricular work but it must be related to the work accomplished by the myocardial fibers which contribute to the change in circumference.

The errors involved in the use of a single ventricular dimension (circumference or diameter) as an index of changing ventricular volume are not quite as gross as they might seem at first. The changes in the dimensions of the ventricular chambers during each systolic ejection are relatively small, ranging around 5 per cent under most conditions and rarely reaching 10 per cent. If the left

ENERGY RELEASE OF THE MYOCARDIUM

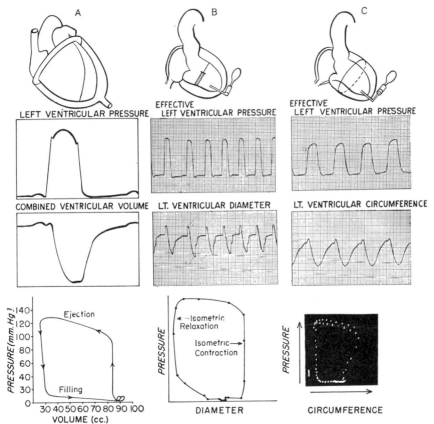

FIGURE 12. *A,* When the left ventricular pressure is plotted against the combined ventricular volume obtained from cardiometer records, a loop is produced which describes pressure-volume relations of this complicated system. If such a loop could be produced by plotting the pressure and volume of the left ventricle alone, the area within the loop would represent the stroke work, or energy release by the ventricle during a cardiac cycle. (After Burch, G. E., Ray, C. T., and Cronvich, J. A.: *Circulation,* 5:504–513, 1952.)

B, A continuous plot of left ventricular diameter against left ventricular pressure produced a loop which bears some resemblance to the loop in *A.*

C, A continuous plot of left ventricular pressure against left ventricular circumference was recorded on the face of a cathode ray oscilloscope to produce a loop. The area of these loops probably reflects the energy released by the myocardial fibers which contribute to the change in circumference being measured.

RELATION OF CIRCUMFERENCE
TO VOLUME

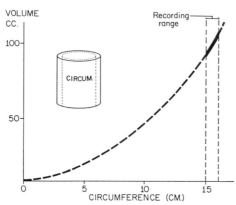

FIGURE 13.   Use of circumference rather than volume in the computation of work by the ventricular wall introduces errors. Since the changes in ventricular circumference during the cardiac cycle are small in relation to the total circumference, the deviation of the relationship from linearity is not so obvious over this small recording range.

ventricle were regarded as a cylinder of constant length, the changes in volume with changes in circumference would be those plotted in Figure 13. Within the very small recording range of changing circumference, the relationship between circumference and volume approaches linearity. A more significant source of error is the fact that not all parts of the ventricle contract simultaneously or to the same extent. For example, during iso-volumetric contraction, the change in ventricular length precedes the concentric constriction of the ventricular circumference (see Fig. 15, Chap. 2). Despite the limitations of the method, the display of pressure-circumference loops during changes in cardiac performance can provide useful information regarding the nature of compensatory adjustments. Such changes can be conveniently displayed by superimposing a loop obtained during the control period on a loop formed during a response. For example, the pressure-circumference loops in Figure 14 reveal that the increase in energy release during exercise was achieved by

an increase in ventricular distention, an increase in the ventricular systolic pressure and by greater systolic ejection. All of these factors increase the area of the pressure-circumference loops ("stroke work").

In the response to *l*-epinephrine, the pressure circumference loops increase in area primarily because of increased diastolic filling associated with the bradycardia and greater systolic ventricular pressure (Fig. 14). Norepinephrine increases the area of the work loops by inducing greater diastolic filling with no obvious change in ventricular filling pressure and by inducing increased ventricular systolic pressure and greater systolic ejection (Fig. 14).

Continuous Analysis of Ventricular Performance with Electronic Computers.   The pressure-dimensional loops illustrated in Figure 14 provided interesting information, but the loops could be recorded only intermittently during the experiment. A more complete analysis of the performance of ventricular function includes the recording of the ventricular diameter and pressure and of the blood flow through the aorta. From these three parameters a wide variety of important functions can be derived continuously by means of electronic computers (see Fig. 15). Recording the fundamental data on a multichannel Ampex tape recorder for subsequent computer analysis has made possible study of a number of pertinent variables. For example, the signals from the pressure transducer are applied to an appropriate differentiating circuit to provide deflections which indicate continuously the slope or rate of change of the ventricular pressure curve. The apex of the upward deflection represented the steepest slope during the isovolumetric pressure rise, and the trough of the downward deflection represented the steepest slope of the pressure fall at the end of systole. In another computation the signal from the aortic flowmeter was applied to a simple integrating circuit which added the increments of flow during successive small periods of time. The resulting record shows a step during each systole; the height of each step indicates the quantity of blood flowing through the root of the aorta during each stroke. Another differentiating circuit provides an indication of the rate of change of the diameter recorded with the sonocardiometer. The rate of change of volume is equal to flow. To the extent that the diameter is a representation of volume, the rate of change of diameter should resemble the aortic flow record.

The product of the rate of change of volume (flow) and the pressure is a definition of power (the rate of doing useful work). Similarly, the rate of change of diameter continuously multiplied by the effective ventricular pressure provides a record illustrating a function of the "power" developed by the sample of myocardium which produces the diameter change. The successive steps of the "work" record could be added over specific intervals (i.e., 5 seconds) to derive the accumulated "work" per unit time as a product of "stroke work" and heart rate. A more accurate indication of the "power" and "work" developed by the entire ventricle can be obtained by directly multiplying the instantaneous aortic flow by the effective ventricular pressure. The heart rate is continuously registered by a ratemeter triggered by the rising phase of each successive pressure pulse.[41] The steps representing stroke flow can be added successively during a set interval to secure an indication of the

EXERCISE AND EPINEPHRINE EFFECTS ON LEFT VENTRICULAR PERFORMANCE

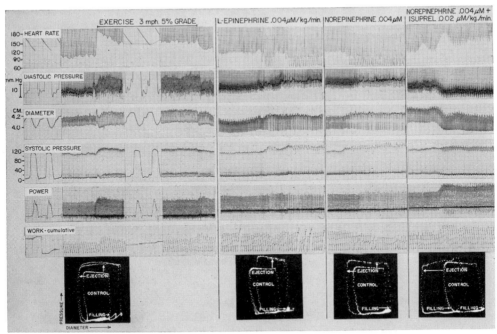

FIGURE 14. The left ventricular performance is presented in terms of numerous variables, including effective ventricular pressure, left ventricular diameter and additional information derived from analogue computers. The pressure-diameter loops also indicate the nature of the ventricular responses. Note that exercise characteristically produces rather extreme tachycardia while *l*-epinephrine and norepinephrine produce bradycardia. (After Rushmer, R. F., and West, T. C.: *Circulation Res.*, 5:240-246, 1957.)

CONTINUOUS ANALYSIS OF VENTRICULAR PERFORMANCE

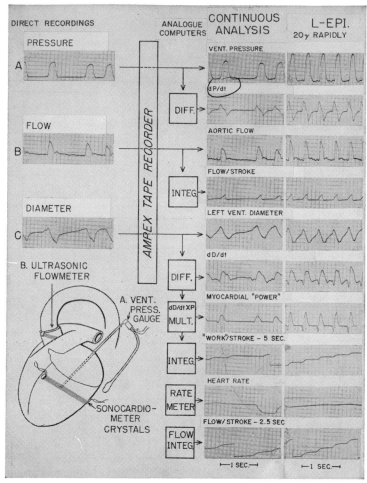

FIGURE 15. *A*, Effective ventricular pressure is recorded by a differential transformer pressure gauge through indwelling catheters extending from the back to the left ventricle and to the intrapleural space. *B*, Instantaneous aortic flow is recorded continuously by a pulsed ultrasonic flowmeter. *C*, Ventricular diameter is recorded in terms of the transit time of ultrasonic waves between two crystals mounted on opposite sides of the chamber.

These three variables are simultaneously recorded on tape and then played back for analysis by means of analogue computers to provide continuous records of ventricular pressure, rate of change of ventricular pressure (dP/dt), instantaneous aortic flow, aortic flow per stroke, left ventricular diameter, rate of change of diameter (dD/dt), a function of "power" of the sample of myocardium producing the change in diameter, a function of the work per stroke of this sample (integrated over 5 second intervals), heart rate and aortic flow integrated over 2.5 seconds.

cardiac output over short intervals (i.e., 2 or 3 seconds) instead of the average output over a full minute. Additional details of the electronic apparatus employed for these studies have been described in the *Proceedings of the Institute of Radio Engineers.*[41]

Various combinations of these primary and derived parameters have been recorded during many experimental and spontaneous cardiovascular responses in healthy unanesthetized dogs. For example, the complete battery of recording equipment can be employed to provide an inclusive definition of the meaning of "increased contractility." The term "contractility" refers to the property or capacity of cells to shorten in response to an appropriate stimulus. On the other hand, the expression "increased contractility" is usually employed to imply a more "vigorous" contraction or a more complete systolic ejection. At times the term is used to describe those changes in the contractile properties of myocardium of the sort caused by the administration of epinephrine.

THE NATURE OF INCREASED VEN-TRICULAR CONTRACTILITY

To illustrate the salient features of "increased contractility," a response to *l*-epinephrine (20 μg. rapidly injected into a 14 kg. dog) was specifically selected (Fig. 15). The typical bradycardia was not present and the heart rate was regular at about 140 beats per minute. The peak

effective ventricular systolic pressure was slightly increased; the stroke volume (derived from the flowmeter), the change in diameter and the computed "stroke work" were little changed. On the other hand, the *rate* at which all these variables changed was very greatly increased. In other words, the rate of change of pressure, the peak rate of aortic flow, the rate of change of diameter and the "power" (rate of doing work) were all very significantly increased (Fig. 16). The duration of systole was significantly reduced. Thus, "increased contractility" really means that the ventricular myocardium develops tension more rapidly, shortening occurs more quickly, ejection is faster, the duration of contraction is briefer and the rate of pressure fall or relaxation is speeded up, even when the total ventricular volume, stroke volume and energy release are not greatly changed. The stroke volume may be increased by increased "contractility" predominately by more complete systolic ejection. This represents an important distinction between the increase in stroke volume which may result from increased contractility and that resulting from increased diastolic distention in accordance with Starling's law of the heart. The type of increased left ventricular contractility in Figure 16 is commonly observed during spontaneous cardiac responses to many different situations although each response may be unique in certain respects. For example, during exercise, the stroke change of diameter or stroke volume may be increased by both greater diastolic filling and more complete systolic ejection (see Fig. 14). The nature of the response of the heart under such conditions as changes in posture and exertion will be considered in Chapters 7 and 8, respectively.

The changes in ventricular performance illustrated in Figures 15 and 16 can be consistently induced experimentally by direct stimulation of sympathetic nerves to the heart in dogs[43, 44] and by

COMPONENTS OF INCREASED CONTRACTILITY

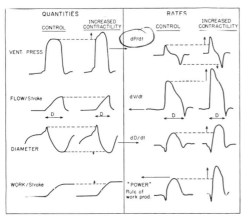

FIGURE 16. The changes in ventricular performance induced by administration of *l*-epinephrine (Fig. 15) demonstrate that the increased "contractility" involved predominately increased in the rates at which the variables change (dP/dt, dV/dt, dD/dt, and "power") without necessarily increasing the quantities (ventricular pressure, flow/stroke, diameter, or work/stroke). The increase in systolic ventricular pressure is primarily the result of increased ejection velocity (dV/dt).

reflex stimulation of these nerves in man.[45] Of even greater interest is the fact that changes of the same kind can be produced by selective stimulation of discretely localized sites in the hypothalamus and subthalamus. In fact, it is possible to reproduce quite accurately the left ventricular responses to exertion without body movement by stimulating electrically very small diencephalic areas in the unanesthetized dog (see Chap. 8).

DIENCEPHALIC INFLUENCES ON VENTRICULAR PERFORMANCE

Neural pathways pass from the hypothalamus and subthalamus to and through the medullary region to terminate at the intermediolateral cell columns of the spinal cord (see Fig. 11). The hypothalamus has long been regarded as the font of the autonomic nervous system and has been repeatedly explored by neurophysiologists using changes in arterial pressure as their principal criterion of sites of cardiovascular control. Thus, various regions in the diencephalon have been labeled "pressor" or "depressor areas" on the basis of elevation or reduction of systemic arterial pressure.[46] Although the anterior hypothalamus is generally regarded as being the site of predominantly depressor areas and the posterior hypothalamus as being largely pressor in its influence, recent exploration of these areas[47, 48] has demonstrated that powerful depressor responses can be induced easily and consistently from many locations (Fig. 17). For example, a very pronounced reduction in heart rate and systolic ventricular pressure and reduced rates of change in pressure and cumulative aortic flow were produced by stimulation in the ventral nuclear group of the thalamus. After the electrode tip was moved 2 mm. ventrad in the H_1 field of Forel, stimulation resulted in a very powerful pressor response (Fig. 17). This response included a transient, explosive acceleration in heart rate, greatly elevated systolic ventricular pressure and rate of change of pressure, and augmented aortic peak flow rates and accumulated flow (cardiac output). Marked changes in respiratory patterns—panting—accompanied these cardiovascular changes.

Stimulation of selected areas of the brain stem quite easily produced cardiovascular changes much greater than any seen during spontaneous activity in these dogs. Moreover, a very wide variety of cardiac responses has been produced by stimulation at different sites during exploration of these central regions (Fig. 18). At the sites indicated by the histologic sections, virtually every conceivable response was elicited and could be repeatedly induced. Of considerable interest was the fact that by selecting records from a rather large collection, examples could be found in which the changes were almost completely restricted to a single feature of cardiac function: heart rate, left ventricular diameter or left ventricular systolic pressure and left ventricular diastolic pressure. Despite the variation in the kinds of cardiovascular responses which are apparently embodied in the diencephalic mechanisms, stimulation of the same site in different animals consistently produced precisely the same pattern of response. In fact, a cardiac response closely simulating the changes typically observed during treadmill exercise can be quite consistently reproduced by electrical stimulation in the H_2 field of Forel (see Chap. 8).

Hypothalamic Function in Cardiac Control

A wide variety of different autonomic functions are represented in the base of the brain. The anatomy, function and interrelations of the central levels of autonomic function were reviewed in considerable detail in 1940.[46] For example, the hypothalamus plays an extremely important role in the regulation of body temperature in both animals and man.

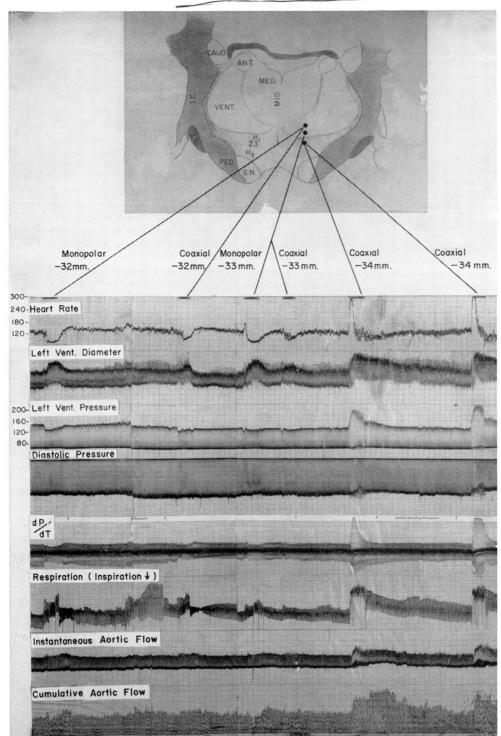

FIGURE 17. Changes in ventricular performance in terms of the variables illustrated in Figure 15. At the upper point, stimulation produced reduction in heart rate, increased ventricular diameter, reduced ventricular systolic pressure, diminished rate of change of pressure (dP/dt), altered respiration and little change in aortic flow. Two millimeters lower, the electrode was in the zona incerta and stimulation produced an extremely high transient tachycardia, increased diameter, increased ventricular systolic pressure, increased diastolic pressure, greatly increased rate of change of pressure, and increased aortic flow. The sites producing these profound changes are apparently discretely localized in the diencephalon.

VARIABLE EFFECTS FROM DIFFERENT DIENCEPHALIC STIMULATION POINTS

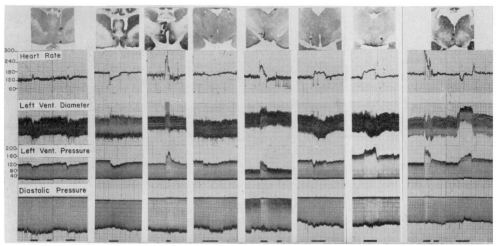

FIGURE 18.   Exploration of various sites in the diencephalon with stimulating electrodes demonstrated that many distinctive patterns of ventricular response can be elicited from different regions. Note that in some sites more or less isolated changes occur in one variable with little change in the others. However, repeated stimulation of a particular site consistently produces similar responses in the same or in different animals.

Heat loss mechanisms (panting and sweating) can be induced by local heating of the preoptic and supraoptic regions in cats. The hypothalamus is apparently involved in sleep and waking; decreased activity of the hypothalamus results in somnolence and increased activity in this region leads to increased bodily activity. Somatic movements, including changes in posture and even running movements, can be produced by stimulating certain regions in the diencephalon. Many forms of overt sexual activity involve stereotyped behavior of a sort which may be influenced by the hypothalamus. This region also serves outward expressions suggesting rage. Each of these responses involves compensatory adjustments in the peripheral blood flow and also in cardiac function. Thus, it is not surprising to find that different portions of the hypothalmic region can induce such varied cardiovascular responses as are illustrated in Figure 18. Certainly mere identification of "pressor" and "depressor" areas is completely inadequate to indicate the finer detail of the compensatory reactions.

Cerebral Control of Cardiac Function

Activity of portions of the cerebral cortex induces changes in overt behavior, and stimulation in these areas also results in some form of cardiovascular response. Thus, motor areas of the cerebral cortex, from which voluntary motion apparently stems, can also induce changes in the distribution of blood flow and increased cardiac activity. Excision of orbital surface of the frontal lobe produces extreme hyperactivity, including continuous pacing. Stimulation of this region has often been reported to induce pressor responses.[46] The cingulate gyrus has been implicated in the control of emotional behavior and apparently is a potent autonomic effector area. These few examples serve to emphasize the general principle that those portions of the central nervous system in which stimulation produces behavioral responses are also capable of causing cardiovascular effects.[49] This statement does not imply that the cardiovascular responses are necessarily appropriate for the type of behavior produced because this correlation has not been demonstrated. However, the incorporation of nervous pathways capable of influencing autonomic function appears to represent an important feature of the organization of the central nervous areas controlling behavior. This type of architecture represents a potential mechanism by which patterns of autonomic adjustment may be automatically associated with particular types of behavior.

SUMMARY

The quantity of blood pumped by the heart per unit time (cardiac output) is determined by two main factors: (1) the heart rate and (2) the stroke volume. Normally each heart beat is initiated by a conducted wave of excitation generated by pacemaker cells in the S-A node. The frequency of discharge of the pacemaker is determined by the balance between the retarding effect of nerve impulses descending the vagus nerve and the accelerating effect of the sympathetic nerve impulses reaching this region. If the heart rate is increased experimentally by an artificial pacemaker directly exciting the atrium at a progressively greater rate, the stroke output of the ventricles diminishes and the cardiac output may not increase. Thus, acceleration of the heart rate alone is not necessarily an effective means of increasing cardiac output.

The quantity of blood ejected by the ventricles is represented by the difference between the volume at the end of diastolic filling and the volume at the end of systolic ejection. An increase in the diastolic distention of the ventricles produces an increase in the energy released during the subsequent systole in accordance with Starling's law of the heart. This law was derived and confirmed by studying the isolated or exposed hearts of dogs under rigid experimental conditions in which the investigator assumed complete control. It is not as readily recognized during spontaneous activity by intact animals. The ventricular myocardium derives several advantages from function at large diastolic dimensions in addition to the well known increase in isometric contractile tension attained through the increased elongation of the muscle fibers. The tension developed by myocardium contracting without a change in length, falls off sharply as the muscle is permitted to shorten (during systolic ejection). The contractile tension is more depleted either by a greater amount of shortening or a faster rate of shortening. To eject a particular volume the amount of myocardial shortening is greatly reduced when the ventricles function at large diastolic and systolic dimensions. The contractile tension which is lost and stored in the form of interfascicular tension between layers of muscle fibers is also diminished by a reduction in relative myocardial shortening. On the other hand, the contraction tension required to elevate ventricular pressure to a particular level is increased by diastolic distention in accordance with the law of Laplace. Thus, the dimensions at which the ventricles function must represent the resultant of several interacting factors.

In addition to the functional and architectural factors indicated above, the contractile properties of the myocardium can be greatly influenced by the stimulation of sympathetic nerves to the heart. Under the influence of these nerves, the ventricles develop tension more rapidly, shorten more rapidly, eject blood more rapidly, develop more power and can attain a much higher maximum contractile tension. The duration of systole is shortened so that, in spite of greatly accelerated ejection, the volume ejected may be not greater than during the control period. On the other hand, increased stroke volume may be produced by greater systolic ejection, by more diastolic distention or by a combination of both factors. The parasympathetic nerves are apparently distributed only to the S-A node, the A-V node and, diffusely, the atrium but not to the ventricular myocardium. Thus, changes in ventricular "contractility" are achieved by variations in sympathetic, but not by parasympathetic, discharge to the ventricles.

The cardioregulatory areas in the medulla influence the autonomic discharge to the heart as a portion of the pressoreceptor mechanism for maintaining systemic arterial pressure (see Chap.

6). The diencephalic and hypothalamic regions contain cardiovascular controls in complex neural mechanisms involved in temperature regulation, the intake of food and fluid, emotional and sexual behavior and many other patterns of behavior. It follows, then, that a wide variety of cardiovascular responses can be induced by electrical stimulation at various sites in the brain stem. Also areas of the cerebral cortex where stimulation induces changes in overt behavior also induce cardiovascular adaptations of one sort or another. Thus, there exists the possibility that the architecture of the central nervous system provides for combined patterns of somatic and autonomic adaptations.

II. Clinical Estimation of Cardiac Output

Since the maximum capability of the heart can be evaluated only by determining the cardiovascular response to a load, a method for directly measuring cardiac output during exertion would be very valuable in cardiac diagnosis and prognosis. Unfortunately, direct measurements of cardiac function in man, although desirable, are virtually impossible because the heart is quite inaccessible for the determination of either stroke volume or absolute volume. Perhaps the most direct method is the calculation of changes in cardiac volume from the cardiac silhouette on roentgenographic plates.[50, 51] However, this method has serious limitations because the individual cardiac chambers cannot be distinguished on routine roentgenograms, so the computed values represent the total volume of all four chambers. In recent years, a wide variety of techniques has been proposed to determine cardiac output by indirect methods. The basic principles and limitations of some of the techniques currently in vogue will be described.

THE FICK PRINCIPLE

Blood flow through an organ can be determined if a substance is either removed from, or added to, the blood during its flow through the organ. Applied to the lungs, the Fick principle is used to calculate the volume of blood required to transport the oxygen taken up from the alveoli per unit time. The fundamental concept is deceptively simple and can be illustrated schematically by representing the oxygen-carrying capacity of the blood as beakers on a conveyer belt (Fig. 19).

Measurement of Oxygen Consumption

Of necessity, the oxygen consumption is generally measured over a period of several minutes. The accuracy of oxygen uptake determinations from the clinical B.M.R. apparatus is generally inadequate for this purpose. A preferred technique consists of collecting in a spirometer all of the air expired during carefully timed intervals and analyzing samples for oxy-

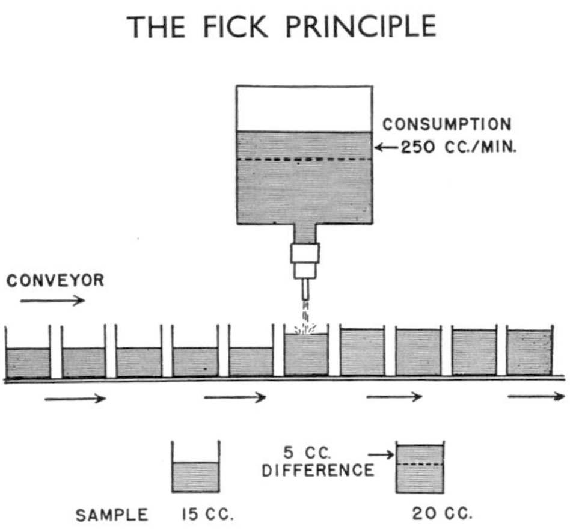

THE FICK PRINCIPLE

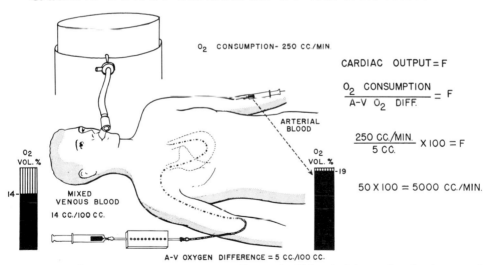

CONSUMPTION
←250 CC./MIN.

CONVEYOR
→

5 CC.
DIFFERENCE →

SAMPLE   15 CC.   20 CC.

FIGURE 19. If each beaker on a conveyer belt receives 5 cc. of fluid as it passes under a dispenser delivering 250 cc. per minute, the beakers must pass the dispenser at a rate of 50 per minute (250/5) to carry that quantity of fluid. Similarly, if each 100 cc. of blood takes up 5 cc. of oxygen from the lungs (A-V oxygen difference) and 250 cc. of oxygen are consumed each minute, 50 increments of 100 cc. (5000 cc.) of blood must have passed through the lungs each minute. This is the Fick principle as it is applied to the calculation of cardiac output (see Fig. 20).

gen content (Fig. 20). Comparing the oxygen content of the total exhaled volume with a similar volume of ambient air provides the data required to compute the oxygen uptake accurately.

The Arteriovenous Oxygen Difference

The arterial blood throughout the body normally has a uniform oxygen content. However, to determine a significant A-V oxygen difference, it is necessary to obtain samples of *mixed* venous blood. The quantity of oxygen contained in venous blood depends upon the vascular bed from which it is returning (see Fig. 2, Chap. 4). For example, blood from the kidneys and skin remains highly saturated with oxygen while blood from the coronary vessels and exercising muscle is largely depleted of oxygen. The oxygen contents of venous blood from other tissues vary between these extremes. Due to laminar flow in the venous channels, currents of blood with a

CARDIAC OUTPUT DETERMINED BY THE FICK PRINCIPLE

O_2 CONSUMPTION- 250 CC./MIN.

CARDIAC OUTPUT = F

$$\frac{O_2 \ \text{CONSUMPTION}}{\text{A-V} \ O_2 \ \text{DIFF.}} = F$$

$$\frac{250 \ \text{CC./MIN.}}{5 \ \text{CC.}} \times 100 = F$$

$$50 \times 100 = 5000 \ \text{CC./MIN.}$$

ARTERIAL
BLOOD

O_2
VOL.%

O_2
VOL.%
-19

14-   MIXED
VENOUS BLOOD

14 CC./100 CC.

A-V OXYGEN DIFFERENCE = 5 CC./100 CC.

FIGURE 20. Computing cardiac output according to the Fick principle requires simultaneous determination of oxygen consumption and the arteriovenous oxygen difference. Exhaled air is collected to measure oxygen consumption per minute. Blood is withdrawn from the pulmonary artery through a catheter into a cuvette oximeter, so that the oxygen content of mixed venous blood can be read from a galavanometer. Arterial oxygen content is measured in a sample of blood from any systemic artery. The A-V oxygen difference in cubic centimeters of oxygen per 100 cc. of blood is obtained by subtracting the oxygen content of the mixed venous sample from the arterial oxygen content.

relatively high oxygen content may accompany streams with lower values in the same vein. The oxygen saturation of blood in the superior vena cava differs from that in the inferior vena cava and these two streams of blood do not mix completely within the right atrium. The Lipiodol streamers in Figure 11, Chapter 2, graphically illustrate this fact. Mixing of blood does occur in the right ventricle and is almost complete by the time the blood has entered the pulmonary arteries. The oxygen content of a sample of blood obtained from the pulmonary artery represents an average value for venous blood which can be used to establish the arteriovenous oxygen difference for calculating cardiac output by the Fick principle.

Cardiac Catheterization.   In 1929, Forssmann[52] demonstrated that a catheter can be passed through the venous channels into the right chambers of the human heart (Fig. 20). Cournand and his associates[53, 54] established the safety of the procedure and stimulated widespread utilization of the method. The technique of cardiac catheterization has been described in detail by Cournand,[55] Warren,[56] Sosman[57] and Dexter.[58]

Measurement of Blood Oxygen Content. Arterial and venous oxygen content can be directly measured with the Van Slyke apparatus, which is a time-consuming but accurate procedure in the hands of highly qualified technicians. For rapid determinations of blood oxygen content, a photoelectric method has been developed and compares favorably with Van Slyke determinations. Blood for analysis is drawn through a cuvette oximeter (Fig. 20), where it is transilluminated by a constant intensity light source, and the transmitted light is registered simultaneously in two spectral regions: approximately 750 to 900 millimicrons and 600 to 750 millimicrons, respectively. The former is near infra-red light in wave length and is transmitted by both oxyhemoglobin and re-

duced hemoglobin to approximately equal degrees. The other photocell responds to red light, which is transmitted well by oxyhemoglobin and to a very slight degree by reduced hemoglobin. The ratio between the light intensities recorded from the two wave lengths can be read in terms of absolute percentage of oxygen saturation after the apparatus has been satisfactorily calibrated by means of Van Slyke analysis. Various spectrophotometric techniques have been successfully employed for the measurement of blood oxygen content. In experienced hands, these devices more than make up for the slight reduction in accuracy through the ease with which serial determinations can be obtained in rapid sequence while the patient is being studied.

Sources of Error

The conventional expression of the Fick principle,

$$\text{Cardiac output} = \frac{O_2 \text{ consumption}}{\text{A-V } O_2 \text{ difference}}$$

presupposes that the values are obtained simultaneously and are constant during measurement. Both the cardiac and the respiratory cyclic activity may exhibit changes and introduce errors in calculations of cardiac output. Even if blood samples are drawn continuously or repeatedly during the determination of oxygen consumption, they represent time averages, not volume averages. The factors which may cause errors in sampling and computations of cardiac output have received considerable attention.[59, 60] Under resting conditions, the A-V oxygen difference is probably fairly constant. During inhalation of low oxygen mixtures serious errors may be encountered. Shunts between the pulmonary and systemic circuits also induce rather large errors in the calculation of systemic flow. Special formulas have been developed to calculate the volume flow of blood through such shunts.[55]

The accuracy of cardiac output determinations depends upon the cumulative magnitude of the errors in sampling and analysis of the blood oxygen content and oxygen consumption.[54, 61] It is generally stated that the cardiac output determined by the direct Fick method has an an accuracy of ± 10 per cent. This is true when groups of data are averaged, but the error may be considerably greater in an individual case.

A test which may produce an alteration in the factor being measured must be carefully controlled. From the patient's point of view, cardiac catheterization is a rather heroic procedure which may give rise to considerable apprehension. The possibility that cardiac output is abnormally increased to a variable extent during catheterization must be constantly considered.

Objective determinations of cardiac output have been of great value in advancing our knowledge of circulatory dynamics, with particular reference to pulmonary function in health and disease. However, the search for an objective test of cardiac reserve was not ended by the development of cardiac catheterization, because the procedure is too complicated for routine clinical use and is not entirely suitable for use during strenuous exertion. A normal value for cardiac output at rest is often obtained even when the cardiac reserve is seriously depleted. If cardiac catheterization provided no information beyond the resting cardiac output, its utilization would be largely limited to fundamental investigation. However, several additional types of information can be gained from catheterization which are particularly useful in the diagnosis of congenital malformations of the heart. These include detection of defects in the partitions of the heart (see Fig. 11, Chap. 14, obstruction of valves (see Fig. 9, Chap. 12) or vascular channels (see Fig. 12, Chap. 14) and pulmonary capillary or

venous pressure, indicated by pressures from catheter tips wedged in terminal pulmonary arteries (see Fig. 10, Chap. 12). Burton[62] discussed the value and misuse of wedged-catheter pressures and advanced compelling arguments against "spoiling a scientific measurement by building upon it such a house of cards, the deceptive façade of which may well mislead the trusting clinician into buying it."

Catheters have been inserted into the coronary sinus to withdraw blood which has supplied the myocardium.[63] From samples of this type it has been possible to calculate the oxygen consumption and myocardial efficiency of the left ventricular myocardium (see Chap. 15).

THE STEWART PRINCIPLE

The volume of fluid in a container can be calculated by adding a known quantity of dye and measuring the concentration of the material after it has become evenly dispersed through the fluid (Fig. 21A). The volume is calculated according to the formula $V = A/C$, where V is the volume of fluid, A is the amount of dye added and C is the concentration of the dye in each cubic centimeter of the fluid. Stewart[64, 65] demonstrated that his method can also be applied to fluids in motion. Hamilton and his associates[66, 67] verified the usefulness of the method in calculating the flow through glass models and in the circulation. Moore et al.[68] obtained a good correlation between the dilution method and the direct Fick method.

General Principles

The computation of a volume of stationary fluid by determining the dilution of a known quantity of dye is perfectly straightforward (Fig. 21). Similarly, the volume flow through a simple tubular system can theoretically be determined with considerable accuracy by determin-

THE INDICATOR DILUTION TECHNIQUE

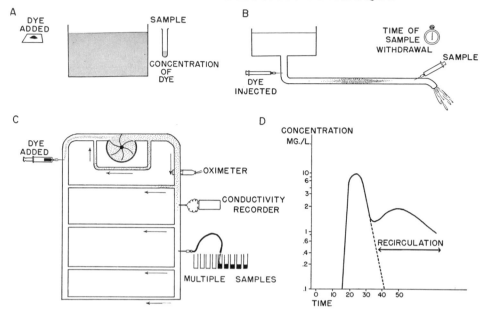

FIGURE 21.   *A,* The volume of stationary fluid in a reservoir can be determined by completely mixing a known amount of dye and analyzing a sample for the concentration of the dye.

B, The volume flow through a simple tube can be estimated by injecting a known quantity of dye, withdrawing a sample at constant rate during the passage of the dye-containing fluid and determining the mean concentration of the sample.

C, A hydraulic model simulating the circulatory system illustrates the fact that an indicator substance may pass through short circuits and begin to recirculate before the mass of dye has passed the sampling point. Therefore it is necessary to devise means by which the amount of recirculating dye can be separated from the amount of dye sampled during its initial passage to arrive at a reliable mean concentration.

D, If the concentration of the dye passing a sampling point is plotted on semi-log paper, the descending limb after the peak can be extended to the baseline as a straight line. The area under the initial curve can be used to derive the mean concentration of the dye during its first circulation.

ing the average concentration of a known quantity of dye and the time during sampling according to the formula $F = A/Ct$, where F is flow, A is quantity of dye injected, C is the average concentration of dye in the sample and t is the duration of sample withdrawal (Fig. 21*B*). Under these conditions, the Stewart principle is quite as accurate as the Fick principle. However, conditions in the human circulation are more complex, as indicated by the hydraulic model in Figure 21*C*. Part of the dye injected at one point in this model has completely traversed the short circuits and begun to recirculate before the material has reached the more distant regions. The average concentration

of the indicator substance can be measured by (1) collecting multiple samples in rapid succession, (2) continuously recording blood conductivity after saline injections or (3) making oximeter or densitometer recordings when dyes are injected. In any case, the concentration of indicator flowing past the point of recording reaches a peak, begins to descend and then increases again owing to recirculation. If the once-circulated dye can be separated from the recirculated dye, cardiac output can be computed with considerable accuracy.

One of the techniques originally described by Stewart[65] included the following steps. A control sample of blood was withdrawn. Hypertonic salt solution was then injected. The arrival of the increased concentration of salt in a peripheral artery was signalled by a change in the tone from a telephone connected to a Wheatstone bridge, one leg of which responded to a change in the conductivity of the blood in the artery. A single sample of blood was then collected from the peripheral artery throughout the entire interval during which the mixture was passing the collecting cannula. To determine the concentration of the injected salt solution in this sample, the control sample was titrated with the same salt solution until the conductivities of the two samples were identical. Note that the only difference between the formula for determining the volume of fluid in a container $(V = A/C)$ and the formula for volume flow $(V = A/Ct)$ is the factor of time (t) during which the sample is collected.

The fundamental requirements for this method are (1) the injection of a material which can be accurately analyzed and which does not leave the blood during the test, and (2) a sample of arterial blood which indicates the average concentration of the material during its first circulation through the arterial tree. Various dyes as well as saline solutions have been used with varying degrees of success and the average concentration has been determined by either repetitive sampling or by continuous recording.

Accuracy of the Indicator Dilution Technique

Hamilton and Remington[66, 69] demonstrated that when a foreign substance is injected into a vein at a constant rate, it begins to recirculate before a concentration plateau is established. They warned against the use of diffusible substances, some of which may be lost during passage through the heart and lungs, and urged the use of dyes such as T-1824

(Evans blue) which tend to remain in the blood stream.

In addition to errors in collecting and measuring samples and in determining the time intervals, Stewart[64] discussed the following sources of error: (1) incomplete mixture of the solution with the blood, (2) variations in velocity in the central and peripheral laminae or blood, (3) loss of blood from sampling and (4) dilution of the blood by large injections. He felt that the errors from these sources were not serious. Wiggers[70] has described important refinements of the procedure which should improve its accuracy. White[71] developed a method for continuously recording the conductivity of blood during saline injections so that repeated determinations can be made with less effort.

PRESSURE PULSE CONTOUR METHOD

The Relation of Pulse Pressure to Stroke Volume

Erlanger and Hooker[72] recognized that the product of the pulse pressure and the heart rate indicated cardiac output, with the following reservations: "In order to be able to obtain a knowledge of the absolute velocity of blood flow from a knowledge of the pulse-pressure and pulse rate, it is necessary to know:

"1. The rate of systolic output. For if a given amount of blood be driven into the aorta with different rates the maximum pressure would be higher when this rate is rapid than when it is slow.

"2. The rate of flow from the arteries into the veins. For this flow continues during cardiac systole and consequently variations in the rate of this flow would vary the height to which the force of the heart would raise the systolic pressure.

"3. The distensibility of human arteries at different pressures. The distensibility diminishes as the pressure increases; consequently at a high pressure it would require a smaller systolic output to pro-

THE PULSE CONTOUR METHOD

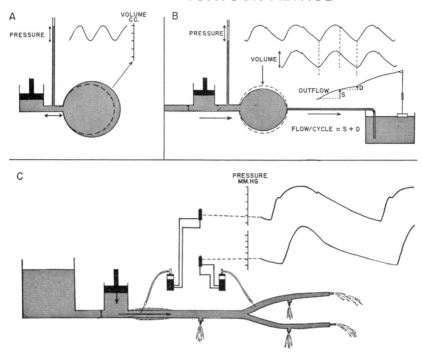

FIGURE 22.   *A,* The changes in the volume of the balloon can be determined by measuring the pressure if the pressure-volume relations are constant.

B, If fluid is pumped into a balloon and flows out through a tube offering some resistance, the flow through the system can be estimated from the pressure fluctuations. The volume and pressure within the balloon increase during ejection from the pump, but outflow occurs throughout the entire cycle. If pressure fluctuations are used to indicate changes in volume, the flow from the system can be estimated by determining the flow out of the system during diastole (D) and adding a computed value for outflow from the system during the stroke (S).

C, In the circulatory system, the pulse of pressure does not reach all parts of the elastic pressure reservoir simultaneously and its contour changes as it passes through the system (see also Fig. 3, Chap. 5). Under these conditions, the volumes entering and leaving various portions of the system must be considered individually to reach maximum accuracy. Since this is not practical in intact animals or man, the computation of cardiac output from pressure pulses has been greatly simplified. However, each step toward simplification of the method involves sacrifice of accuracy.

duce a pulse-pressure of a given magnitude than at a low pressure.

"4. The amount of blood in the systemic arteries under various conditions. The fall of pressure during diastole depends upon the relative amount of blood that escapes into the veins, not upon the absolute amount.

"We do not know how large any one of these factors is, but it seems probable that, under more or less normal conditions, none of them would produce a very large error. Upon this assumption we are perhaps justified in using the product of

the pulse-pressure by the pulse rate as an index to the relative velocity of blood flow."

Clearly the stroke volume would be directly proportional to arterial pulse pressure only if the pressure-volume relations of the arterial system were not only constant and uniform among individuals, but linear from high pressure to low. That this is not the case has been emphasized previously (see Chap. 1). However, the blood pressure is controlled, and if the differences in arterial distensibility were not too great, a reasonable approximati of stroke volume could be determined from the pulse pressure. Remington[73] presented a set of volume factors from known stroke volumes and pulse pressures, corrected for body size and distensibility curves. From this table, stroke volume/sq. m. body surface could be predicted with an error of about 25 per cent. According to Hamilton and Remington[74] pulse pressure correlates roughly with stroke volume determined by the dye dilution technique (r = 0.88). Over the normal pressure range, a pressure rise of 1 mm. Hg was equivalent to about 1 cc. of stroke volume/sq. m. For some purposes, this degree of accuracy might be quite sufficient. However, a great deal of effort has been expended in attempts to increase the precision with which stroke volume is derived from the pressure-pulse contour. This is no simple matter considering the complexity of the situation.

Analysis of Pulse Contours

If fluid is injected into a distensible container with fixed volume elasticity, the volume in the system can be calibrated in terms of the internal pressure (Fig. 22A). Once the volume-pressure relations are established, the volume contained can be determined by noting the pressure in the system. However, if fluid can escape from the system (Fig. 22B), the elastic chamber will remain distended only if fluid is pumped in at the same average rate as it leaks out. Under these circumstances, the pressure will increase as the chamber is distended and will decrease between pumping strokes as the fluid leaves the system. The difference between the maximal and minimal pressures indicates the amount of fluid injected at each stroke less the amount which left the system during the ejection period. If the distensible chamber is a long, narrow cylinder with elastic walls, the fluid ejected by the pump is not instantaneously distributed through the system and the recorded pressure will be distorted by reflected waves. A similar situation obtains within the arterial system of the body (see Fig. 3, Chap. 5).

Hamilton and Remington[74] recognized that prediction of stroke volume from pressure pulses must depend upon evaluation of the "individual arterial distensibility, knowledge of the pulse pressure in the arterial tree and its several parts, and the estimation of arteriolar drainage." They developed a table indicating the capacity of the various portions of the arterial tree at different pressures and another showing the pulse wave transmission times to the parts of the arterial tree at various diastolic pressures. These data were employed in the analysis of pressure pulses. A very good correlation with the dye dilution method (0.994) was found when the stroke volume computations were based upon details of the pressure pulse contours, transmission times to the various parts of the arterial tree and the distensibility of those parts. Remington et al.[75] and Warner[76] subsequently reported a simplified technique which facilitates analysis of the pressure pulse with little increase in the error. In spite of these favorable results, Wiggers[77] stated: "While the published data do not lend themselves to statistical analysis, they certainly do not demonstrate that the pulse contour method is reliable for determining the cardiac index in serial determinations on a given animal." In spite of this rather dim view, the pulse contour method has one very important potential advantage. It permits computation of the stroke volume of individual cycles even though its accuracy may be limited.

BALLISTOCARDIOGRAPHY

The concept that a sudden motion of the blood in one direction must produce a recoil of the body in the opposite direction is not a new idea. In 1887, Gordon[78] compared the ballistic forces of the body to the recoil of a gun. In 1905 Henderson[79] used a "swinging table" to record the movements along the longitudinal axis of

BALLISTOCARDIOGRAPHY

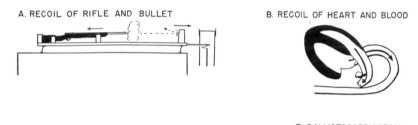

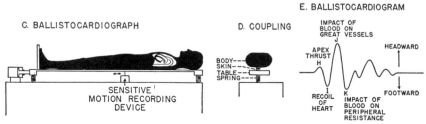

FIGURE 23.   *A*, The recoil of a rifle during discharge of a cartridge can be recorded by attaching it rigidly to a spring-mounted table. The record would become seriously distorted if the bullet ricocheted from a barrier on the table during the recoil of the rifle.

B, The blood ejected by the ventricles travels in several directions simultaneously, imparting its energy to the body at every turn. For this reason, measurements of the recoil of the body in one direction only are inadequate.

C, A low-frequency spring-mounted table which has been critically damped has been recommended for ballistocardiography because the body cannot be rigidly fastened to the table. The tissues in contact with the table have an elasticity which is equivalent to interposing a spring between the body and the table top.

D, If the springs supporting the table are stiff in relation to the elasticity of the tissues, the recorded patterns tend to reflect the elastic properties of the tissues supporting the body as the forces are imparted by the heart and blood.

E, Ballistocardiographic records consist of a series of deflections which have been related to the events of the cardiac cycle. Although the forces developed by the heart and blood affect the recorded patterns, a consistent relationship between these deflections and stroke volume is probably fortuitous for the most part.

a patient reclining on its surface. The changing velocity of the moving blood within the circulatory system caused the table to oscillate during each successive cardiac cycle.

General Principles

The recoil of a rifle is frequently employed as an analogy to explain the basic principles of ballistocardiography. If a rifle is rigidly fastened on a spring-mounted table, a discharging cartridge propels the bullet out of the barrel and displaces the rifle in the opposite direction (Fig. 23*A*). Recording the movements of the table in these circumstances might provide information concerning the magnitude of the powder charge (energy re-

lease) if other conditions are known. If the magnitude of the powder charge and the muzzle velocity were unknown, the weight of the bullet (mass ejected) could not be computed from the recorded deflections. The analysis would be seriously complicated if, during the recoil of the rifle, the speeding bullet struck a steel plate mounted on the same table. Since the blood does not leave the system, the recoil of the heart and body from ejection of blood into the arteries is even more complex. For example, the blood ejected from the two ventricles moves simultaneously in several directions after leaving the heart. Its energy is imparted to the body at every turn. Routine ballistocardiograms indicate movements of the body in only one direction. Simultaneous recordings in three dimensions are extremely difficult to analyze. Finally, the records may be seriously distorted by such factors as the coupling between the body and the table. The elasticity of the skin acts as a spring interposed between the moving body and the table top, and may profoundly influence the recorded deflections. This difficulty can be alleviated by recording from patients on a light table floating on a layer of mercury,[80] but this is not a practical solution.

Evaluation of Ballistocardiography

Starr and his associates[81] extended Henderson's observations and reawakened interest in the recoil phenomena by stating that the size of the initial waves, I and J, is related to the cardiac output, and that the form of the ballistic curve is determined by the shape of the curve of blood velocity in the great vessels.[82] Dow and Hamilton[83] studied the recoil of models simulating the circulation and concluded that the form and frequency of the recorded waves are associated with the standing waves in the "aorta" of the model (see Fig. 3, Chap. 5). Actually, the size of the initial deflection is determined by the acceleration of the fluid (the rate at which velocity of ejection is built up) and not at all by the total stroke output. Nickerson and Curtis[84] demonstrated that with high frequency apparatus of the type used by Starr, the size and shape of the deflections are determined almost completely by the elastic properties of the skin (the coupling between the body and the table). For this reason, critically damped ballistocardiographic apparatus with very low frequency (less than 1.5 c.p.s.) produces much more reliable records. Using a simple, low-frequency ballistocardiograph, Hamilton *et al.*[85] demonstrated that the mass of the body itself renders the ballistocardiograph an imperfect recorder of rapid oscillations. The recorded oscillations are the resultant of vascular and body movements as they may be in phase and reinforce one another, or be out of phase and cancel each other. Reconstruction of the ballistocardiographic records led to the following description of the causes of the various oscillations. The H wave begins with movements that take place during isometric contraction and are the most variable. The I wave is the result of a partly cancelled footward thrust developed as blood is ejected from the heart into the ascending aorta and pulmonary artery. The J wave has a complex origin, including the deceleration of blood in the heart, ascending aorta and pulmonary artery, and the acceleration of blood in the descending aorta. Although the usual ballistocardiogram represents movements along the longitudinal axis of the body, the generated forces are actually in three dimensions. For example, the I wave is the resultant of forces acting toward the left, ventrad and caudad. This is reasonable, considering the orientation of the heart within the thorax. The calculation of cardiac output from ballistic waves is an empirical procedure which cannot give values with inherent validity.

Currently, simplified ballistocardiographic apparatus is receiving extensive clinical use.[86] The obvious limitations of the method do not preclude the recognition of empirical relationships between various types of cardiac dysfunction and characteristic ballistocardiographic patterns. Since the amplitude of the deflections is influenced by the rate at which blood is accelerated, variations in the pattern should reveal alterations in the force of ventricular ejection.

SUMMARY

Cardiac output can be determined through the use of cardiac catheterization according to the Fick principle. The theory is basically sound. The accuracy of the determinations depends upon the cumulative errors caused by deviations from the "steady state" conditions required for application of this theory. Very significant errors result whenever respiratory or circulatory conditions are inconstant.

The indicator dilution technique is also basically sound for computing flow through simple tubular systems. In the circulatory system, application of the Stewart principle is complicated by problems related to recirculation of the indicator. With proper precautions, this technique affords values comparable to those derived from cardiac catheterization.

Theoretically, stroke volume can be determined from an analysis of the arterial pulse contour. However, many sources of error are present, including intangible factors such as differences in arterial distensibility among individuals. If the pulse contour method can be calibrated by the Fick principle in a particular subject, it becomes much more reliable. If the magnitude of the potential errors is recognized, the pulse contour method has considerable practical value since stroke volume of individual cycles can be estimated.

Ballistocardiography has been widely used to compute values presumed to represent stroke volume or cardiac output. Reliable recordings of body movements in response to ballistic forces during the cardiac cycle may be related to the rate or force of ventricular ejection, but even the basic principles of the method fail to reveal any direct relationship between the magnitude of the deflections and the volume of blood ejected. This fact does not preclude the establishment of empirical relations between specific ballistocardiographic patterns and certain forms of cardiovascular disease.

REFERENCES

1. BOZLER, E. The activity of the pacemaker previous to the discharge of a muscular impulse. *Amer. J. Physiol.*, 136:543–552, 1942.
2. WEST, T. C., FALK, G., and CERVONI, P. Drug alteration of transmembrane potentials in atrial pacemaker cells. *J. Pharmacol. Exp. Ther.*, 117:245–252, 1956.
3. HUNT, R. Direct and reflex acceleration of the mammalian heart with some observations on the relations of the inhibitory and accelerator nerves. *Amer. J. Physiol.*, 2:395–470, 1899.
4. ALEXANDER, R. S. Tonic and reflex functions of medullary sympathetic cardiovascular centers. *J. Neurophysiol.*, 9:205–217, 1946.
5. RANDALL, W. C., McNALLY, H., COWAN, J., CALIGUIRI, L., and ROHSE, W. G. Functional analysis of the cardioaugmentor and cardioaccelerator pathways in the dog. *Amer. J. Physiol.*, 191:213–217, 1957.
6. RUSHMER, R. F. Autonomic balance in cardiac control. *Amer. J. Physiol.*, 192:631–634, 1958.
7. BRONK, D. W., PITTS, R. I., and LARRABEE, M. G. Role of hypothalamus in cardiovascular regulation. *Res. Publ. Ass. Res. Nerv. Ment. Dis.*, 20:323–341, 1940.
8. STEVENSON, I. P., and DUNCAN, C. H. Alterations in cardiac function and circulatory efficiency during periods of life stress as shown by changes in the rate, rhythm, electrocardiographic pattern and output of the heart in those with cardiovascular disease. *Res. Publ. Ass. Res. Nerv. Ment. Dis.*, 29:799–817, 1950.
9. HICKAM, J. B., CARGILL, W. H., and GOLDEN, A. Cardiovascular reactions to emotional stimuli; effect on the cardiac output, arteriovenous oxygen difference, arterial pressure, and peripheral resistance. *J. Clin. Invest.*, 27:290–298, 1948.
10. FEIL, H., GREEN, H. D., and EIBER, D. Voluntary acceleration of heart in a subject showing the Wolff-Parkinson-White syndrome. *Amer. Heart J.*, 34:334–348, 1947.
11. DOWLING, C. V., SMITH, W. W., BERGER, A. R., and ALBERT, R. E. The effect on blood pressure in the right heart, pulmonary artery and systemic artery of cardiac standstill produced by carotid sinus stimulation. *Circulation*, 5:742–746, 1952.
12. RUSHMER, R. F. Circulatory collapse following mechanical stimulation of arteries. *Amer. J. Physiol.*, 141:722–729, 1944.
13. LEWIS, T. Lecture on vasovagal syncope and carotid sinus mechanism with comments on Gowers' and Nothnagel's syndrome. *Brit. Med. J.*, 1:873–876, 1932.
14. BAZETT, H. C., and McGLONE, B. Note on pain sensations which accompany deep punctures. *Brain*, 51:18–23, 1928.
15. HENDERSON, Y. Volume curve of the ventricles of the mammalian heart and the significance of this curve in respect to the mechanisms of the heart beat and the filling of the ventricles. *Amer. J. Physiol.*, 16:325–367, 1906.
16. WIGGERS, C. J. Determinants of cardiac performance. *Circulation*, 4:485–495, 1951.
17. PATTERSON, S. W., PIPER, H., and STARLING,

E. H. The regulation of the heart beat. *J. Physiol.*, 48:465–513, 1914.

18. WIGGERS, C. J., and KATZ, L. N. The contour of the ventricular volume curves under different conditions. *Amer. J. Physiol.*, 58: 439–475, 1922.

19. STARLING, E. H. *Principles of Human Physiology*, 3rd ed. Philadelphia, Lea & Febiger, 1920, 1315 pp.

20. STEAD, E. A., and WARREN, J. V. Cardiac output in man. *Arch. Int. Med.*, 80:237–248, 1947.

21. FOWLER, N. O., FRANCH, R. H., and BLOOM, W. L. Hemodynamic effects of anemia with and without plasma volume expansion. *Circulat. Res.*, 4:319–324, 1956.

22. GOWDEY, C. W., HATCHER, J. D., and SUNAHARA, F. A. Cardiovascular responses in dogs to large intravenous infusions. *Canad. J. Biochem.*, 32:282–292, 1954.

23. SUNAHARA, F. A., HATCHER, J. D., BECK, L., and GOWDEY, C. W. Cardiovascular responses in dogs to intravenous infusions of whole blood, plasma, and plasma followed by packed erythrocytes. *Canad. J. Biochem.*, 33:349–360, 1955.

24. RUSHMER, R. F., and CRYSTAL, D. K. Changes in configuration of the ventricular chambers during the cardiac cycle. *Circulation*, 4:211–218, 1951.

25. RUSHMER, R. F., CRYSTAL, D. K., and WAGNER, C. The functional anatomy of ventricular contraction. *Circulat. Res.*, 1:162–170, 1953.

26. NYLIN, G. On the amount of, and changes in, the residual blood of the heart. *Amer. Heart J.*, 25:598–608, 1943.

27. FRIEDMAN, C. E. The residual blood of the heart. A clinical x-ray and pathologico-anatomical study. *Amer. Heart J.*, 39:397–404, 1950.

28. BING, R. J., HEIMBECKER, R., and FALHOLT, W. An estimation of the residual volume of blood in the right ventricle of normal and diseased human heart in vivo. *Amer. Heart J.*, 42:483–502, 1951.

29. KJELLBERG, S. R., RUDHE, U., and SJÖSTRAND, T. The amount of hemoglobin and the blood volume in relation to the pulse rate and cardiac volume during rest. *Acta physiol. scand.*, 19:136–145, 1949.

30. FERGUSON, T. B., SHADLE, O. W., and GREGG, D. W. Effect of blood and saline infusion on ventricular end diastolic pressure, stroke work, stroke volume and cardiac output in the open and closed chest dog. *Circulat. Res.*, 1:62–68, 1953.

31. RUSHMER, R. F., FINLAYSON, B. L., and NASH, A. A. Shrinkage of the heart in anesthetized, thoracotomized dogs. *Circulat. Res.*, 2:22–27, 1954.

32. LUNDIN, G. Mechanical properties of cardiac muscle. *Acta physiol. scand.*, 7 (Suppl. 20):7–86, 1944.

33. GASSER, H. S., and HILL, A. V. The dynamics of muscular contraction. *Proc. Roy. Soc.*, B96:398–437, 1924.

34. BUCHTHAL, F., KAISER, E., and KNAPPEIS, G. G. Elasticity, viscosity and plasticity in the cross-striated muscle fibre. *Acta physiol. scand.*, 8:16–37, 1944.

35. BRECHER, G. A. Critical review of recent work on ventricular diastolic suction. *Circulat. Res.*, 6:554–566, 1958.

36. RUSHMER, R. F., SMITH, O. A., JR., and FRANKLIN, D. L. Mechanisms of cardiac control during exercise. *Circulat. Res.*, 7:602–627, 1959.

37. ANZOLA, J., and RUSHMER, R. F. Cardiac responses to sympathetic stimulation. *Circulat. Res.*, 4:302–307, 1956.

38. RANDALL, W. C. and ROHSE, W. G. The augmentor action of the sympathetic cardiac nerves. *Circulat. Res.*, 4:470–475, 1956.

39. FRANKLIN, D. L., ELLIS, R. M., and RUSHMER, R. F. Aortic blood flow in dogs during treadmill exercise. *J. Appl. Physiol.* 14:809–812, 1959.

40. FRANKLIN, D. L., BAKER, D. W., ELLIS, R. M., and RUSHMER, R. F. A pulsed ultrasonic flowmeter. *IRE Trans. Med. Electron.*, ME6:204–206, 1959.

41. BAKER, D., ELLIS, R. M., FRANKLIN, D. L., and RUSHMER, R. F. Some engineering aspects of modern cardiovascular research. *Proc. Inst. Radio Engrs.* 47:1917–1924, 1959.

42. RUSHMER, R. F., FRANKLIN, D. L., and ELLIS, R. M. Left ventricular dimensions recorded by sonocardiometry. *Circulat. Res.*, 6:684, 1956.

43. SHIPLEY, R. E., and GREGG, D. E. The cardiac response to stimulation of the stellate ganglion and cardiac nerves. *Amer. J. Physiol*, 143:396–401, 1945.

44. KELSO, A. F. and RANDALL, W. C. Ventricular changes associated with sympathetic augmentation of cardiovascular pressure pulses. *Amer. J. Physiol.*, 196:731–734, 1959.

45. KJELLBERG, S. R., RUDHE, U., and SJÖSTRAND, T. The influence of the autonomic nervous system on the contraction of the human heart under normal circulatory conditions. *Acta physiol. scand.*, 24:350–360, 1952.

46. FULTON, J. F., RANSON, S. W., and FRANTZ, A. M. The hypothalamus and central levels of autonomic function. *Res. Publ. Ass. Nerv. & Ment. Dis.*, 20:1–980, 1940.

47. SMITH, O. A., JR., JABBUR, S. J., RUSHMER, R. F., and LASHER, E. P. Role of hypothalamic structures in cardiac control. *Physiol. Rev.*, 40 (Suppl. 4): 136–145, 1960.

48. SMITH, O. A., JR., RUSHMER, R. F., and LASHER, E. P. Similarity of cardiovascular responses to exercise and diencephalic stimulation. *Amer. J. Physiol.* 198:1139–1142, 1960.

49. RUSHMER, R. F., and SMITH, O. A. Cardiac control. *Physiol. Rev.*, 39:41–68, 1959.

50. MEEK, W. J., and EYSTER, J. A. E. Cardiac size and output in man during rest and mod-

erate exercise. *Amer. J. Physiol.*, 63:400–401, 1923.

51. KJELLBERG, S. R., LONROTH, H., and RUDHE, U. The effect of various factors on the roentgenological determination of the cardiac volume. *Acta radiol.*, 35:413–427, 1951.

52. FORSSMANN, W. Probing of the right heart. *Klin. Wschr.*, 8:2085–2087, 1929.

53. COURNAND, A., and RANGES, H. A. Catheterization of right auricle in man. *Proc. Soc. Exp. Biol. Med.*, 46:462–466, 1941.

54. COURNAND, A., RILEY, R. L., BREED, E. S., BALDWIN, DEF., and RICHARDS, D. W. Measurement of cardiac output in man using technique of catheterization of right auricle or ventricle. *J. Clin. Invest.*, 24:106–116, 1945.

55. COURNAND, A., BALDWIN, J. S., and HIMMELSTEIN, A. *Cardiac Catheterization in Congenital Heart Disease.* New York, The Commonwealth Fund, 1949.

56. WARREN, J. V. Determination of cardiac output in man by right heart catheterization. *Meth. Med. Res.*, 1:224–232, 1948.

57. SOSMAN, M. C. Venous catheterization of the heart. I. Indications, technics and errors. *Radiology*, 48:441–450, 1947.

58. DEXTER, L. Venous catheterization of the heart. II. Results, interpretations and value. *Radiology*, 48:451–462, 1947.

59. VISSCHER, M. B., and JOHNSON, J. A. The Fick principle: analysis of potential errors in its conventional application. *J. Appl. Physiol.*, 5:635–638, 1953.

60. STOW, R. W. Systematic errors in flow determinations by the Fick method. *Minnesota Med.*, 37:30–35, 1954.

61. WARREN, J. V., STEAD, E. A., JR. and BRANNON, E. S. The cardiac output in man: a study of some of the errors in the method of right heart catheterization. *Amer. J. Physiol.*, 145:458–464, 1946.

62. BURTON, A. C. Peripheral circulation. *Ann. Rev. Physiol.*, 15:213–246, 1953.

63. BING, R. J., HAMMOND, M. M., HENDELSMAN, J. C., POWERS, S. R., SPENCER, F. C., ECKENHOFF, J. E., GOODALE, W. T., HAFKENSCHIEL, J. H., and KETY, S. S. The measurement of coronary blood flow, oxygen consumption, and efficiency of the left ventricle in man. *Amer. Heart J.*, 38:1–24, 1949.

64. STEWART, G. N. Researches on the circulation time and on the influences which affect it. *J. Physiol.*, 22:159–183, 1897.

65. STEWART, G. N. The output of the heart in dogs. *Amer. J. Physiol.*, 57:27–50, 1921.

66. HAMILTON, W. F., and REMINGTON, J. W. Comparison of the time concentration curves in arterial blood of diffusible and nondiffusible substances when injected at a constant rate and when injected instantaneously. *Amer. J. Physiol.*, 148:35–39, 1948.

67. KINSMAN, J. M., MOORE, J. W., and HAMILTON, W. F. Studies on the circulation: injection method: physical and mathematical considerations. *Amer. J. Physiol.*, 89:321–330, 1929.

68. MOORE, J. W., KINSMAN, J. M., HAMILTON, W. F., and SPURLING, R. G. Studies on the circulation. II. Cardiac output determinations; comparison of the injection method with the direct Fick procedure. *Amer. J. Physiol.*, 89:331–339, 1929.

69. HAMILTON, W. F. Circulatory system: heart output. Pp. 191–194 in *Medical Physics*, vol. 1, O. GLASSER, ed. Chicago, Year Book Publishers, 1950.

70. WIGGERS, H. C. Cardiac output and total peripheral resistance measurements in experimental dogs. *Amer. J. Physiol.*, 140:519–534, 1944.

71. WHITE, H. L. Measurement of cardiac output by a continuously recording conductivity method. *Amer. J. Physiol.*, 151:45–57, 1947.

72. ERLANGER, J., and HOOKER, D. R. An experimental study of blood-pressure and of pulse-pressure in man. *Johns Hopk. Hosp. Rep.*, 12:145–378, 1904.

73. REMINGTON, J. W. The relation between the stroke volume and the pulse pressure. *Minnesota Med.*, 37:105–110, 1954.

74. HAMILTON, W. F., and REMINGTON, J. W. The measurement of the stroke volume from the pressure pulse. *Amer. J. Physiol.*, 148:14–24, 1947.

75. REMINGTON, J. W., HAMILTON, W. F., WHEELER, N. C., and HAMILTON, W. F., JR. Validity of pulse contour method for calculating cardiac output of the dog, with notes on effect of various anesthetics. *Amer. J. Physiol.*, 159:379–384, 1949.

76. WARNER, H. R. Quantitation of stroke volume changes in man from the central pressure pulse. *Minnesota Med.*, 37:111–115, 130, 1954.

77. WIGGERS, C. J. *Physiology of Shock.* New York, The Commonwealth Fund, 1950.

78. GORDON, J. W. On certain molar movements of the human body produced by the circulation of the blood. *J. Anat., Lond.*, 11:533–536, 1877.

79. HENDERSON, Y. The mass-movements of the circulation as shown by a recoil curve. *Amer. J. Physiol.*, 14:287–298, 1905.

80. TALBOT, S. A., DEUCHAR, D. C., DAVIS, F. W., JR., and SCARBOROUGH, W. R. The aperiodic ballistocardiograph. *Johns Hopk. Hosp. Bull.*, 94:27–33, 1954.

81. STARR, I., RAWSON, A. J., SCHROEDER, H. A., and JOSEPH, N. R. Studies on the estimation of cardiac output in man, and of abnormalities in cardiac function, from the heart's recoil and the blood's impacts; the ballistocardiogram. *Amer. J. Physiol.*, 127:1–28, 1939.

82. STARR, I., and SCHROEDER, H. A. Ballistocardiogram. II. Normal standards, abnormalities commonly found in diseases of the
heart and circulation, and their significance.
J. Clin. Invest., 19:437–450, 1940.

83. Dow, P., and HAMILTON, W. F. An analysis,
by hydraulic models, of the factors operating
to produce the typical ballistocardiogram.
Amer. J. Physiol., 133:263, 1941.

84. NICKERSON, J. L., and CURTIS, H. J. The design of the ballistocardiograph. *Amer. J.
Physiol.*, 142:1–11, 1944.

85. HAMILTON, W. F., Dow, P., and REMINGTNO,
J. W. The relationship between the cardiac
ejection curve and the ballistocardiographic
forces. Amer. J. Physiol., 144:557-570, 1945.

86. DOCK, W., and TAUBMAN, F. Some technics
for recording the ballistocardiogram directly
from the body. *Amer. J. Med.*, 7:751–755,
1949.

Chapter 4

PERIPHERAL VASCULAR CONTROL

I. Mechanisms of Peripheral Vascular Control

The human body is composed of billions of cells, variously specialized, grouped and organized to perform many different functions. Unlike self-sufficient unicellular organisms which draw their sustenance from a relatively large expanse of surrounding water, body cells exist within a confined space. They can survive and function only so long as their immediate environment contains an adequate supply of essential nutrient materials and a limited concentration of waste products. In other words, the temperature, pH and concentration of various substances must be maintained within certain limits. A living cell continuously utilizes certain types of molecules (oxygen, glucose, amino acids, etc.). As the quantities of these substances are depleted in the immediate environment of the cell, other molecules of the same species move toward this region of reduced concentration in response to a diffusion gradient (see Fig. 2, Chap. 1). The rate of diffusion is determined by the concentration gradient and the distance between the blood and the cells (Fig. 1).

The capillaries permeate every tissue of the body and the blood is rarely more than 0.1 mm. from any cell. They are only about 0.017 mm. in diameter but their total length is almost 60,000 miles.[1] Thus the blood and tissue fluids are exposed to a tremendous expanse of capillary surface through which materials may be exchanged. Cells which consume essential materials rapidly must either be situated near capillaries or operate effectively at low concentrations of the various vital materials. Thus, tissues with high metabolic rates (brain, muscle, kidney, etc.) characteristically have dense capillary networks through which blood flows rapidly. By this mechanism, high concentrations of essential substances are maintained near the capillary walls, providing steep gradients for diffusion. Cells with lower requirements lie farther from the capillaries and are less affected by cessation of blood flow. Elimination of waste products proceeds in the reverse direction propelled by diffusion gradients with maximum concentrations at the site of production in the cells.

The delivery of substances to the tissues thus involves two steps: transportation by the blood to the capillary beds and local delivery by diffusion. The efficiency of the circulatory apparatus depends upon the success with which it provides adequate diffusion gradients within the tissues.

If, for example, the metabolic activity of skeletal muscle suddenly increased without a change in blood flow, the concentration of oxygen in and around the cells would drop, the diffusion gradient would steepen, the rate of diffusion would accelerate and the arteriovenous oxygen difference would widen (Fig. 1B). On the other hand, if an increased blood flow

98

completely compensated for the increased oxygen utilization, oxygen delivery would be increased without a change in the arteriovenous oxygen difference and with little drop in tissue oxygen tension. Circulatory adjustment to the varying metabolic demands of skeletal muscle is never adequate to prevent a reduction in the oxygen content of venous blood, i.e., an increase in the arteriovenous difference.

Influenced by common personal experience, we are inclined to view peripheral vascular control primarily in terms of delivery of oxygen to the tissues, as is implied by Figure 1. Oxygen is used at a prodigious rate in relation to the available stores during exertion. When the circulation is restored after occluding the arterial supply to the arm or leg for a few minutes, the flushing of the skin, the throbbing of the limb and the return of the power of contraction all attest to the essential role of the blood supply in the function of muscles and skin. Indeed, this greatly accelerated blood flow (reactive hyperemia) after temporary arterial occlusion is generally attributed to vasodilation induced by depressed oxygen content in the tissues and to accumulation of carbon dioxide, lactic acid and other "metabolites" in the tissues. In addition this mechanism has been widely invoked to explain the vasodilation that produces accelerated blood flow in most regions of the body at one time or another. Actually, the substance or substances responsible for reactive hy-

OXYGEN EXTRACTION IN ACTIVE AND INACTIVE TISSUES

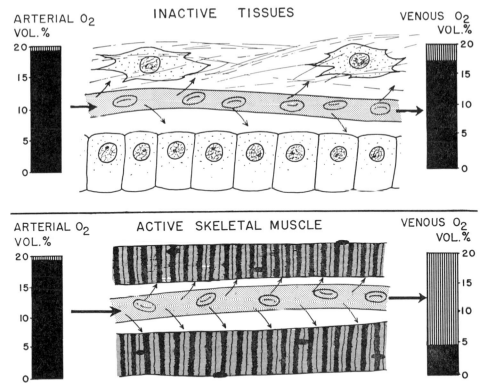

FIGURE 1. The quantity of oxygen extracted from the blood during its flow through capillaries is determined by the relationship between the rate of oxygen utilization and the blood flow.

A, Slight oxygen extraction and small arteriovenous oxygen differences occur in tissues with relatively small oxygen requirements and active blood flow, e.g., skin.

B, Tissues which release energy at rapid rates, e.g., contracting muscle, extract a major portion of the oxygen from the blood.

THE ARTERIOVENOUS OXYGEN DIFFERENCES IN VARIOUS TISSUES

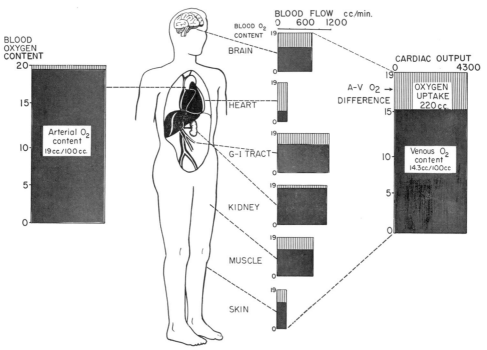

FIGURE 2.   The blood flow through some tissues is voluminous in relation to the oxygen requirements (kidney and skin). In contrast, the myocardium extracts most of the oxygen from the blood.
The arteriovenous oxygen differences represent the relationship between blood flow and oxygen utilization in various tissues.

peremia has not been identified (see *Chemical Dilators* below).

When we experience fatigue in muscles after exhausting exercise, it certainly "feels as though" the products of metabolism had been collecting in the muscles. When muscles feel too "fatigued" to function they can still contract vigorously as demonstrated by a simple experiment. An electrical stimulus delivered through the skin over the point where the motor nerve enters a skeletal muscle, will readily activate the muscle. This responsiveness can be shown by fixing an electrode over the point where a motor nerve enters a muscle that will flex a finger. The subject voluntarily flexes this finger against a spring resistance in time with a metronome until the muscle is so "fatigued" that it no longer depresses the spring.

Electrical stimulation delivered through the electrode at the same rate will immediately produce rhythmic contractions just as powerful as those at the beginning of the experiment. The point of this demonstration is that the so-called "fatigue" in the muscle does not result from accumulated products of metabolism. The sensation of "tiredness" does not even originate within the muscle or the peripheral nerve. The voluntary flexion of the muscle must be interrupted by depression or "fatigue" within the neural chains in the central nervous system.

Normal Oxygen Distribution

In most tissues other than skeletal muscles and myocardium, adjustments of blood flow in relation to oxygen consumption or metabolic activity would be completely inappropriate. For example, the oxygen consumption in skin is quite trivial and yet extremely large amounts of blood may flow through this organ to support its function of dissipating heat. Similarly, the amount of blood flowing through the kidney is very large in relation to its metabolic activity. Thus, only a small fraction of the oxygen presented to the kidney substance is taken up and the blood leaving the kidney does not differ greatly from arterial blood.

To illustrate these points, the quantity of blood flowing each minute through several organs is plotted on the abscissa in Figure 2. The quantity of oxygen presented to the tissues in the arterial blood was 19 cc. per 100 cc. of blood (ordinate in Fig. 2). Thus, the area of each rectangular figure represents the quantity of oxygen presented to each organ each minute. The black area represents the quantity of oxygen in the venous blood leaving the organ and the remaining area (vertical lines) indicates the amount of oxygen extracted by the tissue. Note the very small quantity of oxygen extracted from blood in the kidney. Myocardium extracts about 70 per cent or more of the oxygen presented to it. Resting skeletal muscle utilizes only about one-third of the oxygen in the blood it receives, but contracting skeletal muscle extracts about three-fourths of the oxygen from the blood. Thus, the difference between the oxygen contents of arterial and venous blood (A-V oxygen difference) varies widely from tissue to tissue. The average A-V oxygen difference at rest, based on mixed venous blood, ranges around 4 to 6 cc. per 100 cc. of blood.

Resistance to Blood Flow

The blood pumped by the heart is distributed to the various tissues according to their functions. The rate at which the blood flows through the vascular channels is dependent upon the energy lost in the form of friction. Little pressure energy is

dissipated in the long arterial conduits (Fig. 9, Chap. 1), but the pressure gradient becomes steeper as the blood flows through the smaller and smaller branches toward the periphery. Thus, a substantial fraction of the pressure head available in the aorta is dissipated as the blood flows through the terminal arteries, arterioles and capillaries. The amount of pressure dissipated is regulated by variations in the caliber of the vascular channels. The extent to which the vessels change their diameters for this type of regulation becomes progressively greater and more significant toward the peripheral ramifications of the arterial tree. The wall of the aorta contains a substantial quantity of elastic tissue (about 40 per cent by weight). The proportion of elastic tissue diminishes and the proportion of smooth muscle is greater in the more peripheral arterial branches (Fig. 3).

The pressure within the lumen of the blood vessels must be supported by tension in their walls in accordance with the law of Laplace ($P = T/r$); so that the greater the radius of the tube, the greater the wall tension required to support a given internal pressure (see Fig. 11, Chap. 1). The tension supported by various components of the vascular wall has been analyzed by Burton.[2] The tensile strength of the elastic tissue in the aorta is capable of supporting three times the normal aortic pressure, providing a good margin of safety. The force required to break the collagenous tissue in the aorta is so great that in most experiments the clamps holding the tissue slip before breakage occurs. The caliber of the vascular channels is adjusted by changing tension exerted by smooth muscle (see Fig. 3), which can maintain tension for a long time with a very small expenditure of energy.[2]

Critical Closing Pressure. By virtue of Laplace's law, active tension exerted by smooth muscle in the wall of a cylindrical tube may produce a fundamental instability. Suppose that when the wall

COMPONENTS OF VASCULAR WALLS

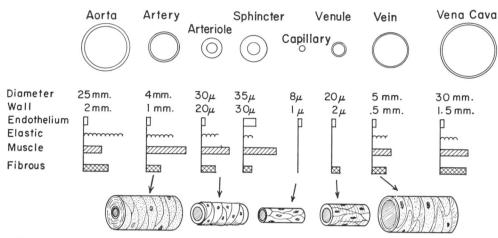

FIGURE 3.   The relative amount of elastic tissue and fibrous tissues is largest in the aorta and least in small branches of the arterial tree. Smaller vessels have more prominent smooth muscle in the media. Capillaries consist only of endothelial tubes. The walls of the veins are much like the arterial walls, but are thinner in relation to their caliber.

tension is precisely balanced against the pressure in a blood vessel $(P = T/r)$ the tension exerted by the smooth muscle is slightly increased. The radius of the vessel decreases slightly, and the tension required to maintain the pressure is further reduced so that the radius continues to shrink. If this occurred, the caliber would progressively diminish until the lumen of the vessel closed. Thus, if smooth muscle predominates in the wall, as in arterioles, precapillary sphincters and arteriovenous shunts, the vessels would tend to be either fully open or fully closed. Burton proposed the concept of a *critical closing pressure* at which the lumina of such small vessels would close because the wall tension was being supported predominantly by smooth muscle. According to this concept, the sites of controlled resistance in the terminal vascular networks should be either wide open or closed. Microscopic examination fails to confirm this prediction completely since graded variations in the caliber of vessels and sphincters can be observed. However, the control of capillary flow distribution clearly involves changing patterns of closure of the vascular sphincters (see Fig. 4*A*).

The concept of critical closing pressure neglects the influence of the thickness of the vascular walls. In vessels with walls which are thick in relation to the radius, $P = T\delta/r$ where P is the pressure, T is the tension in the wall, δ is the thickness of the wall and r is the radius of the tube.[3] With constriction of the vessel, the wall becomes thicker. Internal stresses develop in the wall as the lumen is progressively constricted until extremely great tension must be developed to obliterate the lumen completely (Fig. 4*B*).

Mechanisms of Vascular Closure.   The lumina of larger arteries can be reduced but are not completely obliterated by contraction of the smooth muscle in the walls. Reduction in the caliber of such arteries involves severe deformation of the smooth muscle cells, the internal elastic membrane and the endothelial cells. The forces required to completely occlude the lumen can be simulated by encircling a piece of gum rubber tubing with a strong ligature or string and pulling on its two ends in an attempt to close the lumen. Small terminal arteries, arterioles and precapillary sphincters can be completely constricted by contraction of the investing smooth muscle. In this process, the endothelial cells change shape and are molded to plug the lumen (Fig. 4B).

Functional Anatomy of Peripheral Vascular Control. Zweifach[4] has described two distinct types of capillaries: arteriovenous capillaries and "true" capillaries. The A-V capillaries are "thoroughfare" channels with fairly direct courses from the arterioles to the venules. In general, blood flows continuously through the A-V capillaries, the rate of flow being varied through changes in the caliber of the muscular arterioles and of the A-V capillaries themselves. A-V capillaries are invested with smooth muscle, which is abundant at the arteriolar end and more diffusely distributed toward the venular regions (Fig. 5). Branching from the A-V capillaries are the "true" capillaries, which are intricately joined to form complex networks lying between adjacent thoroughfare channels. The "true" capillaries have no smooth muscle except for muscular cuffs (precapillary sphincters) at their points of origin from the A-V capillaries. Capillaries from the vascular network rejoin the A-V capillaries near the venular end, but there are no smooth muscle sphincters at these junctions. If all the precapillary sphincters serving a capillary bed closed simultaneously, blood would not flow through these channels. However, at any one instant, some precapillary sphincters are open and others are closed. At intervals of one-half to three minutes some sphincters close and others open. The caliber of the A-V channels also fluctuates asynchronously.

Dilatation and constriction of the A-V capillaries and the different combinations of dilated precapillary sphincters produce

VASOCONSTRICTION

A. CONSTRICTION OF SMALL VESSELS

Dilated   Constricted

Smooth Muscle

Endothelium

B. WALL THICKNESS

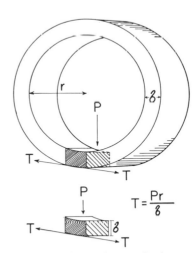

$$T = \frac{Pr}{\delta}$$

FIGURE 4. *A*, If a thick-walled tube constricts concentrically until the lumen is completely occluded, the internal circumference must become zero. The occlusion of the lumen in a constricted blood vessel is achieved by deformation and rounding of endothelial cells to form a central plug.

B, According to the Laplace relationship, the wall tension is determined by the product of the internal pressure and radius. The relation holds for tubes with very small wall thickness in relation to the radius. In a thick-walled tube with dimensions which change over a wide range of caliber, the wall thickness must be considered (i.e., if the cylinder constricts to very small dimensions as in *A*). Under these conditions $T = \dfrac{Pr}{\delta}$.

VASOMOTION IN A CAPILLARY NETWORK

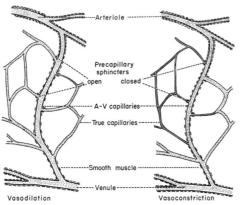

FIGURE 5. Capillary networks, in some tissues at least, consist of arteriovenous capillaries (thoroughfare channels) and "true" capillaries. The blood flow through the different portions of the capillary bed is affected by contraction and relaxation of smooth muscle in the arterioles, A-V capillaries and precapillary sphincters. Phasic changes in the caliber in these regions produce cyclic alterations in the amount and distribution of blood flow through the various true capillaries (vasomotion).

a continuously changing pattern of flow through the capillary networks. In a particular segment of the capillary bed, the blood may flow rapidly through one channel for a period of time, then cease to flow or even flow in the opposite direction depending on which sphincters are open. The phasic changes in the caliber of the arterioles, A-V capillaries and precapillary sphincters have been termed "vasomotion" (Fig. 5). The rate of blood flow through the individual channels is an expression of a gradient in capillary pressure. Blood flow is rapid when capillary pressure in the arteriolar end of an A-V capillary is high in relation to venular pressure. When flow ceases, the pressure throughout the capillary approximates that in the venules.

The functional significance of vasomotion is being intensively investigated. It is apparent that this aspect of vascular control has important implications for normal function. For example, phasic vasomotor

activity is expressed in periodic changes in the volume of the finger[5] and in fluctuations in the arterial blood pressure. The existence of vasomotion implies a more precise regulation of capillary blood flow in response to local tissue demands than could result if control were exerted only by the arterioles. At the same time, descriptions of capillary blood pressure become more complicated because the pressure levels and gradients are continuously changing. However, certain generaliza·tions can be made. If the pressure in the venules remains constant, vasomotion would affect only the pressure gradients from arterioles to venules. When the arterioles, A-V capillaries and precapillary sphincters are dilated, the pressure gradients along the channels are steep and blood flow is rapid. When the caliber of these channels is reduced by constriction, more potential energy is lost as friction before the blood reaches the capillaries. The pressure at the arteriolar end of the capillaries is thus lowered, the pressure gradients become shallow or are eliminated and blood flow diminishes or ceases. Total blood flow through a tissue is increased by prolonging the intervals of vasodilatation and reducing the periods of vasoconstriction. The organization of capillaries illustrated in Figure 5 is believed to occur in those tissues which have widely varying levels of activity. Vasomotion, as a characteristic pattern of peripheral circulatory control, has been observed in a number of tissues including rat mesentery, bat wing, subcutaneous connective tissues and canine and human hearts.

Mechanisms of Vascular Regulation

The quantity of blood flowing through various vascular beds and its distribution among the myriad vascular channels depend primarily upon changes in the caliber of the sites of controlled resistance brought about by active changes in the tension exerted by smooth muscle cells. Histologic examination of vascular smooth muscle fails to reveal structural differences from one vessel to another. Yet the functional disparity between the vessels of different organs is so great that a single substance will produce constriction in one organ and dilation in another.

The concept that autonomic nerve fibers terminate on each smooth muscle cell in the vascular system has been widely accepted. According to Lutz and Fulton,[6] however, some vascular smooth muscle has dual innervation (constrictor and dilator), only vasoconstrictor or vasodilator nerves serve some vascular smooth muscle and a third class of muscle cells apparently does not receive any innervation. Vascular smooth muscle without a nerve supply reacts to both epinephrine and acetylcholine (the transmitter substances for the sympathetic and parasympathetic nervous systems respectively), and vessels highly sensitive to acetylcholine may have no demonstrable cholinergic innervation. Some vascular beds respond to changes in the carbon dioxide tension in arterial blood; others dilate in response to unidentified metabolites. Thus, concise descriptions of peripheral vascular control are impossible because the system is very complex and because not nearly enough is known about it. For the present discussion, some of the more important controls will be considered in terms of neural, hormonal, chemical and physical mechanisms. Then, the factors which appear to be prominent in the control of certain key organs will be discussed.

Sympathetic Vasomotor System. Neural control over the peripheral vascular system is dominated by the sympathetic division of the autonomic nervous system. Nerve cell bodies lying in the intermediolateral cell column of the thoracic division of the spinal cord give off axons that pass out the ventral root and synapse either in the ganglia of the sympathetic chain or in accessory ganglia. The postganglionic axons follow the segmental nerves to the peripheral vessels or pass directly to perivascular plexuses through which the fibers pass to the periphery. The terminal branches of the sympathetic constrictor fibers pass to vascular smooth muscle and apparently release transmitter substances which induce contraction or relaxation of the smooth muscle components in the walls.

The collections of nerve cell bodies in the intermediolateral column serve as spinal vasomotor centers, receiving impulses over afferent fibers entering the spinal cord from various structures and also receiving regulatory impulses descending from higher neural structures (Fig. 6). Immediately after cervical spinal section in man the blood pressure tends to be poorly sustained.[7] Since the spinal lesion has interrupted descending pathways but has neither injured the cells at the thoracic level nor interfered with their afferent input, this condition indicates that volleys of impulses descending the spinal cord normally modulate the discharges of the spinal vasomotor centers. Sometime later such patients regain vascular reactivity. This reactivity is a function of the spinal centers and is reflex in nature. For example, when the spinal cord is bombarded by impulses aroused by experimental distention of the bladder, the systemic arterial pressure may rise to 300 mm. Hg or more.

Medullary Centers. Electrical stimulation of some areas in the medulla oblongata[8] produces prompt elevation in blood pressure (pressor areas) and stimulation of other medullary areas causes a sharp reduction in blood pressure (depressor areas; Fig. 6). These regions are generally termed the vasoconstrictor and vasodilator "center," respectively. These so-called centers are not strictly localized but are diffuse networks of interconnected

CENTRAL CONTROL OF SYMPATHETIC VASOCONSTRICTION

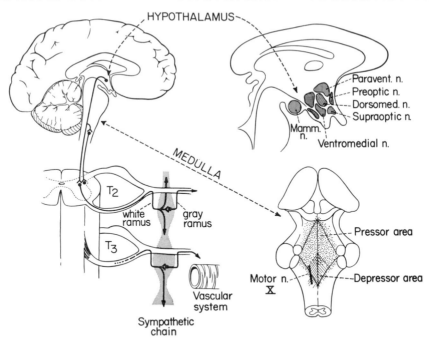

FIGURE 6. Sympathetic constrictor nerves, distributed to peripheral vascular system, originate from the intermediolateral cell column of the thoracic cord. Impulses descend from the medullary region and the hypothalamus to modulate the sympathetic nerve discharge. The hypothalamus plays an important role in autonomic control of many different visceral functions. Changes in systemic arterial pressure can be readily produced by stimulation of the "pressor" and "depressor" areas in the medulla. (After Alexander.[8]) However, these medullary areas may actually represent pathways from higher levels down to the spinal cord, rather than "vasomotor centers."

neuron groups. The nature of the interaction between the pressor and depressor zones is not known, and they are continuously influenced by impulses from many sources such as pressoreceptors, chemoreceptors, somatic afferent sources and the higher levels of the nervous system (see below). These medullary centers of cardiovascular regulation appear to be essential to normal control of systemic arterial pressure (see Chap. 6).

Diencephalic Centers. The region of the hypothalamus contains control centers integrating reactions which involve the vascular system. As mentioned in Chapter 3, these reactions include temperature regulation, water balance, thirst and hunger and cardiovascular responses to exertion (see Chap. 8). Electrical stimulation of discrete hypothalamic and sub-

thalamic sites produces profound changes in the heart rate, ventricular contractility and arterial pressure and also dilation of blood vessels in skeletal muscle by means of the familiar sympathetic cholinergic vasodilator fibers (see below).

Impinging on the hypothalamic centers are nerve impulses from many parts of the brain including the motor and premotor cortex, the frontal cortex, the orbital cortex, the temporal lobe, the amygdala, the insula and the cingulate gyrus.[9, 10] In general, if electrical stimulation of an area in the brain consistently yields behavior responses, cardiovascular responses are also induced. Conversely, if electrical stimulation of a cerebral area does not induce cardiovascular responses, it rarely evokes behavioral changes.

Sympathetic Constrictor Nerves. The sympathetic constrictor fibers exert their most profound effects on the blood vessels of skeletal muscle, the skin and the splanchnic bed (see Figs. 13 and 15). The sympathetic constrictor nerve fibers apparently exert their action on smooth muscle at the so-called alpha (α) receptor sites at which *l*-epinephrine and norepinephrine also act (Fig. 7*A*). The blood vessels of skeletal muscles are served by both adrenergic constrictor fibers and cholinergic dilator fibers. The constrictor fibers to the skin are involved in conservation of heat, and the direct vascular connections between the small arteries and small veins (arteriovenous anastomoses) in the skin are directly controlled by the hypothalamic heat loss center. Through these channels large volumes of blood pass directly from the terminal arteries into the voluminous venous plexuses for heat dissipation. The arteriovenous anastomoses are completely dominated by the constrictor fibers, dilating maximally when the constrictor nerves are cut. In other areas, severance of the constrictor fibers leave the blood vessels with considerable constrictor "tone" (i.e., they are partially constricted).

Sympathetic Vasodilator System. Stimulation of the sympathetic chain in the lumbar region of cats or dogs may cause initial dilation followed by constriction in the vascular beds within skeletal muscle. When the constriction was eliminated by adrenergic blocking drugs, pure vasodilation was obtained.[9] The vasodilator response was restricted to skeletal muscle, and was potentiated by eserine and eliminated by atropine.[9] A substance like acetylcholine was found in the effluent perfusate from such muscles.[10] These observations form the basis for the concept of a sympathetic cholinergic vasodilator system (Fig. 7*B*). It is believed that this system originates in the motor cortex and that impulses descend from there to the hypothalamus, pass through the medullary centers, and leave the spinal cord

with the sympathetic nerves to induce vasodilation of the blood vessels in skeletal muscles. When the sympathetic constrictor fibers to the skeletal muscle are blocked or inactivated, the blood vessels dilate somewhat, but continue to display considerable basal tone (partial constriction). Upon stimulation of the sympathetic cholinergic vasodilator system the blood flow may become five or six times greater.

Axon Reflex. Stimulation of the peripheral ends of severed dorsal roots (afferent fibers) produces vasodilation in skin vessels. This response was formerly ascribed to activity of motor fibers issuing from the spinal cord against the stream of the sensory fibers that normally enter the cord by this route. A preferred explanation for this phenomenon is the hypothetical axon reflex. According to this concept, sensory nerve fibers in the skin may have collateral fibers distributed to adjacent blood vessels (Fig. 7*B*). Impulses generated from the sensory endings may pass directly to the dilator termination in the blood vessel as well as to the spinal cord. Such a mechanism has been invoked to explain the dilatory effects of certain irritants and mechanical stimulation of the skin.

Parasympathetic Dilator Mechanism. Stimulation of the parasympathetic nerves supplying certain glands (e.g., salivary glands) induces a profuse secretion and an intense vasodilation. Existence of parasympathetic vasodilators was postulated to explain the hyperemia. Recently Hilton and Lewis[11] have presented evidence that the glandular cells, activated by the parasympathetic fibers, release an enzyme (bradykinin) into the interstitial spaces. There this enzyme acts on tissue proteins to split off a polypeptide which diffuses to vessels in the vicinity, and produces vasodilation (see Fig. 7*B*). Bradykinin was apparently recoverable from the glandular excretion, and, after saline was perfused under the skin during profuse

VASOMOTOR CONTROL

A. GENERAL VASOMOTOR CONTROL MECHANISMS

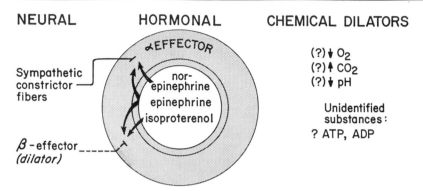

NEURAL   HORMONAL   CHEMICAL DILATORS

Sympathetic constrictor fibers

αEFFECTOR

nor-epinephrine
epinephrine
isoproterenol

β-effector (dilator)

(?)$\downarrow O_2$
(?)$\uparrow CO_2$
(?)$\downarrow$ pH

Unidentified substances:
? ATP, ADP

B. SPECIAL VASOMOTOR MECHANISMS

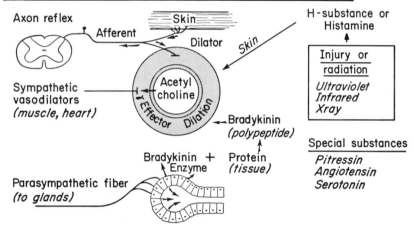

Axon reflex
Afferent
Skin
Dilator
Skin

H-substance or Histamine

Injury or radiation
Ultraviolet
Infrared
Xray

Sympathetic vasodilators (muscle, heart)

Acetyl choline

Effector Dilation

Bradykinin (polypeptide)

Bradykinin + Enzyme
Protein (tissue)

Special substances
Pitressin
Angiotensin
Serotonin

Parasympathetic fiber (to glands)

FIGURE 7. *A*, Vasoconstriction or vasodilation can be produced in various tissues by means of many neural, hormonal and chemical mechanisms. Sympathetic fibers, and circulating norepinephrine and *l*-epinephrine are widely believed to act as specific sites (α effectors). The β effectors are not innervated. The chemical dilators are proposed mechanisms for explaining vasodilation following temporary occlusion of blood supply to a vascular bed (reactive hyperemia).

B, The special vasomotor mechanisms are found prominently in the skin although the sympathetic vasodilators (muscle and heart) and the postulated bradykinin mechanism affect glands. No definite role in normal vascular regulation has been assigned to the special constrictor substances, vasopressin (Pitressin), angiotensin and serotonin.

sweating, a substance like bradykinin was recovered in the perfusate.[12] Thus, the bradykinin mechanisms may be involved in the vasodilation of the skin which accompanies profuse sweating. It is tempting to postulate that the same type of mechanism is involved in the vasodilation which accompanies other visceral activity induced by parasympa-thetic activity (e.g., that in the gastro-intestinal tract).

Hormonal Mechanisms. Impulses arriving at the terminals of the autonomic nervous system exert their influence on the effectors by release of transmitter substances. In the parasympathetic nervous system, this transmitter is acetylcholine, a rather potent vasodilator substance in some vascular beds. Through Euler's investigations,[13] the transmitter substance for sympathetic constrictor fibers has been identified as norepinephrine, which is found in high concentration in sympathetic nerves and in tissues with an intact sympathetic innervation. This substance differs from *l*-epinephrine, which is excreted primarily from chromaffin cells in the adrenal medulla and from other chromaffin cells scattered in different parts of the body, particularly in the heart. In man, norepinephrine produces vasoconstriction in those vascular beds where it produces any response at all. In contrast, *l*-epinephrine also has a vasodilator action in skeletal muscle, and perhaps in the heart, and a powerful effect on myocardial contractility. The distinction between these two substances is not nearly so obvious in the dog (see Fig. 14, Chap. 3).

The Concept of Vascular Receptors. Catechol amines exert either of two effects on the vascular beds in skeletal muscle—vasoconstriction or vasodilation. Norepinephrine is a powerful vasconstrictor, but *l*-epinephrine can have either a dilator or a constrictor action depending upon the circumstances. Ahlquist[14] was therefore led to propose that two distinct types of receptors, or binding sites—α and β receptors—are involved at the smooth muscle. (Since the term "receptor" might be misconstrued to mean the sensory or afferent receptors of reflex activity, the word "effector" has been substituted for "receptor" in Figure 7.)

It is thought that norepinephrine acts only on the α receptors and that these receptors excite the constrictor mechanism. *l*-Epinephrine is also believed to have the same effect when acting on α receptors. If these receptors are blocked by an appropriate drug (azapetine; Ilidar), then injected *l*-epinephrine produces vasodilation by its action on the receptors (Fig. 7). The β receptor is blocked by

very large doses of adrenergic blocking agents and is believed to be without innervation. The β receptors are believed to be confined to the blood vessels in skeletal muscle and perhaps in myocardium. Gamma (γ) receptors are believed responsible for the cholinergic vasodilation initiated by the sympathetic vasodilator in skeletal muscle.

The pharmacology of vascular smooth muscle, including the concept of receptors, has been effectively reviewed by Furchgott.[15] Green and Kepchar[16] have also published an excellent review of this and other aspects of peripheral vascular control. Although existence of these receptors, or effectors, has excited much interest among physiologists, it seems doubtful that the circulating catechol amines are very important in the normal peripheral vascular control. On the other hand, the action of norepinephrine as the transmitter substance for the sympathetic constrictor nerves is undoubtedly important in the control of certain vascular beds.

Acetylcholine. The transmitter substance issuing from the parasympathetic nerve endings is quite definitely acetylcholine. If the proposed bradykinin mechanism (Fig. 7B) withstands the tests of time and critical evaluation, direct action of acetylcholine in vascular smooth muscle as a normal control mechanism need be postulated only for the sympathetic cholinergic vasodilator fibers which serve skeletal muscle and perhaps the coronary vessels. Intravenously administered acetylcholine produces vasodilation in various vascular beds, but this effect is probably not a significant facet of normal peripheral vascular control. The cholinesterase levels in the blood are so high that circulating acetylcholine is rapidly destroyed. Thus, very large doses must be administered intravenously to produce vascular effects.

Chemical Dilators. It is common experience that, if the blood supply to a limb is obstructed for a few minutes and then released, the skin supplied by these vessels flushes a vivid red. Such vasodilation induced by temporary occlusion of the blood supply is termed *reactive hyperemia*. Roy and Brown[17] studied these vascular reactions and concluded that it "seems to us to throw much light on the manner in which the local circulation is carried on under normal conditions. It shows us that there is a local mechanism independent of the centres in the medulla and spinal cord by which the degree of dilation of the vessels is varied in accordance with the requirements of the tissues." This was in 1879; the same views are widely held today and we are still unable to identify the substance, substances or other mechanisms which actually induce the vascular dilation in reactive hyperemia or during increases in the metabolic activity of the tissues. Lewis[18] described a series of astute observations and subscribed to the view that the vasodilator substance is a normal metabolite.

Unidentified Vasodilator Substances. The effects of obstructed blood flow or increased metabolism which are perhaps the most obvious include: diminished oxygen tension in the tissues, increased carbon dioxide and lowered pH due to accumulation of acid metabolic products. As a matter of fact, perfusion with arterial blood of diminished oxygen content may produce vasodilation in some organs, particularly the heart, skeletal muscles, skin and, to a lesser extent, the gastrointestinal tract. If the low oxygen were the immediate cause of the vasodilation, however, the blood flow should return to control levels by the time the oxygen debt is repaid. On the contrary the oxygen debt is overpaid in both skin[19] and muscle,[20] and the excess blood flow may vary from 50 to 200 per cent of that necessary to repay the calculated oxygen debt.[21] Furthermore the increased flow

may persist after the venous oxygen content has returned to normal or even attained supernormal values. Carbon dioxide apparently plays an important role in vasomotor control only in the cerebral circulation (see Figs. 13 and 15). Thus vascular control by carbon dioxide and hydrogen ion concentration has been questioned. Infusion of lactate without a change in pH produces no demonstrable change in blood flow through extremities.[22]

At the present time reactive hyperemia is attributed to vasodilator metabolite(s) accumulating during hypoxia, but the cause is not histamine. In short, the vascular reaction must be attributed to *unidentified vasodilator substance(s)*.[16] To provide such a hypothetical substance with an attractive name might gain some measure of reassurance but will certainly not accelerate progress toward its identification. In fact, the label "unidentified vasodilator substance" is used in Figures 7, 13 and 15 as a signpost directing attention to an important unsolved problem.

Adenylic Acid Derivatives. Adenosine triphosphate (ATP) is an important source of energy for metabolism. During the release of energy, this substance is converted into adenosine diphosphate (ADP). If ADP were a strong vasodilator, it might qualify as a mechanism for adjusting the blood flow in accordance with metabolic demands. Considerable evidence has been compiled to demonstrate that ATP, ADP, adenosine monophosphate and even adenosine have vasodilator effect.[15, 23] They all probably act on the same inhibitory sites to permit vasodilation, but ATP and ADP are more powerful than the others. Although these substances deserve further study, there is no evidence that they are released from cells so that they might act on the vascular smooth muscle. One difficulty in such studies is that the vascular beds are so exquisitely sensitive to these substances that the concentrations necessary for vasodilation are less than can be detected with current methods.

Vasopressin (Pitressin). The neurohypophysis excretes a polypeptide, vasopressin, which has a fairly strong vasoconstrictor action in coronary vessels. This substance does not appear to react at the effector (receptor) sites involved by epinephrine, serotonin or histamine.[15] The close spatial and functional relations between the hypothalamic centers and the neurohypophysis certainly suggest that release of vasopressin might contribute to vascular control, but no specific action of this mechanism has ever been demonstrated. Vasopressin is composed of eight amino acids, a characteristic shared by two other substances which induce smooth muscle contraction: oxytocin, which induces contraction of the uterus, and angiotensin.

Angiotensin. Under some circumstances the kidney releases a protein, renin, that acts on a blood protein (renin substrate) to produce angiotensin I, which is composed of ten amino acids. This decapeptide does not affect the caliber of a blood vessels, but under the influence of converting enzyme it loses two amino acids to form angiotensin II, which has potent vasoconstrictor qualities (see Fig. 8, Chap. 6). The synthesis of these substances is a most notable achievement by Page and his collaborators.[24] This mechanism was explored in a search for the cause of systemic arterial hypertension, and has been proposed as one of the mechanisms for normal peripheral vascular control which go awry in patients developing hypertension. Since the cellular sources of renin are not known, the mechanism or mechanisms by which its production is accelerated or depressed are completely obscure. The sensing element which monitors the concentration of angiotensin I or II or renin in blood has not been discovered, and it thus seems pre-

mature to assign this mechanism a role in normal peripheral vascular control. This subject will receive more attention in Chapter 6.

Serotonin. The serum of clotted blood causes contraction of blood vessels. Since the substance responsible for this reaction could easily complicate research on hypertension, Page and his colleagues[25] investigated the problem and isolated a substance called serotonin or, more exactly, 5-hydroxytryptamine. When injected intravenously this substance has a very complex action on the pulmonary circulation,[26] which otherwise is quite unresponsive (Figs. 13 and 15). Serotonin also is a vasodilator in peripheral beds, notably the coronary vessels; however, under normal conditions it is confined within platelets and mast cells, and release into the blood stream has not been demonstrated. Thus, its role in normal vascular control remains doubtful.

H-substance and Histamine. Mechanical stimulation of the skin (e.g., by firm stroking) produces a sequence of vascular changes including local vasoconstriction, a surrounding vasodilation or flare and, finally, local swelling or edema. Lewis[18] attributed this "triple response" to the release of "H-substance" from the injured tissue. This substance is generally identified as histamine, which can be derived from histidine by splitting off carbon dioxide. Experimentally, histamine causes vasodilation in the terminal capillary beds but constriction of the larger arterial branches.[15] Histamine-like substances are generally considered to be present during vascular responses to tissue injury caused by such forms of radiation as ultraviolet light (sunburn), infrared (thermal burns) and roentgen rays, and by mechanical stress and trauma. However, this substance is not apparently involved in normal control.

Myogenic Responses. In 1902 Bayliss[27] reported experiments which indicated

FLOW RECORDINGS FROM VARIOUS SITES

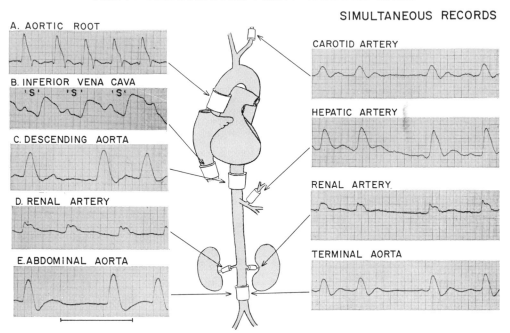

FIGURE 8. Ultrasonic flowmeters mounted on arteries and veins at various sites continuously register the instantaneous flow velocity of the blood passing through the flow sections. The wave forms of the flow patterns are characteristic in different locations (see text). The four records on the right were obtained simultaneously from the carotid artery, hepatic artery, renal artery and terminal abdominal aorta in an active healthy dog.

that "the muscular coat of the arteries reacts, like smooth muscle in other situations, to a stretching force by contraction" independent of the nervous system. More recently Folkow[28] and others[29, 30] have investigated this concept that elevated internal pressure produces vasoconstriction in denervated vascular beds. The evidence of this type of reaction is quite universally indirect. Without any questioning of these observations it seems illogical, as McDonald and Taylor[31] have pointed out, to emphasize this mechanism as the physiologically dominant one since it would appear to act as a positive feedback loop and so to be completely unstable. "Thus, a rise in blood pressure would cause a vasoconstriction which would cause further rise in pressure."[31] If smooth muscle is indeed capable of a myogenic response, then it must act in

conjunction with, and be governed by, built-in sensing and control systems.

Effects of Control Mechanisms on Flow Distribution

When ultrasonic flowmeters are installed on arteries or veins, the instantaneous flow through these regions can be continuously registered during the spontaneous activity of healthy dogs and during reactions experimentally induced in the presence or absence of anesthesia.[32] Typical cyclic patterns of normal flow recorded by this means from selected sites in the canine circulatory system are shown in Figure 8.

The instantaneous volume flow through the aortic root attains a very high peak very early in systole. There is then a relatively gradual reduction in flow, terminated by a sharp drop which accompanies closure of the aortic valves. The patterns of instantaneous flow in the descending thoracic and abdominal aortas and in the hepatic, superior mesenteric and carotid arteries resemble each other in showing a more gradual attainment of peak flow, followed by sluggish oscillations which extend into the diastolic interval. In the renal artery, the flow is distinctive. The pattern here shows an early abrupt peak and a later secondary hump during systole and a gradual decline in flow during diastole. The flow in the renal vascular bed does not fall to zero during the cycle. Normally, some blood is flowing in the renal artery during any phase of the cardiac cycle.

The records presented on the right side of Figure 8 were obtained simultaneously. This technique has provided the first opportunity for continuous registration of the changing distribution of blood to various vascular beds during spontaneous activity and during experimental procedures.

Flow Distribution During Spontaneous Activity. The instantaneous flow through the superior mesenteric or hepatic artery, the renal artery and the terminal abdominal aorta of intact dogs was continuously recorded while the animals were engaged in various activities including: reacting to a startling event, standing erect with the head up (60 degrees), standing with the head down (50 degrees), sitting, drinking water, entering a treadmill and exercising at 3 m.p.h. on a 12 per cent grade (Fig. 9). As the changes in the wave form of the instantaneous flow do not indicate the changes in volume flow per unit time, the flow records have been integrated with an analogue computer so that the flow during intervals of 2.5 seconds is accumulated. In this manner the influences

FLOW DISTRIBUTION DURING SPONTANEOUS ACTIVITY

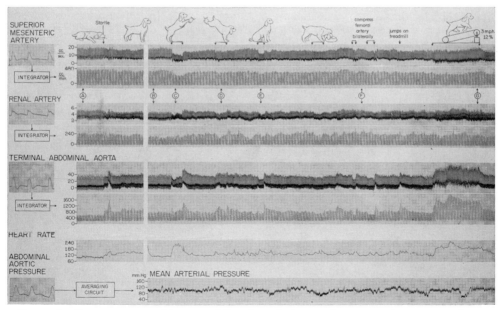

FIGURE 9. Instantaneous and integrated flow through the superior mesenteric artery, renal artery and terminal abdominal aorta as recorded simultaneously and continuously in an intact dog during a series of cardiovascular adjustments to spontaneous activity including startle reaction, standing erect with head up, head down, eating, constriction of femoral arteries bilaterally, entering treadmill and exercise. Note that blood flow per unit of time (integrated) through the superior mesenteric and renal arteries changes very little during most responses except standing with head up. Flow to the hindquarters increased greatly during treadmill exercise.

EFFECTS OF HORMONES ON FLOW DISTRIBUTION

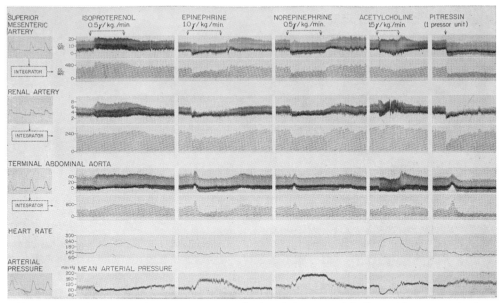

FIGURE 10.   Isoproterenol, norepinephrine, *l*-epinephrine, acetylcholine and vasopressin have rather profound effects on the flow through the superior mesenteric and renal arteries and the terminal aorta. The response is observed during spontaneous activity. This suggests that experimental use of these hormones is a poor substitute for normal control mechanisms.

of both changes in wave form and changes in heart rate are taken into account, and the height of the resulting deflection is an accurate measure of volume flow during a particular period. The contribution of each stroke can be identified from the distance separating pairs of darker spots representing diastole on the integrated flow line.

Each of the spontaneous actions listed above was associated with obvious deflections in the records of instantaneous flow. The integrated flow per unit of time through the superior mesenteric and renal arteries, however, remained remarkably constant, although slight changes accompanied the startle reaction and standing erect with the head up. In all seven dogs studied, volume flow was remarkably constant in the renal artery and in the superior mesenteric or hepatic artery during virtually all forms of spontaneous activity which were studied. On the other hand, the integrated flow as

well as the instantaneous flow in the terminal abdominal aorta was very responsive to most forms of activity. During exercise the forward flow of blood through the hindquarters never ceased, a condition indicating both a considerably reduced peripheral resistance and a greatly increased blood flow. The mean pressure in the abdominal aorta was quite constant except during standing erect with the head up. The heart rate increased notably during the startle reaction, standing erect and exercise.

Effects of Hormones.   When isoproterenol was administered intravenously, there was greatly augmented flow through all vessels monitored (Fig. 10). This increase was accompanied by a drop in mean arterial pressure, reflecting a pronounced reduction in vascular resistance. A great increase in maximum flow velocity also suggested greater myocardial contractility. All in all, the amplitudes and wave forms of the instantaneous flow patterns were radically different from normal and the altered wave forms of flow through the renal artery were distinctive.

The effects of epinephrine and norepinephrine on the blood flow, heart rate and arterial pressure resembled each other. The instantaneous flow and integrated flow per unit time were diminished in all three arteries, the reductions in renal and mesenteric or hepatic flow being significant with small doses and very great with large doses. In response to a rather large injection of either hormone the renal flow promptly decreased and approached zero for a brief period. The reaction of the renal, mesenteric and hepatic arteries to injected hormones is very great in comparison with that observed during spontaneous activity. Thus, the results of employing these hormones to study vascular control are not necessarily applicable to normal conditions.

When acetylcholine was administered by way of a leg vein, rather bizarre responses ensued (Fig. 10). Tachycardia, diminished mean arterial pressure, indications of reduced flow through the superior mesenteric artery, little change in the flow through the lower aorta, and a delayed increase in renal blood flow were seen. The explanation for these events is not readily apparent. Since acetylcholine is rapidly destroyed in the blood, its effects on the heart rate and baroreceptor reflexes may predominate over its effects on the peripheral vascular beds.

Vasopressin (Pitressin) acted to reduce the blood flow through all arteries studied. The aortic and mesenteric flow remained depressed for some 20 minutes, but the renal flow promptly returned toward control levels. The systemic arterial pressure was elevated, and the heart decelerated.

The distribution of blood flow following administration of these hormones is not obviously related to the responses during spontaneous activity. Some other regulatory mechanism must therefore predominate in the cardiovascular adjustments to spontaneous changes in activity.

Effects of Diencephalic Stimulation. Stimulation of selected sites in the diencephalon produced a wide variety of flow patterns in dogs under chloralose anesthesia. Changes in flow distribution reminiscent of those during exercise consistently resulted from stimulation in the region of the H_2 fields of Forel; stimulation of this region was already known to cause changes in cardiac function comparable to the changes accompanying exercise.[33] In the studies of blood flow, repeated stimulation as the electrode was advanced at 1 mm. increments toward this area produced the changes illustrated in Figure 11. No significant alterations followed stimulation at the first two points selected. After the electrode was advanced only 1 mm., the superior mesenteric and renal flows definitely decreased and the flow through the terminal aorta increased. Stimulation after the electrode was moved 1 mm. farther produced an even greater response, but, as the electrode was advanced still farther, the response lessened. The influence of diencephalic stimulation on the blood flow through these arteries and the promptness of the response indicate that their nerve supplies were intact. Thus, the relative slightness of the changes in superior mesenteric and renal flow during spontaneous activity probably cannot be attributed to damage of essential innervation during application of the flow sections.

Basic Requirements for Cardiovascular Control

Many of the mechanisms which might induce changes in the caliber of the peripheral blood vessels are illustrated in Figure 7. The tissues and organs served by the vascular system have widely varying functions and ranges of activity. If the changing requirements of tissues for

EFFECTS OF DIENCEPHALIC STIMULATION
ON FLOW DISTRIBUTION

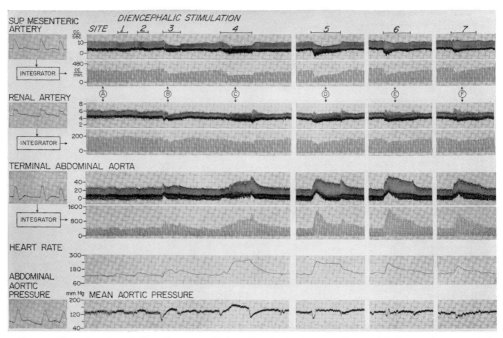

FIGURE 11. A series of stimuli was applied as the electrode was advanced in 1 mm. increments to and through the H_2 fields of Forel. The changes in flow distribution resemble those observed during spontaneous exercise by the same animal. Stimulation in this diencephalic region simultaneously produces these changes in flow distribution, changes in cardiac rate and function resembling the exercise response (see Fig. 6, Chap. 8), increased respiratory ventilation and, on some occasions, running movements.

blood flow had no priority or coordinating mechanism, the circulatory responses might easily become chaotic and break down, e.g., during running on a hot day after a full meal. At the risk of oversimplification, the fundamental requirements for cardiovascular regulation can be described in terms of uncomplicated hydraulic systems.

A common form of such systems consists of a large tank supported at sufficient height to give a head of pressure. In such a system, the pump can be set to operate at constant speed, variations in demand being accommodated at the expense of the reserve volume in the tank. However, this type of system could not easily be adapted to man or animals because a large quantity of blood would have to be carried around above the head. Portabil-

ity can be achieved only if the capacious storage tank is replaced by a small pressure tank. In this case, however, an increase in outflow from the system must be rapidly and precisely compensated by adjusting the output of the pump.

Consider a model circulation consisting of a pump, a compression chamber and several variable orifices (Fig. 12). By adjustments in stroke volume, stroke frequency and total outflow resistance, the mean pressure in the system can be maintained at constant levels for indefinite periods of time. If the stroke frequency and outflow resistance are properly set, the pressure in the system never drops to zero between strokes. Once such an equilibrium is established, alterations in any one of the three variables will be immediately reflected in changes in pressure within the system. To maintain a constant pressure, any alteration in one variable must be simultaneously balanced by adjustments in the others so that inflow always equals outflow. For example, if the stroke frequency is increased and the outflow resistance is not changed, the stroke volume must be reduced until pump output is restored to previous levels. Similarly, opening one outflow orifice more widely would pro-

duce a fall in pressure unless the resistance to outflow from other valves was increased or the pump output was rapidly augmented by an increase in either stroke volume or stroke frequency. In this system, maintenance of a constant mean pressure automatically provides a precise balance between inflow and outflow. This schematic model illustrates the fundamental principle by which the cardiac output is continuously adjusted to com-

PRESSURE GRADIENTS

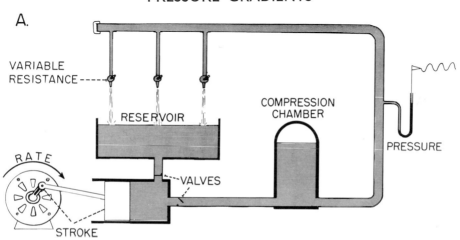

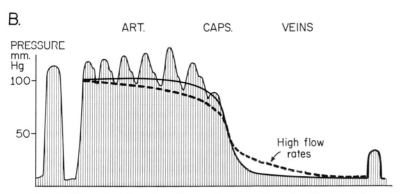

FIGURE 12.   *A*, The principles of cardiovascular control can be illustrated by a simple hydraulic model. In this system, the pressure head is determined primarily by the relation between the resistance to outflow and the pump output (stroke volume $\times$ heart rate). To maintain the pressure at a constant level, any change in outflow resistance must be promptly compensated by an adjustment in the pump output. The pressure head, outflow resistance and pump output are so intimately related that none can be altered without effect on the others.

B, The pressure gradient along the arteries and veins is very shallow under resting conditions. However, if the blood flow is greatly accelerated, the pressure gradient in the terminal arteries and veins becomes steeper, diminishing the pressure gradient along the small vessels (arterioles, capillaries and venules).

pensate for changes in peripheral resistance. The mean arterial blood pressure tends to stay within a relatively narrow range both at rest and during activity. To the extent that the requirements of the tissues for blood flow are reflected by their changes in peripheral resistance, cardiac output is continuously adjusted to equal the total blood flow in all the tissues.

The quantity of blood flowing through a set of vessels per unit of time is determined by two factors: (1) the pressure gradient from the arteries to the veins and (2) the resistance of the vascular bed as influenced by constriction in the smaller and terminal branches. The mechanisms by which the systemic arterial blood pressure is maintained within a reasonable range despite wide fluctuations in the distribution and total quantity of blood flowing through the peripheral tissues are described in Chapter 6. In the following discussion of the mechanisms of vascular control, the arterial pressure head will be considered to be relatively fixed.

Pressure Gradients at High Flow Rates. Despite the gradual reduction in the caliber of the long arterial trunks, the pressure drop along them is very slight (2 to 4 mm. Hg from the axillary to the radial arteries) at rest in a cool environment. As a result, flow along the arteries is normally slow (Figure 12B). However, peripheral vasodilation in the extremities of man during reactive hyperemia may accelerate the flow rates as much as ten times. Under such conditions, the pressure drop between the brachial and radial arteries increases from 5 mm. Hg to 25 mm. Hg.[34] The rate of pressure drop along the terminal branches of the arterial system also steepens so that the pressure at the arterioles is markedly depressed. The increased pressure required to propel the increased flow along the veins also results in a high pressure head at the venules because central venous pressure cannot be greatly depressed. Thus, in the

presence of high flow rates through a segment of the vascular tree, the arterial and venous pressure gradients are steepened and the pressure drop across the arterioles and capillary networks are reduced far below the normal resting conditions. Under these conditions, the resistance to flow through the larger arterial and venous conduits assumes major importance in the dissipation of pressure energy during flow.

Vascular Control in Specific Tissues

The anatomic arrangement and environmental conditions of arteries, arterioles and sphincters vary from one vascular bed to another, but the smooth muscle cells which invest these vessels and induce changes in their caliber look the same in all vascular beds. Nevertheless, the vascular smooth muscle in different tissues responds in widely different ways under the influence of the mechanisms illustrated in Figure 7. Under these conditions, control of the vascular system cannot be considered in general terms. The characteristics of the vascular responses peculiar to each major tissue or organ must be detailed individually. In the following discussion, the organs of the body will be discussed roughly in the order of increasing reactivity or diversity of mechanisms inducing vasomotor responses. Green and Kepchar's[16] excellent review is a valuable reference to supplement the following discussion.

Brain. The cerebral vasculature is probably most resistant to vasomotor influences to be found in the body. According to Kety,[35] the cerebral blood flow of healthy young men is about 54 ml. per 100 gm. of brain tissue per minute and the respiratory quotient is approximately unity, indicating that carbohydrate is the prime source of energy. The energy requirement of the brain is about 20 watts, compared to the thousands of watts required by electronic computors.

It is well established that autonomic nerves supply the cerebral vessels. This innervation may influence the cerebral blood flow in lower animals, but there is little evidence of its effectiveness in man. After reviewing a great many potential factors, Sokoloff[36] concluded, "an overall view of the action of drugs on the cerebral circulation is the great resistance of the cerebral blood flow to change" (Fig. 13). Increased carbon dioxide tension has the most potent effects on cerebral vessels, but it rarely elevates cerebral flow as much as twofold. Reduced oxygen tension in the arterial blood has also been reported to dilate cerebral vessels.[37]

Reflecting the constancy of the over-all cerebral metabolism, the total cerebral blood flow is remarkably constant. However, the blood flow is not uniform throughout the brain substance, varying from 0.14 ml. per gram in spinal white matter to 1.8 ml. per gram in the inferior colliculus.[38] Primary sensory areas sub-serving visual, auditory and somatosensory functions receive significantly higher blood flows than do other cortical areas. Under thiopental anesthesia, the differences in blood flow through sensory areas disappear.

Lungs. The pulmonary circulation appears to be almost as unresponsive as the cerebral to normal controlling mechanisms (Fig. 13). The pulmonary vascular bed is an extremely low resistance system (Chap. 1), and its resistance readily becomes even less. Thus the amount of blood flowing through this system can increase two or three times with very little increase in the pressure gradient from the pulmonary artery to the left atrium. Because definitive demonstration of any active vasomotor change induced by neural, hormonal or chemical agents has proved very difficult, the reduction in resistance as flow increases has been ascribed to passive distention of the vascular bed. At higher pulmonary blood flow rates, however, the pressure gradient in-

VASOMOTOR MECHANISMS IN VARIOUS TISSUES

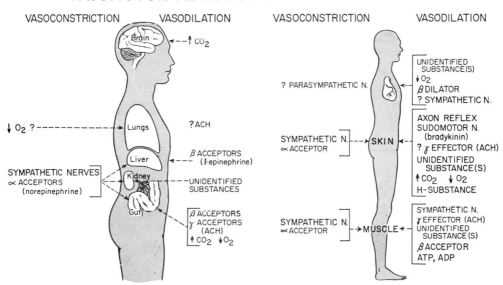

FIGURE 13. Vascular beds in some tissues are very unresponsive to all normal vasomotor mechanisms; e.g., cerebral vessels are slightly affected by CO_2 and pulmonary vessels by O_2 content. The splanchnic vascular bed is quite reactive and responds to many different controlling mechanisms. The vascular reactivity of the coronary vessels is difficult to determine because most of the mechanisms affect cardiac function as well. The vessels of skin and muscle respond to a very large number of different control mechanisms and are extremely reactive.

creases in direct proportion to the flow rate as though the vascular bed had reached a maximum cross-sectional area and was behaving more like a system of rigid tubes.[39]

Hypoxia apparently induces some vasoconstriction, which would tend to shunt blood from collapsed or inactive lung parenchyma toward regions where gases could be interchanged. Fairly large concentrations of acetylcholine infused directly into the pulmonary artery produce a slight and questionable fall in pulmonary arterial pressure.[39] There is, however, no evidence that either hypoxia or acetylcholine is normally a regulator of pulmonary vessels.

The evidence on the action of vasodilator drugs on pulmonary vessels is inconclusive. They are constricted by serotonin, and under these conditions respond with vasodilation to acetylcholine, histamine and adenosine triphosphate.[40] The functional significance of this observation remains obscure. Some evidence for a parasympathetic innervation of the lung activated by stimulation of the carotid chemoreceptors has been presented by Daly and Daly,[41] but such a mechanism would play little or no role in normal control (see Chemoreceptors, Chap. 6).

It thus seems safe to consider the pulmonary vascular bed as one that does not share in peripheral vasomotor alterations. This attitude appears entirely logical since all of the cardiac output flows through the lungs. There is no obvious need for a means of changing the distribution of blood flow from one part of the lungs to another under normal conditions, because all parts serve the same function.

Liver. The liver, like the lung, is a low-pressure system served by two vascular systems. A major portion (about four-fifths) of the blood flowing through the liver arrives by way of the portal vein under low pressure after having passed through the capillaries in the gastrointestinal tract upstream. The remainder enters under the systemic arterial pressure head by way of the hepatic artery. Both stimulation of sympathetic nerves and norepinephrine apparently produce some constriction of both the hepatic and portal arterial systems, but the effects are relatively mild.[42] Since epinephrine, isoproterenol and acetylcholine have little or no effect on either vascular system, neither β nor γ effectors are believed to exist here. Reactive hyperemia does not follow temporary occlusion of the blood flow. Thus, the liver is a system that is quite unresponsive to the available control systems.

Spleen. Stimulation of the splenic nerve greatly increases the vascular resistance and activates the mechanism by which the cells concentrated in the spleen are dumped into the active circulation. The changes in resistance apparently are mediated by norepinephrine; the emptying mechanism by *l*-epinephrine. Dilation follows administration of extremely small concentrations of cholinergic substances, although existence of a parasympathetic innervation has not been demonstrated.

Kidney. The splanchnic sympathetic nerves exert a vasoconstrictor effect on the renal vessels. Norepinephrine and *l*-epinephrine act on effectors to produce constriction. Temporary occlusion of renal blood flow results in reactive hyperemia induced by unidentified dilator substances. Above a certain critical pressure (i.e., 70 mm. Hg) the blood flow through the kidney tends to remain quite constant in spite of progressively elevated arterial perfusion pressure. This has been been termed *autoregulation* and may result from elevation of perivascular pressures in step with increases in perfusion pressure, so that flow remains relatively constant. Gottschalk[43] demonstrated that the pressures in the tubules and the peritubular capillaries remain essentially the same despite parallel changes in both resulting from alterations in venous and ureteral pressures.

Gastrointestinal Tract. The splanchnic nerves are profusely distributed to the vessels of the splanchnic bed and are believed to play an important role in the maintenance of systemic arterial blood pressure. These nerves apparently act through α effectors so that administration of norepinephrine induces similar effects on this bed. Significant dilation follows injection of isoproterenol, indicating the presence of β effectors. Mild dilation from administration of acetylcholine suggests the presence of γ effectors. However, according to presently available information, the autonomic nerves act on the α effectors but not on the β effectors. Carbon dioxide produces vasodilation when present in the extremely high concentrations produced by inhalation of gas mixtures containing 5 to 15 volumes per cent.[44] Since such levels are beyond the physiologic range, the resulting dilation has very limited significance.

Heart. The terminal coronary vessels penetrate the walls of the heart. There they are compressed by the contracting myocardium, particularly that in the wall of the left ventricle (see Chap. 9). During ventricular systole, the outflow from the coronary veins is accelerated and the inflow through the coronary arteries is impeded. However, the pumping action of ventricular systole apparently does not facilitate blood flow. Sudden arrest of the heart immediately increases both the arterial inflow and the venous outflow, indicating that ventricular contraction impedes flow through the coronary vessels.[45] More vigorous contraction of the myocardium, induced by catechol amines or sympathetic stimulation, tends to increase simultaneously the work load on the myocardium and the impedence to coronary flow. A close relation between the cardiac effort, the myocardial oxygen consumption and the coronary flow has been repeatedly reported.[21, 46] Gregg[45] pointed out that most of the oxygen is normally removed from the coronary blood so that the oxygen content of coronary sinus (venous) blood cannot be reduced very much. Therefore increased oxygen delivery must be achieved primarily by increased coronary flow. Furthermore, spurious correlations between coronary flow and myocardial oxygen consumption result from the fact that the calculation of myocardial oxygen consumption involves values for coronary blood flow and vice versa.[47] Under these conditions, high correlations occur automatically and thus have little significance.

The effects of administered norepinephrine, epinephrine and acetylcholine on coronary flow are equivocal, so it is not certain whether these hormones are constrictors or dilators. In the fibrillating or potassium-arrested heart, catechol amines appear to have a constrictor action.[48] The influence of sympathetic nerves on coronary resistance is also open to question. According to some investigators, the parasympathetic nerves exert a constrictor action; others believe that sympathetic dilators are active here as in skeletal muscle.

It seems likely that low oxygen tension or low oxygen content in the blood produces coronary dilation, but this dilation could reflect the effects of unidentified vasodilator substances since the coronary vessels exhibit reactive hyperemia. Carbon dioxide and altered pH apparently have no effect. According to Green and Kepchar,[16] the only agents which consistently cause constriction of the coronary arterioles are vasopressin and angiotensin. Many drugs appear to produce coronary dilation but have no known functional significance in normal control.

Skeletal Muscle. The blood vessels supplying skeletal muscles generally are now believed to have double sympathetic innervation. The sympathetic constrictor fibers activate typical α receptors and, apparently, participate in the generalized sympathetic discharges which tend to support systemic arterial blood pressure.[49] When this sympathetic constrictor mechanism is eliminated, the blood vessels of muscle maintain a substantial degree of vasoconstriction.[50] Sympathetic vasodilator fibers act through cholinergic γ receptors, which can produce maximal dilation and can be readily blocked by atropine. The sympathetic vasodilator system is confined to skeletal muscle and is apparently dissociated from the control of the blood pressure regulatory system of the medullary vasomotor areas. Instead, the nerve impulses which ultimately reach the sympathetic vasodilator nerve endings have been traced from the motor cortex of the cerebrum near the cruciate sulcus to the supraoptic part of the hypothalamus, to the collicular area and through the medullary regions, apparently bypassing the medullary cardioregulator centers, to impinge rather directly on the sympathetic outflow in the spinal cord.[51, 52] Roddie and Shepherd[53] have demonstrated vasodilation within forearm muscles induced by elevation of the legs, the response being mediated by a sympathetic vasodilator reflex.

Thus there are four postulated mechanisms by which vasodilation in skeletal muscle may be achieved: (1) inhibition of the sympathetic constrictor mechanism (twofold to threefold increase), (2) activation of the sympathetic vasodilator system (fivefold to sixfold increase), (3) the β effectors, and (4) unidentified vasodilator substances present immediately after exercise (sixfold to tenfold increase). The β effectors are not innervated but are activated by circulating l-epinephrine or injected isoproterenol (Fig. 7). The function of this mechanism in normal body economy has not been established.

The skeletal muscles are prone to develop extremely intense reactive hyperemia following temporary occlusion of their blood supply. This state is attrib-

MUSCULAR PUMPING MECHANISMS

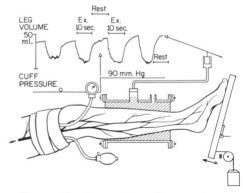

FIGURE 14.   Contraction of leg muscles compresses the veins of the leg with sufficient force to drive blood out under a sphygmomanometer cuff inflated to 90 mm. Hg as evidenced by the changing volume in a leg plethysmograph. (After Barcroft and Swan.[56]) This experiment suggests the mechanism by which the venous pressure in the legs is depressed during normal walking (see Fig. 5, Chap. 7).

uted to unidentified metabolic vasodilator substances. In patients whose sympathetic nervous system has been excised,[54] extreme vasodilation can be achieved in skeletal muscle by exercise and by reactive hyperemia.

Extremely small quantities of adenosine triphosphate (ATP) produce profound vasodilation in skeletal muscle. A similar degree of vasodilation can be produced by adenosine diphosphate (ADP). In fact, these substances are such potent dilators that the effective doses for the skeletal vessels defy chemical detection. Although ATP and ADP are fine potential candidates for the position of "unidentified vasodilator substances," their role has not been conclusively demonstrated.

The contraction of skeletal muscle impedes blood flow just as ventricular contraction does (see above). Thus, the blood flow through an extremity is greater immediately after the cessation of exercise than during the exertion itself.[55] The compression of blood vessels by contracting muscle can actively pump venous blood against a very high resistance (Fig. 14). Barcroft and Swan[56] performed an experiment in which they used a plethysmograph to register the expression of blood from the calf during voluntary muscular contractions (one per second for 10 seconds then rest 10 seconds). During one rest period the blood pressure cuff about the leg was inflated to 90 mm. Hg, but the quantity of blood expressed from the leg under the cuff was the same during the next exercise period as during the control (Fig. 14). This experiment suggests that muscular contraction can express blood from veins distended by a pressure as great as 90 mm. Hg. This ability is important in dependent extremities as part of the vascular response to arising (see Chap. 7).

Skin. The skin has the most complex assortment of available control mechanisms (Fig. 13) and contains a vascular bed which is most accessible for study by physiologists and clinicians. The result is an imposing, almost overwhelming mass of literature that defies precise description.

The predominant neural control is exercised by the sympathetic vasoconstrictor nerves; the mediator is probably norepinephrine. In contrast with vessels in muscle, skin vessels dilate maximally when the sympathetic constrictor influence on them is eliminated. Consequently, the full range of cutaneous flow can be achieved by release of constrictor tone. No sympathetic or parasympathetic vasodilator fibers directly affecting cutaneous vessels have been described. Injection of acetylcholine induces a slight dilation of these vessels which suggests the presence of γ effectors that are not innervated. Stimulation of the peripheral ends of several dorsal roots produces vasodilation which can best be explained in terms of an axon reflex (see Fig. 7B). The normal course of impulses in such a mechanism is from sensory nerve endings in the skin to collaterals which directly impinge on blood vessels. Recent evidence suggests that the parasympathetic supply to the

sweat glands (sudomotor) triggers the release of an enzyme (bradykinin enzyme) that acts on tissue proteins to form bradykinin which diffuses to adjacent blood vessels and induces a vasodilation of the deep and superficial vascular plexuses. (Fig. 7).

The skin exhibits severe reactive hyperemia following temporary occlusion to blood supply. Thus, it can be postulated that unidentified vasodilator substances participate in the control of the skin vessels. A vasomotor role of low oxygen or elevated carbon dioxide has not been established.

Local warming of the skin produces a vasodilation which is believed to result from release of constrictor tone through central reflexes rather than from a direct action of the heat on the blood vessels. These reflexes probably involve the hypothalamic temperature regulating centers, acting through sympathetic vasoconstrictor nerves. Excessive cold applied to the skin may produce a brief vasodilation which may be independent of the nerve supply.

Finally, flushing of the skin from embarrassment or emotional stimuli represent vascular changes induced from higher levels of the nervous system.

Summary

The basic principles of peripheral vascular control are generally considered in terms of mechanisms by which the blood flow through various tissues are adjusted in relation to metabolism and the oxygen requirement. Actually, many tissues have functional requirements for blood flow which are unrelated to the oxygen consumption (e.g., kidney, skin, liver, and perhaps the gastrointestinal tract; Fig. 15). In fact, the principal tissues that require blood flow related to their metabolic rates (oxygen uptake) are the striated muscles: myocardium and skeletal muscles. After temporary occlusion of the

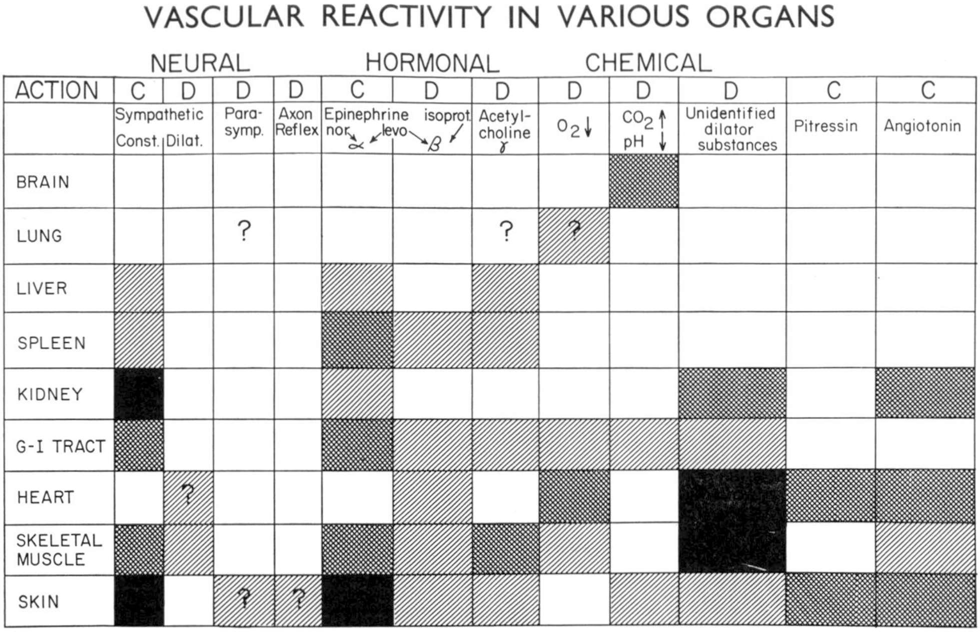

VASCULAR REACTIVITY IN VARIOUS ORGANS

ACTION	NEURAL				HORMONAL				CHEMICAL				
	C	D	D	D	C	D	D	D	D	D	D	C	C
	Sympathetic Const.	Dilat.	Para-symp.	Axon Reflex	Epinephrine nor (α)	levo (β)	isoprot	Acetyl-choline (γ)	$O_2\downarrow$	$CO_2\uparrow$ pH$\downarrow$	Unidentified dilator substances	Pitressin	Angiotonin
BRAIN										▨			
LUNG			?					?	?				
LIVER	▨				▨		▨						
SPLEEN	▨				▨		▨						
KIDNEY	■										▨		▨
G-I TRACT	▨				▨		▨						
HEART		?			▨		▨		▨		■	▨	▨
SKELETAL MUSCLE	▨	▨			▨		▨		▨		■		▨
SKIN	■		?	?	▨		▨				▨	▨	▨

FIGURE 15.   The responsiveness of the various vascular beds illustrated in Figure 13 is here indicated schematically by the density of the shading under each of the neural, hormonal and chemical factors. The action of the mechanisms is indicated by C for constriction and D for dilation. The question marks indicate that the response is controversial. Note that both the diversity of the response and the intensity of the response tend to be much greater in the gastrointestinal tract, heart, skeletal muscle and skin than in the brain, lung, liver and spleen.

blood supply to these tissues they exhibit a most powerful reactive hyperemia apparently caused by unidentified metabolic vasodilator substances.

The blood flow, oxygen extraction and vasomotor control are quite different in the various vascular beds. The neural control mechanisms are clearly important in the regulation of blood flow through many tissues, but not all. Neural controls are based principally on the sympathetic constrictor system, which continuously maintains varying degrees of constriction within the vascular beds. In addition there is a sympathetic vasodilator system, which is restricted to skeletal muscle (and, perhaps, the heart). Vasodilation is attributed currently to parasympathetic activation of certain structures, notably glands, with resulting formation of bradykinin by an enzyme released from the gland into the interstitial tissues.

Circulating autonomic hormones, l-epinephrine, norepinephrine and acetylcholine have powerful vasomotor activity when injected, but their role in normal peripheral vascular control remains questionable. The vasodilator substances which seem to accumulate when tissues metabolize in an environment containing inadequate oxygen, have not been definitively identified and represent an important challenge in this field.

The vascular reactivity in various organs is strikingly different (Fig. 15). For example, the cerebral circulation is little affected by neural or hormonal substances and is mildly dilated by increased carbon dioxide tension. Control of the pulmonary circulation is difficult to demonstrate experimentally. The coronary vessels dilate readily in response to metabolic vasodilator substances but are otherwise quite nonreactive so far as can be determined experimentally. In contrast, the splanchnic bed, kidneys, liver and spleen are fairly responsive to a variety of mechanisms, and skeletal muscles and the skin are influenced by a bewildering number of factors.

II. Pathophysiology of Peripheral Vascular Control

The organs of the body are functionally dependent, to varying degrees, on an adequate blood flow through their capillary networks. Disturbances in the control of this flow become manifest as symptoms which may or may not be related to the basic function of the organ involved. For example, vascular disturbances in the skin of the extremities may result in exaggerated responses to changes in temperature. On the other hand, inadequate blood flow through the coronary arteries may produce pain felt over the pericordium and down the left arm. A few examples of the disturbances in peripheral vascular control will illustrate some problems that may confront physicians during routine practice.

Raynaud's Disease

The primary purpose of the vasomotor control of the cutaneous vessels is the maintenance of a proper heat balance so that the core of the body remains at a fairly constant temperature. Under experimental conditions, localized heating of specific anterior hypothalamic sites produces peripheral vasodilation and inhibits shivering, while cooling of nearby sites produces appropriate cutaneous vasodilation.[57] Thus, the hypothalamus is equipped with a thermostatic type of control which theoretically can induce appropriate cardiovascular adjustments to compensate for changes in the temperature of the blood arriving at these regulatory areas. There can be little doubt that nerve impulses originating in the temperature receptors in the skin ultimately impinge upon the hypothalamic centers for temperature regulation.

The appropriate vascular response to an excessive loss of heat is a vasoconstriction in the portions of the skin where heat is most rapidly dissipated—i.e., the fingers and toes and possibly the tips of the nose and ears.

Persistently cold moist hands and feet are fairly common in any large segment of the population, particularly among young emotional persons, often girls. When they grasp something cold, the skin may turn almost white. They suffer with cold feet more or less continuously during winter months. With advancing age, the peripheral vasoconstriction of the skin of the

RAYNAUD'S DISEASE

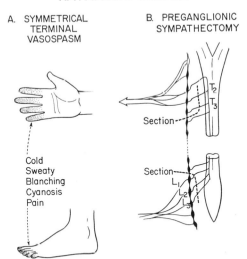

A. SYMMETRICAL TERMINAL VASOSPASM

B. PREGANGLIONIC SYMPATHECTOMY

FIGURE 16. A severe vasoconstriction of the skin vessels of the most distal extremities produces severe symptoms, apparently the result of hyperreactive vascular responses in fingers, toes and sometimes nose and ears. Preganglionic interruption of the sympathetic outflow to these vessels provides some relief, but the response is not wholly satisfactory because the denervated vessels acquire increased sensitivity to circulating vasomotor substances.

hands and feet tends to disappear. However, in some of these young people the tonic contraction of the terminal vessels may progress symmetrically to involve all of the toes, the fingers and, rarely, the tip of the nose. In response to either exposure to cold or intense emotional stimuli, the blood vessels in these areas constrict until the skin becomes white or bluish because only a limited quantity of blood is progressing slowly through the capillaries. When the condition is severe, the asphyxia becomes so intense that the tissues die, and gangrene appears at the tips of the phalanges (Fig. 16).

According to White, Smithwick and Simeone,[58] several responsible mechanisms can be postulated: (1) increased vasomotor impulses acting on normal blood vessels, (2) normal sympathetic activity acting on hyperreactive terminal vessels, and (3) diseased vessels which are partially occluded in combination with varying degrees of sympathetic activity. Any of these mechanisms could induce the objective and subjective changes in cutaneous flow. In any event, the excessive vasoconstriction is inappropriate for the external environmental conditions, and, on this basis, elimination of the sympathetic discharge to affected areas should alleviate the symptoms. To determine which patients would benefit from surgical removal of the sympathetic outflow, procaine block of these nerves makes it possible to discern how much relief from vasoconstriction could be expected.

The first operative procedures involved merely sectioning the postganglionic fibers destined for arms and legs; immediate relief of the symptoms was obtained, temporarily. However, the symptoms recurred in a matter of days or weeks and often became more intense than they were before the sympathectomy. It is now known that when the sympathetic nerves to smooth muscles are severed, the denervated muscles develop greatly increased sensitivity to the transmitter substances normally released at the nerve endings. Thus, the recurrence of symptoms after sympathectomy reflected severe vasospasm induced by circulating catechol amines. For example, exposure to cold or intense emotion may induce the release of epinephrine and norepinephrine from the adrenal glands. These hormones then circulate through the blood to the hypersensitive smooth muscle, inducing sustained contraction and persistent vasospasm in the denervated regions. Since the hypersensitization is greatest in the structure directly denervated (law of denervation), the degree of hypersensitivity of the smooth muscle is materially less if preganglionic rather than postganglionic sympathetic nerves to the extremities are sectioned (Fig. 16). Preganglionic sympathectomy for the upper extremities is achieved by sectioning T_2 and T_3 and cutting the sympathetic chain below T_3. The leg is preganglionically sympathectomized by excising ganglia L_1, L_2 and L_3.

Although sympathectomy often alleviates symptoms of Raynaud's disease, the patients are rarely cured. In fact, it is not certain that excessive sympathetic discharge to cutaneous vessels of the digits is the primary cause of the condition. Although the concentration of epinephrine and norepinephrine in venous blood collected at the wrist was greater than normal in 10 out of 11 patients with Raynaud's disease,[59] such an abnormal concentration could result from excess production of catechol amines or from some interference with their metabolism and inactivation.[60] Thus, it is clear that much remains to be learned concerning the mechanisms by which nerves and hormonal substances control cutaneous vessels. Such knowledge will undoubtedly improve the rationale and effectiveness with which the functional disturbances can be treated.

Angina Pectoris

Atherosclerosis of the coronary arteries tends to obstruct blood flow to the myocardium and often leads to the development of a periodic severe pain occurring over the precordium and extending down the left arm. Most commonly, the pain is felt during effort (e.g., walking briskly up hill on a frosty day) and tends to diminish and disappear after resting. Transient spasm of the coronary arteries is often assigned an important role in the development of angina pectoris, even though it is very difficult to induce vasoconstriction in this vascular bed. Indeed, neural control of coronary vessels is not readily demonstrated, and myocardial ischemia is a potent vasodilator (e.g., reactive hyperemia). Angina pectoris is discussed in more detail in a subsequent section (see Chap. 9).

Migraine

The typical attack of migraine begins with visual disturbances, including blurring, spots and lights flashing before the eyes and often transient blindness or hemianopsia. After a varying period, a violent headache develops—generally unilateral and often pounding or boring in quality. Nausea and vomiting are common features of an attack. The headache may persist a few hours or even a few days. During a search for pain-sensitive arteries on the exposed brain of conscious human subjects, it was found that distention or stretching of the walls of an artery would reproduce the pain of migraine.[61] Intravenous injection of histamine, a powerful dilator of cerebral vessels, also induces pain like that of spontaneous migraine attacks. The visual disturbances which precede the typical migraine attack are generally attributed to intense vasoconstriction or spasm in blood vessels serving the visual system of the brain. Considering how unresponsive the cerebral vessels are to a wide variety of vasoactive materials, it seems remarkable that these vessels will either constrict so vigorously or dilate so completely that these violent symptoms can be produced. At the present, however, no alternate explanation appears more attractive.

Pulmonary Embolism

The lungs are functionally suited to the filtering of particles, air bubbles, fragments of clotted blood and other foreign substances from the blood returning from the systemic veins (see Fig. 24, Chap. 1). The lungs have a very large factor of safety since complete excision of the entire right lung is followed by amazingly little disturbance of respiratory or circulatory function. However, sudden obstruction of a pulmonary arterial branch supplying only a portion of one lung all too frequently produces sudden death. This phenomenon occurs most often when a blood clot in a systemic vein breaks loose and is carried to the lungs.

The most commonly offered explanation for the fatal increase in pulmonary arterial blood pressure is a reflex vasoconstriction involving pulmonary vessels in a segment of the lung much larger than that directly affected by the embolus. Although the pulmonary vascular bed is supplied by vasomotor nerves, it is so unresponsive that variations in pulmonary vascular resistance are difficult to achieve experimentally. Serotonin (5-hydroxytryptamine), which is present in high concentration in blood platelets, is known to have a powerful constrictor effect on pulmonary vessels. It has therefore been assumed that serotonin may be responsible for the increased pulmonary resistance. Even if this mechanism is applicable to this problem it is difficult to visualize how serotonin can be released from a blood clot wedged in a pulmonary artery and can find its way to other parts of the pulmonary vascular tree. Another explanation is suggested by observations that widespread pulmonary embolization with very small particles induces reflex pulmonary vasoconstriction by activating afferent fibers from the lungs that ascend the vagus nerve.

Disturbances of General Vasomotor Control

Vasoregulatory Asthenia. A large group of patients with subjective and disabling heart symptoms lack signs of disease or dysfunction of the heart demonstrable by the usual clinical examination. Holmgren et al.[62] recently described a group of such patients who had symptoms referable to the cardiovascular system and limited capacity for exertion demonstrated by quantitative tests. Under resting conditions, the cardiac output was elevated in these patients and their arteriovenous oxygen difference was diminished. During exercise, the blood flow through the working muscles was apparently smaller than normal, limiting the exercise tolerance. Interestingly enough, the exercise tolerance of such patients can be significantly improved by graded physical training.[63] In view of the complexity of the various mechanisms regulating the peripheral circulation, it is remarkable that such functional disorders caused by inappropriate cardiovascular responses are not more common.

The same type of symptoms and findings as those described under the heading of "vasoregulatory asthenia" have also been catalogued as neurocirculatory asthenia, soldier's heart, neurasthenia and anxiety. The confusion surrounding this type of disturbance is common to psychosomatic disorders in general but this fact makes them no less distressing to the patient.

Abnormal Control of Peripheral Resistance. The control of total peripheral resistance is an essential feature of the regulation of systemic arterial blood pressure (see Fig. 12). The mechanisms involved in maintaining systemic arterial pressure within a relatively restricted range are discussed in Chapter 6. Factors which may produce excessive total peripheral resistance in the presence of normal cardial output tend to induce systemic arterial hypertension (see also Chap. 6).

In some individuals the systemic arterial blood pressure is maintained at a relatively low level (e.g., 90/70 mm. Hg) and many of these suffer transient loss of vision (blackout) or even loss of consciousness when they suddenly stand up (see Chap. 7). This so-called "orthostatic hypotension" is a common complaint after bilateral removal of the sympathetic chains as a treatment for severe hypertension.

Summary

The principal disturbances of local blood flow result from excessive constriction and inadequate perfusion of the tissues, with local discomfort or destruction of the tissues as the result. Raynaud's disease involves an exaggeration of the normal vasomotor response in the digits to cold or emotion. In view of the diversity of the mechanisms controlling blood flow in the skin, it is not surprising that such conditions might develop in some fraction of the population. Actually, Raynaud's disease is quite rare. Much more common are angina pectoris and migraine headaches, apparently reflecting spasm of coronary vessels and excessive dilation of cerebral vessels, respectively. It is extremely difficult to demonstrate any powerful or even significant control over either of these two beds. They are both remarkably unresponsive to neural control mechanisms under experimental conditions. Similarly, the changes in pulmonary vascular resistance accompanying pulmonary embolism are difficult to explain in terms of common experimental or clinical observations. We must consider the possibility that none of these phenomena is related to the normal control mechanisms. They may instead be vascular responses induced by abnormal conditions which have no role in the normal regulatory process.

The disturbances of general vasomotor control are represented by relatively rare instances of excessive vasodilation which limits the exercise tolerance and by abnormally high peripheral resistance which leads to elevation of the systemic arterial pressure (see Chap. 6). Slow or weak vasoconstrictor responses on arising may lead to orthostatic hypotension, which is discussed in Chapter 7.

REFERENCES

1. ZWEIFACH, B. W. The microcirculation o the blood. *Sci. Amer.*, 200:54–60, 1959.
2. BURTON, A. C. Relation of structure to function of the tissues of the wall of blood vessels. *Physiol. Rev.*, 34:619–642, 1954.
3. PETERSON, L. H., JENSEN, R. E., and PARNELL, J. Mechanical properties of arteries in vivo. *Circulat. Res.*, 8:622–639, 1960.
4. ZWEIFACH, B. W., and KOSSMANN, C. E. Micromanipulation of small blood vessels in the mouse. *Amer. J. Physiol.*, 120:23–35, 1937.
5. BURCH, G. E. A new sensitive portable plethysmograph. *Amer. Heart J.*, 33:48–75, 1947.
6. LUTZ, B. R., and FULTON, G. P. Smooth muscle and blood flow in small blood vessels. Pp. 13–23 in *Factors Regulating Blood Flow*, G. P. Fulton and B. Zweifach, eds. Washington, Amer. Physiol. Soc., 1958.
7. WHITTERIDGE, D. Cardiovascular reflexes initiated from afferent sites other than the cardiovascular system itself. *Physiol. Rev.*, 40 (Suppl. 4): 198–200, 1960.
8. ALEXANDER, R. S. Tonic and reflex functions of medullary sympathetic cardiovascular centers. *J. Neurophysiol.*, 9:205–217, 1946.
9. FOLKOW, B. Nervous control of blood vessels. *Physiol. Rev.*, 35:629–663, 1955.
10. ERICI, I., FOLKOW, B., and UVNÄS, B. Sympathetic vasodilator nerves to the tongue of the cat. *Acta physiol. scand.*, 25:1–9, 1952.
11. HILTON, S. M., and LEWIS, G. P. The relationship between glandular activity, bradykinin formation and functional vasodilatation in the submandibular salivary gland. *J. Physiol.*, 134:471–483, 1956.
12. Fox, R. H., and HILTON, S. M. Sweat gland activity, bradykinin formation and vasodilation in human forearm skin. *J. Physiol.*, 137:43p–44p, 1957.
13. VON EULER, U. S. *Noradrenaline*. Springfield, Ill., C. C Thomas, 1956, 382 pp.
14. AHLQUIST, R. P. Adrenergic drugs. Pp. 378–407 in *Pharmacology in Medicine*, vol. 2, V. A. Drill, ed. New York, McGraw-Hill, 1958.
15. FURCHGOTT, R. F. The pharmacology of vascular smooth muscle. *Pharmacol. Rev.*, 7:183–265, 1955.
16. GREEN, H. D., and KEPCHAR, J. H. Control of peripheral resistance in major systemic vascular beds. *Physiol. Rev.*, 39:617–686, 1959.
17. ROY, C. S., and BROWN, J. G. The blood pressure and its variations in the arterioles, capillaries and small veins. *J. Physiol.*, 2: 323–359, 1879–1880.
18. LEWIS, THOMAS, *The Blood Vessels of the Human Skin and Their Responses*. London, Shaw & Sons Ltd., 1927, 322 pp.
19. PATEL, D. J., and BURTON, A. C. Reactive hyperemia in the human finger. *Circulat. Res.*, 4:710–712, 1956.
20. YONCE, L. R., and HAMILTON, W. F. Oxygen consumption in skeletal muscle during reactive hyperemia. *Amer. J. Physiol.*, 197:190–192, 1959.
21. KORNER, P. I. Circulatory adaptations in hypoxia. *Physiol. Rev.*, 39:687–730, 1959.
22. WIEDERHEILM, CURT. Personnal communication.
23. FOLKOW, B. The vasodilator action of adenosine triphosphate. *Acta physiol. scand.*, 17: 311–316, 1949.
24. PAGE, I. H., McCUBBIN, J. W., SCHWARZ, H., and BUMPUS, F. M. Pharmacologic aspects of synthetic angiotonin. *Circulat. Res.*, 5:552–555, 1957.
25. PAGE, I. H. Serotonin (5-hydroxytryptamine): the last four years. *Physiol. Rev.*, 38: 277–335, 1958.
26. ROSE, J. C., and LAZARO, E. J. Pulmonary vascular responses to serotonin and effects of certain serotonin antagonists. *Circulat. Res.*, 6:282–293, 1958.
27. BAYLISS, W. M. On the local reactions of the arterial wall to changes of internal pressure. *J. Physiol.*, 28:220–231, 1902.
28. FOLKOW, B. A study of the factors influencing the tone of denervated blood vessels perfused at various pressures. *Acta physiol. scand.*, 27:99–117, 1953.
29. COLES, D. R., KIDD, B. S. L., and PATTERSON, G. C. The reactions of the blood vessels of the human calf to increases in transmural pressure. *J. Physiol.*, 134:665–674, 1956.
30. JOHNSON, P. C. Myogenic nature of increase in intestinal vascular resistance with venous pressure elevation. *Circulat. Res.*, 7:992–999, 1959.
31. McDONALD, D. A., and TAYLOR, M. G. The hydrodynamics of the arterial circulation. *Progr. Biophys. Biophys. Chem.*, 9:105–173, 1959.
32. FRANKLIN, D., BAKER, D., VAN CITTERS, R. L., and RUSHMER, R. F. Blood flow distribution in intact dogs by ultrasonic flowmeters. *Fed. Proc.*, 19:90, 1960.
33. SMITH, O. A., JR., RUSHMER, R. F., and LASHER, E. P. Similarity of cardiovascular responses to exercise and to diencephalic stimulation. *Amer. J. Physiol.*, 198:1139–1142, 1960.

34. WALLACE, J. M., and STEAD, E. A. Fall in pressure in radial artery during reactive hyperemia. *Circulat. Res.*, 7:876–879, 1959.

35. KETY, S. S. The physiology of the cerebral circulation in man. Pp. 324–340 in *Circulation*, J. McMichael, ed. Oxford, Blackwell Scientific Publications, 1958.

36. SOKOLOFF, L. The action of drugs on the cerebral circulation. *Pharmacol. Rev.*, 11:1–85, 1959.

37. LASSEN, N. A. Cerebral blood flow and oxygen consumption in man. *Physiol. Rev.*, 39:183–238, 1959.

38. SOKOLOFF, L. Factors regulating the total and regional circulation of the brain. Pp. 79–88 in *Factors Regulating Blood Flow*, G. P. Fulton and B. Zweifach, eds. Washington, Amer. Physiol. Soc., 1958.

39. COURNAND, A. Control of the pulmonary circulation in normal man. Pp. 219–237 in *Circulation*, J. McMichael, ed. Oxford, Blackwell Scientific Publications, 1958.

40. RUDOLPH, A. M., KURLAND, M. D., AULD, P. A. M., and PAUL, M. H. Effects of vasodilator drugs on normal and serotoninconstricted pulmonary vessels of the dog. *Amer. J. Physiol.*, 197:617–623, 1959.

41. DALY, I. DE B., and DALY, M. DE B. The effects of stimulation of the carotid body chemoreceptors on pulmonary vascular resistance in the dog. *J. Physiol.*, 137:436–446, 1957.

42. GREEN, H. D., HALL, L. S., SEXTON, J., and DEAL, C. P. Autonomic vasomotor responses in the canine hepatic arterial and venous beds. *Amer. J. Physiol.*, 196:196–202, 1959.

43. GOTTSCHALK, C. W. Hydrostatic pressures in individual tubules and capillaries of the rat kidney. Pp. 65–72 in *Factors Regulating Blood Flow*, G. P. Fulton and B. Zweifach, eds. Washington, Amer. Physiol. Soc., 1958.

44. BRICKNER, E. W., DOWDS, E. G., WILLITTS, B., and SELKURT, E. E. Mesenteric blood flow as influenced by progressive hypercapnia. *Amer. J. Physiol.*, 184:275–281, 1956.

45. GREGG, D. W. Regulation of the collateral and coronary circulation of the heart. Pp. 163–186 in *Circulation*, J. McMichael, ed. Oxford, Blackwell Scientific Publications, 1958.

46. KATZ, L. M., and FEINBERG, H. The relation of cardiac effort to myocardial oxygen consumption and coronary flow. *Circulat. Res.*, 6:656–669, 1958.

47. SCOTT, J. C., and BALOURDAS, T. A. The interpretation of "spurious" correlations in coronary flow literature. *Circulat. Res.*, 7:169–172, 1959.

48. BERNE, R. M. Effect of epinephrine and norepinephrine on coronary circulation. *Circulat. Res.*, 6:644–655, 1958.

49. YOUMANS, P. L., GREEN, H. D., and DENISON, A. B., JR. Nature of the vasodilator and vasoconstrictor receptors in skeletal muscle of the dog. *Circulat. Res.*, 3:171–180, 1955.

50. LOFVING, B., and MELLANDER, S. Some aspects of the basal tone of the blood vessels. *Acta physiol. scand.*, 37:134–141, 1956.

51. ELIASSON, S., LINDGREN, P., and UVNÄS, B. The hypothalamus, a relay station of the sympathetic vasodilator tract. *Acta physiol. scand.*, 31:290–300, 1953.

52. LINDGREN, P., and UVNÄS, B. Vasoconstrictor inhibition and vasodilator activation—two functionally separate vasodilator mechanisms in the skeletal muscles. *Acta physiol. scand.*, 33:108–119, 1955.

53. RODDIE, I. C., and SHEPHERD, J. T. The reflex nervous control of human skeletal muscle blood vessels. *Clin. Sci.*, 15:433–440, 1956.

54. STEIN, I. D., HARPUDER, K., and BYER, J. Effect of sympathectomy on blood flow in the human limb. *Amer. J. Physiol.*, 152:499–504, 1948.

55. BARCROFT, H., and DORNHORST, A. C. The blood flow through the human calf during rhythmic exercise. *J. Physiol.*, 109:402–411, 1949.

56. BARCROFT, H., and SWAN, H. J. C. *Sympathetic Control of Human Blood Vessels*. London, Edward Arnold, 1953.

57. FREEMAN, W. J., and DAVIS, D. D. Effects on cats of conductive hypothalamic cooling. *Amer. J. Physiol.*, 197:145–148, 1959.

58. WHITE, J. C., SMITHWICK, R. H., and SIMEONE, F. A. *The Autonomic Nervous System: Anatomy, Physiology and Surgical Application*, 3rd ed. New York, The Macmillan Co., 1952, 569 pp.

59. PEACOCK, J. H. Peripheral venous blood concentration of epinephrine and norepinephrine in primary Raynaud's disease. *Circulat. Res.*, 7:821–827, 1959.

60. BURN, J. H. *Functions of Autonomic Transmitters*. The Abraham Flexner Lectures, series no. 13. Baltimore, Williams & Wilkins Co., 1956, 228 pp.

61. WOLF, S. G., and WOLFF, H. G. *Headaches; Their Nature and Treatment*, 1st ed. Boston, Little, Brown & Co., 1953, 177 pp.

62. HOLMGREN, A., JONSSON, B., LEVANDER, M., LINDERHOLM, H., SJÖSTRAND, T., and STROM, G. Low physical working capacity in suspected heart cases due to inadequate adjustment of peripheral blood flow (vasoregulatory asthenia). *Acta med. scand.*, 158:413–436, 1957.

63. HOLMGREN, A., JONSSON, B. LEVANDER, M., LINDERHOLM, H., MOSSFELDT, F., SJÖSTRAND, T., and STROM, G. Physical training of patients with vasoregulatory asthenia. *Acta med. scand.*, 158:437–446, 1957.

Chapter 5

PRESSURE MEASUREMENTS

The three principal attributes of circulating blood are (*a*) flow, (*b*) volume and (*c*) pressure. Various methods for measuring cardiac output (see Chap. 3) provide information concerning total blood flow through the heart, but of these three important variables, only blood pressure is routinely measured in patients. By means of hypodermic needles and catheters, intravascular pressures in virtually all portions of the human cardiovascular system have been intensively studied and many ingenious pressure recording devices have been developed for these purposes.

Attempts to describe the flow, volume and pressure in the circulatory system by measuring only the pressure correspond to attempts to analyze the functional characteristics of a television set by using only a voltmeter. Nonetheless, direct pressure measurements have intrinsic value in determining certain of the conditions under which the circulatory system is functioning.

MEASUREMENT OF STATIC PRESSURES

A vertical column of fluid in a manometer and an accurate ruler are the only tools needed for measuring steady pressures. It is well to remember that even the most intricate pressure measuring devices require calibration by such simple pressure indicators. Thus, the fluid manometer is the basic instrument for pressure recording, and for many applications may be preferable to the expensive, complicated and insensitive electronic pressure transducers now in vogue.

Peripheral Venous Pressure

The venous pressure can be measured by a needle connected through a three-way stopcock to a vertical manometer. From the syringe, sterile saline is expressed into the manometer to a level above the possible venous pressure (Fig. 1*A*). The valve on the stopcock is then turned so the vertical tube becomes continuous with the needle. The saline runs into the vein until the vertical height of the column of saline is in equilibrium with the venous pressure at the point of the needle.

Alternatively, the phlebomanometer of Burch and Winsor[1] is well suited to measurement of pressure in both large and small peripheral veins (Fig. 1*B*). In this apparatus, a small needle is fastened to a capillary tube which is connected by a rubber tube to a small air chamber, the capacity of which can be adjusted to elevate the pressure in the system. A water manometer indicates the air pressure within the tubes. Sterile saline is drawn into the capillary tube until the meniscus lies at a reference line. When the needle is inserted into a vein, the meniscus will move farther along the capillary tube if the venous pressure exceeds the pressure within the phlebomanometer. By eleva-

131

MEASUREMENT OF PERIPHERAL VENOUS PRESSURE

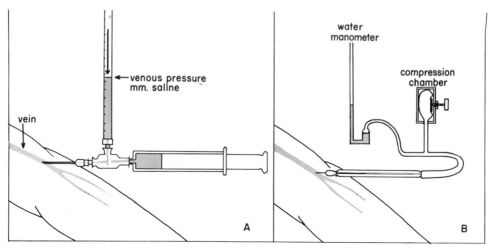

FIGURE 1. *A*, Venous pressure can be measured by a simple vertical manoneter filled with saline and connected to a needle which has been thrust into a vein. The fluid column in the vertical tube descends until its pressure is in equilibrium with venous pressure at the point of measurement.

B, The phlebomanometer of Burch and Winsor[1] consists of a small hypodermic needle fastened to a glass capillary partially filled with sterile fluid. The remainder of the system except the water manometer is filled with air. The manometer registers the pressure in the system as adjusted by twisting the screw on the compression chamber until the fluid in the glass capillary is stationary. The pressure in the water manometer then indicates venous pressure when corrected for capillary and hydrostatic pressures in the needle and observation tubing.

tion of the pressure in the system, the meniscus can be brought to a standstill at the reference line when the pressure in the manometer equals the venous pressure. A correction (about 20 mm. H_2O) must be made for the capillarity of the needle and observation tube. A more compact version of this instrument has been described by Sodeman.[2]

The average pressures in superficial veins measured in a large number of normal supine humans are illustrated in Figure 1, Chapter 7. The average venous pressure in *small* tributaries at the wrist and ankle attains levels of 139 to 188 mm. H_2O (10 to 14 mm. Hg). In all regions of the body, veins of corresponding size have similar pressures. Individual values obtained from similar sites in different individuals varied as much as 100 mm. H_2O. However, in each individual a gradient in venous pressure from the distal portion of the extremities toward the heart was apparent.

The Significance of Venous Pressure. The veins originate at the capillaries and terminate at the heart. Thus, venous pressure has important bearing on the function of both the capillaries and the heart. The pressure in the smallest peripheral veins is a basis for deducing the minimal pressure in the capillaries of the region, since the capillary pressure must exceed venous pressure. The effective pressure in the large intrathoracic veins reflects the diastolic filling pressure of the ventricles.

Right atrial pressure ranges just above or below atmospheric pressure but the pressure in extrathoracic veins is 2 to 5 cm. H_2O higher. A rather sudden drop in pressure often occurs as the veins penetrate the thoracic walls, where the extravascular pressure becomes subatmospheric. According to Duomarco *et al.*,[3] branches of the superior vena cava in normal erect subjects are collapsed from the point of entrance into the thorax to a level a few centimeters above the right atrium. The sudden drop in pressure indicates local constriction at or near the point at which the veins pass through the thoracic musculature. In any case, the venous pressure in the arms does not normally reflect right ventricular diastolic pressure. However, if central venous pressure rises, e.g., in congestive failure, the difference between intrathoracic and extrathoracic venous pressure disappears, and the brachial venous pressure becomes a fairly reliable indicator of central venous pressure.

The Phlebostatic Level. To obtain comparable values in different individuals or in a series of measurements, the venous pressure is frequently measured at the level of the right atrium. For this purpose, Winsor and Burch[4] described a reference line (the phlebostatic axis) which passes transversely through the thorax midway between the anterior and posterior surfaces of the trunk at the level of the fourth interspace at the sternum (Fig. 2A). The phlebostatic level is a horizontal plane at the level of the phlebostatic axis. Venous pressures anywhere in the body can be measured as the vertical height of a fluid column above this plane (Fig. 2B).

BASELINE FOR CENTRAL VENOUS PRESSURE

A. PHLEBOSTATIC AXIS

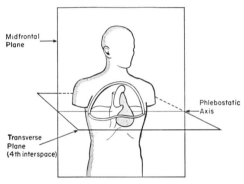

B. PHLEBOSTATIC LEVEL

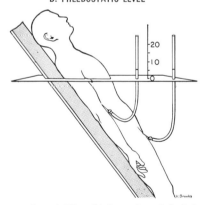

FIGURE 2.   A, The phlebostatic axis is defined as the line of junction between two planes: a mid-frontal plane and a plane at right angles passing through the junction of the fourth rib with the sternum. The phlebostatic axis passes through or near the mid-portion of the right atrial chamber.

B, The phlebostatic level is used as the zero reference for venous pressures measured in different locations with the body in various positions. The phlebostatic level is a horizontal plane passing through the phlebostatic axis.

Extravascular Pressures

Water manometers are generally employed for measuring tissue pressures in various sites. For example, pressures in the skin, subcutaneous tissue and muscle have generally been recorded with apparatus resembling the phlebomanometer (Fig. 1B). Cerebrospinal fluid pressure is usually measured with simple vertical manometers of the type illustrated in Figure 1A.

MEASUREMENT OF ARTERIAL BLOOD PRESSURE

Measuring arterial blood pressure involves determining both the systolic and the diastolic pressure. These two pressure levels actually represent the amplitude of the arterial pressure pulse at the point of measurement. For this reason, the origin and characteristics of the arterial pulse wave deserve consideration.

The Arterial Pulse

At the onset of ventricular ejection, blood flows into the aorta faster than it leaves through the arterioles. The inertia of the long columns of blood in the arteries opposes acceleration. Blood ejected by the left ventricle accumulates in the

ARTERIAL PRESSURE PULSE

A. DISTORTION OF THE ARTERIAL PULSE WAVE ALONG THE AORTA

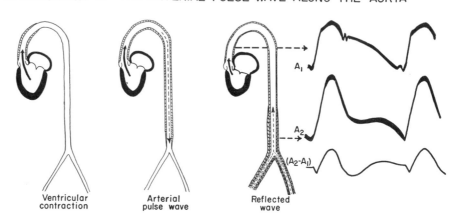

Ventricular
contraction

Arterial
pulse wave

Reflected
wave

B. THE VELOCITY OF BLOOD FLOW AND ARTERIAL PULSE IN THE AORTA

Blood flow

Pulse wave

velocity
meters/sec.

FIGURE 3.   *A,* The arterial pressure pulse is a wave of pressure which passes rapidly along the arterial system. Blood suddenly ejected into the ascending aorta at the beginning of systole has insufficient energy to overcome all the inertia of the long columns of blood in the arteries. Therefore, blood tends to pile up and distend the ascending aorta, causing a sudden local increase in pressure. Blood is then forced into the next portion of the aorta, extending the region of distention and initiating a pulse of pressure which travels rapidly along the arteries toward the periphery. These waves of pressure, reflected by peripheral structures, travel back toward the heart and become superimposed on the advancing pulse wave. This produces a higher peak of systolic pressure, a slurring of the incisura and a lower diastolic pressure in the femoral artery. If the peripheral arterial pulse wave is subtracted from the pulse recorded at the arch of the aorta, the resulting wave form ($A_2 + A_1$) suggests a natural frequency of the peripheral arterial system.

B, The pulse wave velocity (4 to 5 m. per second) is much faster than the velocity of blood flow (less than 0.5 m. per second). The pulse wave velocity is determined by the elasticity of the arterial walls which, in turn, depends upon their distensibility in relation to the blood pressure.

first portion of the aorta (Fig. 3*A*), increasing the tension in the walls of this region. The increased pressure and wall tension in the root of the aorta force blood into the adjacent segment of aorta which, in turn, is stretched and develops increased tension. In this way, a pulse of pressure moves rapidly down the aorta at a velocity which is determined by the elasticity of the walls and the pressure of the blood (Fig. 3*B*).

During the latter part of systole ventricular ejection slows. Blood leaves the arterioles faster than it enters from the left ventricle, and the pressure in the

root of the aorta falls. Ventricular pressure drops rapidly to a level below the arterial pressure, and the aortic valves close. Closing of the valves involves a retrograde surge of blood in the root of the aorta which produces a notch or incisura in the descending limb of pressure pulses recorded from this region.

The arterial pulse is altered in its form as it passes rapidly through the arterial system.[5, 6] A comparison of the pressure tracings obtained from the root of the aorta and from the lower abdominal aorta (Fig. 3) discloses in the latter a more steeply rising wave front, a higher peak pressure of shorter duration and a secondary oscillation (dicrotic wave). These changes in wave form have been variously attributed to effects of reflected pressure waves rebounding from the periphery (see Fig. 3), attenuation or damping of various frequency components of the pulse wave, differences in the propagation velocity of different frequencies in the pressure pulse and steady-state oscillation of the arterial system.[5-9] The relative contributions of these postulated mechanisms to the distortion of the arterial pulse wave remain highly controversial on technical grounds and will not be considered further. In the peripheral arteries, the systolic pressure is considerably higher and the diastolic pressure is slightly lower than they are at the root of the aorta. For example, the systolic pressure in the femoral artery of a recumbent subject may exceed the systolic pressure in the brachial artery by 15 to 25 mm. Hg. However, the mean arterial pressure (Fig. 6) is slightly higher at the aortic arch than at the periphery (see Fig. 9, Chap. 1).

Sphygmomanometry

Since the pulse waves rapidly spread through the arterial system and are modified to varying degrees, the arterial pressure at any instant varies throughout the arterial tree. Determinations of arterial pressure generally represent the maximal and minimal pressure of the pulse wave at the point of measurement.

The most accurate records of arterial pressure pulses are obtained through intra-arterial needles connected to suitable pressure recordings systems (see below). To reproduce the wave as it appears in the artery, the recording paper would have to move at the velocity at which the pulse travels past the needle (Fig. 3B). Since this is impractical, the records are generally obtained on paper moving relatively slowly, and the pulse waves are compressed in time (Fig. 4).

The arterial blood pressure is generally measured with a sphygmomanometer consisting of an inelastic cuff containing an inflatable rubber bag. The rubber bag is connected by rubber tubing to a rubber bulb and to a device which continuously records the pressure within the cuff (e.g., a mercury manometer, Fig. 4). When the cuff is snugly applied to the arm, inflation of the rubber bag compresses the tissues under the cuff. If the rubber bag is inflated to a pressure which exceeds the peak of the arterial pulse wave, the artery is continuously collapsed and no pulse wave can be palpated in the artery peripheral to the occlusion. If the pressure in the cuff is gradually reduced, a point will be reached at which the peak of the pulse wave slightly exceeds the pressure in the surrounding tissues and in the rubber bag (Fig. 4). At that level, the pulse becomes palpable and the pressure indicated on the mercury manometer is a measure of the peak of the arterial pulse or systolic pressure. The spurt of blood flowing through the artery under the cuff rapidly accelerates the column of blood in the peripheral arterial tree, producing turbulence and distinctive sounds (Korotkoff sounds) which can be heard through a stethoscope applied over the artery just below the cuff.[10] As the pressure in the cuff is reduced farther, the difference between systolic pressure and cuff pressure progressively widens and the artery is open during a greater proportion of the time. In general, the quantity of blood surging under the cuff is similarly increased, and the sounds heard through the stethoscope tend to become louder. When the pressure in the cuff falls below the minimal pressure of the arterial pulse wave, the artery remains open continuously and the emitted sounds become muffled because the blood flows continuously and the degree of acceleration

SPHYGMOMANOMETRY

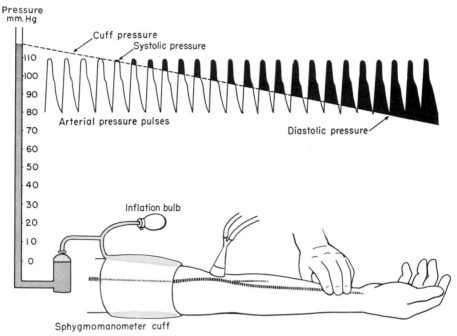

FIGURE 4.   When the pressure within the sphygmomanometer cuff is increased above arterial blood pressure, the arteries under the cuff are occluded and no pulse can be palpated at the wrist. As the cuff pressure is gradually released, the systolic peaks of pressure finally exceed cuff pressure and blood spurts into the arteries below the cuff, producing palpable pulses at the wrist. The sudden acceleration of blood below the cuff produces vibrations which are audible through a stethoscope. The pressure in the mercury manometer at the time the pulse is heard or felt indicates systolic pressure. As cuff pressure is further diminished, the sounds increase in intensity and then rather suddenly become muffled at the level of diastolic pressure where the arteries remain open throughout the entire pulse wave. At still lower pressures, the sounds disappear completely when laminar flow is re-established.

of the blood by the pulse wave is suddenly reduced. At still lower cuff pressures, the sounds disappear altogether as laminar flow is re-established.

The pressure at which the sounds become muffled has been generally accepted as the diastolic pressure. However, Bordley *et al.*[11, 12] recommended that the cessation of sounds should be substituted for this established end-point. This recommendation was termed a major setback to medical science by Burton,[13] and compelling reasons for ignoring the proposal were presented in a most stimulating review.

Sources of Error in Measuring Arterial Pressure. Significant errors in arterial blood pressure readings result from improper selection or application of sphyg-

momanometer cuffs.[14, 15] The pressure which exists in the rubber bag is transmitted to the greatest depth at the center of the cuff. If the cuff is sufficiently wide and is properly adjusted, the pressure indicated by the manometer extends to the tissues immediately surrounding the artery (Fig. 5A). However, if the limb is too thick in relation to the width of the cuff, the pressure around the artery may be significantly less than that recorded from the rubber bag (Fig. 5B). Under these conditions, the cuff pressure required to collapse the artery must exceed the pressure which exists in the artery at that point. Thus, the systolic (and diastolic) pressure readings will be too high. If the cuff is loosely applied (Fig. 5C) so that the rubber bag must be partially inflated before it exerts pressure on the tissues, the area of contact is seriously reduced, corresponding to a very narrow cuff.

The Auscultatory Gap. In some patients, the sounds emitted from the artery below the cuff disappear over a fairly large range in pressure between the systolic and diastolic pressures. The cause of this auscultatory gap is not known. If the cuff pressure is increased only to levels within the range of the auscultatory gap, the pressure at the lower end of this silent range may be noted as indicating a normal systolic pressure when, in fact, the true systolic pressure is excessively high. Since the pulse wave persists in the range of the auscultatory gap, this source of error can be eliminated by routinely checking systolic pressure by both the auscultatory and the palpatory methods (Fig. 4).

Mean Arterial Blood Pressure. Since the arterial blood pressure fluctuates during each cardiac cycle, the mean arterial pressure is often used in clinical and experimental reports. The arithmetic average of the systolic and diastolic pressures would be an accurate indication of the mean arterial perfusion pressure if the arterial pressure pulse were a true sine wave (see Fig. 6). However, the arterial pulse wave in no way resembles a sine wave and the arithmetic average of systolic and diastolic pressures is not an accurate expression of the mean pressure. The true mean arterial pressure can be determined by damping out the pulses or by integrating the arterial pulse wave on accurate records of the pressure pulse. Vertical lines are dropped from corresponding points on arterial pulse waves to the zero pressure line. The arterial pressure pulses then correspond to a serrated upper border of a rectangular area. If the area enclosed by these lines, measured by means of a planimeter, is divided by the length of the horizontal base line (Fig. 6, line L), the quotient represents the vertical distance above the zero line (Fig. 6, line H) at which the mean arterial pressure lies. By this method the mean arterial pressure is usually about one-third of the way between diastolic and systolic pressures, but varies with the configuration of the arterial pulse wave.

TRANSMISSION OF CUFF PRESSURES TO THE TISSUES OF THE ARM

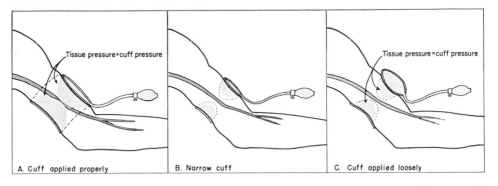

FIGURE 5.   *A,* When a sphygmomanometer cuff of sufficient width in relation to the diameter of the arm is properly applied, the tissue pressure around deep arteries under the cuff equals cuff pressure. However, pressure under the edge of the cuff does not penetrate as deeply as that under the center of the cuff.

B, A cuff which is too narrow in relation to the diameter of the limb does not transmit its pressure to the center of the limb. Under these conditions, the cuff pressure must greatly exceed arterial pressure to produce complete occlusion of the artery, and erroneously high systolic and diastolic pressures will be read from the mercury manometer.

C, If a cuff of sufficient width is applied too loosely, it becomes rounded before exerting pressure on the tissues and produces the same sort of error as a narrow cuff.

MEAN ARTERIAL PRESSURE

DETERMINATION OF MEAN ARTERIAL PRESSURE

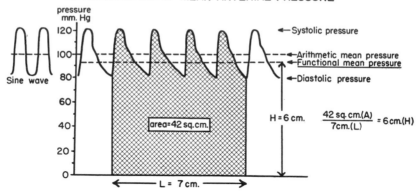

FIGURE 6.   If the systolic pressure is 120 mm. Hg and the diastolic pressure 80 mm. Hg, the arithmetic mean pressure is 100 mm. Hg. If the arterial pulse wave were symmetrical (a sine wave), this value would represent the average perfusion pressure. However, the interval during which the arterial pressure is less than 100 mm. Hg is longer than that during which it is elevated above this level, so the functional mean pressure is less than 100 mm. Hg. The functional mean pressure is determined by dividing the area of the shaded region (area = 42 sq. cm.) by the horizontal dimension (L = 7 cm.) to determine the height of a rectangle having the same area (H = 6 cm.). The functional mean pressure tends to be higher than diastolic pressure by about one-third the pulse pressure, but this estimate does not apply to pulse waves having different contours, e.g., with changes in heart rate.

Continuous Recording of Arterial Blood Pressure

Measurement of arterial blood pressures has long played an important role in cardiovascular research. Recent developments in cardiac catheterization and the pulse-contour method of computing cardiac output have created widespread interest in accurately recording both pulmonary and systemic arterial pressures. Pressure transducers, suitable for recording the rapidly fluctuating arterial and intraventricular pressures, have certain essential requirements which should be understood by anyone who either uses them or wishes to appraise the multitude of clinical reports involving such equipment.

A mercury manometer is inadequate for recording pressures which fluctuate widely and rapidly, especially when the extremes of pressure are significant. The inertia of the fluid and the resistance to its flow into the manometer keep the fluid level from following the rapid changes in pressure. If a mercury manometer is connected directly to an artery through a hypodermic needle, the mercury column oscillates slightly above and below the mean pressure. The manometer obviously does not indicate the magnitude of either the systolic or the diastolic pressure. The same problem arises in measuring the widely fluctuating pressures in the ventricular cavities. Thus, more complicated apparatus is required to measure arterial and ventricular pressures accurately.

Rapidly fluctuating pressures can be accurately recorded only by apparatus with an adequate frequency response. The frequency response is a measure of the rate at which a recording system responds to a sudden change in pressure. The factors which determine the responsiveness of a pressure-sensitive device can best be described in terms of simple mechanical systems.

Mechanical Pressure Transducers. A common pressure transducer consists of a tambour with a rubber membrane coupled to a writing lever. If the rubber membrane is quite flaccid, very slight pressures will stretch the membrane and displace the writing lever (Fig. 7A). In response to an increased pressure, a considerable quantity of fluid must pass along the tubing and enter the tambour to produce a corresponding displacement of the membrane and writing lever. The inertia of the fluid and lever opposes a rapid response to a change in pressure, and the rubber membrane provides a relatively weak force to restore the fluid and lever to their original positions when the pressure is reduced. Clearly, such a system could not respond rapidly enough to follow the fluctuating arterial pressure. The natural frequency of a pressure transducer can be visualized in terms of a mass suspended on a spring. The smaller the mass and the stiffer the spring, the faster the oscillations which occur after a displacement from the rest position. When the mass of the fluid and of the lever is large in relation to the tension of the membrane, the oscillations are slow. If the rubber membrane is very tense, the frequency response is increased, but the sensitivity (deflection per unit of pressure) is correspondingly reduced (Fig. 7B).

Optical Manometers. A reduction in the mass of the moving parts makes possible greater sensitivity without a sacrifice of the frequency response. The inertia of the writing lever can be eliminated by

MECHANICAL PRESSURE RECORDERS

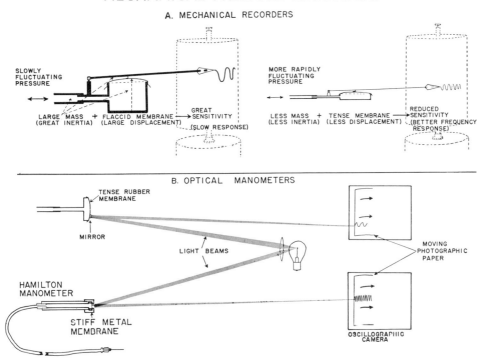

FIGURE 7. *A*, Pressure recording ordinarily involves the displacement of some type of elastic membrane. To displace the membrane, fluid must move into the recording capsule. The inertia of the fluid, the membrane and the recording mechanisms tends to resist displacement. When the moving mass is large and the membrane is flaccid, the recording system may be very sensitive to slowly fluctuating pressures, but will not respond to rapid changes in pressure. Reducing the moving mass and utilizing stiff membranes diminish sensitivity but improve the frequency response.

B, Optical manometers amplify the movements of stiff membranes by utilizing a weightless beam of light as a lever to produce rapid response with sufficient sensitivity. For example, the Hamilton manometer is equipped with a stiff beryllium-copper membrane which may respond reliably to frequencies in excess of 150 c.p.s.

ELECTRICAL PRESSURE TRANSDUCERS

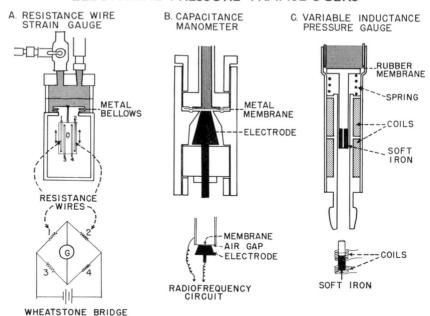

FIGURE 8.   *A*, The unbonded resistance wire strain gauge (Statham gauge) consists of a metal bellows which is compressed by increased pressure within the chamber. Downward displacement of the bellows is transmitted to a metal slide supported by four sets of strain-sensitive wires wound under tension and connected to form a Wheatstone bridge. Displacement of the metal slide stretches two sets of wires and relaxes the other two. These changes in resistance imbalance the bridge in proportion to the applied pressure. The resulting voltage output from the bridge is amplified and recorded by various means.

B, The electrical capacitance diaphragm manometer is a condensor formed by an electrode (black) separated from a stiff metal membrane by a carefully adjusted air gap. Displacement of the membrane changes the thickness of the air gap. This results in a change in capacitance which is recorded by a radio frequency circuit. (From Lilly.[17])

C, Variations in magnetic flux in two coils of wire can be produced by movements of an iron slug positioned within the coils. In a differential transformer pressure transducer, the iron slug is fastened to the center of an elastic membrane so that changes in pressure produce changes in magnetic flux. (From Gauer and Gienapp.[19])

using a beam of light. A small mirror eccentrically mounted on the membrane diverts a beam of light onto the slit of a recording camera (Fig. 7*B*). Bulging of the membrane by increased pressure deflects the beam to a degree related to the magnitude of the applied pressure.

Utilizing the increased sensitivity provided by a long weightless beam of light, Hamilton incorporated a beryllium-copper membrane with an eccentric mirror into a rigid system to produce a pressure recording device with a frequency response ranging above 150 cycles per second (Fig. 7*B*). This manometer has

been the accepted standard for accurate recording of arterial blood pressure. A more complete description of different mechanical pressure transducers was presented by Green.[16]

Electrical Pressure Transducers.   In this electronic age it is not surprising that slight movements of stiff membranes should be used to affect currents or voltages which can be amplified by vacuum tube amplifiers. Various types of electronic pressure transducers are available in which movements of membranes produce changes in (*a*) resistance, (*b*) capacitance or (*c*) inductance (Fig. 8*A*, *B*, *C*).

In each case, stiff membranes with small fluid displacement and relatively high frequency response can be used because the output signals can be amplified enough to activate recording galvanometers of various types.

Variable Resistance Manometers. Resistance wire strain gauge manometers respond to a change in pressure with a change in the resistance to the flow of electrical currents when strain-sensitive wire is exposed to varying degrees of stretch. A small bellows, used in place of a membrane, is compressed by increased pressure in the chamber (Fig. 8*A*).

Variable Capacitance Manometers. A stiff metal membrane separated from an electrode by a very small air gap constitutes a condenser (Fig. 8*B*). Movements of the membrane in relation to the electrode vary the capacitance, which can be measured by means of a radio frequency circuit. Such an instrument was described by Lilly in 1942,[17] and improved models of this manometer are now available commercially. The membrane displacement of this device is extremely small (computed volume displacement, 0.00001 cc. per 100 mm. Hg). This characteristic permits successful recording of fluctuating pressures through long tubes of small caliber.[18] The zero base line of this device tends to be more unstable than that of the unbonded resistance wire strain gauge.

Variable Inductance Pressure Gauges. The inductance of a coil can be altered by changing the position of an iron slug within its magnetic field. For example, if an iron slug connected to the center of an elastic membrane is mounted within two coils, deflection of the membrane moves the iron slug within the coils, changing their inductance. Thus, changes in the inductance of the coils, recorded through an appropriate bridge circuit, indicate the amount of membrane displacement during fluctuations in pressure. Gauer and Gienapp[19] developed such an instrument which was so small it could be attached to the end of a cardiac catheter and introduced directly into the heart and great vessels. A differential transformer pressure transducer has been mounted within the thorax to record intraventricular pressures in dogs (see Chap. 3).

Amplification. The output of unbonded strain gauge pressure transducers is sufficient to activate directly a sensitive moving-coil type of galvanometer (Fig. 9*A*). In this case the deflections are amplified by an optical system in which a light beam is deflected into an oscillograph camera. This system is extremely stable, and will retain the same sensitivity and zero base line for a long time. Such gauges can be obtained for a wide variety of pressure ranges so that either very large or very small pressure deviations can be recorded. Once pressure recording is begun, it is difficult to vary the sensitivity of the system. However, an amplifier can be used with optical galvanometers to adjust the sensitivity during recording. To some investigators, photographic recording is undesirable because the record cannot be observed as it is inscribed, and processing the paper records is a nuisance.

It is common practice to amplify electronically the signal emitted by the various pressure transducers to provide power sufficient to drive insensitive galvanometers. In recent years, direct writing recording instruments have become very widely used to record electrocardiograms and other physiologic phenomena. The inertia of direct writing galvanometers is so great that their frequency response is limited and extensive amplification is required to produce any deflection at all. Nevertheless, it is possible to obtain accurate recordings of arterial and ventricular pressures under direct vision with such instruments (see Chap. 8). Many types of pressure transducer-amplifier combinations are available and a common type is illustrated schematically in Figure 9*B*. A carrier wave type of strain

AMPLIFICATION OF TRANSDUCER SIGNALS

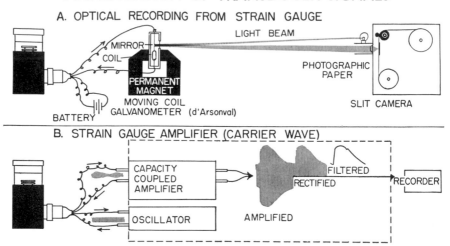

FIGURE 9.   The weak signals from electronic pressure transducers generally require some form o amplification.

A, A Statham strain gauge powered by a constant voltage source and connected to a coil-type galvanometer provides a very stable pressure recording system. The deflections of the galvanometer can be amplified by an optical system deflecting a beam of light onto a strip of moving photographic paper.

B, Carrier wave amplifiers are frequently employed in conjunction with pressure transducers. An oscillator supplies an alternating current of constant voltage to a Statham strain gauge. Fluctuations in resistance in the bridge produce variations in the amplitude of this carrier wave. The modulated carrier wave is then amplified and the resulting signal is then rectified, filtered and recorded by suitable galvanometers.

gauge amplifier consists of an oscillator by which an alternating current of constant amplitude is supplied to the Wheatstone bridge of the strain gauge. In passing through the bridge, the alternating current is modulated by the changing resistances in the bridge resulting from variations in pressure. In other words, the amplitude of the alternating current is continuously affected by the varying resistances in the Wheatstone bridge which are, in turn, determined by the pressure applied to the bellows (Fig. 9*B*). The output of the gauge enters a capacity-coupled amplifier which amplifies the modulated carrier wave. Then the signals are rectified and the carrier wave is filtered out, leaving a D.C. voltage which powers a suitable recording device. This general approach is widely used with many modifications to amplify the signals from different types of transducers.

Recorders.   Three basic types of recording devices are employed to record pressure pulses: (*a*) optical galvanometers, as in Figure 9*A*, (*b*) direct-writing galvanometers and (*c*) cathode ray oscilloscopes. The advantages and limitations of optical galvanometers and direct-writing instruments have been mentioned above. Cathode ray oscilloscopes are well suited for the study of very rapidly fluctuating pressures, including heart sounds. In this instrument, the amplified signals deflect an electron beam which has negligible inertia. Such devices offer practically no frequency limitation. The patterns are displayed on the face of the cathode ray tube and may be observed directly or photographed.

No ideal pressure recording system exists. For any particular application the transducer, amplifier and recorder must be matched to obtain optimal performance. This process invariably involves compromise of sensitivity, convenience, stability or frequency response. The nature and significance of frequency response is widely misunderstood even by some individuals routinely engaged in physiologic recording.

The Frequency Response of Recording Systems. It is generally agreed that a high fidelity reproduction of a wave form can be recorded by a system which has a uniform response to the tenth harmonic of its fundamental frequency. With a heart rate of 240 beats per minute, the pulse frequency is 4 per second and the tenth harmonic of this frequency is 40 c.p.s. Such a high frequency response is deemed necessary if the most rapid changes in pressure during the pulse are to be faithfully recorded.

Although it is possible to determine the frequency response characteristics of the transducer, amplifier and galvanometer individually, it is more important to test the dynamic response of the entire system assembled for use. When the transducer is connected to a fluid-filled catheter or through tubing to a hypodermic needle, the frequency response of the gauge may be greatly reduced. The fluid in the system represents a mass which must move with changes in pressure, and its inertia markedly reduces the frequency response of the gauge. When the diaphragm is displaced by an increased pressure, its elasticity must overcome the inertia of the entire mass of fluid within the connecting tubes. The mass of fluid can be reduced by using tubing of small caliber, but only at the price of increasing the frictional resistance to movement of fluid. Thus, some of the pressure energy is dissipated as friction in fluid within narrow tubes. Increasing the frictional resistance of a system is a form of "damping." Careful matching of the frequency response of the system with an optimal degree of damping can greatly improve the response characteristics (Fig. 10). Damping is attained by reducing the caliber of the catheter or tube, by locally constricting the tubing with a clamp or by inserting a short section of tube with appropriate caliber.

Virtually identical arterial and ventricular pulse contours have been obtained with damped systems having uniform response to 5, 30, and 50 c.p.s.[20] The frequency response and the degree of damping of any system should be routinely established by methods indicated in Figure 10. Such a procedure eliminates inaccurate records caused by temporary malfunction of the system. For example, a small bubble remaining in the tubing or gauge after it is filled with fluid reduces the frequency response of the system to very low levels because air is much more elastic than the diaphragm.

Artifacts from the Movement of Cardiac Catheters. Pressures from within the heart and great vessels are frequently measured through long catheters. Owing to movements of the heart, the tip of the catheter may oscillate in time with the cardiac cycle. Such movements produce artifacts which are superimposed upon the pressure pulses and often attain amplitudes equivalent to 10 mm. Hg. These motion artifacts are much more prominent when recorded with high frequency systems and are largely eliminated by using an optimally damped system responding uniformly to 5 c.p.s.[21]

SUMMARY

Stable or slowly fluctuating pressures can be accurately recorded with simple water or mercury manometers. Arterial blood pressure can be measured indirectly by sphygmomanometry. Accurate direct recording of rapidly fluctuating arterial or ventricular pressures can be accomplished by means of either mechanical manometers or electronic transducers of various types. It is vitally important to test the frequency response and degree of damping of any system which is employed for accurate registration of rapidly fluctuating pressures.

THE DYNAMIC RESPONSE CHARACTERISTICS OF PRESSURE RECORDING SYSTEMS

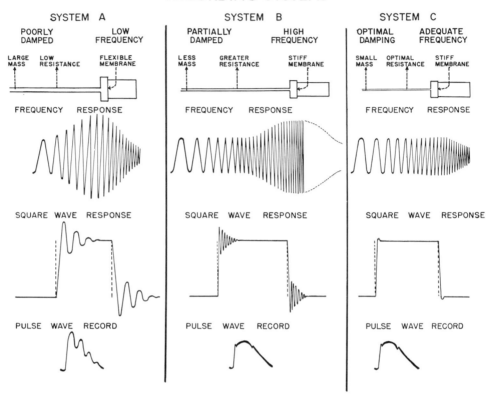

FIGURE 10.   The response characteristics of a recording system should be carefully established and rechecked frequently.

System *A* has a large mass of fluid in a large caliber tube and a flexible membrane. Thus, the system is very sensitive to changes in pressure, but is poorly damped. If fluctuating pressures of constant amplitude and progressively increasing frequency are applied to the end of the tube, the output from the system increases with higher frequencies up to the natural frequency of the system and then declines. The characteristics of the system can be more easily checked by suddenly raising or abruptly lowering the pressure (a square wave of pressure). In this particular system, the recorded deflection was considerably delayed in reaching the new pressure level (slow rise time). The deflection had considerable overshoot and oscillations persisted at the natural frequency of the system for a considerable time (poor damping). This system would be entirely unreliable for recording arterial pressure pulses.

System *B* has a stiff membrane and partial damping. Pressure waves of equal amplitude produced a response of uniform height over a considerable range of frequency. However, the deflections became exaggerated near the natural frequency of the system. In response to a square wave, the rise time was very short and the oscillations at the natural frequency of the system died down rather promptly. This system would be adequate for recording pressure pulses unless certain portions of the pulse had frequencies near the natural frequency of the system. The square wave response should be determined just before using such a system because a single small air bubble in the catheter or the gauge may so reduce the response characteristics that system *B* acts like system *A*.

In system *C* the membrane is more flexible than that in system *B*, but system *C* has been critically damped. In other words, the output from the system is uniform throughout a wide range of frequencies. A square wave of pressure produced a rapid response and a very slight overshoot, but no sustained oscillations. A critically damped system accurately reproduces arterial pressure pulses even though its uniform frequency response is limited to 20 or even 10 c.p.s. (From records presented by Lambert, E. H., and Jones, R. E.: *Proc. Staff Meet. Mayo Clin.*, 23:487–493, 1948.)

REFERENCES

1. BURCH, G. E., and WINSOR, T. The phlebo-manometer. A new apparatus for direct measurement of venous pressure in large and small veins. *J. Amer. Med. Ass.*, 123:91–92, 1943.

2. SODEMAN, W. A. Direct venous pressure determinations by use of a new instrument. *Amer. Heart J.*, 43:687–690, 1952.

3. DUOMARCO, J. L., RIMINI, R., and SAPRIZA, J. P. Attempted evaluation of venous pressure by angiocardiography. *Rev. argent. cardiol.*, 17:15–28, 1950.

4. WINSOR, T., and BURCH, G. E. Phlebostatic axis and phlebostatic level, reference levels for venous pressure measurements in man. *Proc. Soc. Exp. Biol., N.Y.*, 58:165–169, 1945.

5. HAMILTON, W. F., and DOW, P. An experimental study of the standing waves in the pulse propagated through the aorta. *Amer. J. Physiol.*, 125:48–59, 1939.

6. ALEXANDER, R. S. Transformation of the arterial pulse wave between the aortic arch and femoral artery. *Amer. J. Physiol.*, 158:287–293, 1949.

7. PETERSON, L. H. The dynamics of pulsatile blood flow. *Circulat. Res.*, 2:127–139, 1954.

8. WARNER, H. R. A study of the mechanism of pressure wave distortion by arterial walls using an electrical analog. *Circulat. Res.*, 5:79–84, 1957.

9. McDONALD, D. A., and TAYLOR, M. G. The hydrodynamics of the arterial circulation. *Progr. Biophys.*, 9:105–173, 1959.

10. ERLANGER, J. Studies in blood pressure estimation by indirect methods. II. The mechanism of the compression sounds of Korotkoff. *Amer. J. Physiol.*, 40:82–125, 1916.

11. BORDLEY, J., III, CONNOR, C. A. R., HAMILTON, W. F., KERR, W. J., and WIGGERS, C. J. Recommendations for human blood pressure determinations by sphygmomanometers. *Circulation*, 4:503–509, 1951.

12. BORDLEY, J., III, CONNOR, C. A. R., HAMILTON, W. F., KERR, W. J., and WIGGERS, C. J. Recommendations for human blood pressure determinations by sphygmomanometers. *J. Amer. Med. Ass.*, 147:632–636, 1951.

13. BURTON, A. C. Peripheral circulation. *Annu. Rev. Physiol.*, 15:213–246, 1953.

14. THOMSON, A. E., and DOUPE, J. Causes of error in auscultatory blood pressure measurements. *Rev. Canad. Biol.*, 8:337, 1949.

15. WENDKOS, M. H., and ROSSMAN, P. L. The normal blood pressure in the lower extremity. *Amer. Heart J.*, 26:623–630, 1943.

16. GREEN, H. D. Circulatory system: methods. Pp. 208–222 in *Medical Physics*, O. Glasser ed. Chicago, Year Book Publishers, 1950.

17. LILLY, J. C. The electrical capacitance diaphragm manometer. *Rev. Sci. Instrum.*, 13:34–37, 1942.

18. PETERSON, L. H., DRIPPS, R. D., and RISMAN, G. C. A method for recording the arterial pressure pulse and blood pressure in man. *Amer. Heart J.*, 37:771–782, 1949.

19. GAUER, O. H., and GIENAPP, E. A miniature pressure-recording device. *Science*, 112:404–405, 1950.

20. ELLIS, E. J., GAUER, O. H., and WOOD, E. H. An intracardiac manometer: its evaluation and application. *Circulation*, 3:390–398, 1951.

21. WOOD, E. H., LEUSEN, I. R., WARNER, H. R., and WRIGHT, J. L. Measurement of pressures in man by cardiac catheters. *Circulat. Res.*, 2:294–303, 1954.

Chapter 6

SYSTEMIC ARTERIAL PRESSURE

I. Control of Arterial Pressure

The distribution of blood flow through the various peripheral vascular beds is controlled primarily by changes in caliber at the sites of resistance in the vessels leading to the capillary networks (Chap. 4). This form of flow control depends upon the maintenance at all times of an adequate pressure head within the systemic arterial system. Some stabilizing mechanism must exert an over-all regulation of systemic arterial pressure to prevent circulatory collapse when several major areas of the body simultaneously require increased blood flow. For example, running at full speed on a hot day after a full meal would theoretically require increased blood flow through the active skeletal muscles, the skin and the gastrointestinal tract. If all these vascular beds suddenly dilated, the arterial blood pressure would drop precipitously and blood flow through vital regions (the heart and brain) would be jeopardized. A monitoring system which senses systemic arterial pressure and induces appropriate cardiovascular compensations to maintain this pressure within a relatively narrow range will automatically adjust the balance between inflow and outflow so that the total flow through capillary networks does not exceed the capacity of the pump.

The requirements of a pressure-regulating system are indicated schematically

in Figure 1. By adjustment of the pump motor and the resistance valves, the pressure head can be set at a predetermined level. Pressure-sensing elements which continuously monitor this pressure can act upon a black-box control system. In such a system, wider opening of one resistance valve increases the outflow from the high pressure side, dropping the pressure head. This lowers the output from the pressure transducers which in turn acts on the control system to close other resistance valves, speed up the pump, or do both. In other words, the pressure level is set, the pressure-sensing elements detect a shift in pressure from this level as an error signal, and proper corrective adjustments to return the pressure to the "normal" level are instituted.

The systemic arterial pressure is apparently controlled essentially in this manner. There are, however, some complications. First, the process by which the "normal range" of systemic arterial pressure is originally set at a mean of about 90 mm. Hg is not obvious. Second, to detect an error, the pressure-sensing elements must continuously register absolute pressure above atmospheric pressure even though they are stretch receptors located in flexible walls apparently capable of varied distensibility. The pressure-sensing mechanism must integrate a fluctuating arterial pressure and induce responses which are related to changes in mean pressure rather than to changes in either the systolic or the diastolic pressure. For this reason, the factors which influence the systemic arterial pressure deserve consideration.

SYSTEMIC ARTERIAL PRESSURE PULSES

The principal function of the arterial system is to accept the repetitive spurts of blood injected by the heart and to convert this intermittent inflow into a relatively steady outflow through the peripheral resistance vessels into the capillary networks. The geometry of the vascular bed and the visco-elastic properties of the arterial walls play important roles in the conveying of blood down the long arterial channels with a minimal loss of pressure head but with a damping of the violent pressure fluctuations in the peripheral vessels (see Fig. 9, Chap 1).

Systolic Pressure

During the latter part of systole the rapidly attained peak pressure in the root of the aorta is well maintained as a rounded summit by the slower ejection from the left ventricle (Fig. 2). The peak systolic pressure in the central aorta is determined largely by the left ventricular stroke volume, the peak rate of ejection and the distensibility of the aortic walls. For example, the slow ejection of a small stroke volume into an easily distensible aorta produces a small elevation in systolic pressure. A rapid ejection of a large volume into a rigid aorta produces a large rise in systolic pressure, as does a normal stroke volume injected at normal velocity

CONTROL OF ARTERIAL BLOOD PRESSURE

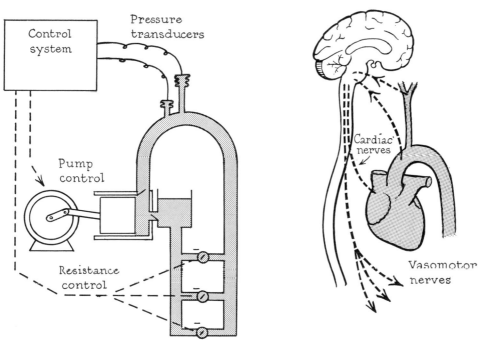

FIGURE 1. The pressure head in a simple hydraulic system could be controlled by means of pressure-sensing elements transmitting signals proportional to pressure through leads to a black-box integrating system which appropriately adjusts the pump output and valve settings in response to any deviation from some preset level. The corresponding elements for the control of arterial blood pressure include carotid sinus and aortic arch pressoreceptors feeding into the nervous system which provides integration of nerve impulses to the pump and peripheral vascular system.

FACTORS AFFECTING SYSTOLIC AND DIASTOLIC ARTERIAL PRESSURE

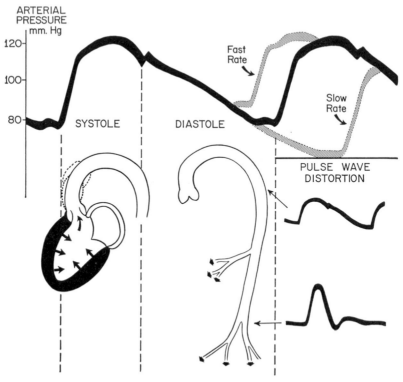

FIGURE 2.   The systolic pressure is determined primarily by the rate and volume of ventricular ejection in relation to the arterial distensibility. The diastolic pressure is determined by the rate of diastolic pressure drop (related to peripheral resistance) and the heart rate as it affects the duration of diastole. The pulse wave is distorted by damping and reflections as it travels along the arterial trunks such that the peak systolic pressure is higher and the diastolic pressure is flatter but the mean arterial pressure is only slightly less than at the arch of the aorta.

into a rigid atherosclerotic artery. The greatly accelerated ventricular ejection associated with increased ventricular contractility also produces greatly increased systolic pressure in the aorta (see Figs. 15 and 16, Chap. 3).

Diastolic Pressure

After ventricular systole is completed, the aortic valves are closed by a retrograde surge of blood, represented on the pressure pulse by the dicrotic notch (see Fig. 2). After the aortic valves snap shut, the arterial pressure gradually falls as blood flows out through the myriad of peripheral vascular networks. The rate

at which the diastolic pressure falls is determined by the pressure achieved during the systolic interval, the rate of outflow through the peripheral resistances and the diastolic interval. If the next systole were delayed for 3 or 4 seconds, the arterial pressure would continue to fall, asymptotically approaching a level of about 10 mm. Hg. The minimal diastolic pressure is determined primarily by the total peripheral resistance and by the heart rate (Fig. 2). The pulse pressure (the maximum systolic minus the minimum diastolic pressure) is increased by the factors that increase systolic pressure and reduce diastolic pressure.

Distortion of the Arterial Pulse During Transmission

The form of the arterial pressure pulse changes as it passes down the arterial tree (Fig. 2). The systolic wave becomes considerably higher, is more sharply peaked and falls abruptly; the gradual decline in diastolic pressure becomes replaced by several damped oscillations. These changes in the form of the pulse have been variously attributed to (a) pressure waves reflected from the periphery[1] or from abdominal aortic branches,[2] (b) a damping transmission line,[3] (c) the resonant frequency and damping coefficient of the arterial walls, and (d) highly damped steady-state oscillations (see also Fig. 5, Chap. 3). Although the exact cause has not been completely determined, it is clear that the pulse pressure becomes progressively greater as the pulse traverses the major branches of the arterial tree, so that the systolic pressure peak in the femoral or brachial arteries reaches values as much as 15 to 20 mm. Hg higher than those in the central aorta.

It is important to recognize that an increase in systolic pressure, with an increase in both pulse pressure and mean pressure, can occur without a change in peripheral resistance by three different mechanisms: (a) increased stroke volume, (b) increased ejection rate and (c) reduced arterial distensibility. These events can be exaggerated by the distortion of the pressure pulse during its transmission to the site of measurement at the brachial artery.

ARTERIAL STRETCH RECEPTORS (PRESSORECEPTORS)

The role of receptors in the walls of cardiovascular structures in the regulation of the circulation and respiration has been studied by many investigators,[6-10] whose work has recently been reviewed by Heymans and Neil.[11] The aortic depressor nerve was discovered by Cyon and Ludwig in 1866. Since then, a great deal of information has been gathered regarding the function of neural elements in the reflex regulation of the cardiovascular system.

Carotid Sinus

At the bifurcation of the common carotid artery into the internal and external branches there is a local dilation of the very first portion of the internal carotid artery called the carotid sinus. It has a much thinner wall than other arteries of the same size because the smooth muscle in its media is relatively sparse, particularly on the ventromedial surface where the sinus nerve arises. In this part of the media, the smooth muscle is almost

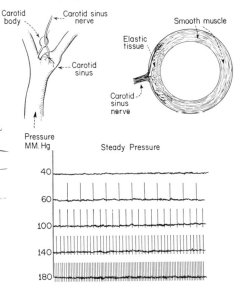

CAROTID SINUS STRETCH RECEPTORS

FIGURE 3. Nerve endings sensitive to stretch or distortion are located in the wall of a localized expansion at the origin of the internal carotid artery. At this site the walls contain an unusually large amount of elastic tissue and the smooth muscle of the media is somewhat deficient. Such an arrangement is particularly suited to the monitoring of pressure by these receptors, which discharge at greater and greater frequencies in response to increasing steady pressures, maintained artificially. (After Heymans and Neil, Reflexogenic Areas of the Cardiovascular System.)

CAROTID SINUS REFLEXES

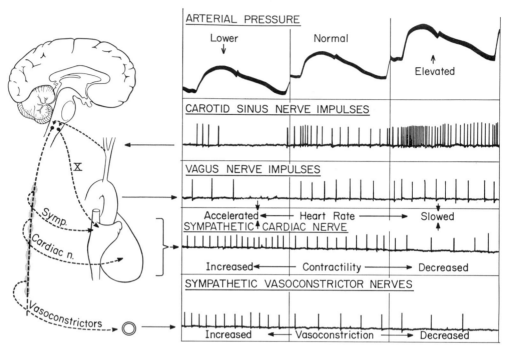

FIGURE 4.   Single stretch receptors in the carotid sinus discharge at frequencies dependent upon the arterial pressure. When the arterial pressure is lower, the pressoreceptor impulse frequency diminishes, the vagus nerve impulses diminish and sympathetic cardiac nerve impulses increase (accelerating the heart) and the sympathetic vasoconstrictor fibers become more active and increase peripheral resistance. The net effect is to raise the blood pressure. If the arterial pressure rises above the normal set value, the impulse frequency increases on carotid sinus nerves, reducing the sympathetic discharge and increasing the vagal discharge. Slowing of heart rate and peripheral vasodilation restore the blood pressure to normal again.

completely replaced by elastic fibers and the adventitia is fairly dense. The sensory endings in the wall of the sinus have multiple branchings like a vine (Fig. 3). Impulses are set off at the very fine terminations, apparently by any type of distortion. The thinning of the media seen in the carotid sinus is believed to occur at other places where such distortion receptors lie, including sites along the common carotid arteries, the aortic arch and the brachiocephalic artery.[11] Although these nerve endings are sensitive to any form of distortion of the wall in which they lie, they serve as pressure-sensitive elements since they are located in elastic segments of walls supporting high and fluctuating internal pressure. To be effective in reg-

ulation the receptors should monitor "absolute" arterial pressure, but they can theoretically be influenced by changes in the distensibility of the walls resulting from smooth muscle contraction or stiffening of the walls with aging.

Bronk and Stella[7] recorded the action potentials in single afferent nerve fibers from stretch receptors located in isolated and perfused carotid sinus. Within the sensitivity range of a receptor, an increase in distending pressure was associated with an increase in the frequency at which the receptor discharged impulses. One receptor may increase its discharge rate from zero to maximum frequency when the pressure ranges from 30 to 200 mm. Hg, and others may function within different ranges of pressure. [8,9] The overlap of sensitivity between fiber groups assures responses from very low to very high pressures. If the isolated carotid sinus is distended with a steady pressure, the discharge frequency is also steady over a long period. In other words, the stretch receptors do not exhibit fatigue or adaptation. If the carotid sinus is distended by a fluctuating pressure, bursts of impulses occur during a rapid rise of pressure. Similar bursts of impulses appear during the abrupt increase in arterial pressure (Figs. 4 and 5). Thus, the discharge rate of the receptors is increased not only by the pressure in the artery but also by the rate of rise of pressure. The nerve fibers from the stretch receptor endings in the carotid sinus travel by way of the glossopharyngeal (IXth) nerve and those from the aortic arch pass by way of the vagus (Xth) nerve to the "cardiovascular regulatory centers" in the medulla (see Fig. 6, Chap. 4).

Pressoreceptor Reflexes. An increase in arterial pressure increases the rate of discharge from the stretch receptors. These impulses impinge upon the medullary centers to slow the heart by stimulating the motor nucleus of the vagus and inhibiting the "cardio-accelerator center," which acts through the cardiac sympathetic nerves. The increased sympathetic discharge also enhances atrial and ventricular contractility. At the same time, the medullary "vasoconstrictor center" is inhibited, so that the total peripheral resistance is reduced. Of all the potential mechanisms for changing peripheral resistance (see Fig. 7, Chap. 4), the excitation or inhibition of the sympathetic vasoconstrictor outflow is the only one which has a demonstrated role in the control of arterial pressure.

STRETCH RECEPTORS IN THE ATRIA AND CAROTID ARTERY

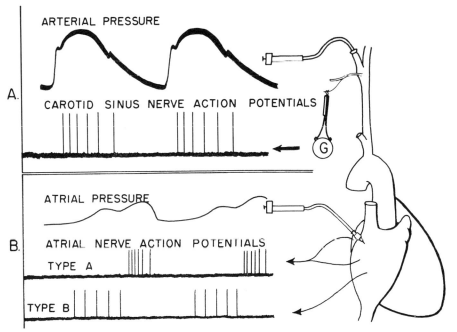

FIGURE 5. *A*, Individual stretch receptors in the carotid sinus discharge impulses at a frequency dependent primarily upon the arterial pressure (after Bronk and Stella[7]).

B, Stretch receptors from the atria have been divided into two groups: type A, which discharge during atrial systole, and type B, which discharge during atrial diastole (after Paintal, *J. Physiol.*, 121: 341–359, 1953).

Although the distortion receptors actually respond to stretch, the words "pressoreceptor" and "baroreceptor" are usually used to describe the reflexes induced by activation of these fibers. To avoid confusion, these terms will be employed in the following discussion with the reservation that they may eventually prove to be somewhat misleading.

Theoretically, the cardiovascular system can respond to an elevation in blood pressure with a reduction in heart rate, a reduction in stroke volume or a reduction in total peripheral resistance. In general, the vasomotor effects have been assigned the predominant role, and the protection of the arterial pressure level during hemorrhage has also been ascribed primarily to increased peripheral resistance. The growing tendency, however, is to recognize the importance of both cardiac output and peripheral resistance in such reactions. For example, Carlsten *et al.*[12] reported that direct stimulation of the carotid sinus nerve in man produced reflex bradycardia, peripheral dilation in the forearm and reduced pulse pressure— ascribed to reduced stroke volume. On the other hand, no baroreceptor effect on the pulmonary vascular system could be demonstrated.[13] This finding is consistent with the impression that the pulmonary vasculature is highly nonreactive to neural or humoral control mechanisms and does not participate in general systemic vascular responses (see Chap. 4).

The pressoreceptor mechanism illustrated in Figures 1, 3, 4 and 5, acting alone, would appear to provide a simple and straightforward explanation for the maintenance of systemic arterial blood pressure within a very narrow range. Actually, the arterial pressoreceptors constitute only one of many different sources of potent influences on cardiovascular responses. Thus, the regulation of systemic arterial pressure must involve the net result of many interacting mechanisms.

Chemoreceptors. The carotid body, lying near the carotid bifurcation, is a reddish glomus structure which is profusely supplied with nerves and has one of the most active blood supplies in the body (equivalent to 2000 cc. per 100 gm. of carotid body tissue). The carotid bodies are stimulated by reduced oxygen, increased carbon dioxide and lowered pH in the arterial blood perfusing them. Conditions which stimulate the chemoreceptors lead to elevated systemic arterial pressure. These chemoreceptors are strongly stimulated by experimental occlusion of the carotid sinus, a fact which complicates studies of pressoreceptor mechanisms. Other chemoreceptors of similar nature are found near the aortic arch. Since the oxygen content and pH of arterial blood are diminished and its carbon dioxide content is increased only when the cardiovascular-pulmonary system is overtaxed or incompetent, such chemoreceptors probably have no function during normal conditions of rest. It may also be that they become involved in responses to activity only under extreme conditions.

Stretch Receptors at Various Sites

In various experiments the results have suggested the presence of stretch receptors at many sites in the cardiovascular system including the descending thoracic aorta, abdominal vessels, cerebral vessels, lungs, atria and even the ventricular walls.[6, 14] Most of these receptors have not been implicated in the control of blood pressure. Thus, bradycardia reportedly follows distention of the left ventricular wall.[15] Rapid infusion of fluids into the systemic veins was once widely believed to be a mechanism for inducing tachycardia in association with increased venous return (Bainbridge reflex). Receptors suitable for such a response have not been found, and the original observations have not been consistently confirmed. In fact, acceleration, deceleration or no change in heart rate has recently been reported to result from intravenous infusions into isolated hearts, denervated hearts or hearts in intact animals.[16] In contrast, profound bradycardia and fainting responses, resembling the reactions induced by pressure applied to the carotid sinus in persons with hypersensitive carotid receptors, can be produced by mechanical stimulation of peripheral arteries and veins. Stretch receptors in the left atrium have been postulated as contributors to the control of blood volume (see Chap. 16). Paintal[17] has described the discharges from vagal afferent nerve fibers which fired during atrial contraction (A fibers) or during atrial filling (B fibers), as illustrated in Figure 5. A role for these impulses in hemodynamic regulation has not been demonstrated.

The complexity of the neural reflex mechanisms which may significantly affect the systemic arterial pressure under different conditions is illustrated in Figure 6. Included are the fibers from pressoreceptors and chemoreceptors, atrial afferent fibers and visceral afferents from the various organs within the abdomen and from the blood vessels throughout the body. Virtually all of these reflex actions induce lowered blood pressure and slow the heart rate. In contrast, application of cold or painful stimuli to the skin produce elevated blood pressure and tachycardia. Pathways from the higher centers of the nervous system also produce powerful vascular adaptations, associated with rage, embarrassment, fainting, etc. Practically all of these pathways descend through the medulla and reach the vascular system and the heart by way of the

NEURAL MECHANISMS FOR PERIPHERAL VASCULAR CONTROL

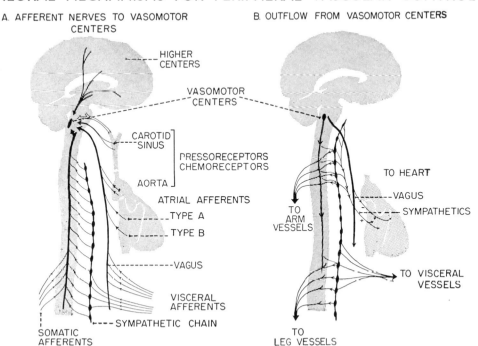

FIGURE 6. *A*, The vasomotor centers in the medulla receive afferent impulses originating from many different areas in the body, including the higher centers of the nervous system, pressoreceptors from the heart and great vessels, afferent nerves from the viscera and somatic pain afferents.

B, Impulses discharged from the vasomotor centers descend the spinal cord and influence cell bodies in the intermediolateral cell column which in turn initiate sympathetic nerve impulses conducted to the blood vessels in all parts of the body.

sympathetic outflow (Fig. 6B) plus the vagal distribution to the heart.

SUMMARY

A large number of factors and mechanisms *influence* the systemic arterial blood pressure. All the factors which affect cardiac function in terms of the heart rate, stroke volume and rate of ejection also affect the pulse pressure and, to some extent, the mean pressure. In general, the peak amplitude of the rise in systolic pressure is a manifestation of the rate and amount of systolic ejection by the left ventricle. In addition, the systemic arterial pressure is influenced by the peripheral resistance produced by all the neural, hormonal and chemical mechanisms discussed in Chapter 4. Finally, the wide variety of visceral and somatic afferent impulses converging on the medulla may significantly alter the level of the blood pressure.

Although all of these mechanisms are potentially capable of changing the blood pressure, none of them could be regarded as regulating it. Regulation of the blood pressure must involve a sensing mechanism (arterial pressoreceptors), an integrating mechanism (medullary or higher centers) and an effector mechanism (autonomic outflow), so that a deviation in arterial pressure is automatically compensated. So far as we know, only the pressoreceptor reflexes qualify as a regulatory mechanism. Such a mechanism is inherently static, tending to cause a return to a particular level. Other factors (e.g., pain, cold, emotion) tend to produce a deviation of the blood pressure and are not known to have the sensing mechanisms required for stabilization. Whenever any of these factors causes a significant change in systemic arterial pressure, that factor must have been able to override, suppress or modify the pressoreceptor mechanism. The many mechanisms which can produce a deviation of the systemic arterial pressure from its baseline condition are unquestionably responsible for the great variation in blood pressure noted when it is repeatedly measured in one person. On the other hand, the potency of the pressoreceptor mechanism is displayed in the fact that, among most normal individuals, the blood pressure remains within a fairly circumscribed range with a fairly constant mean value. The causes of sustained increased systemic arterial pressure should be considered from this point of view.

II. The Causes of High Blood Pressure

The cardiovascular system is equipped with a simple pressure regulating mechanism of the sort illustrated in Figure 1. Theoretically, such a system should ensure prompt compensation for any change in blood pressure. Such extreme stability of the systemic arterial pressure is achieved consistently in animals and men under surgical anesthesia. Under these conditions, the systemic arterial pressure remains remarkably constant over extended periods of time unless the level of anesthesia changes or external influences are introduced. The same situation is achieved in decerebrate animals, indicating that an important source of fluctuation in systemic arterial pressure stems from overriding or "resetting" of the regulating system by higher levels of the nervous system.

In normal human subjects, systemic arterial pressure diminishes more than 20 mm. Hg during sleep, reaching a minimum at 3:00 or 4:00 A.M.[18] The "basal" blood pressure has been defined as the arterial pressure present when all physical, emotional and metabolic activities are reduced to a physiologic minimum.

This state is rarely achieved, so the "basal" blood pressure has been approximated with measurements made before the subject arises from a good night's sleep. This, too, is difficult to accomplish routinely, so many investigators collect their data on patients who have reclined quietly in a comfortable, soothing environment for at least 30 minutes, ten to twelve hours after the previous meal. Even under these conditions a single determination of systemic arterial pressure is almost meaningless because of fluctuations, so that average values from repeated measurements must be used. The emotional reaction to the act of recording the blood pressure can be alleviated by measuring blood pressure repeatedly for half an hour.[19] The difficulties involved in obtaining reproducible "basal" blood pressure values have been stressed to indicate how much caution must be used in interpreting the "casual" blood pressure recorded routinely in a physician's examining room or in a hospital.

VARIABILITY IN SYSTEMIC ARTERIAL PRESSURE

In addition to emotions, expressed or repressed, a great many factors affect the systemic arterial pressure. A complete list is beyond the scope of this book, so a few examples will have to suffice.

1. Technical Errors. The values obtained by sphygmomanometry may be in error for a number of reasons including the width of the cuff, the method of applying it, the position of the arm in relation to heart level, the rate of pressure release, and the subjective nature of the end points (see Fig. 5, Chap. 5).

2. Posture. Assumption of the erect posture usually produces a transient reduction in systolic pressure and a more sustained increase in diastolic pressure, with a reduction in pulse pressure (see Chap. 7).

3. Exercise. Physical exertion generally induces an increase in both systolic and pulse pressures. These increases may persist for varying periods after the termination of the exertion (see also Chap. 8).

4. Eating. Ingestion of a large meal is usually followed by a significant increase in systolic pressure.

5. Diurnal Variation. From early morning until dinner time, the blood pressure tends to rise progressively by about 15 to 20 mm. Hg.

6. Temperature. In warm weather the blood pressure tends to diminish somewhat.

7. Race. Chinese, Filipinos, Puerto Ricans, East Africans, Indians, Arabs and aboriginal Australians seem to have lower blood pressure than do North American or Western European peoples.

8. Weight. The blood pressure tends to increase with greater body weight. The incidence of patients with "high" blood pressure is greater among groups that are overweight.

9. Sex. The blood pressure is lower among women under 40 years of age and higher in women over 50 years of age than in men in the corresponding age groups.

10. Age. Both systolic and diastolic arterial pressures increase with age, so that different standards must be established for the various age groups (see Fig. 7).

Additional discussion of these factors appears in the excellent texts by Master et al.,[18] Smirk,[19] Pickering[20] and Page and Corcoran.[21]

HOW HIGH IS HIGH?

The "normal" arterial blood pressure is commonly said to be 120/80 mm. Hg. This statement is clearly meaningless from a practical point of view if one considers all the causes of variability listed above and described in the first part of this chapter (see also Chap. 4). The commonly accepted upper limit for normal blood pressure, 140/90 mm. Hg., has been established largely by life insurance companies during the past four decades.

RANGE OF NORMAL ARTERIAL PRESSURE

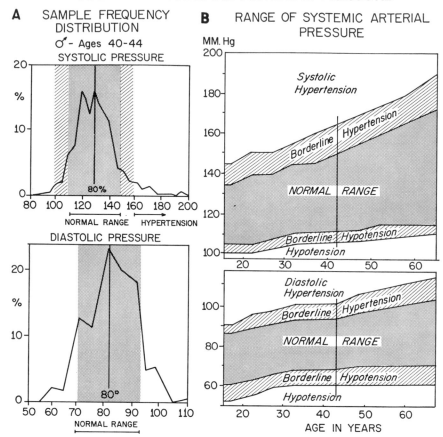

FIGURE 7. *A,* In males age 40 to 44, the normal arterial blood pressure is generally described in terms of range of values which will include a major portion of normal subjects (80 per cent in this graph). The "normal systolic pressure range" extends from 110 to 150 mm. Hg. Abnormal blood pressure is defined as extending above and below some borderline range.

B, Assembling the frequency distributions for various age groups demonstrates a distinct tendency for broadening of the normal systolic and diastolic pressure ranges and a tendency for higher pressures in older people. This fact must be considered in defining "high blood pressure" or hypertension.

Actually, single values for the upper limits of systolic and diastolic pressure are unacceptable because they fail to take into account the sources of variability.

The problem of physiologic variability is most effectively approached by statistical methods, based on frequency distribution. Master and his colleagues[18] proposed new and broader limits for the range of normal blood pressure after studying 15,706 persons in 11 industrial plants. A frequency distribution curve of diastolic and systolic pressures was established for each five-year group of men

and women. A sample frequency distribution for men 40 to 44 years old is shown in Figure 7A. The mean value for systolic pressure was 130 mm. Hg. The normal range was arbitrarily set to include 40 per cent of the subjects above and 40 per cent of the subjects below the mean. By definition, 80 per cent of the population was considered "normal." The borderline range included the next 7.5 per cent of all observations, and the remaining values (2.5 per cent) above the borderline were regarded as "abnormally high blood pressure." Note that this partitioning arbitrarily defines "high blood pressure" as the values found in the top 2.5 per cent of each group in Figure 7. The ranges of "normal," "borderline" and "abnormal" for men are presented in Figure 7; the ranges for women are quite similar.

The progressive rise in mean values and borderline ranges in the older age groups is interpreted as a tendency for blood pressure to increase with age. However, some individuals may have little or no increase in systemic arterial pressure with advancing age and others may develop high pressures more rapidly than indicated by these figures. Pickering[20] directed attention to the fact that the individuals with high blood pressure represent only the upper end of the frequency distribution curves and not a separate group or population. He presented evidence of a hereditary tendency towards elevation of systemic arterial pressure. On this basis, the blood pressure could be regarded as a graded characteristic, like height, so that individuals with "high blood pressure" cannot be consistently distinguished from persons in the "normal range." According to Pickering, an effort to draw an arbitrary line between "normal" and "high" blood pressure is futile; the distinction has importance primarily because life expectancy is depressed in relation to the elevation of systemic arterial pressure.

Since the mean systemic arterial pressure increases with age in a sample population, the number of people with blood pressures over some arbitrary level (e.g., 140/90 mm. Hg) is very great indeed. In many persons the blood pressure fluctuates more widely and tends to rise more rapidly than in the general population. In a small percentage of these people, elevation of blood pressure is obviously or suggestively associated with a recognizable disease state. However, in a vast majority of them the development of

"hypertension" cannot be explained at present. In this last large category the elevated blood pressure is called "primary" or "essential" hypertension, signifying that it seems to arise without a distinctive or recognizable cause.

HYPERTENSION ASSOCIATED WITH SPECIFIC DISEASE PROCESSES

Elevated systemic arterial pressure is not a disease state; it is one sign (among many) which is common to a variety of physiologic and pathologic conditions. From the vast pool of individuals displaying this sign, a few patients may be identified in whom the elevated arterial pressure is the direct result of a specific cause and can be alleviated by removal of that cause (Fig. 8). A rare form of tumor consisting of chromaffin cells like those in the adrenal medulla (pheochromocytoma) provides an exceptionally good example.

Adrenal Gland Dysfunction

Pheochromocytoma. Chromaffin cells in the adrenal medulla and elsewhere in the body normally secrete norepinephrine and *l*-epinephrine. When chromaffin cells multiply to produce a tumor or adenoma, these catechol amines are released periodically into the circulating blood to produce bouts of severe symptoms consisting of mounting hypertension, palpitation, headaches, anxiety and tremor, nausea, vomiting, blanching and coldness of the skin— in short, the signs and symptoms of a massive release of sympathetic transmitter substances. The blood pressure is elevated intermittently and tends to return toward normal in the intervals between attacks. These attacks may last for minutes or days and induce severe exhaustion. In some patients the blood pressure fluctuates widely but remains persistently elevated. The signs, symptoms, duration, course, diagnostic tests and treatment are discussed in detail elsewhere[19-21] and will not be considered here. Suffice to say that complete removal of the chromaffin tumor abolishes the symptomatic attacks. In some patients in whom the attacks have been eliminated by surgery, the systemic arterial pressure remains elevated for reasons which are not at all clear. The persistence of elevated blood pressure after elimination of its cause leads to the concept that hypertension begets hypertension (see below).

Adrenal Cortical Tumors. Changes in the blood pressure are consistently observed in patients with diseases affecting the adrenal cortex. For example, hypertension occurs in about 85 per cent of patients with Cushing's syndrome—an adrenogenital syndrome resulting from excessive excretion of adrenocortical hormones and consisting of sexual precocity, hermaphroditism, virilism of females or feminization in males, and obesity. The elevated blood pressure is the most important cardiovascular manifestation of the disease. The incidence of hypertension is also high in patients with cortical adenomata but without the other signs of Cushing's syndrome.[19] At present it is impossible to identify the abnormality in cortical steroid metabolism which is responsible for the hypertension. Administration of desoxycorticosterone acetate (DOCA) produces hypertension in rats; the hypertensive effect of this hormone is accentuated by the administration of salt.[22] The same results can be achieved in human subjects. As might be expected, diminished function of the adrenal cortex (Addison's disease) is characterized by diminished systemic arterial pressure.

The potentiating effect of sodium chloride administered along with adrenal cortical hormones suggests a role for aldosterone in the induction of hypertension. Aldosterone, one of the steroid hormones normally excreted by the adrenal cortex, acts on the kidney tubules to induce retention of sodium and accelerated excretion of potassium. A few

patients with primary aldosteronism resulting from tumors of the adrenal cortex have been described, and in most of them the systemic arterial pressure was above normal levels. Some investigators[23] express the view that the patterns of salt exchange in human hypertension parallel the patterns demonstrated in hypertension experimentally induced by adrenal cortical hormones and by restricted renal blood flow. Reduction in the blood pressure of patients with hypertension of various types has been accomplished in many laboratories and clinics by stringent restriction of salt consumption.

The precise mechanism by which salt excess might be linked to the development of systolic hypertension remains obscure. No single hypothesis satisfactorily explains the many conflicting observations. For example, in rats fed very large quantities of sodium chloride there is an elevation of blood pressure which correlates well with the percentage of sodium chloride in the diet.[24] Furthermore, the pathologic changes seen in rats with severe salt-induced high blood pressure resembled those observed in human patients with malignant hypertension, and the life expectancy of the animals was materially reduced. However, administration of potassium chloride along with the excess sodium chloride ameliorated the hypertension and pathologic changes, extending the life expectancy. Whereas most patients with excessive production of aldosterone exhibit elevated systemic arterial pressure, those who experience intermittent aldosteronism associated with periodic paralysis are no more susceptible to hypertension than the population at large. To confound the problem even more, hypertension can also be induced by administration of the cortical hormones which influence metabolism of glucose rather than salt, and this effect may actually be enhanced if the salt intake is reduced. Skelton[25] demonstratcd that hypcrtension can be induccd in the presence of hypofunction of the adrenal gland. For example, if one adrenal gland is excised and the medulla and most of the cortex is removed from the other, hypertension is more readily induced during the regeneration of the cortical tissue than when the regenerating gland is removed.

The kidney obviously plays an important role in the action of mineralocorticoids and in the retention or elimination of electrolytes. Thus, it is not possible to dissociate the adrenal cortical effects from kidney function. Furthermore, administration of excessive amounts of such cortical hormones leads to widespread lesions in arterial walls within the kidney (nephrosclerosis) and pathologic degeneration of renal substance. Such changes are also prominent in Cushing's disease. Attention has therefore been directed to participation of thc kidneys in provoking elevated systemic arterial pressure.

Kidney Diseases

More than 100 years ago Richard Bright recognized a relation between protein in the urine and pathologic changes in the kidney with hypertrophy of the left ventricle attributable to changes in the "quality" or composition of the blood which lead to constriction of the small vessels. This remains a fair description of increased peripheral resistance associated with altered kidney function.

The systemic arterial pressure is elevated during a wide variety of kidney diseases—in fact nearly all. A few of these disorders are indicated in Figure 8.

Interference with the arterial blood supply to the kidney or external compression of the renal parenchyma may be associated with elevated systemic arterial pressure. For example, the systemic arterial pressure may increase in patients with unilateral obstruction of the renal artery

ESSENTIAL HYPERTENSION

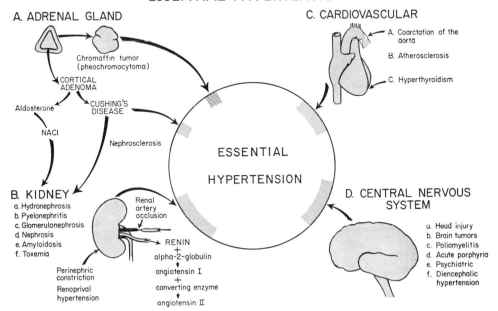

FIGURE 8. Elevation of the systemic arterial pressure is a common feature in many different disease processes involving the adrenal glands, kidneys, brain and cardiovascular system (see text). Of the very large population with elevated systemic arterial pressure, only a small proportion have these specific disease processes. The very large remainder are defined as having "essential hypertension" which means that its cause is undetermined.

or its branches. Such lesions are commonly caused by encroachment upon the arterial lumen by local mural thickening (atherosclerosis) or by local constriction of the vessel. In a majority of such patients, successful elimination of the obstruction or excision of the affected kidney is curative. Such recovery provides strong evidence that the kidney itself is involved in the production of this form of hypertension. The number of patients with these disorders is relatively small, but they represent the counterpart in man of the experimental hypertension which Goldblatt produced years ago by graded constriction of the renal arteries of animals. It is now generally agreed that any mechanism which interferes with the blood supply to the renal parenchyma may be expected to cause elevation of systemic arterial pressure. Impairment of the renal circulation leads to the release of an enzyme, renin, into the plasma.[26] There it acts upon a specific alpha-2-globulin to release angiotensin I, which consists of ten amino acids. As mentioned in Chapter 4, this substance itself is not active as a vasoconstrictor, but an enzyme in the plasma converts it to vasoconstrictive angiotensin II by splitting off two of the amino acids.

The renal pressor mechanism is believed to be activated by many different forms of kidney disease, most of which can be presumed to disturb renal blood flow by one means or another. Included among these disorders are hydronephrosis, pyelonephritis, glomerulonephritis, nephrosis, amyloidosis and toxemia of pregnancy. For example, obstruction of the ureter (e.g., by kidney stones) leads to expansion of the pelvis and compression of the kidney parenchyma. Pyelonephritis is stated to produce obliteration and destruction of the medium-sized renal arteries; atherosclerotic occlusion of the renal arteries may or may not be complicated by pyelonephritis. Glomerulonephritis, an inflammatory re-

action in the kidney usually following streptococcal infections, causes obstruction of glomerular capillaries.

By a different mechanism, excision of both kidneys leads to a severe increase in systemic blood pressure. This increase is best demonstrated when the survival of experimental animals is being supported by means of artificial kidneys. This form of hypertension ("renoprival" hypertension) is distinctly different from that produced by the renin mechanism and is probably more closely related to the electrolyte metabolism normally involving both the kidneys and the adrenal cortical hormones. Such hypertension may be encountered in terminal states of renal disease.

Finally, pathologic changes in blood vessel walls are reported to occur when the blood pressure is elevated from any cause. The walls of the blood vessels and particularly the arterioles in many different tissues may thicken, but the thickening tends to be concentrated in the renal vessels. There is considerable evidence that experimental hypertension is sufficient to induce hyalinization and hypertrophy of the vascular smooth muscle and degeneration of the intima in renal vessels.[27] Once established, these lesions impede renal blood flow and the renin-angiotensin mechanism may sustain hypertension even after the primary cause has been eliminated (see below).

Cardiovascular Hypertension

Systemic arterial pressure may rise as a result of changes within the cardiovascular system itself. The cardiovascular disorders causing elevated blood pressure are exemplified by coarctation of the aorta, generalized atherosclerosis of the systemic arteries and periarteritis nodosum (Fig. 8).

Near the site of the ductus arteriosus a constriction of the thoracic aorta occasionally occurs as a developmental defect. This local constriction reduces the lumen of the aorta to a very small channel and greatly impedes the flow of blood from the arch to the descending thoracic aorta. Collateral channels develop around this obstruction, but blood pressure is usually far above normal in the systemic arteries arising above the constriction. In the past, this hypertension in the upper part of the body was attributed to interference with the blood supply to the kidneys, as indicated in the preceding section. However, an occasional patient develops such an obstruction below the renal arteries and still displays hypertension.[19] Moreover, the diastolic pressure in the lower extremities may be higher than normal.[21] Surgical correction of the aortic constriction is followed by a prompt fall of blood pressure, which returns to normal over a few days.

Generalized Atherosclerosis. Atherosclerosis spread throughout the arterial tree has the effects suggested by the common lay term, *hardening of the arteries*. The arterial walls become somewhat stiff and less distensible. For this reason, the systolic pressure tends to increase decidedly. If the condition is uncomplicated, the diastolic pressure is normal, indicating that peripheral resistance is not affected. Since virtually all other causes of hypertension produce primarily increased peripheral resistance, inclusion of the systolic hypertension of atherosclerosis in discussions of elevated blood pressure often leads to unnecessary semantic difficulties. The same is true of some types of hypertension resulting from increased cardiac output without an increase in total peripheral resistance, including the hypertension accompanying hyperthyroidism and certain forms of neurogenic hypertension.

Diseases of the Central Nervous System

Elevated blood pressure is associated with diverse pathologic and functional disturbances of the central nervous system such as head injury, brain tumors, selective destruction of brain tissue as in rare cases of poliomyelitis, acute porphyria, psychiatric disturbances, cardiovascular hyperreaction and disturbances of the pressoreceptor mechanism (Fig. 8). This list by itself indicates that hypertension can result from damage to selected portion of the central nervous system or from overactivity of other regions. To illustrate these conditions, a few will be described briefly.

Increased Intracranial Pressure. Head injuries or strategically placed brain tumors may lead to a rise in the pressure of the cerebrospinal fluid surrounding the central nervous system. Under these conditions, the systemic arterial pressure tends to increase as the cerebrospinal fluid pressure rises. This consequence is commonly attributed to compression of the brain stem in the medullary regions which contain centers of cardiovascular regulation.[19]

Destructive Lesions. Some patients with acute poliomyelitis involving the brain stem (bulbar paralysis) develop severe hypertension; the lesions lie in the medial portion of the medullary reticular substance. In general, the hypertension is transient.

Occasionally severe mental disturbances are combined with neural lesions resulting from peripheral neuritis and ascending myelitis. Examination of the urine discloses excessive excretion of porphyrin as a result of abnormal pigment metabolism. Such patients are prone to display disturbances of autonomic function (vomiting, constipation, cramping abdominal pain) as well as hypertension with tachycardia. The hypertension appears and subsides in relation to the psychoneurotic behavior.

Psychiatric Disturbances. Widespread recognition of the fact that excitement and other psychologic factors may greatly influence the level of systemic arterial pressure has led many investigators to examine the incidence of hypertension among patients with neuroses or psychoses. The results are not clear-cut because conflicting evidence has been obtained by different approaches. However, the consensus of current opinion is a conservative or doubtful attitude toward this mechanism as a dominant cause of chronic hypertension. Pickering[20] concluded, "there is nothing inherently improbable in the idea. At the same time there is nothing conclusive about the evidence."

Diencephalic Syndrome. A labile form of hypertension associated with blotchy flushing of the face and upper chest, cold pale extremities, tachycardia and hyperperistalsis may be induced by embarrassment and excitement in young and middle-aged women. This group of symptoms and signs has been termed the "diencephalic syndrome" because it can be brought on by diffuse stimulation of the human diencephalon.

Patients with hypertension related to disturbances of the nervous system frequently display tachycardia and increased cardiac output. In patients with diseases of the adrenal glands, kidneys or cardiovascular system, on the other hand, the hypertension is generally the result of increased peripheral resistance with little or no increase in heart rate or cardiac output. This distinction should be kept in mind when attempting to assign a cause to hypertension of unknown origin.

Surprisingly enough, the wide variety of causes of elevated systemic arterial pressure discussed above are responsible for a very small proportion of the cases of abnormally high blood pressure. The remainder represents patients with "primary" or "essential" hypertension (Fig. 8).

ESSENTIAL HYPERTENSION

According to Page and Corcoran,[21] the causes of sustained hypertension can be identified in only about 5 to 10 per cent of such patients; the remaining 90 to 95 per cent are generally classified as having "essential" or "primary" hypertension (see Fig. 8). A more realistic term would be "hypertension of undetermined origin." During excision of the sympathetic chain in an effort to alleviate hypertension, direct inspection of the adrenal glands and kidneys is possible to supplement the results of routine function tests. Smithwick[28] operated upon about 2800 patients with hypertension; of them only 1.8 per cent were found to have renal or adrenal disease. Although unilateral renal disease may have been overlooked in some patients, the total incidence was not believed to be more than 2 or 3 per cent.

The Nature of Essential Hypertension

Essential hypertension is a term applied to high blood pressure which cannot be attributed to a specific lesion. Since blood pressure rises progressively with age faster in some individuals than in others— the patients with essential hypertension are those at the high end of the frequency distribution curves for each age. Inheritance, environment and sex may affect the rate at which the blood pressure rises. In general, the higher the blood pressure, the shorter the life expectancy. Headache and vertigo are common complaints of such patients and cerebral vascular accidents (strokes) are frequent complications. The elevated systemic arterial pressure leads to left ventricular hypertrophy. Since vascular disease may interfere with coronary blood supply, congestive heart failure occurs frequently in later stages.

In most patients with benign hypertension, the blood pressure fluctuates more widely than normal, but rises progressively and slowly over many years. In a small percentage of such patients, the hypertension becomes "malignant" or rapidly progressing. Characteristic vascular changes in the retina of the eye (hypertensive neuroretinopathy)appear early in this phase of the disease, and kidney function often becomes rapidly impaired. Patients with malignant hypertension have a very limited life expectancy, usually succumbing within a few months but occasionally surviving one or two years. Left ventricular failure or cerebral vascular accidents may cause death before renal failure becomes fully developed.

Causes of Essential Hypertension

The problem of establishing the cause of "essential" hypertension is comparable to attempting to determine the origin of fever in a group of patients after all known causes have been specifically eliminated. A great deal of effort has been expended in attempts to determine which of the mechanisms illustrated in Figure 8 might be responsible for such hypertension. The search for renal hypertension without renal disease, adrenal hypertension without adrenal dysfunction, vasomotor hypertension without central nervous system abnormality and cardiovascular hypertension without cardiovascular lesions has provided much controversy and semantic confusion but has shed little light on the subject at hand.

Exclusion of Standard Mechanisms. During the early stages of essential hypertension none of the hypertensive mechanisms illustrated in Figure 8 can be shown to be operative. Electrolyte metabolism and excretion are entirely within normal limits. Renal blood flow and function are normal, and the extent of atherosclerotic lesions is not greater than that among patients with normal blood pressure. The presence of neural lesions cannot be demonstrated.

Although there is considerable evidence that angiotensin may be involved in certain spontaneous and experimental hypertensive states, it seems doubtful that this mechanism is the common exciting cause of "essential" hypertension for several reasons.[20] During the early phases of moderate hypertension in younger persons, the kidneys appear to be entirely normal functionally and anatomically. Dogs with moderate hypertension from unilateral renal ischemia may have no evident renal vascular disease in the other kidney. Abnormal amounts of renin have not been found consistently in human patients with primary hypertension. Finally, patients with congestive heart failure may have easily demonstrable increases in the amount of renin in the plasma without having hypertension. Thus it is difficult to believe renin in *undetectable* concentrations in the plasma of hypertensive patients is the cause of their high blood pressure. One of the most confusing elements in the puzzle stems from evidence that hypertension is self-perpetuating.

Hypertension Begets Hypertension. Since patients with "essential" hypertension exhibit no identifiable cause of it, the therapy of it has been largely directed toward reduction of the blood pressure by various means. Without casting doubt on the wisdom or success of this approach, one should recognize that the implied basis of this therapy is that elevated systemic arterial pressure acts in some manner to produce even greater increases in this pressure. It is true that the elevation of the systemic pressure produced by several experimental procedures may persist after the exciting cause has been removed. One explanation of this phenomenon depends upon the pronounced tendency toward development of degenerative lesions in the walls of the renal blood vessels.[29] According to one view, this "nephrosclerosis" impedes blood flow through the renal parenchyma, exciting the renin mechanism so that the amount of circulating angiotensin II increases and produces generalized vasoconstriction. Theoretically, then, elevated systemic arterial pressure from any cause would become self-sustaining through the development of nephrosclerosis and the original cause might disappear, effectively confounding

CAROTID SINUS SENSITIVITY IN HYPERTENSIVE DOGS

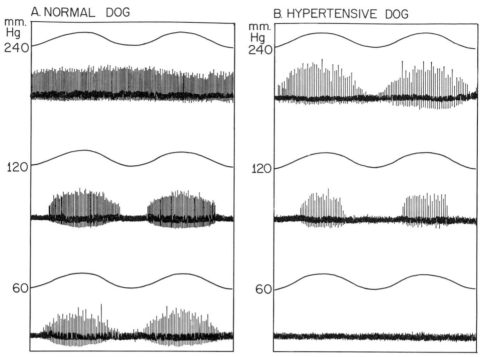

FIGURE 9.   The frequency of discharge of carotid sinus stretch receptors was recorded during induced pressure fluctuations at various mean pressure levels in normal control dogs and in dogs with chronic renal hypertension. The carotid sinus discharge frequency at the same pressure levels was much lower in the hypertensive dogs suggesting reduced sensitivity of the pressure monitoring system. (After McCubbin, Green and Page, *Circulat. Res.*, 4:205–210.)

investigators. Experimental hypertension induced by neural mechanisms (section of the carotid sinus nerves or chronic stimulation of sympathetic nerves) is not generally associated with renal lesions, nor is this type of hypertension self-perpetuating. Another mechanism for self-sustaining hypertension could be related to resetting of the pressoreceptor mechanism.

Resetting the Pressoreceptor Mechanism. Kubicek *et al.*[30] produced arterial hypertension which was sustained over several weeks (up to 38 days) by continuous electrical stimulation of the splanchnic nerves. Within 20 hours of sustained stimulation the systemic arterial pressure rose significantly; but the pulse rate was normal, indicating that the pressoreceptor mechanism was no longer attempting to compensate. As soon as the stimulation

was interrupted, the blood pressure began to fall toward the control level and the heart rate accelerated. In other words, the pressoreceptor mechanism had been reset to the new higher level and was acting to oppose the fall of pressure. This resetting could occur at the cardiovascular control centers in the central nervous system or at the peripheral receptors in the carotid sinus.

Interestingly enough, McCubbin *et al.*[31] demonstrated that the frequency at which carotid sinus stretch receptors discharged in response to a given pressure was clearly lower in chronically hypertensive dogs than in normal animals (Fig. 9). In other words, the peripheral pressoreceptors themselves apparently can adapt to a sustained increase in arterial pressure, with only a slight lag. The adapted pressoreceptor mechanism would act to sustain the pressure at the higher level to which it had been reset rather than to compensate toward "normal." Adaptation of the integrating centers in the nervous system might also occur. The concept of resetting of the pressoreceptor mechanism is not a wholly satisfactory explanation of the sustained elevation of systemic arterial pressure because the blood pressure does tend to return to normal levels over longer periods of time when the stimulus to neurogenic hypertension is removed. A more sustained depression of carotid sinus pressoreceptor activity would result from pathologic changes in the walls of the vessel that would restrict their distensibility.

Atherosclerosis of the Carotid Sinus. The carotid sinus region is a site of predilection for atherosclerosis.[32] This has been recognized since Burns first described the condition in 1811. Pathologic thickening and even calcification may occur here when other portions of the arterial tree are relatively unaffected. Such changes may begin at relatively early ages (as young as 19 years). If the wall of the carotid sinus is stiffened by this process, the amount of stretch in the wall for a particular pressure range would be reduced, curtailing the stretch on the distortion receptors in the wall. Under these conditions, the nerves might still be quite responsive to external compression and yet display greatly reduced discharge frequency from changes in internal pressure. Kezdi[33] emphasized that the distensibility of the carotid arterial wall may also be reduced by contraction of the smooth muscle. Although this mechanism seems attractive enough to warrant considerable interest, it has received relatively little attention.

Distribution of Blood Flow in Hypertensive Patients

In patients with essential hypertension, the pulse rate and cardiac output are normal, and the elevated arterial pressure results from increased total peripheral resistance. When the mean arterial pressure is significantly elevated, the distribution of blood flow through the various vascular beds must be decidedly abnormal unless all of them participate more or less equally in the vasoconstriction (Fig. 10). For example, if the mean arterial pressure were doubled by vasoconstriction confined to the splanchnic bed, the blood flow would be greatly restricted in the splanchnic region and would increase throughout all other vascular networks. The different vascular beds vary widely in their responsiveness to vasomotor influences, as indicated in Figures 7, 13 and 15 in Chapter 4. For example, the cerebral circulation is grossly unresponsive to all vasomotor influences except carbon dioxide. At the other extreme the skin vessels respond actively to a bewildering array of mechanisms. If we could determine the manner in which the cardiac output is partitioned among the various tissues in patients with hypertension and could reproduce this kind of flow distribution by some reasonable mechanism, a step might be taken toward elucidating the cause of hypertension.

Many measurements by different investigators, summarized by Pickering,[20] indicate that the blood flow through the brain, through the splanchnic bed and liver and through the skin is the same in hypertensive and in normal individuals. This signifies that vasoconstriction in these vascular beds increased the vascular resistance until it just balanced the increased perfusion pressure. The blood flow through the muscle was somewhat more than normal, indicating incompletely compensatory vasoconstriction. The blood flow through the kidneys was reduced, suggesting somewhat excessive constriction of renal vessels. Considering the wide range of responsiveness of the various vascular beds, this pattern of flow distribution is a most surprising result be-

FLOW DISTRIBUTION IN HYPERTENSIVE PATIENTS

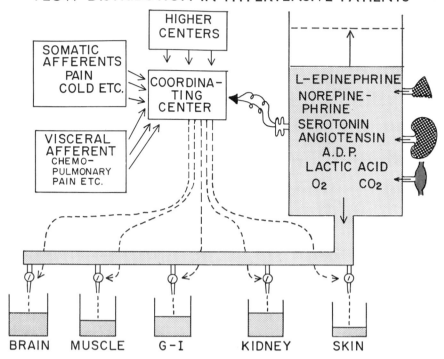

FIGURE 10. Patients with abnormally high blood pressure are reported to have normal blood flows through most tissues including the brain, splanchnic bed, liver and skin. The flow through the kidneys is somewhat diminished and through the skeletal muscle is somewhat enhanced. The maintenance of essentially normal flow distribution in the presence of elevated pressure head means that all of the vascular beds participate almost equally in the degree of vasoconstriction. This is a remarkable phenomenon considering the wide variety of influences on peripheral resistance illustrated above and the differences in responsiveness of the various vascular beds described in Chapter 4.

cause it is unlike that produced by any of the mechanisms indicated in Figure 11 of Chapter 4. For example, what mechanism would provide normal blood flow through the unresponsive cerebral vessels in the presence of a greatly increased perfusion pressure?

Pressure-Flow Relations and Autoregulation. During perfusion of the kidney at progressively higher pressure, flow increases as the pressure head increases until a level of about 80 mm. Hg is reached. The flow then remains relatively unchanged as the perfusion pressure is increased to as much as 200 mm. Hg. This observation signifies that the resistance of the renal vessels increases as the perfusion pressure rises. Among the concepts advanced to explain this controversial phe-

nomenon is the idea that the increased perfusion pressure leads to increased filtration, higher extravascular pressure and external compression of the vessels so that resistance increases and flow remains about the same.[34, 35] Such a mechanism would function best in vascular beds confined within connective tissue or bony compartments (e.g., brain, eye, bone, kidney). It would at least tend toward equalization of blood flow in various vascular beds in spite of changes in perfusion pressure, unaccompanied by direct vasomotor effects. Evidence in favor of autoregulation in vascular beds outside the kidney is sparse indeed. Another alternative is a generalized vasoconstriction of about equal extent in all vascular networks.

Generalized Vasoconstriction. Theoretically, the mean arterial blood pressure would be doubled if half of the vascular channels were completely closed or if the circumference of all the resistance vessels were reduced by only about 20 per cent. Generalized reduction in circumference is more effective than a decrease in the number of *channels* open because the pressure gradient and resistance to flow are related to the reciprocal of the radius to the fourth power $(1/r^4)$ in accordance with Poiseuille's law (see Fig. 6, Chap. 1). In blood vessels with appreciably thick walls, the reduction in external circumference would be even less and would most certainly be imperceptible without the most meticulous quantitative measurements. Several mechanisms might be involved in a generalized vasoconstriction sufficient to induce hypertension.

The administration of norepinephrine or nitroglycerin produces a greater response in hypertensive patients but its duration is the same as in normal subjects. This observation led Conway[36] to conclude that the increased reactivity might result from structural changes in the arterial wall. Furthermore, some of the increased resistance in hypertensives was not overcome by nitrite, indicating that the vessels could not dilate as greatly as could those in normal subjects. Gaskell[37] found that abnormally high vascular tone persisted in the vessels of the finger after digital nerve block in patients with persistent hypertension. This tone was attributed to an "abnormal force" exerted by the vascular smooth muscle not under the immediate control of the nervous system.

Hypertrophy in the medial layers of the arterial walls is a prominent feature in the resistance vessels of patients with hypertension. Such hypertrophy might result from repetitive or continuous exposure to elevated internal pressure or from intermittent increases in sympathetic constrictor nerve activity. Folkow *et al.*[38] postulated that thickening of the arterial walls would reduce the vascular lumen and also significantly increase the degree of vascular constriction induced by a specific degree of smooth muscle shortening. They demonstrated that the resistance through "maximally" distended forearm vessels was higher in hypertensive than in normal subjects. Furthermore, a 30 per cent shortening of the smooth muscle could theoretically increase the resistance as much as two times.

Vascular Swelling. Tobian and Binion[39] found an increased concentration of water and sodium in the renal artery and psoas muscle in humans with hypertension and in the aortic walls of hypertensive rats. Swelling of the arteriolar walls was regarded as a potential cause of increased peripheral resistance since a 13 per cent swelling of the arteriolar wall was computed to increase flow resistance by 54 per cent. A retention of salt and water might represent a change in the electrolyte metabolism in such patients, and low-salt diets might then alleviate hypertension by reducing the fluid content of the vascular walls. Edema of the vascular walls would be roughly equivalent to medial hypertrophy.

Unidentified Vasoconstrictor Substances. Finally, vasoconstrictor substances yet to be identified might be primarily responsible for the production of essential hypertension. Such substances should have more or less equal effects on such vascular beds as those in the brain and skin and the splanchnic bed, with a slightly more intense effect on renal vessels and a slightly less intense effect on vessels of the skeletal musculature (see Fig. 10).

SUMMARY

Elevated systemic arterial pressure is a clinical sign which is common to a wide variety of disease states. The many potential mechanisms for the production of sustained high blood pressure are generally grouped into four main classes: endocrine (primarily adrenal glands), renal, cardiovascular and neural. Several specific diseases in each category are characteristically associated with elevated systemic arterial pressure. All these causal mechanisms combined will account for only about 5 to 10 per cent of all patients with high arterial blood pressure. The remaining 90 to 95 per cent of these patients have "essential" hypertension or elevated arterial pressure of unknown origin. Among these patients, the blood pressure rises at different rates. In a small percentage, the blood pressure rises abruptly ("malignant hypertension"); death usually supervenes within a year from severe heart failure, advanced kidney disease or cerebral vascular accident.

The cause of essential and malignant hypertension is not known. Attempts to explain this condition in terms of recognized mechanisms which elevate the blood pressure have been unsuccessful. The distribution of blood flow in the presence of this hypertension is very nearly normal even though the total peripheral resistance is increased. This distribution means that the degree of increased resistance must be more or less equal in all major vascular beds. None of the vasomotor control mechanisms discussed in Chapter 4 produces such widespread, uniform constrictor responses. It thus seems reasonable to seek other mechanisms affecting the various vascular beds which might be responsible for a progressive increase in blood pressure.

First, the presence of elevated arterial blood pressure apparently tends to be self-perpetuating in that it tends to persist after the initiating cause is removed. This persistence may be due to the development of sclerotic vascular lesions in the renal vessels (nephrosclerosis) in the presence of systemic hypertension. Furthermore, the pressoreceptor mechanisms can be shown to be reset to higher levels when the blood pressure is elevated for even a few hours. Thus, the neural control mechanisms may actually tend to sustain a hypertension rather than to induce compensatory reactions to restore the pressure to the control levels. The carotid sinus area is exceptionally susceptible to the development of atherosclerosis. The stiffening of the walls would tend to reduce the sensitivity of the stretch receptors in them, and reflexly induce vasoconstriction in the peripheral vascular system.

Generalized vasoconstriction in the various vascular beds might result from structural changes in the resistance vessels. For example, the smooth muscle in the media apparently hypertrophies in these vessels. If this condition develops in response to repeated vasoconstrictor impulses or to repeated episodes of transient elevation of systemic arterial pressure, a sustained increase in peripheral resistance would occur. Also, the same degree of shortening of the smooth muscle would produce greater constriction of the vessels owing to the greater thickness of their walls. Edema of the vascular walls due to increased concentrations of sodium and water in them has been demonstrated in hypertensive patients. This edema would have the same functional effect as hypertrophy of the smooth muscles in the media. Finally, currently unidentified vasoconstrictor substances may be discovered and may turn out to be the primary cause of the progressive rise in systemic arterial pressure observed in this large group of patients.

REFERENCES

1. HAMILTON, W. F., and Dow, P. An experimental study of the standing waves in the pulse propagated through the aorta. *Amer. J. Physiol.*, 125:48–59, 1939.
2. ALEXANDER, R. S. The genesis of the aortic standing wave. *Circulat. Res.*, 1:145–151, 1953.
3. PETERSON, L. H., and GERST, P. H. Significance of reflected waves within the arterial system. *Fed. Proc.*, 15:144–145, 1956.

4. WARNER, H. R. A study of the mechanism of pressure wave distortion by arterial walls using an electrical analog. *Circulat. Res.*, 5: 79–84, 1957.

5. McDONALD, D. A., and TAYLOR, M. G. The hydrodynamics of the arterial circulation. *Prog. Biophys.*, 9:105–173, 1959.

6. HEYMANS, C., DELAUNOIS, A. L., and VAN DEN HEUVEL-HEYMANS, G. Tension and distensibility of carotid sinus wall, pressoceptors and blood pressure regulation. *Circulat. Res.*, 1:3–7, 1953.

7. BRONK, D. W., and STELLA, G. The response to steady pressures of single end organs in the isolated carotid sinus. *Amer. J. Physiol.*, 110: 708–714, 1935.

8. LANDGREN, S. On the excitation mechanism of the carotid baroceptors. *Acta physiol. scand.*, 26:1–34, 1952.

9. LANDGREN, S., NEIL, E., and ZOTTERMAN, Y. The response of the carotid baroceptors to the local administration of drugs. *Acta physiol. scand.*, 25:24–37, 1952.

10. LEUSEN, I., DEMEESTER, G., and BOUCKAERT, J. J. La regulation de la pression arterielle apres hemorragie. *Acta cardiol.*, 11:556–566, 1956.

11. HEYMANS, C., and NEIL, E. *Reflexogenic Areas of the Cardiovascular System*. Boston, Little, Brown & Co., 1958, 271 pp.

12. CARLSTEN, A., FLOKOW, B., GRIMBY, G., HEMBERGER, C. A., and THULESIUS, O. Cardiovascular effects of direct stimulation of the carotid sinus nerve in man. *Acta physiol. scand.*, 44:138–145, 1958.

13. DALY, I. DEB., and DALY, M. DEB. Observations on the changes in resistance of the pulmonary vascular bed in response to stimulation of the carotid sinus baroreceptors in the dog. *J. Physiol.*, 137:427–435, 1957.

14. AVIADO, D. M., JR., and SCHMIDT, C. F. Reflexes from stretch receptors in blood vessels, heart and lungs. *Physiol. Rev.*, 35:247–300, 1955.

15. AVIADO, D. M., JR., and SCHMIDT, C. F. Cardiovascular and respiratory reflexes from the left side of the heart. *Amer. J. Physiol.*, 196:726–730, 1959.

16. PATHAK, C. L. Alternative mechanism of cardiac acceleration in Bainbridge's infusion experiments. *Amer. J. Physiol.*, 197:441–444, 1959.

17. PAINTAL, A. S. The conduction velocities of respiratory and cardiovascular afferent fibres in the vagus nerve. *J. Physiol.*, 121:341–359, 1953.

18. MASTER, A. M., GARFIELD, C. L., and WALTERS, M. B. *Normal Blood Pressure and Hypertension*. Philadelphia, Lea & Febiger, 1952, 144 pp.

19. SMIRK, F. H. *High Arterial Pressure*. Oxford, Blackwell Scientific Publications, 1957, xxxvi, 764 pp.

20. PICKERING, G. W. *High Blood Pressure*. New York, Grune & Stratton, 1955, viii, 547 pp.

21. PAGE, I. H., and CORCORAN, A. C. *Arterial Hypertension: Its Diagnosis and Treatment*, 2nd ed. Chicago, The Year Book Publishers, 1949, 400 pp.

22. MILLS, L. C. Clinical observations on the general effects of steroids and the adrenal cortex on blood pressure and relationship to hypertension. Pp. 232–242 in *Hypertension: The First Hahnemann Symposium on Hypertensive Disease*, J. Moyer, ed. Philadelphia, W. B. Saunders Co., 1959.

23. GREEN, D. M., JOHNSON, A. D., BRIDGES, W. C., and LEHMANN, J. H. Stages of salt exchange in essential hypertension. *Circulation*, 9:416–424, 1954.

24. MENEELY, G. M. The effect of salt and other electrolytes in hypertension. Pp. 250–261 in *Hypertension: The First Hahnemann Symposium on Hypertensive Disease*, J. Moyer, ed. Philadelphia, W. B. Saunders Co., 1959.

25. SKELTON, F. R. A study of the natural history of adrenal-regeneration hypertension. *Circulat. Res.*, 7:107–117, 1959.

26. PAGE, I. H., BUMPUS, F. M., and SCHWARZ, H. J. Angiotensin. *Sci. Amer.*, 200:54–58, 1959.

27. MUIRHEAD, E. E., and STIRMAN, J. A. Structural alterations of systemic vessels in response to systemic hypertension. Pp. 109–121, *Pulmonary Circulation*, W. Adams and J. Veith, eds. New York, Grune & Stratton, 1959.

28. SMITHWICK, R. H. Surgery in the treatment of hypertension of adrenal and renal origin. Pp. 633–640 in *Hypertension: The First Hahnemann Symposium on Hypertensive Disease*, J. Moyer, ed. Philadelphia, W. B. Saunders Co., 1959.

29. MASSON, G. M. C., McCORMACK, L. J., DUSTAN, H. P., and CORCORAN, A. C. Hytensive vascular disease as a consequence of increased arterial pressure. *Amer. J. Path.*, 34:817–833, 1958.

30. KUBICEK, W. G., KOTTKE, F. J., LAKER, D. J., and VISSCHER, M. B. Adaptation in the pressor-receptor reflex mechanisms in experimental neurogenic hypertension. *Amer. J. Physiol.*, 175:380–382, 1953.

31. McCUBBIN, J. W., GREEN, J. H., and PAGE, I. H. Baroceptor function in chronic renal hypertension. *Circulat. Res.*, 4:205–210, 1956.

32. ADAMS, W. E. *The Comparative Morphology of the Carotid Body and Carotid Sinus*. Springfield, Ill., Charles C Thomas, 1958, 272 pp.

33. KEZDI, P. Control by the superior cervical ganglion of the state of contraction and pulsatile expansion of the carotid sinus arterial wall. *Circulat. Res.*, 2:367–371, 1954.

34. SHIPLEY, R. E., and STUDY, R. S. Changes in renal blood flow, extraction of inulin, glomerular filtration rate, tissue pressure and urine flow with acute alterations of renal artery blood pressure. *Amer. J. Physiol.*, 167: 676–688, 1951.

35. SCHER, A. M. The mechanism of autoregu-

lation of renal blood flow. *Nature (Lond.)*, 184:1322–1323, 1959.

36. CONWAY, J. Vascular reactivity in experimental hypertension measured after hexamethonium. *Circulation*, 17:807–810, 1958.

37. GASKELL, P., and DOISY, A. Persistence of abnormally high vascular tone in vessels of the fingers after digital nerve block in patients with chronic high blood pressure.

Circulat. Res., 7:1006–1010, 1959.

38. FOLKOW, B., GRIMBY, G., and THULESIUS, O. Adaptive structural changes of the vascular walls in hypertension and their relation to the control of the peripheral resistance. *Acta physiol. scand.*, 44:255–272, 1958.

39. TOBIAN, L., JR., and BINION, J. T. Tissue cations and water in arterial hypertension. *Circulation*, 5:754–758, 1952.

Chapter 7

EFFECTS OF POSTURE

I. Circulatory Response to Arising

The cardiovascular system is generally studied in supine subjects or animals. Circulatory dynamics are most stable while the individual is lying down because many of the arteries and veins are horizontally oriented at or near heart level. When one stands upright, many of the arteries and veins are oriented vertically and large hydrostatic pressures are produced by the long, uninterrupted columns of blood. The arterial, capillary and venous pressures are markedly elevated in the dependent extremities and the circulatory system must promptly make appropriate compensatory adaptation.[1-4] If these compensatory mechanisms are insufficient or retarded, orthostatic hypotension results. Fainting reactions are

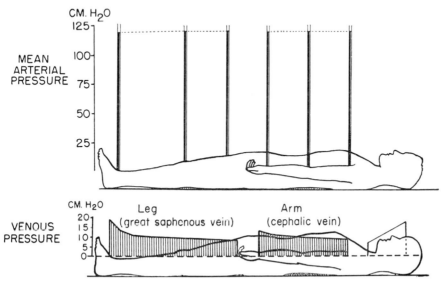

MEAN ARTERIAL AND VENOUS PRESSURES IN
RECLINING SUBJECTS

FIGURE 1. *A*, The mean arterial pressure diminishes but slightly from the arch of the aorta to the arterial branches, e.g., the radial. This pressure gradient is responsible for the flow of blood through the system.

B, The peripheral venous pressure also has a very gradual diminution in pressure from the periphery toward the heart. In the smaller venous branches the pressure gradient is considerably steeper. (After Ochsner *et al.*[5])

171

frequently produced in erect subjects by stimuli that would have virtually no effect on the supine individual. Recognition that much of man's effective existence is spent in the erect position makes it appropriate to consider the cardiovascular adjustments required in this position.

VASCULAR PRESSURES IN RECLINING SUBJECTS

When the long axis of the body is horizontal, the long columns of blood are at or near heart level. The mean pressure throughout the entire systemic arterial tree is fairly uniform except for the slight pressure gradients incident to the frictional energy loss during flow through these tubes (Fig. 1). The mean arterial pressure diminishes only a few millimeters of mercury during flow of the blood from the aorta to arterial branches the size of the radial artery at the wrist. In the same way, the venous pressure declines only slightly between the smallest venous branches in the extremities and the large central venous channels. The pressure in peripheral veins of various calibers was measured at various points over the body surface by Ochsner et al.[5]; their data are schematically illustrated in Figure 1B. Note that the pressure in the smallest peripheral veins averaged about 17 mm. Hg in the lower extremity, and that capillary pressure must exceed the pressures in the corresponding veins.

PRESSURES PRODUCED BY HYDROSTATIC COLUMNS

The pressure in a rigid tube containing a continuous column of stationary fluid is determined by the vertical distance from the point of measurement to the top of the fluid (Fig. 2A). At lower levels within the tube, the pressure in the fluid progressively increases owing to the action of gravity on the column of fluid above each point of measurement. Strictly speaking, the meniscus of the fluid represents an interface between the fluid medium and the at-

mosphere, so the total pressure equals the hydrostatic pressure in the fluid column plus the ambient atmospheric pressure. In the present discussion the hydrostatic pressure will be considered in relation to the specific gravity of the fluid and the vertical distance from the point of measurement to the level at which fluid pressure equals pressure immediately outside the tube.

The venous system consists of a series of collapsible tubes so there is no interface between the venous blood and the external environment of the vein. If at any point along the vein, the pressure within it equals the external tissue pressure, the vessel collapses at that level. If a thin-walled tube containing no air is arranged as indicated in Figure 2B, the fluid from the reservoir will flow through the tube in response to a pressure gradient. The tube collapses at a level just above that of the outflow tube. Below this level, the internal pressure exceeds the external pressure and the tube is distended by hydrostatic pressures which increase progressively toward the lower portion of the system. Above the zero level, the pressure within the collapsed tube is equal to the external pressure. Technically, a free-falling body has no weight because all the potential energy is converted into kinetic energy (movement) or lost as friction (heat). Thus, even though there is fluid flowing through the collapsed portion of the tube, the lateral pressure exactly equals the external pressure. If a normal man assumes a semi-reclining position with his head and trunk oriented about 30 to 45 degrees from the horizontal plane, the lower portion of the jugular vein is distended, but at some point along its course the vein becomes collapsed because venous pressure equals tissue pressure. This represents the level of zero effective venous pressure.

When a normal man is standing, the level of zero effective venous pressure is within the thorax (Fig. 2C). If there is a continuous column of blood extending from the foot to heart level, the pressure in an ankle vein should be about 85 mm. Hg (125 cm. H₂O). It has been demonstrated experimentally that this is approximately true so long as the subject remains relaxed and motionless. Similarly, if the mean arterial blood pressure at heart level is 90 mm. Hg the arterial blood pressure at the ankle should be increased by a corresponding amount, i.e., to about 175 mm. Hg, neglecting the slight frictional losses during flow indicated in Figure 1. Since the arterial and venous pressures in dependent extremities are increased to the same extent by hydrostatic pressure, the energy lost during circulation through dependent parts is no greater than that lost when the same vascular bed is at heart level. The pressure differences between arteries and veins at the ankle are the same as those at heart level. The frictional energy loss along a tube is not increased when it is formed in-

THE NATURE AND SIGNIFICANCE OF HYDROSTATIC PRESSURES

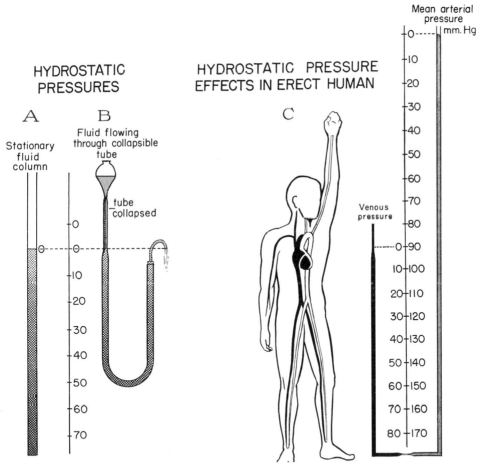

FIGURE 2. *A*, The pressure in a column of fluid is dependent upon its specific gravity and the vertical distance from the point of measurement to the meniscus.

B, A collapsible tube is distended only so long as the internal pressure exceeds the external pressure. These two pressures are exactly equal in the portion of the tube which is collapsed.

C, In the erect position, the arterial and venous pressures are both increased by some 85 mm. Hg at the ankle. With the arm held above the head, the arterial pressure at the wrist is about 40 mm. Hg and the effective venous pressure is zero down to a level just above the heart.

THE EFFECTS OF DEPENDENCY ON THE FLOW OF FLUID

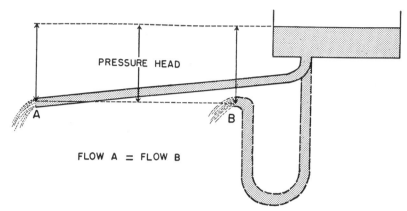

FIGURE 3.   This simple model illustrates the point that assuming the erect position per se places no additional burden upon the heart. Since the frictional energy loss is essentially the same, the same energy release (pressure head) provides equal flow from *A* and *B*.

to a U tube. For example, the pressure head is the same for tubes *A* and *B* in Figure 3 and the flow from each tube is essentially identical. Forming a tube into a dependent loop does not increase the amount of energy required to propel fluid through the tube. Thus, the erect position does not require an increased energy output by the heart, but capillary pressure increases tremendously in the dependent parts of the body.

CEREBRAL CIRCULATION

Whenever a man is erect, the pressure in the cranial cavity drops well below atmospheric pressure while the pressure in the lower spinal canal is well above this value. It has long been recognized that cerebrospinal fluid protects the cerebrospinal vascular bed. The cerebrospinal fluid pressure and the cerebral venous pressure vary together because these fluids are confined within a relatively rigid chamber (Fig. 4). The intravenous and extravenous pressure must be precisely equal at all levels of the cerebrospinal cavity regardless of its position or orientation (see Fig. 4).

Since the hydrostatic columns in the arteries, capillaries and veins are precisely balanced by equal changes in extravascular hydrostatic pressure,[6] the cerebrospinal circulation exhibits a stability not exceeded in any other tissue of the body. The pressure gradient from the arteries to the veins is precisely equal across all capillary beds. The only mechanism for altering flow through any part of the enclosed circulation is by means of local vasoconstriction or vasodilation. However, the cerebral circulation is remarkably unresponsive to the usual neural, humoral or chemical mechanisms (see Fig. 7, Chap. 4). The blood flow through the cerebrospinal vessels is extremely constant, a condition compatible with the more or less uniform oxygen requirements of the central nervous system. The effective capillary pressure is also very similar at all levels within the cerebrospinal canal, and the fluid balance postulated by Starling (see Fig. 15, Chap. 1) is probably in effect in all capillary networks. Net filtration probably does not occur in cerebral capillaries other than those of the choroid plexus, which has the specialized function of producing cerebrospinal fluid. In fact, many substances in the blood are greatly impeded in their movement into the cerebrospinal fluid, a fact ascribed to the so-called "blood-brain barrier." Recently Pappenheimer *et al.*[7] reported that certain substances are actively transported from the cerebropsinal fluid into the blood stream. This process apparently uses mechanisms requiring expenditure of energy just as do mechanisms involved in the function of the kidney tubules.

The circulatory pattern and extravascular support within the eye are quite analogous to those of the cerebrospinal cavity. The ciliary body is a structure specialized to produce capillary filtrate (aqueous humour). A similar kind of external support of the vascular beds probably obtains within bones.

COUNTER PRESSURES IN PERIPHERAL CIRCULATION

It is obvious that a capillary pressure exceeding a pressure of 85 mm. Hg in an ankle vein must also greatly exceed the maximum colloid osmotic pressure of the plasma proteins (about 30 mm. Hg). If the effective capillary pressure throughout the vascular networks of a region sig-

nificantly exceeds the maximal colloid osmotic pressure, fluid will filter from all parts of the capillary system, resorption will be impossible, and accumulation of fluid in the tissue spaces (edema) can result. It is important to consider the extent to which this kind of situation is alleviated in various regions of the body by such mechanisms as (a) the balancing of intravascular pressures by extravascular or tissue pressure, (b) the reduction of the hydrostatic columns in veins by "pumping" action and (c) the return of unabsorbed capillary filtrate to the circulation by way of the lymphatic system.

Intramuscular Tissue Pressure

In reclining subjects the intramuscular pressure ranges from 2 to 5 cm. H_2O in muscles with loose fascial investment,[8] e.g., biceps brachii and gastrocnemius. Slightly higher values have been obtained from anterior tibial and soleus muscles, which are invested with a tight fascial

THE RELATION OF CEREBROSPINAL FLUID PRESSURE TO VENOUS PRESSURE

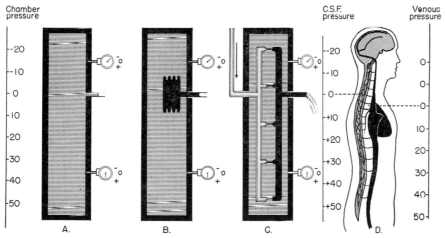

FIGURE 4. In a rigid container filled with fluid, the pressure at the level of the horizontal tube equals atmospheric pressure. Below this level the pressure progressively increases owing to the hydrostatic column of fluid. Above the reference level, the pressure progressively diminishes below atmospheric pressure. This situation is unaltered by the presence of a distensible barrier between the contents of the chamber and the outlet tube. If fluid flows into the chamber through rigid tubes and out through collapsible tubes, the pressure within the collapsible tubes is precisely equal to the pressure outside the tube at any level within the rigid system. By the same token, the venous pressure determines the cerebrospinal fluid pressure within the cerebrospinal cavity.

PUMPING ACTION OF MUSCLES DURING WALKING

A. COMMUNICATIONS BETWEEN SUPERFICIAL AND DEEP VEINS   **B. THE REDUCTION OF VENOUS PRESSURE DURING WALKING**

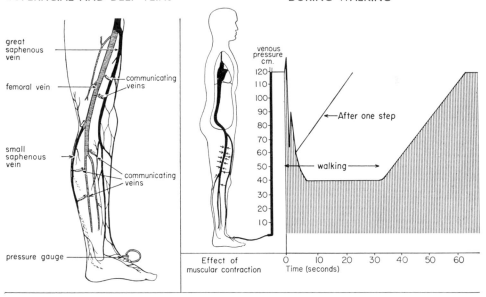

FIGURE 5.   *A*. Venous blood may ascend the leg along both deep and superficial channels, which are in communication at many points. To reduce the venous pressure at the ankle, each vertical column of blood draining the area must be interrupted at some point in the leg.

B. After taking one step the venous pressure in a dorsal vein of the foot is markedly reduced and then gradually ascends to the control level; repetitive steps keep the venous pressure depressed (after Pollack and Wood[12]).

sheath. After the subject has been tilted into the erect position, intramuscular pressures rise abruptly a few centimeters of water and then gradually increase to values of 20 or 30 cm. H_2O in muscles with tight fascial covering. Maximal pressures developed during voluntary muscular contraction are rarely reported to be over 50 cm. H_2O, although the venous pressure in the legs exceeds this amount.[9, 10] In muscles without tight fascial sheaths the increase in pressure is relatively slight during maximal voluntary contraction. For example, pressure in the rectus femoris could not be raised above 20 cm. H_2O by maximal effort.[8] Although the recorded values for intramuscular pressure are surprisingly low, muscular contraction has important cardiovascular significance. A relationship between low intramuscular pressure and **syncope** has been demonstrated by

Mayerson and Burch.[10] Even more impressive is the fact that voluntary muscular contraction can apparently force blood under a cuff inflated to levels of 90 mm. Hg (see Fig. 14, Chap. 4). By some unknown means, contraction of skeletal muscle in the legs is sufficient to compress the veins of the legs even when their internal pressure is very high.[11] This is the basis of a muscular pumping mechanism by which the venous pressure in dependent extremities may be significantly lowered during ordinary walking or shifting of position.

Muscular Pumping Mechanisms. The veins of the extremities are equipped with many valves located at strategic positions along their course. So long as blood flows continuously throughout the peripheral venous system, the valves along all the venous channels are open and the columns of blood are not interrupted at any point. Under these conditions, the pressure in the veins at the dorsum of the foot is equal to that in a vertical column of blood extending from the point of measurement to heart level (Figs. 2, 5). If the subject takes one step (Fig. 5), the venous pressure at the ankle drops to a level equivalent to that in a column of fluid extending to the knee and then gradually returns to the previous level at a rate determined by the volume flow of blood through the limb.[12] There are alternate pathways by which blood from the foot may ascend the leg. If any single uninterrupted column of blood from ankle to heart persisted after the step, the venous pressure at the dorsum of the foot would not be altered. Thus, muscular contraction must produce complete or partial emptying of both the deep and superficial veins within the leg or thigh. As the muscles relax, columns of blood are supported by closed intravenous valves. According to Höjensgard and Stürup,[13] the pressure in the deep and superficial leg veins may be reduced simultaneously during walking. The superficial veins must empty into the deep veins of the thigh so that all the veins above the knee are decompressed. This could be accomplished by complete emptying of veins or by segmenting the columns of blood so that each valve in the thigh is closed and supports a column of blood which does not extend to the valve above. As blood flows through the capillaries into the veins, the partially collapsed deep and superficial veins gradually refill, elevating the pressure at the dorsum of the foot back to the initial levels. Repetitive movements of the lower extremities, as in walking, maintain the venous pressures at the lower level (Fig. 5) if each successive step occurs before the venous columns in the thighs are refilled.

This muscular pumping mechanism has important functional connotations: (a) It drastically lowers the venous and capillary pressures, reducing the effective capillary filtration pressures. (b) It reduces the volume of blood contained within the veins of the leg and to this extent these veins act as a reservoir which releases excess blood during muscular exercise (see below). (c) It momentarily accelerates the return of venous blood from the legs at the onset of walking or running. After the pumping mechanism is established, the rate of venous return again depends upon the rate of blood flow through the capillaries into the veins. When venous blood flows upward from the leg into the abdomen, the pressure in the veins of the thigh must exceed the pressure in the abdominal portion of the inferior vena cava, which has no valves. In general, the veins within the abdomen are filled with uninterrupted columns of blood under a pressure equivalent to that of a vertical column extending slightly above heart level.

Intra-abdominal Pressure

The abdominal cavity is filled with organs having a specific gravity approximating that of blood. The hydrostatic pressure of a vertical column of abdominal organs is similar (Fig. 6) to that which would be produced if the abdomen were filled with fluid.[14-16] At rest the venous pressure apparently exceeds the intra-abdominal pressure by only 5 to 10 cm. H_2O at any level within the abdomen in either the supine or the erect position. However, the diaphragm and the abdominal walls may simultaneously exert tension during deep inspiration or straining, so that the over-all intra-abdominal pressure exceeds venous pressure in the thorax and compresses the abdominal veins. Blood is forced onward into the veins of the thorax because retrograde flow out of the abdominal cavity is prevented by closure of venous valves. Since the diaphragm can exert no force in the upward direction, intrathoracic pressure never exceeds intra-abdominal pressure.

TRANSMURAL PRESSURES OF ABDOMINAL VEINS

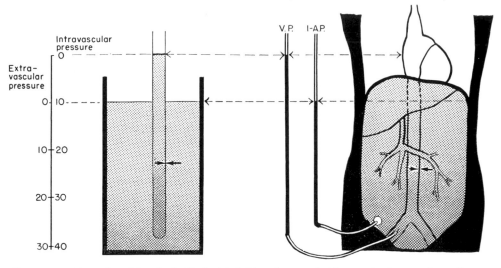

FIGURE 6.   If a collapsible tube is filled with fluid and suspended in a tank of water, the walls must support only the difference in pressure between the inside and the outside. In the case illustrated, the walls of the tube support no more than 10 cm. H_2O pressure at any level in the tube. The abdomen contains movable organs with a specific gravity similar to that of blood. For this reason the transmural pressure of intra-abdominal veins is less than 10 cm. H_2O at any level in the abdominal cavity.

Intrathoracic Pressure

The collapsed volume of the lungs is much smaller than the capacity of the thoracic cage. Since the lungs are stretched or distended to fill their allotted space, the elastic tissue is under stretch even at the end of a forced expiration. This elastic tension of the pulmonary tissue is expressed as a subatmospheric intrathoracic pressure which exerts a distending force on the structures within the chest. An elastic tube filled with fluid is further distended if the tube is confined within a chamber containing a subatmospheric pressure. The level of zero transmural pressure occurs at the point where the internal fluid pressure is balanced by the extravascular pressure. The central venous pressure measured with a catheter ranges slightly above or slightly below the atmospheric pressure. The transmural pressure of the veins and atria, however, is greater than the recorded values because of the subatmospheric pressure in

the thorax. If the negative intrathoracic pressure is applied to the top of an external fluid column connected to an intrathoracic vein (Fig. 7), the top of the fluid

TRANSMURAL PRESSURE IN THE THORAX

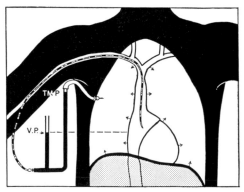

FIGURE 7.   The central venous pressure recorded with a catheter approximates atmospheric pressure. The transmural pressure of the intrathoracic vessels is actually represented by the combined effects of intrathoracic and intravascular pressures. The intrathoracic pressure exerts a distending influence on vasculature within the thorax.

column is elevated by the "suction" of the subatmospheric intrathoracic pressure. The "effective" venous pressure within the chest is indicated by such a manometer. The distending influence of the subatmospheric intrathoracic pressure tends to increase the transmural pressures throughout the thoracic cavity. It augments the central venous pressure in distending the large veins and the heart, reducing, to this extent, the lower end of the pressure gradient from the periphery to the right ventricle.

The intrathoracic pressure fluctuates during normal respiratory activity, averaging about -5.4 cm. H_2O (-4 mm. Hg) at the end of a normal expiration. Inspiration further distends the lungs, lowering the pressure to about -10.8 cm. H_2O (-8 mm. Hg). Increased respiratory excursions produce correspondingly greater fluctuations in the intra-

thoracic pressure. Changes in intrathoracic and intra-abdominal pressure associated with diaphragmatic movements provide a pumping mechanism that facilitates transfer of blood into the thorax.

The Abdominothoracic Pumping Mechanism

During inspiration, the contracting diaphragm descends and the intrathoracic pressure is lowered by increased stretch of the inflated lungs. Simultaneously, the abdominal organs are displaced downward and forward; this displacement tends to stretch the anterior abdominal wall and increases the over-all intra-abdominal pressure. Thus, during inspiration, the gradient in pressure between the abdomen and the thorax is increased and the flow of blood into the thoracic veins is accelerated (Fig. 8). In addition, the shortening of the inferior vena cava

ABDOMINOTHORACIC PUMP

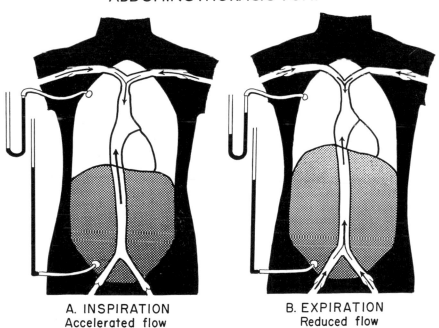

A. INSPIRATION
Accelerated flow into thorax

B. EXPIRATION
Reduced flow into thorax

FIGURE 8. *A*, During inspiration, reduced intrathoracic pressure coupled with increased intra-abdominal pressure accelerates the flow of blood from the abdominal veins into the thorax.

B, During expiration, flow into the thorax is retarded by simultaneous increase in intrathoracic pressure and reduction in intra-abdominal pressure.

reduces its capacity, contributing to the blood flow into the thorax.[17] The increased intra-abdominal pressure temporarily impedes flow from the periphery into the abdomen; flow is accelerated after the intra-abdominal pressure is lowered during the subsequent expiratory movement.

Exhalation releases tension within the inflated lungs and the intrathoracic pressure rises toward atmospheric pressure. Intra-abdominal pressure is reduced as the diaphragm relaxes and ascends. The inferior vena cava becomes elongated and accommodates more blood.[17] Thus, blood flow from abdomen to thorax is accelerated during inspiration and slowed during expiration. If expiration is continued beyond the normal range by active contraction of the abdominal muscles, the diaphragm is stretched as it is elevated beyond the position of rest so that intra-abdominal pressure is increased more than intrathoracic pressure rises. Since the diaphragm applies force only toward the abdominal cavity, and elastic tension in the lungs is continuously present, intra-abdominal pressure always exceeds intrathoracic pressure. By this mechanism, a favorable pressure gradient from abdomen to thorax is always maintained under normal conditions.

CONTROL OF CENTRAL VENOUS PRESSURE

The pressure in the intrathoracic portions of the superior and inferior venae cavae is of great importance because the transmural pressure in these veins represents the distending pressure of the heart. A positive effective filling pressure must be maintained in these veins at all times regardless of the position of the body, the magnitude of the blood volume, the redistribution of blood in dilated capillary beds or the accumulation of blood in distended dependent veins. Otherwise, filling of the heart would be deficient during the diastolic intervals. On the other hand,

excessive pressure in these veins would raise the gradient in pressure in both the venous and the lymphatic systems, which would promote accumulation of fluid in the tissues. The maintenance of central venous pressure between these two critical levels requires that the venous system compensate for variations in total blood volume and changes in its distribution.[18, 19] The right ventricular pressure during diastole represents the minimal pressure in the systemic venous system, since it is the point of outflow from the entire system. At rest in the horizontal position, the right ventricular pressure varies between +2 and −2 mm. Hg during diastole. Angiocardiographic studies[20] have revealed that, in the supine position, both the superior and inferior venae cavae are distended with blood. In the erect position, the inferior vena cava is distended, but the superior vena cava is partially collapsed just above the level of the right atrium. The point of collapse of the veins represents the level at which the effective venous pressure (intravascular pressure minus extravascular pressure) is essentially zero. If the pressure in the inferior vena cava fell until the point of collapse was just below the right atrium, the effective filling pressure of the right ventricle would be zero. Thus, a decrease in venous pressure of only a few centimeters of water in the right atrium would represent a serious impairment of right ventricular filling. This contingency is prevented by continuous and precise adjustments in the venous reservoir system to maintain the central venous pressure at levels only slightly above that of the right atrium regardless of the body's position.

The mechanism which controls the central venous pressure is best described by a schematic diagram (Fig. 9). Consider a distensible tube filled with water until there is a slight positive internal pressure when it is horizontal. In the vertical position, the fluid level in the tube would descend because the hydrostatic pressure would produce greater distention of the dependent portions. The fluid level could be restored to the previous height only by compression of some portion of the tube (Fig. 9). Exactly the same considerations apply whether the fluid is stationary or is flowing through the tube (see Fig. 2). The central venous pressure is only slightly above atmospheric pressure in normal reclining subjects. When the individual assumes a vertical position, the hydrostatic pressures produce a distention of the dependent veins which may accumulate relatively large quantities of blood (more than 500 cc.). Unless some portions of the venous vascular bed were compressed, effective central venous pressure would probably fall below that of the heart. A major portion of this blood may come from the lungs (see Chap. 1). However, external compression of veins by skeletal muscles in the legs, and probably by contraction of large venous channels and other venous reservoirs, restores the central venous pressure so that it is just above the pressure in the right atrium. The exact mechanisms controlling this important adjustment have not yet been elucidated (see Chap. 16).

The probability that central venous pressure is precisely controlled was strengthened by exposing animals to positive and negative radial acceleration on a large centrifuge.[6] Under forces as great as five times the force of gravity (5 g) the pressures in "dependent regions" became very high, but the level at which venous pressure remained essentially unchanged was at or near heart level whether these forces were directed toward the head or toward the lower parts of the body. Since the capacity of the veins below the diaphragm greatly exceeds that of those above the diaphragm, the

MAINTENANCE OF CENTRAL VENOUS PRESSURE

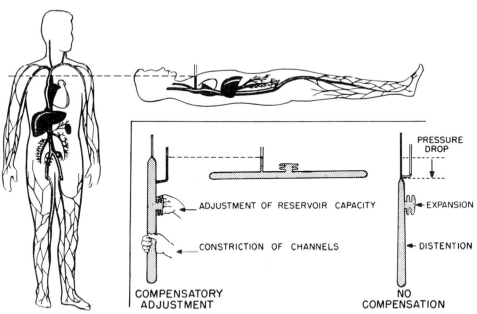

FIGURE 9.   The veins in various regions of the body tend to be distended to about the same degree when a subject is recumbent. In the erect position the hydrostatic columns of blood produce distention of the vessels below the heart and collapse of veins above the heart. Since most of the venous reservoir capacity is below heart level, the central venous pressure theoretically could fall below heart level unless compensatory adjustments were promptly instituted. These compensatory mechanisms are illustrated schematically as a constriction of venous channels and regulation of reservoir capacity (see also Chap. 4).

EFFECTS OF RECLINING ON VENTRICULAR FUNCTION

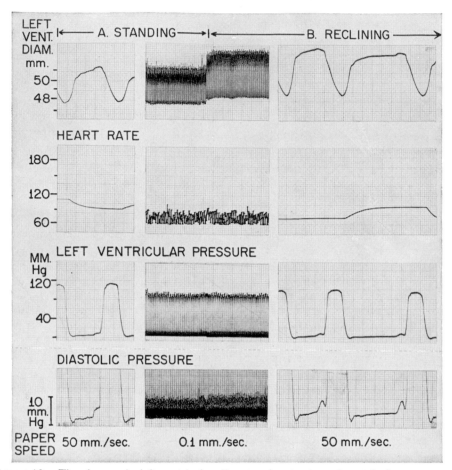

FIGURE 10.   The changes in left ventricular diameter, heart rate and ventricular pressures as a healthy dog, standing with his trunk horizontal, spontaneously reclines. Note that the diastolic distention increased in spite of a slight drop in mean atrial pressure. The increased stroke deflections in the diameter record indicate an increase in stroke volume which has been amply confirmed by aortic flowmeters. These changes are in accordance with Starling's law of the heart.

large hydrostatic pressures would tend to cause massive accumulations of blood in dependent regions when the forces acted from head to feet. Control of central venous pressure must certainly involve regulation of the capacity of the venous reservoirs.

THE EFFECTS OF POSTURE ON VENTRICULAR SIZE

In earlier times the ventricular chambers were thought to be nearly empty at the end of each systole. This impression probably stemmed from observation of

hearts exposed by thoracotomy, which induces marked shrinkage of the heart (see Fig. 5, Chap. 3). Measurements under more normal conditions consistently indicate that relatively large volumes of blood remain within the ventricular chambers at the end of a normal ventricular systole.[21, 22] In fact, the ventricles apparently eject only about half of the end diastolic volume.[23, 24] In normal human subjects and in patients with heart disease resting quietly in the supine position the heart functions at or near its maximum dimensions.[25, 26] In resting recumbent dogs, the left ventricle tends to attain its maximum dimensions as recorded by gauges of diameter, length and circumference.[27]

The rapid increase in the left ventricular diameter of a dog during a change from the standing (with trunk horizontal) to the reclining position is illustrated in Figure 10. The abrupt diastolic distension of the ventricular diameter occurred without any significant change in heart rate, filling time or effective ventricular filling pressure. Apparently, the distensibility of the ventricular myocardium had changed so that there was a greater diastolic distention without a corresponding increase in effective filling pressure. The increase in diastolic dimensions was greater than the increase in systolic dimensions, so that the amplitude of the stroke was increased. The transition from sitting (or standing) to the recumbent position was accompanied by a progressive increase in diastolic dimensions over a series of cardiac cycles in which the stroke deflection increased and the systolic pressure was elevated (Fig. 11*A*, *B*). Thus, the increase in diastolic size was accompanied by an increase in energy release, in accordance with Starling's law of the heart.[26, 28] The diastolic diameter expanded to a maximum as evidenced by the fact that it reached a plateau early in diastole and atrial contraction produced little or no additional distension.

Intravenous infusion of sufficient blood to elevate effective filling pressure as much as 15 mm. Hg failed to increase diastolic diameter as much as 1 mm.[22] After the dog was anesthetized and thoracotomized, the heart was observed as it distended to its "maximum" dimensions when the animal succumbed to asphyxia. The diastolic diameter recorded during the distension produced by

MAXIMAL DIASTOLIC DISTENTION DURING RECUMBENCY

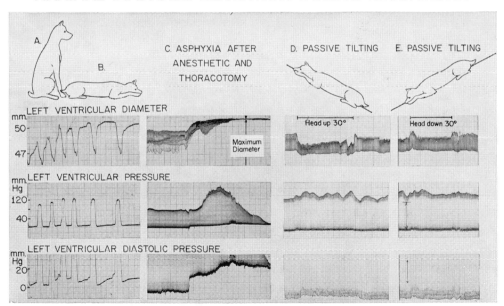

FIGURE 11.   *A*, As indicated in Figure 10, the left ventricular diameter promptly increases during the next few cycles after a dog assumes the reclining position

B, After anesthesia, thoracotomy and asphyxia, the left ventricle distended under direct vision. The ventricular diameter after this extreme distention was essentially the same as in the recumbent position in *A*, indicating that under these conditions left ventricular distention may be "maximal" for that ventricle.

C, Changes in ventricular diameter with changes in posture are not due to the effort because they occur during passive tilting with the head up but to a much lesser extent with the head down.

asphyxia was essentially the same as that recorded previously while the dog was relaxed (Fig. 11*B*).

The reduction in ventricular size was not due to the exertion involved in standing since both the diastolic diameter and the stroke deflection were reduced when the head was passively tilted up 30 degrees (Fig. 11*C*). However, vertical orientation of the trunk per se is not an essential factor in the reduction in heart size and stroke volume because the trunk is horizontal during both reclining and standing in the dog. Furthermore, the heart size promptly diminishes to about the same extent if the animal merely lifts his head in response to an unexpected noise. In other words, the cardiac chambers function at or near their maximum dimensions in the relaxed recumbent dog and their size is promptly reduced in all other circumstances observed.

A reduction in stroke volume on arising has been consistently observed in normal human subjects;[29] the average heart rate is slightly accelerated, but the net effect is a diminution in cardiac output. The same observation was made on intact dogs in which aortic flow was measured continuously by means of an indwelling ultrasonic flowmeter.[30] A reduction in cardiac output when the erect position is assumed indicates that the total flow through the peripheral circulation has been curtailed, presumably by vasoconstriction in some peripheral vascular bed.

The Concept of Venous Return

The stroke volume of the heart-lung preparation was generally increased by elevating the venous reservoir. This experimental technique formed the basis for the concept that a prominent factor in the initiation of increased cardiac output was an increase in "venous return" in many cardiovascular responses. A precise definition for the term "venous return" is difficult to derive since it has been em-

ployed in many different ways so that it has, at one time or another, included increased volume flow into the ventricles, increased velocity of flow in the central veins, increased central venous pressure, increased filling pressure in the ventricles, etc. However, there might be general agreement that stroke volume and cardiac output are increased by greater venous return when the central venous pressure, the volume flow into the ventricles, the diastolic ventricular volume, the stroke volume and the cardiac output are all increased. On the basis of these criteria, the increase in stroke volume and cardiac output occurring when an erect man or dog lies down is a most clear-cut example of the results of an increased venous return. Similarly, the reduced stroke volume and cardiac output accompanying standing could be described in terms of reduced venous return. An exaggerated form of this response is seen when positive radial acceleration with centrifugal forces of three to five times the force of gravity (3 to 5 g) are applied. Under these conditions, the ventricles become progressively smaller until they appear to empty maximally during each systole. In general, reduced "venous return" is a useful concept in describing the effects of gravitational forces acting from head to seat. Evidence of changes in venous return in the initiation of circulatory responses cannot be easily recognized in other spontaneous circulatory adjustments by normal animals or man (e.g., exercise, see Chap. 8). In patients with congestive heart failure (see Chap. 16), the ventricles become enlarged and the circulation adapts to an increased load by an increase in central venous pressure but without a corresponding increase in stroke volume. In other words, the failing heart exhibits signs of an increased "venous return" having been invoked unsuccessfully in response to demands for increase cardiac output.

THE EFFECTS OF STANDING ON PERIPHERAL FLOW DISTRIBUTION

When a normal person arises from the recumbent to the erect position, less blood flows through the splanchnic bed and the dependent extremities (Fig. 12). For example, the estimated blood flow through the liver decreased on the average from 1713 cc. to 1070 cc. per minute in a group of human subjects.[31] The blood flow through the hand promptly diminishes and then rises somewhat to reach a mean level just below that recorded in the reclining subject.[32] The blood flow through the legs decreases significantly, and the oxygen content of femoral venous blood is reduced, indicating that a much greater proportion of the oxygen reserve is utilized. A most pronounced reduction in flow through renal and superior mesenteric arteries occurred when the dogs in Figure 9, Chapter 4, stood on their hind legs with the trunk held erect. According to recent evidence, the arteriovenous oxygen difference in blood passing through the leg increases about twofold without a demonstrable increase in oxygen consumption, and oxygen extraction is augmented by this amount even if the leg bears no weight.[33]

Teleologic explanations for vasoconstriction in the dependent leg are not difficult to imagine. In the erect position, the long columns of blood elevate the pressure in both the arteries and veins of the legs. An increase in the internal pressure within the arteries, arterioles, capillaries and venules by 50 to 90 mm. Hg would tend to produce distention of all these vessels, producing a passive vasodilation throughout these vascular beds unless this tendency were opposed by active vasoconstriction. Vasoconstriction might also serve to diminish the rate at which fluid filters through the dependent capillary beds. If an erect subject moves his legs, as in walking, the venous pressure in the lower legs drops to much lower levels owing to the pumping action of the muscles (Fig. 5). Under these conditions, the pressure gradient from the arteries to the veins may suddenly increase from about 90 mm. Hg to about 140 mm. Hg. This increase would cause considerably augmented flow through the dependent vascular beds. The consequent accelerated outflow from the arterial system, coupled with the reduced stroke volume (Figs. 10 and 11), might produce a precipitous fall in systemic arterial blood pressure unless a peripheral vasoconstriction were promptly induced. The principal sign of a severe reduction in systemic arterial pressure attendant upon standing is a loss of consciousness.

SOME EFFECTS OF ARISING

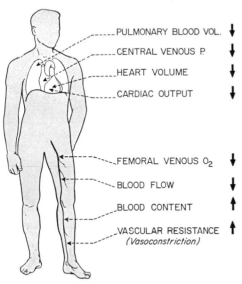

PULMONARY BLOOD VOL. ↓

CENTRAL VENOUS P. ↓

HEART VOLUME ↓

CARDIAC OUTPUT ↓

FEMORAL VENOUS O₂ ↓

BLOOD FLOW ↓

BLOOD CONTENT ↑

VASCULAR RESISTANCE ↑
(Vasoconstriction)

FIGURE 12. Changes in blood distribution and blood flow when a man stands are summarized schematically. Blood content diminishes in the lungs and heart and increases in the legs. Blood flow through the legs and cardiac output both diminish. The oxygen extraction from the blood flowing through the legs is necessarily more complete.

SUMMARY

In the standing adult of average height, the arterial and venous pressures recorded at the ankle are both as much as 85 mm. Hg higher than the pressures in the reclining subject. The pressure difference between the arteries and veins remains unchanged, and the energy release by the heart is no different from that in the supine position so long as muscular exertion is not required. In fact, the cardiac output has been reported to be slightly less when the subjects are relaxed in the upright position than when they are supine. The major circulatory change produced by the hydrostatic columns is an increase in the capillary pressure in the dependent extremities. This pressure reaches levels well above the maximum effective colloid osmotic pressure.

Changes in the position of the body have no functional effect on the vasculature within the cerebrospinal cavity and the eye, and probably not on those in bone, because the extravascular pressure precisely balances the venous pressure.

Contraction of the leg muscles during walking brings into play the so-called "muscular pumping action" which has three effects: (a) At the beginning of muscular contraction, blood is displaced from the veins of the legs owing to external compression. (b) The pressure in the veins and capillaries in the lower extremities tends to be maintained at lower levels during active walking. (c) The arteriovenous pressure difference is increased so that blood flow through the capillaries into the veins would be increased if the state of arteriolar constriction remained unchanged. The quantity of blood flowing through the veins depends upon the rate of flow through the capillaries.

The external pressure provided by the hydrostatic column of abdominal organs tends to balance the hydrostatic pressures in the veins of the abdomen. By this mechanism, the vast splanchnic venous bed is largely protected from being distended by the increased venous pressures developed in the erect position. The subatmospheric pressure within the thorax provides a favorable pressure gradient from abdomen to thorax. Contraction of the diaphragm can act only to increase intra-abdominal pressure and reduce intrathoracic pressure.

The effective or transmural pressure in the thoracic veins, atria and ventricles is greater than that recorded externally because the subatmospheric pressure acts as a distending force. The filling pressure of the right ventricle is normally maintained at very low and constant levels by adjustments in the capacity of the venous reservoir system to compensate for variations in the distribution of blood and in the total blood volume.

II. Postural Hypotension

Diminished systemic arterial pressure, often accompanied by dizziness, sweating, visual disturbances and even loss of consciousness, is fairly commonly produced by sudden assumption of the erect posture after an individual has been relaxed while seated or lying down. The principal effects of arising from the recumbent to the standing position result from the hydrostatic pressures of vertically oriented columns of blood. The arterial and venous pressures increase in the dependent regions of the body. In regions above the heart, the veins collapse and the venous pressure becomes approximately equal to the surrounding tissue pressure. The arterial pressure in these regions diminishes by an amount equivalent to the height of the column of blood above the level of the heart. The cerebral circulation, however, is protected against the effects of the reduction in arterial pressure because the gravitational influences on hydrostatic columns affect equally the intravascular and extravascular pressures within the rigid cerebrospinal canal (see Fig. 4). During standing the arterial pressure at the base of the skull[15] (about 30 cm. above the heart) is about 25 mm. Hg less than the arterial pressure at heart level. The pressure of the cerebrospinal fluid within the skull is also about 25 mm. Hg less than the systemic venous pressure at heart level (i.e., is approximately 25 mm. Hg below atmospheric pressure). Since the arterial, capillary, venous and extravascular pressures within the skull are all reduced by the same amount (25 mm. Hg), the perfusion pressure from the arteries to the veins is not reduced when the erect position is assumed.

So long as the mean arterial pressure within the skull remains 90 mm. Hg above the systemic venous pressure at heart level, cerebral blood flow is not significantly influenced by the effects of standing or even by exaggerated gravitational forces. For example, pilots in aircraft executing high-speed turns are exposed to centrifugal forces four to five times the force of gravity. Observations made while these conditions were simulated on a rapidly spinning human centrifuge show that the pilot's cerebral function remains normal in these circumstances if the arterial blood pressure at the heart is sufficient to support a column of blood to levels above the base of the skull. As the pressure in the carotid sinus falls, the blood pressure at heart level is elevated reflexly until the cardiac output is reduced. When the arterial pressure at eye level drops to about 25 to 30 mm. Hg vision begins to fail and "blackout" occurs. (The intra-ocular pressure is about 20 to 25 mm. Hg.) Pilots tend to lose consciousness when the carotid arterial pressure approaches zero because the arteries outside the cerebrospinal canal collapse and severely impede forward flow. This example demonstrates that gravitational forces (e.g., standing) do not restrict cerebral blood flow even if the arterial pressure at head level is somewhat diminished by the hydrostatic column effect. On the other hand, the cerebral blood flow is affected by a reduction in the systemic arterial pressure that acts to reduce the perfusion pressure, i.e., the pressure gradient from the cerebral arteries to the veins.

The cerebral circulation is unresponsive to virtually all mechanisms normally exerting control over peripheral blood flow (see Figs. 7 and 13, Chap. 4). Although elevation of the carbon dioxide tension may double cerebral blood flow, changes attributable to any of the other mechanisms have not been demonstrated unequivocally, and the cerebral blood flow tends to reflect directly changes in the systemic arterial pressure. Blood flow through muscle or skin can be maintained at high levels in spite of reduced arterial pressure by varying degrees of compensatory vasodilation. Lacking such effective compensatory mechanisms, the cerebral perfusion diminishes with any significant drop in systemic arterial pressure.

The key to the tendency toward fainting in the erect position is the greater likelihood of a reduction in systemic arterial pressure at heart level. A drop in blood pressure signifies either a reduction in cardiac output without vasoconstriction or a drop in peripheral resistance without a corresponding increase in cardiac output (see Chap. 6). Thus, the immediate cause of a fall in blood pressure in the erect position must be diminished cardiac output, diminished peripheral resistance, or a combination of the two.

SYNCOPE (FAINTING)

Fainting is characterized by an abrupt fall in blood pressure, bradycardia, pallor, dizziness, dimming or loss of vision, and unconsciousness.[11, 34] These changes may be induced by many and varied conditions including emotional reactions (e.g., the sight of blood), standing quietly for long periods, hemorrhage and pain—particularly the diffuse, poorly localized pain carried by visceral afferent fibers.[34, 35] Fainting reactions can be elicited experimentally by passively tilting the subject into the erect position during withdrawal of blood by venesection or trapping of blood in the legs with cuffs, after administration of various dilator drugs or during application of painful stimuli.

Because fainting most commonly develops in erect individuals and is promptly alleviated by falling or lying down, many investigators once attributed it to reduced cardiac output resulting from a combination of the bradycardia with pooling of blood in the dependent veins. Since then, evidence obtained in a variety of ways suggests that such a combination is not necessarily concurrent with fainting. Prevention of the bradycardia with atropine does not affect the fall in blood pressure. By means of cardiac catheterization, a reduction in both right atrial pressure and cardiac output was observed after passive tilting and during venesection while the arterial blood pressure was well maintained. At the abrupt onset of the fainting reaction the blood pressure drops precipitously to lower levels (i.e., 60/40) with no drop in cardiac output.

Barcroft[11] accidentally discovered that during fainting reactions the blood flow through skeletal muscle increases greatly owing to both release of vasoconstrictor tone and activation of vasodilator fibers serving skeletal muscles. He compared the blood flows in the forearms of subjects with and without sympathetic nerve block during induced fainting reactions and found a flow through the innervated muscles exceeding that through the denervated muscles. These observations led to the concept of sympathetic vasodilator fibers serving skeletal muscles (see also Fig. 7, Chap. 4). Although the blood flow through the liver diminishes abruptly at the onset of a fainting reaction, the concurrent fall in blood pressure is disproportionately great. This observation suggests the occurrence of some vasodilation in the splanchnic bed as well as in the skeletal muscle.[34] Resistance to blood

flow through the kidney may also be reduced. The loss of consciousness is apparently caused by diminished cerebral blood flow, as evidenced by a marked reduction in the amount of venous blood flowing from the brain.

HYPERSENSITIVE CAROTID SINUS

External pressure on the carotid sinus may activate the pressoreceptor reflex which normally compensates for an abrupt rise in systemic arterial blood pressure. The heart rate slows and the peripheral vessels dilate as though to correct an increased arterial pressure. Thus, the systemic arterial pressure is abruptly but inappropriately reduced, and the individual experiences lightheadedness or even unconsciousness.

In 1933 Weiss and Baker[36] described 15 patients complaining of dizziness and fainting apparently related to unusual sensitivity of the carotid sinus mechanism. Some of these patients developed cardiac standstill for 2 to 12 seconds when pressure was exerted on their necks by tight collars, during shaving or even by the turning of their heads in a particular manner. Digital pressure over the sinus region readily produced the attacks. In six of these patients there was a definite aneurysmal dilation of one or both carotid sinuses, and in three a small tumor pressed on the sinus. In the remaining six patients no gross lesion was noted.

Four main types of syncope can be produced by compression of the carotid sinus: (a) transient cardiac standstill, (b) precipitous fall in blood pressure with slowing of the heart rate, (c) precipitous fall in blood pressure without bradycardia and (d) cerebral syncope now regarded as a form of epilepsy rather than as cardiovascular collapse.

Circulatory collapse accompanied by a precipitous fall in blood pressure, bradycardia, profuse sweating and pallor can be induced in many erect normal subjects by mechanical stimulation of the

at least 2 or 3 seconds. On the contrary, flow through these vessels can increase almost simultaneously (Fig. 5).

An increase in "venous return" might be interpreted as a shift of blood from the periphery to the central veins. For example, the pressure in isolated vein segments rises during exercise owing to constriction of the vein walls.[14] Such a mechanism might be expected to displace blood toward the heart under normal conditions. The liver and spleen are generally regarded as important blood reservoirs, but direct measurements of their

dimensions in healthy dogs reveal no consistent changes during treadmill exercise.[15] Thus, there is little positive evidence that an increase in "venous return," in the most common usage of the term, is essential for initiation of an increase in cardiac output when exercise begins (see also blood distribution in Chapter 16).

Reduced peripheral resistance was obtained experimentally by rapidly pumping blood from a femoral artery into a femoral vein exposed under local anesthesia. The systemic arterial pressure declined and this reduction was accompanied by tachy-

CHANGES IN AORTIC AND VENA CAVAL FLOW
AT THE ONSET OF EXERCISE

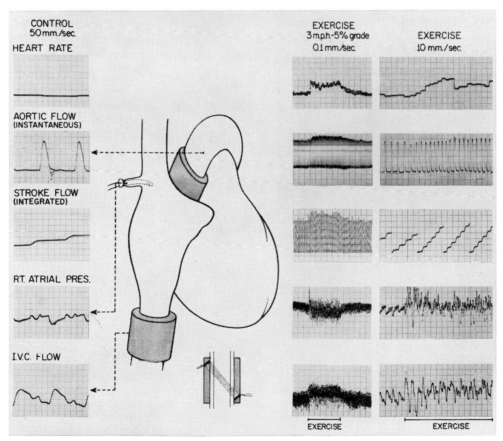

FIGURE 5.   The blood flows through the root of the aorta and through the inferior vena cava increase essentially simultaneously as judged by simultaneous recordings at different paper speeds. Although artifacts appear on some records at the onset of exercise, the slope of the integrated record of stroke flow becomes steeper as the flow through the inferior vena cava rises to a higher level. These changes indicate that the flows into the right ventricle and out of the left ventricle increase essentially simultaneously.

EXERCISE RESPONSE SIMULATED BY DIENCEPHALIC STIMULATION

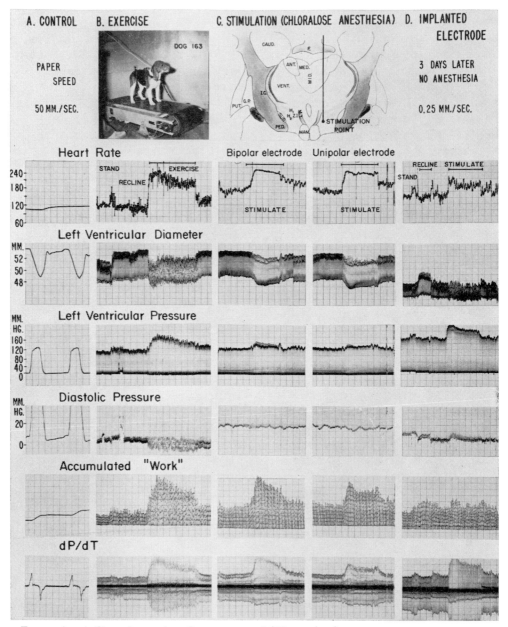

FIGURE 6.   *A,* Control records at fast paper speed (50 mm./sec.).

B, Left ventricular response to exercise on a treadmill at 3 m.p.h. on a 5 per cent grade.

C, On the same day, unipolar and bipolar stimulation in the H_2 fields of Forel under chloralose anesthesia produced changes of the same general type as were recorded during exercise. The electrode was implanted at that site.

D, Three days later, without any anesthesia, stimulation using the implanted electrode reproduced the original left ventricular response to exercise with considerable precision.

cardia. However, the over-all response did not resemble the normal exercise response. When isoproterenol, a synthetic catechol amine, was administered at carefully graded rates, the changes closely simulated the exercise response except for the changes in diastolic ventricular pressure. This mechanism has no obvious relation to normal responses since this substance is not believed to be a normal secretion.

Naturally occurring catechol amines, l-epinephrine and norepinephrine, were infused intravenously in doses calculated to be within the physiologic range. In virtually all experiments on dogs, these substances in physiological doses produced bradycardia along with elevation of the systemic arterial pressure. Under these conditions the normal ventricular exercise response cannot be reproduced unless tachycardia is induced artifically. When the right atrium was stimulated with an artificial pacemaker during infusion of catechol amines, normal exercise responses were simulated with a fair degree of precision.

Stimulation of sympathetic nerves distributed to the heart from the stellate ganglia profoundly affected both the heart rate and the contractility as defined in Chapter 3 (see Fig. 15, Chap. 3). Prompt and sustained tachycardia can be produced by relatively weak stimulation. The ventricular contraction is much more vigorous, as indicated by a more rapid rise in ventricular pressure, a more rapid ejection, a higher peak pressure, a more rapid fall in pressure and a shorter systole. Simulation of the same sympathetic fibers through electrodes implanted in a healthy dog produced changes in ventricular performance of the same general type as those commonly observed during spontaneous exercise.[15]

Stimulation in the central nervous system was next undertaken to locate sites from which impulses could reach the heart through the autonomic pathways. Since the hypothalamic region is generally recognized as the locus of important integrating mechanisms governing autonomic activity, the diencephalon was explored by means of stimulating electrodes.[4, 11, 16-18] The success of the search for sites of electrical stimulation which would produce cardiac responses similar to the natural exercise responses is indicated in Figure 6.

After a typical treadmill exercise response was recorded, the dog was anesthetized with chloralose and an electrode was positioned in the subthalamus (H_2 fields of Forel). Stimulation there produced changes in cardiac function of the proper type, and the similarity of responses to unipolar and bipolar stimulation indicated that the electrode tip was directly in or very near the source of the nerve impulses producing this change. The electrode shaft was cemented to the skull and the animal was permitted to recover. Three days later the same locus was stimulated through the implanted electrode while the unanesthetized dog stood quietly. The response to stimulation reproduced nearly all details of the exercise response with considerable precision (Fig. 6B). The same kind of cardiac responses can be elicited routinely by stimulation of the H_2 fields of Forel or the periventricular gray matter, as evidenced by records from three different dogs (Fig. 7).

When the animal is under chloralose anesthesia, electrical stimulation of these areas often results in increased ventilation and distinct running movements as well as the cardiovascular response. Syncurine completely abolished the limb and respiratory movements but did not affect the magnitude of the cardiac response. If the electrode was moved a very short distance up or down, cardiac responses without running movements or running movements without cardiac responses could be elicited. Unfortunately, the activated neural structures are never ex-

COMPARISON OF RESPONSES TO EXERCISE
AND DIENCEPHALIC STIMULATION

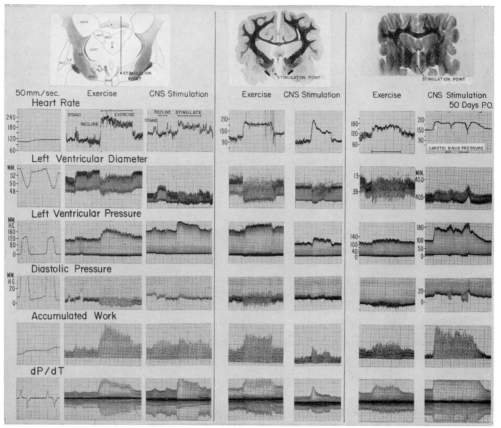

FIGURE 7. Diencephalic stimulation in the region of the H_2 fields of Forel and in the periventricular gray matter produces changes in left ventricular function comparable to those produced by spontaneous exercise.

actly the same during electrical stimulation and normal activity. For this reason, the role of these diencephalic sites in normal function cannot be assessed with confidence by stimulation alone. Additional evidence obtained by selective destruction of such areas is also necessary.

Diencephalic lesions of a very small size were made bilaterally in regions which produced powerful cardiac responses. In one animal with such lesions the ventricular response to exertion decreased progressively during successive treadmill exercises (Fig. 8). By the seventh day after the lesions were made, the animal's ventricular performance did not change significantly when he exercised. Obviously,

he could run only a short time. He then stopped and let the treadmill slide beneath him. During the period after the diencephalon was damaged, the animal displayed other signs of autonomic disturbance including vomiting, diarrhea, reduced food intake and easy fatigability. In spite of these complications it seems evident that the bilateral lesions destroyed pathways or collections of nerve cells important to normal cardiovascular regulation.

Blood Flow in Muscles During Exertion

At the beginning of exercise the flow of blood through the contracting muscles increases greatly to maintain and restore the supply of energy that is being released as work and wasted as heat. Barcroft and Dornhorst[19] presented evidence that contraction of skeletal muscles actually hinders the flow of blood through them; thus, the vasodilation must be great enough to permit very large flows in the intervals between contractions.

The widely accepted concept that vasodilation in active muscle results directly from the diminution of oxygen tension, decline of pH and accumulation of carbon dioxide and other metabolites appears to be logical and to be evidenced by the extreme vasodilation occurring after temporary obstruction of the arterial supply to an extremity (reactive hyperemia). As mentioned in Chapter 4, the evidence that a lowered oxygen level or an elevated carbon dioxide level is normally an important regulator of blood flow to muscles and certain other tissues is tenuous and indirect. The blood flow through the human calf immediately after exercise does not consistently reflect the severity of the preceding exertion[20] and remains elevated after the oxygen debt has been repaid and the heart rate has returned to normal.[21] Then, too, the venous blood from the legs may contain more oxygen during recovery from either exercise or temporary arterial occlusion than during rest.

Most concepts of the intimate nature of the control exercised by metabolites, hormones or neural mechanisms over the peripheral vasculature are based on very indirect evidence and remain extremely controversial.[22] Evidence can be mar-

EFFECT OF DIENCEPHALIC LESIONS ON THE EXERCISE RESPONSE

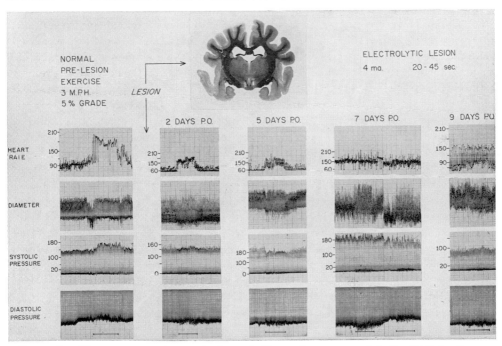

FIGURE 8.   The response to the standard treadmill exercise was recorded. Small bilaterally symmetrical lesions were placed in the H_2 fields of Forel. Two days later the systolic ventricular pressure rise during exercise was slightly reduced. After five days, the systolic ventricular pressure fell during exercise. Seven days after the lesions, the heart rate did not accelerate. After nine days, the animal performed the standard exercise without any significant changes in the recorded variables. The explanation for this sequence is not obvious but it suggests that, before the lesions, these discretely localized sites may have played a significant role in the normal response to exercise.

shalled to support any one of several widely divergent views and the solution to the dilemma does not appear close at hand. It is generally agreed, however, that the sympathetic nerves serving vessels in skeletal muscle are predominantly constrictors. If the constrictor portion of this action is blocked, a vasodilation is elicited by stimulating sympathetic trunks which has been ascribed to a specialized sympathetic vasodilator system (see also Chap. 4).

Sympathetic Vasodilator Fibers to Skeletal Muscle. Nerve fibers are assigned to the sympathetic system on purely anatomic grounds. Although the vast majority of these fibers release a transmitter substance closely resembling norepinephrine, exceptions exist. For example, the fibers innervating the sweat glands of the skin are anatomically sympathetic, but they release acetycholine as a transmitter substance and thus may be blocked by atropine. In recent years an eminent group of Swedish investigators has presented a great deal of experimental evidence[22][24] which suggests that some sympathetic fibers distributed to skeletal muscles (and possibly to the heart) release acetylcholine as a transmitter substance to induce vasodilation.

The use of the term "vasodilator" in this connection deserves additional consideration. After all accessible sympathetic fibers to the extremities are cut, the smooth muscle in vessels serving skeletal muscle retains a fairly high degree of tone, evidenced by the fact that the blood flow increases five- or sixfold when acetylcholine is administered. This effect is blocked by atropine. Activation of the sympathetic vasodilator fibers can also increase the blood flow above the level sustained under "basal tone." This effect can also be blocked by atropine administered in doses too small to affect the vasodilation caused by inhibition of vasoconstrictor tone. Such dual innervation of vessels in skeletal muscle is generally in-

terpreted as mediating two forms of vascular reaction, the vasoconstrictor activity serving in the control of systemic arterial pressure and the vasodilator activity serving to accelerate muscle blood flow promptly at the onset of muscular exertion.[23]

The pathway of the sympathetic vasodilator system has been traced from the motor cortex[25] to the supraoptic area in the hypothalamus, through the medulla and thence down to spinal levels. Quite naturally, it has been suggested that impulses from higher neural levels traverse these connections to elicit vasodilation in skeletal muscles, "in circumstances when a sudden increase in blood flow in the skeletal muscles is needed in order to create optimal conditions for muscular effort."[26]

Redistribution of Blood Flow During Exertion

Contracting skeletal muscles need a greatly increased blood flow, which can be supplied by an increase in cardiac output. The load on the heart can be reduced somewhat by diversion of some flow from relatively inactive tissue to the active muscle. For example, about one-fourth of the total cardiac output at rest flows through the kidney, a quantity far greater than necessary to meet that organ's oxygen requirement. A significant proportion of the renal blood flow could be diverted to serve active muscles at the expense of a reduction in the oxygen content of renal venous blood. If this mechanism is operable, the cells in the renal parenchyma must function in an environment of reduced oxygen tension to achieve the greater oxygen extraction. Curtailment of renal blood flow during exercise not only is a very reasonable concept but is supported by evidence from normal human subjects. For example, Bucht *et al.*[27] catheterized the renal veins and measured renal clearances to determine the blood flow during mild and moderately severe exercise. When the work was slight, the renal blood flow was unchanged but the cardiac output was somewhat augmented. During more strenuous work the renal blood flow decreased by 20 per cent and the cardiac output was almost doubled.

The blood flow through the splanchnic bed and liver might also be curtailed during exertion. During supine exercise the hepatic blood flow, measured indirectly, was about 400 ml. per minute below a mean resting level of approximately 1500 ml. per minute.[28] The extent to which differences in posture would affect these observations is not known (see below). The blood flow in the arm diminishes 50

per cent in the early minutes of exercise, primarily because circulation through the skin decreases;[29] this reduced flow does not persist throughout the exertion. According to Scheinberg et al.,[30] cerebral blood flow increased in subjects walking on a treadmill.

The distribution of blood flow during exercise most commonly has been studied in human subjects by means of indirect methods applied to one portion of the circulation at a time. Installation of ultrasonic flowmeters at several sites in the canine circulation makes possible continuous, simultaneous monitoring of several patterns of flow at rest, during exer-

BLOOD FLOW DISTRIBUTION DURING EXERTION AND DIENCEPHALIC STIMULATION

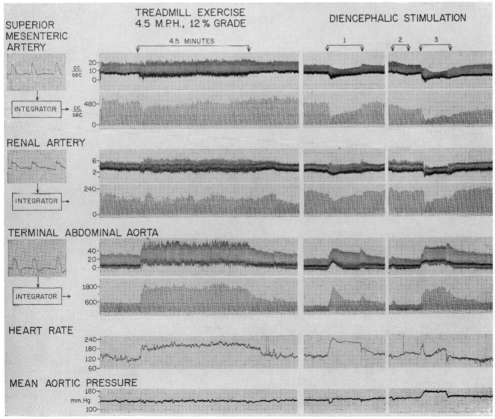

FIGURE 9.   During exercise, the flow through the superior mesenteric and renal arteries may change transiently, but the integrated flow is essentially unchanged, while the flow to the hindquarters is greatly increased. A similar change in flow distribution can be induced by stimulation in the same regions that produced the pronounced changes in cardiac function illustrated in Figure 7.

CONSTANCY OF STROKE VOLUME DURING EXERTION IN DOGS

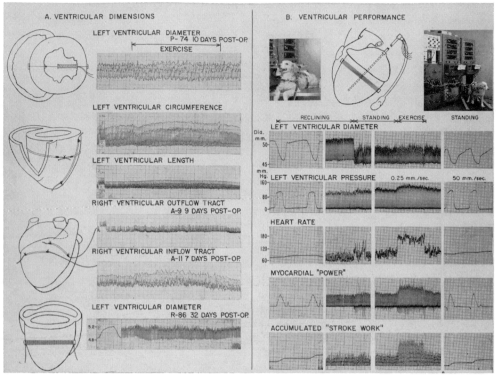

FIGURE 10. *A*, Direct recordings of changing internal left ventricular diameter, external left ventricular circumference and length, various dimensions of the right ventricular wall and the external left ventricular diameter consistently demonstrated little or no shift in baseline or increase in the amplitude of the deflections. This observation indicates that the total ventricular volume and stroke volume remain essentially unchanged in dogs during moderate exercise from a standing control.

B, When a recumbent dog stands up, the diastolic and systolic dimensions abruptly diminish and the stroke deflections become much smaller (see also Figs. 10 and 11, Chap. 7). These changes in ventricular dimensions are much greater than are typically recorded during exertion.

cise and under other conditions (see Fig. 8, Chap. 4). When a dog ran on the treadmill, the flow through the lower abdominal aorta to the hindquarters increased promptly and was sustained throughout the exercise (Fig. 9). The instantaneous flow velocity and the integrated flow (flow per stroke) rose and there were more strokes per minute. In contrast, the blood flow through the renal artery was essentially unchanged, not only in the example presented in Figure 9 but also, consistently, in a series of exercise responses by six dogs. The flow through the hepatic artery to the liver and stomach was substantially reduced, as was the flow through the hepatic por-

tal vein; these observations suggest that the splanchnic flow diminished. The blood flow through the common carotid artery was generally greater than at rest. Since flow through the internal carotid could not be distinguished from that through the external, the flow through soft tissues of the head might have increased without a change in the cerebral vascular bed.

Electrical stimulation of selected sites in the diencephalon consistently influenced flow distribution directionally as exercise did (Fig. 9*B*). These sites were at or near those which induced corresponding changes in cardiac function, hyperpnea and running movements (see above).

Thus, complete patterns of somatic and visceral adaptation (e.g., exercise) can be induced by selective diencephalic stimulation. It should be emphasized, however, that the motor and visceral components can appear individually after stimulation of slightly different diencephalic loci, so that the motor activity is not the cause of the changes in visceral function. Abrahams and Hilton[31] reported that stimulation of certain hypothalamic sites produced muscle vasodilation in anesthetized cats and defense reactions in conscious cats—pupillary dilation, hissing, snarling, massive pilo-erection and running about the cage. According to Fencl et al.,[32] the flow of blood through skeletal muscle increased when "acute emotional stress" was induced by mental arithmetic.

Uvnäs[33] recently noted that, although the vasodilator mechanism induces additional blood flow through muscle, the clearance of radioactive materials from the muscle is somewhat retarded and its oxygen consumption decreases. These observations were interpreted as evidence that the sympathetic vasodilator system tends to open arteriovenous shunts (or arteriovenous capillaries; see Fig. 5, Chap. 4) and to reduce flow through true capillaries. Such a mechanism would at least deliver more blood to the muscles.

RELATION OF TACHYCARDIA TO STROKE DEFLECTIONS

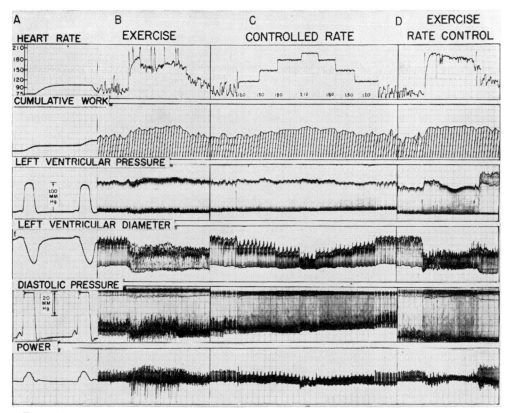

FIGURE 11. A, B, The principal change in left ventricular function during spontaneous exercise is a pronounced acceleration of the heart with little increase in stroke deflections (see also Fig. 10).

C, Stepwise increase in heart rate induced by an artificial pacemaker in the same alert dog produced a progressive decline in diastolic and systolic dimensions and stroke deflections.

D, The changes in heart rate during exercise were precisely reproduced from a tape recording activating the artificial pacemaker and the stroke deflections were greatly diminished as compared with the normal exercise response.

EFFECTS OF CONTROL POSTURE ON EXERCISE RESPONSE

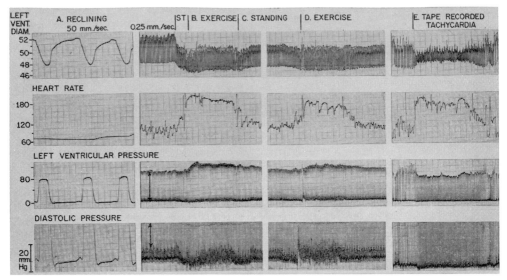

FIGURE 12.   *A*, In reclining dogs, the left ventricular diameter is approximately maximal and the stroke deflections are large.

B, If the animal stands and immediately begins to exercise, the ventricular dimensions and stroke deflections appear to diminish promptly in relation to the exercise.

C, Exercise begun from a standing control demonstrates that the ventricular dimensions and stroke deflections are not greatly affected by the exercise.

It could then be distributed to the true capillaries by an opening of the precapillary sphincters during exercise (i.e., opening induced by local metabolic products).

Postural Effects on the Exercise Response

Over some five years the changes in the ventricular dimensions of healthy dogs were measured hundreds of times by different techniques during various spontaneous adjustments. When the animal had stood quietly on the treadmill during the control period, exercise at 3 m.p.h. on a 5 per cent grade was accompanied by only slight changes in the ventricular dimensions. The diastolic dimensions might increase slightly in some instances; not at all in others. The systolic dimensions might decrease slightly, but, in general, the systolic deflections were not significantly augmented during the moderate exercise employed. The examples in Figure 10*A* represent about the greatest changes in the stroke deflections of the

left and right ventricles recorded by each of three different techniques. These observations suggested that the stroke volume did not increase materially when the standing animal began to run. This conclusion was confirmed by measuring the aortic flow directly with the ultrasonic flowmeter.[34] On the other hand, if the dog was reclining quietly during the control period, the diastolic and systolic ventricular dimensions and the stroke deflections all diminished significantly when he began to exercise (Fig. 10*B*). Clearly the cardiac output was augmented in either case primarily by an increase in heart rate rather than by greater stroke volume.

Tachycardia alone does not effectively increase cardiac output. This fact is shown clearly by the left ventricular response to cardio-acceleration induced by an artificial pacemaker (Fig. 11). Stimulating electrodes were implanted in the region of the sino-atrial node during an aseptic operation in which recording devices were also attached to the heart. After recovery the animal was exercised on the treadmill (Fig. 11*B*). The left ventricular dimensions decreased as the animal stood up and began to run. The stroke deflections were now slightly larger than those after exertion, during a standing control period. Stimulation through the electrodes near the sino-atrial node was then begun to increase the heart rate in a stepwise fashion (Fig. 11*C*). This artificial tachycardia was accompanied by a progressive reduction in the diastolic and systolic dimensions and the stroke deflections. Similarly, an artificially induced tachycardia reproducing the rates recorded during exercise resulted in a markedly reduced stroke deflection (Fig. 11*D*). Thus, an artificial tachycardia does not produce the normal increase in cardiac output because the stroke volume is decreased. The normal exercise response involves no change or a slight increase in the stroke volume because "contractility" (as defined in Fig. 15, Chap. 3) is increased.

The nature of the cardiac response to exertion depends to a considerable extent on the state of the animals during the control period. For example, if a dog is lying quietly on the treadmill during a control period and then stands and begins to exercise abruptly, systolic and diastolic left ventricular diameters diminish along with stroke deflections (Fig. 12*B*). On the other hand, if the animal is standing quietly on the treadmill during the con-

CONSTANCY OF STROKE VOLUME DURING EXERCISE IN MAN

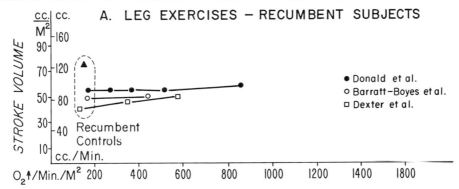

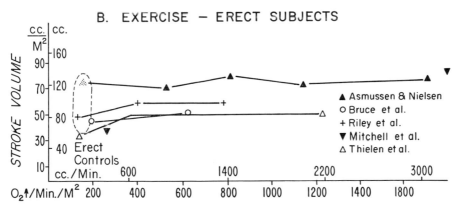

FIGURE 13. *A,* Human subjects exercising in the recumbent position exhibit little increase in stroke volume over a fairly wide range of exercise as judged by the oxygen consumption.
B, Normal human subjects in the erect position have smaller stroke volumes during the control period, and at the onset of exercise the stroke volume increases to a higher level where it tends to remain over a wide range of oxygen consumption. At the extreme levels of exercise, a further increase in stroke volume is observed (see Fig. 2, Chap. 15).

trol period, the left ventricular diameter is not greatly altered when the exercise begins (Fig. 12D).

The constancy of the stroke volume which had been so consistently observed in the animal experiments (Figs. 10 and 12) led to a survey of the literature to determine how the stroke volume behaves during exercise by human subjects.[4, 34] In eight different studies,[35] summarized in Figure 13, the stroke volume changed only slightly over a wide range of exercise levels, graded for severity on the basis of oxygen consumption (see also Fig. 2, Chap. 15). This apparent failure of stroke volume to increase progressively as the work load increased was not consistent with observations by certain investigators, notably Mitchell, Sproule and Chapman.[37] In a personal communication Chapman pointed out that this discrepancy might be partly explained by the fact that the stroke volume during exercise is very little higher than that in the recumbent position. It seems quite possible that the stroke volume in the relaxed recumbent subject is at or near the maximal level ordinarily reached during heavy work. When the individual stands up, his stroke volume, and his heart volume, consistently diminish.[38] Beginning at this smaller baseline, the stroke volume increases promptly with even slight exertion, but does not necessarily increase progressively as the external work becomes more intense. Chapman has, however, presented evidence that there is an additional increase in stroke volume under conditions of maximal exertion.[39] Other investigators have also reported some augmentation of stroke volume during exercise. Musshoff et al.[40] calculated a mean increase in stroke volume of 60 per cent, but their subjects included men with different exercise tolerances. Athletes are generally recognized as being able to utilize stroke volume more effectively during exercise than the average healthy subject can.

Conditions Under Which Stroke Volume Increases. According to Yandell Henderson,[41] the heart rate is slower and the stroke volume is higher in trained athletes than in nonathletes. "The athlete's heart is supernormal." Many other investigators have also observed this tendency,[40, 42] although Freedman et al.[43] could find no differences attributable to training in the way a trained and an untrained athlete meet the tissues' demands for oxygen. In any event, there seems little doubt that, during exertion, the heart rate accelerates less and the stroke volume is higher in trained athletes than in average subjects. Warner et al.[44] demonstrated that, if tachycardia is prevented by artificial control of the heart rate, the cardiac output increases normally during exertion through an increase in stroke volume.

Patients with chronically high cardiac output (resulting from anemia, thyrotoxicosis or an arteriovenous fistula) also tend to have a normal heart rate and an increased stroke volume at rest and to utilize increased stroke volume rather than cardio-acceleration during exertion.[45] The cardiac responses of such patients resemble those of trained athletes.

Normal persons who stand during the control period will generally exhibit an increase in stroke volume at the onset of exertion, be it severe or mild. There is little evidence that stroke volume increases progressively with more strenuous work in average normal subjects. Subjects whose apprehensions induce tachycardia and reduced stroke volume during the control period will tend to display greater increases in stroke volume than relaxed subjects will.

SUMMARY

Traditional concepts of the cardiac response during exertion, based primarily on Starling's law of the heart, have been evaluated for human subjects and intact dogs and found wanting. The patterns of ventricular response to exercise could not be duplicated by many different standard experimental methods including increased "venous return," reduced peripheral resistance, intravenous administration of natural autonomic hormones or by artificial tachycardia. Electrical stimulation of specific areas in the diencephalon reproduced ventricular responses similar to those occurring during exercise both with and without anesthesia. Lesions in the regions which produced these responses have been shown to produce profound changes in the responses to treadmill exercise. In both dogs and man, the stroke volume does not necessarily increase with increased severity of exertion as judged by oxygen consumption. The stroke volume is characteristically smaller during standing control measurements than in the recumbent position. During exercise in the erect position, the stroke volume may increase above the values measured during standing control but rarely exceeds the recumbent controls to any great extent. The stroke volume does not necessarily increase from very mild to quite severe exercise in human subjects. A further increase in stroke volume may occur at maximal levels of exertion.

REFERENCES

1. BARGER, A. C., RICHARDS, V., METCALFE, J., and GUNTHER, B. Regulation of the circulation during exercise. *Amer. J. Physiol.*, 184: 613–623, 1956.
2. FENN, W. O. Acute and sustained high energy output. Pp. 8–17 in *Symposium on Stress* (16–18 March, 1953). Washington, D. C., Army Medical Service Graduate School, 1953.
3. RUSHMER, R. F. Anatomy and physiology of ventricular function. *Physiol. Rev.*, 36:400–425, 1956.
4. RUSHMER, R. F., and SMITH, O. A., JR. Cardiac control. *Physiol. Rev.*, 39:41–68, 1959.
5. STEAD, E. A., and WARREN, J. V. Cardiac output in man. *Arch. Int. Med.*, 80:237–248, 1947.
6. WARREN, J. V., BRANNON, E. S., STEAD, E. A., JR., and MERRILL, A. J. The effect of venesection and the pooling of blood in the extremities on the atrial pressure and cardiac output in normal subjects with observations on acute circulatory collapse in three instances. *J. Clin. Invest.*, 24:337–344, 1945.
7. LILJESTRAND, G., LYSHOLM, E., and NYLIN, G. The immediate effect of muscular work on the stroke and heart volume in man. *Scand. Arch. Physiol.*, 80:265–282, 1938.
8. MEEK, W. J., and EYSTER, J. A. E. Cardiac size and output in man during rest and moderate exercise. *Amer. J. Physiol.*, 63:400–401, 1923.
9. SJÖSTRAND, T. Regulatory mechanisms relating to blood volume. *Minnesota Med.*, 37: 10–15, 1954.
10. RUSHMER, R. F., CRYSTAL, D. K., WAGNER, C., ELLIS, R. M., and NASH, A. A. Continuous measurements of left ventricular dimensions in intact, unanesthetized dogs. *Circulat. Res.*, 2:14–21, 1954.
11. RUSHMER, R. F., SMITH, O. A., JR., and FRANKLIN, D. Mechanisms of cardiac control in exercise. *Circulat. Res.*, 7:602–627, 1959.
12. SUNAHARA, F. A., HATCHER, J. D., BECK, L., and GOWDEY, C. W. Cardiovascular responses in dogs to intravenous infusions of whole blood, plasma, and plasma followed by packed erythrocytes. *Canad. J. Biochem.*, 33:349–360, 1955.
13. FOWLER, N. O., FRANCH, R. H., and BLOOM, W. L. Hemodynamic effects of anemia with and without plasma volume expansion. *Circulat. Res.*, 4:319–324, 1956.
14. MERRITT, F. L., and WEISSLER, A. M. Reflex venomotor alterations during exercise and hyperventilation. *Amer. Heart. J.*, 58: 382–387, 1959.
15. ANZOLA, J., and RUSHMER, R. F. Cardiac responses to sympathetic stimulation. *Circulat. Res.*, 4:302–307, 1956.
16. SMITH, O. A., JR., RUSHMER, R. F., and LASHER, E. P. Similarity of cardiovascular responses to exercise and to diencephalic stimulation. *Amer. J. Physiol.* 198:1139–1142, 1960.
17. RUSHMER, R. F., SMITH, O. A., JR., and LASHER, E. P. Neural mechanisms of cardiac control during exertion. *Physiol. Rev.*, 40 (Suppl. 4): 27–34, 1960.
18. SMITH, O. A., JR., JABBUR, S. J., RUSHMER, R. F., and LASHER, E. P. Role of hypothalamic structures in cardiac control. *Physiol. Rev.*, 40 (Suppl. 4):136–145, 1960.
19. BARCROFT, H., and DORNHORST, A. C. The blood flow through the human calf during rhythmic exercise. *J. Physiol.*, 109:402–411, 1949.
20. HALLIDAY, J. A. Blood flow in the human calf after walking. *J. Physiol.*, 149:17P, 1959.
21. ELSNER, R. W., and CARLSON, L. D. Limb blood flow during recovery from moderate exercise. *Fed. Proc.*, 17:41, 1958.
22. FOLKOW, B. Nervous control of the blood vessels. *Physiol. Rev.*, 35:629–663, 1955.

23. Uvnäs, B. Sympathetic vasodilatory outflow. *Physiol. Rev.*, 34:608–618, 1954.

24. Lindgren, P., and Uvnäs, B. Vasoconstrictor inhibition and vasodilator activation—two functionally separate vasodilator mechanisms in the skeletal muscles. *Acta physiol. scand.*, 33:108–119, 1955.

25. Eliasson, S., Lindgren, P., and Uvnäs, B. Representation in the hypothalamus and the motor cortex in the dog of the sympathetic vasodilator outflow to the skeletal muscles. *Acta physiol. scand.*, 27:18–37, 1952.

26. Eliasson, S., Folkow, B., Lindgren, P., and Uvnäs, B. Activation of sympathetic vasodilator nerves to the skeletal muscles in the cat by hypothalamic stimulation. *Acta physiol. scand.*, 23:333–351, 1951.

27. Bucht, H., Ek, J., Eliasch, H., Holmgren, A., Josephson, B., and Werkö, L. The effect of exercise in the recumbent position on the renal circulation and sodium excretion in normal individuals. *Acta physiol. scand.*, 28:95–100, 1953.

28. Bishop, J. M., Donald, K. W., Taylor, S. H., and Wormald, P. N. Changes in arterial-hepatic venous oxygen content difference during and after supine leg exercise. *J. Physiol.*, 137:309–317, 1957.

29. Bishop, J. M., Donald, K. W., Taylor, S. H., and Wormald, P. N. The blood flow in the human arm during supine leg exercise. *J. Physiol.*, 137:294–308, 1957.

30. Scheinberg, P., Blackburn, L. I., Rich, M., and Saslaw, M. Effects of vigorous physical exercise on cerebral circulation and metabolism. *Amer. J. Med.*, 16:549–554, 1954.

31. Abrahams, V. C., and Hilton, S. M. Active muscle vasodilatation and its relation to the "flight and fight reactions" in the conscious animal. *J. Physiol.*, 140:16P–17P, 1958.

32. Fencl, V., Hejl, Z., Jirka, J., Madlafousek, J., and Brod, J. Changes of blood flow in forearm muscle and skin during an acute emotional stress (mental arithmetic). *Clin. Sci.*, 18:491–498, 1959.

33. Uvnäs, B. Sympathetic vasodilator system and blood flow. *Physiol. Rev.* 40 (Suppl. 4): 69–80, 1960.

34. Franklin, D. L., Ellis, R. M., and Rushmer, R. F. Aortic blood flow in dogs during treadmill exercise. *J. Appl. Physiol.*, 14:809–812, 1959.

35. Rushmer, R. F. Constancy of stroke volume in ventricular responses to exertion. *Amer. J. Physiol.*, 196:745–750, 1959.

36. Rushmer, R. F. Postural effects on the baselines of ventricular performance. *Circulation*, 20:897–905, 1959.

37. Mitchell, J. H., Sproule, B. J., and Chapman, C. B. The physiological meaning of the maximal oxygen intake test. *J. Clin. Invest.*, 37:538–547, 1958.

38. Linderholm, H., and Strandell, T. Heart volume in the prone and erect positions in certain heart cases. *Acta med. scand.*, 162:247–261, 1958.

39. Fisher, J. M., Chapman, C. B., and Sproule, B. J. Effect of exercise on stroke volume in human subjects. *Clin. Res.*, 8:73, 1960.

40. Musshoff, K. von, Reindell, H., Klepzig, H., and Kirchoff, H. W. Herzvolumen, Schlagvolumen und körperliche Leistungsfahigkeit. *Cardiologia*, 31:359–374, 1957.

41. Henderson, Y., Haggard, H. W., and Dolley, F. S. The efficiency of the heart, and the significance of rapid and slow pulse rates. *Amer. J. Physiol.*, 82:512–524, 1927.

42. Musshoff, K. von, Reindell, H., and Klepzig, H. Stroke volume, arterio-venous difference, cardiac output and physical working capacity and their relationship to heart volume. *Acta cardiol.*, 14:427–452, 1959.

43. Freedman, M. E., Snider, G. L., Brostoff, P., Kimelblot, S., and Katz, L. N. Effects of training on response of cardiac output to muscular exercise in athletes. *J. Appl. Physiol.*, 8:37–47, 1955.

44. Warner, H. R., and Toronto, A. F. Regulation of cardiac output through stroke volume. *Circulat. Res.*, 8:549–552, 1960.

45. Bishop, J. M., Donald, K. W., and Wade, O. L. Circulatory dynamics at rest and on exercise in the hyperkinetic states. *Clin. Sci.*, 14:329–360, 1955.

Chapter 9

THE CORONARY SYSTEM

The maximum capacity for sustained exertion or work is ultimately limited by the maximum rate of oxygen delivery to the tissues, as discussed in Chapter 15. A major component of this cardiovascular reserve capacity is the ability of the heart to increase its output of useful work in terms of the volume flow per minute against the pressure in the major arterial trunks. The heart must be supplied with enough oxygen and metabolic fuels to replace continuously the energy expended both as useful work and as energy lost because the heart is less than perfectly efficient as a pump. Since the rest periods between cardiac contractions are very short, the delivery of oxygen by the coronary vessels must rapidly adjust to any change in the work level of the heart. In other words, a progressively increasing oxygen debt can be tolerated only briefly. If the ventricular myocardium releases more energy than is restored during each cycle, the cardiac output must soon diminish until a balance between energy expenditure and energy restoration is again established. As a matter of fact, myocardium exists in an environment of low oxygen tension at all times, judged by the very low oxygen content of the coronary venous blood. Since there is little oxygen left in this blood, increased oxygen delivery to the myocardium must be supported almost exclusively by increased coronary blood flow. For these reasons, it is important to realize that exercise tolerance, cardiovascular reserve capacity and cardiac reserve are frequently limited primarily by the ability to increase coronary flow. The factors which affect coronary flow and its control are of paramount importance in the evaluation of various disease states.

I. The Coronary Circulation

ANATOMY OF THE CORONARY VESSELS

The ventricular walls are supplied by three main arterial trunks. The left coronary artery arises from the left aortic sinus and divides almost immediately into two branches. The anterior descending branch gives off several branches to the anterior septum as it passes along the anterior interventricular groove toward the apex of the heart. The left circumflex branch courses around the base of the left ventricle along the coronary sulcus, and terminates in the posterior descending branch. The right coronary artery, originating in the right aortic sinus, reaches the posterior interventricular groove by way of the coronary sulcus at the base of the right ventricle. From the coronary ring, a number of branches descend to supply the ventricle walls. In addition to the three main coronary trunks, a smaller

213

CORONARY ARTERIES AND COLLATERALS

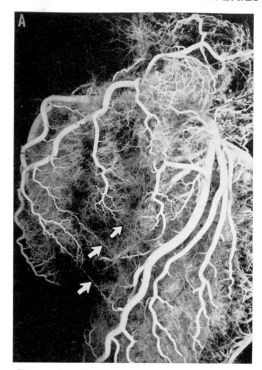
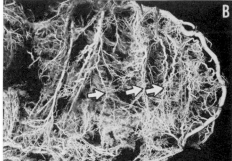

FIGURE 1.   Casts of the coronary arteries disclose the complex branching and the density of the vascular distribution throughout the walls of the heart. Helical collateral vessels connecting different arterial ramifications are indicated by arrows. These photographs are presented through the courtesy of Dr. Giorgio Baroldi, Instituto di Anatomia Patological, University of Milan, Milan, Italy.

conus artery supplies the outflow region of the right ventricle. This artery often arises directly from the aorta. In dogs, the interventricular septum receives a fairly rich vascular supply from septal branches that arise near the origins of the main coronary channels. The conus and septal branches may have great importance in supplying blood flow to vascular beds below obstructions in the main coronary arteries. The profuse networks of coronary vessels supplying the walls of the heart can be most readily appreciated by injecting plastic into the vessels and dissolving away the myocardium[1, 2] (Fig. 1). The pattern of distribution is somewhat variable, particularly in the posterior aspect of the ventricular walls and septum. Schlesinger[3] has described three general patterns of coronary distribution: (1) right coronary preponderance,

(2) a balanced distribution and (3) left coronary preponderance (Fig. 2). Patients with left coronary preponderance are more apt to succumb to coronary occlusion.

Branches from the main coronary vessels descend toward the apex, giving off penetrating branches which divide into dense anastomotic capillary networks roughly paralleling the courses of the myocardial bundles. The distribution of scars following occlusion of specific coronary branches suggests that each bundle of myocardial fibers has an individual blood supply although many communicating channels connect these vascular networks.

Collateral channels connecting the three coronary arterial systems are probably of small caliber. Prinzmetal and his associates[4, 5] performed a number of ingenious experiments on normal animals, demonstrating anastomotic channels from 70 to 180 μ in diameter between the main coronary arterial systems. Wiggers[6] marshalled convincing arguments that these collaterals are not normally significant and will not protect the myocardium from abrupt occlusion of its arterial supply. He pointed out that flow through collateral channels depends upon the magnitude of the pressure difference between the communicating tubes. If the pressures in the various arterial trunks are equal, blood flow through anastomotic connections will be small or absent. Gradual establishment of differential pressures associated with progressive occlusion of a main coronary artery may produce differential pressures sufficient to distend collateral channels.

The major arterial channels are distributed over the external surface of the ventricles. The muscular branches plunge almost perpendicularly into the substance of the ventricular wall and penetrate toward the endocardial surface, giving off branches at various levels to supply the myocardial bundles. The capillary net-

works in the ventricular myocardium have been found to contain metarterioles with smooth muscle cells at irregular intervals along their length. True capillaries, consisting of endothelial tubes, arise as branches of the metarterioles. Cuffs of smooth muscle, or precapillary sphincters, are situated at the origins of the true capillaries.[7] Thus, the coronary capillary network has an organization comparable to that of corresponding small vessels in other tissues (see Fig. 5, Chap. 4).

Direct communications between the small vessels of the coronary circulation and the ventricular chambers have received a great deal of attention in the past. Injection studies of the coronary arteries indicated that some small branches from the terminal arteries penetrate directly through the endocardium (arterioluminal vessels), or join larger channels (arteriosinusoidal vessels) which empty into the right or left ventricular chambers. Thebesian veins pass from the venous end of capillaries, or from deep coronary veins, to the endocardial surface. The main coronary venous drainage tends to retrace the course of the coronary

DISTRIBUTION OF THE CORONARY ARTERIES TO THE VENTRICULAR WALLS

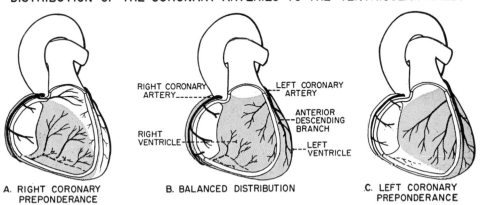

A. RIGHT CORONARY PREPONDERANCE

B. BALANCED DISTRIBUTION

C. LEFT CORONARY PREPONDERANCE

FIGURE 2.   A, The posterior portion of the interventricular septum and part of the posterior aspect of the left ventricle were supplied by the coronary artery in about 48 per cent of a series of postmortem examinations. This distribution has been classified as right coronary preponderance.

B, Balanced coronary distribution occurred in about 34 per cent of specimens.

C, Left coronary preponderance (left coronary artery supplying some of the contiguous right ventricle and virtually the entire interventricular septum) occurred in 18 per cent. Patients with left coronary preponderance appear to be more susceptible to coronary occlusions with myocardial infarction. (After Schlesinger, M. J.: Arch. Path., 30:403–415, 1940.)

arteries, passing toward the atrioventricular groove and terminating in the
coronary sinus, which empties into the
right atrium through its posterior wall.

By direct measurements in isolated
hearts, it is possible to demonstrate that
only about 60 per cent of the blood which
enters the coronary arteries passes out
through the coronary sinus. For many
years, the remaining 40 per cent was
generally regarded as representing the
flow directly into the ventricular chambers through the deep collateral channels,
including the arterioluminal vessels, the
arteriosinusoidal vessels and the Thebesian veins. However, by carefully can-
nulating the anterior cardiac veins, which
lie on the surface of the right ventricle
and empty into the right atrium, Gregg[8]
was able to account for virtually all the
blood which does not flow into the coronary sinus. Nearly all the blood entering
the right coronary artery drains by way
of these anterior cardiac veins, and the
left coronary arterial flow reaches the
right atrium by way of the coronary
sinus. Thus, little or no flow need be ac-
counted for as passing directly into the
ventricular chambers by way of the direct
collateral channels.[9] Further, there is no
evidence that blood ever flows in the reverse direction, from the ventricular
chambers into the coronary capillary
beds, and then out the coronary veins.
Thus, the functional significance of the
Thebesian veins and the arterioluminal
and arteriosinusoidal channels remains
very much in doubt.

FACTORS AFFECTING CORONARY BLOOD FLOW

As in any peripheral vascular bed, the
flow through the coronary vessels must be
determined by the pressure gradient between arteries and veins in relation to the
total resistance offered in the arteries,
capillaries and veins. The coronary vessels occupy a unique position in the vascular system since they serve the pump

which supplies the energy for the circulation of the blood. The coronary branches
penetrate between the myocardial bundles and the contracting myocardium applies an external compression on each
vessel within the ventricular walls. The
external compression is sufficient to completely collapse and occlude the terminal
arteries, capillaries and veins where the
internal pressure is low in relation to the
extravascular pressure. Thus, the resistance to flow through the coronary vascular bed becomes infinitely great in the
occluded vessels deep within the myocardium during systole and drops to some
minimal level during the diastolic interval. These great changes in resistance are
reflected in gross changes in coronary
flow which are repeated during each cardiac cycle.

Changes in Coronary Blood Flow During the Cardiac Cycle

The compression of the coronary vessels within the ventricular walls must depend upon the pressure attained within
the wall during systole. Clearly, the pressure just inside the endothelium of the
ventricles must be a reflection of the intraventricular pressure during both diastole
and systole. The coronary vessels on the
external surface of the ventricles are exposed to the intrapleural pressure, which
is slightly below atmospheric pressure. No
reliable technique has been developed for
direct measurement of the actual extravascular pressures within the ventricular
walls. If each layer of myocardial fibers
contributes equal tension to the development of the intraventricular pressure during systole, the pressure within the wall
must be some form of gradient from the
intrathoracic pressure outside the heart
to the ventricular pressure on the inside.
On the other hand, the distending pressure within the vessels diminishes as the
blood flows through ever-narrowing channels—arteries, arterioles—toward capillaries and veins within the ventricular

walls. Although it is impossible to determine at what levels the extravascular pressure would exceed the intravascular pressure, it is certain that during ventricular systole the terminal arteries, capillaries and veins in the deepest layer of the myocardium are closed while flow may continue through the outermost layers.

Simultaneous measurement of the left coronary arterial inflow and the coronary sinus outflow during constant pressure perfusion demonstrates that left ventricular systole greatly impedes flow into the coronary bed and accelerates flow from the coronary veins (Fig. 3). In fact, the arterial flow may be reversed early in systole as the wave of excitation spreads outward through the left ventricular wall, successively compressing the layers of coronary vessels. Although most of the blood in these vessels is evacuated through the venous channels, some moves in a retrograde direction, up the arteries and through the more superficial layers of the myocardium, so that there is a sharp drop in coronary arterial inflow during early

systole. Coronary arterial inflow falls precipitously and often drops below zero as the retrograde surge of blood reaches even into the major arterial trunks. A forward surge of flow follows during mid-systole and is probably a rebound phenomenon (Fig. 3). In any event, the mean left coronary inflow during left ventricular systole is significantly below the flow rate attained early in diastole, when the relaxing myocardium releases its compression of the deep vessels so that the blood can rush along the arteries into the empty vascular beds deep within the ventricular walls. The outflow from the coronary veins is slowed during most of diastole, indicating that much of the arterial inflow serves to fill the coronary channels emptied during the preceding systole.

Right ventricular pressure is much lower than that in the left ventricle. The pressure which develops within the thin right ventricular wall is so much lower that blood flow into the right coronary artery continues at a fairly high level during both systole and diastole. Thus, right

CORONARY FLOW DURING THE CARDIAC CYCLE

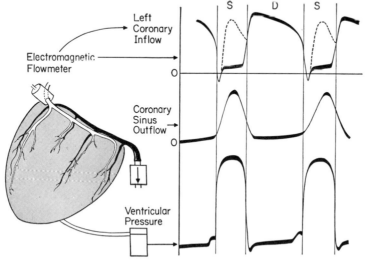

FIGURE 3.   Continuous measurements of coronary arterial flow to the left ventricle indicate that the inflow to the myocardium is greatly impeded during systole. In fact a retrograde surge back toward the aorta often appears in early systole. The coronary sinus outflow is accelerated during ventricular systole, indicating that the contracting myocardial fibers wring out the small coronary vessels and veins. Thus, the flow out of the coronary vessels is greatest when the inflow is diminished by the external compression of the vascular bed within the ventricular walls.

ventricular contraction does not represent nearly as great an impedance to net coronary flow as contraction of the left ventricle.

The alternate compression and release of the intramural coronary vessels corresponds to the pumping action previously described for contracting skeletal muscle (see Fig. 14, Chap. 4). During diastole, blood would flow very rapidly into the emptied channels because it would meet with very little impedance. The concept of a muscle pump suggests that the ventricular contraction might actually facilitate the onward propulsion of blood through the coronary vessels. Wiggers[10] suggested that the contractile force of the heart is a prominent determinant of coronary flow, whether the coronary resistance is increased or decreased. Although this is an attractive hypothesis for automatic coronary regulation, Gregg[8] abruptly stopped the heart during constant pressure coronary perfusion and noted that the left coronary inflow promptly increased (from 123 to 150 ml. per minute within 1 second). This evidence suggests that the normally contracting myocardium impedes coronary flow. Furthermore, this increase in coronary flow is followed after a few seconds by an increase in the venous oxygen content. Calculation of the oxygen consumption of the myocardium for each successive second revealed the uptake of an excess of oxygen immediately after vagal arrest of the heart; the amount was equivalent to the estimated energy release required for 25 systoles. This extra oxygen could properly be called "oxygen debt," and would correspond to about 6 liters of cardiac output in an average sized man at resting levels and might reach higher values were such a man to exercise to capacity.

Effects of Perfusion Pressure on Coronary Flow.

In the studies described in the preceding paragraphs, the coronary arteries were perfused under a constant pressure head to simplify the analysis and interpretation of the experiments. However, a progressive elevation of the coronary artery pressure results in a progressive elevation of the coronary flow per unit time. Both systolic and diastolic flows are generally increased under these conditions. The increase in coronary flow is not closely correlated with the increase in coronary arterial pressure. For example, when sudden clamping of the aorta produces a sudden elevation of coronary arterial pressure, the coronary flow increases promptly and then descends to levels below the control level even while arterial pressure is continuing to rise.[11] These changes indicate that the vascular resistance to coronary blood flow changes during the elevation of the perfusion pressure.

Effects of Anoxia on Coronary Blood Flow.

Dilation of the coronary vascular bed with a great increase in coronary flow per unit of perfusion pressure promptly results during the course of asphyxia. Under these conditions the tension of oxygen decreases and that of carbon dioxide increases in the myocardium. Coronary dilation also occurs in an animal breathing a mixture with a low oxygen tension even if the carbon dioxide elimination is normal. Breathing high concentrations of carbon dioxide does not increase the coronary flow. Thus, diminished oxygen tension in the myocardium may be a mechanism for coronary dilation, while carbon dioxide has little role to play in this event (see also Chap. 4). Theoretically, diminished oxygen in the ventricular wall could provide a simple and automatic system for increasing the coronary flow when the load on the ventricles increases. It is extremely difficult to evaluate the importance of other coronary control mechanisms because they all tend to affect the metabolism of the myocardium which, in turn, alters the oxygen extraction and possibly the oxygen tension in the myocardium. In fact, the oxygen consumption of the myocardium is increased merely by raising the perfusion pressure and the coronary flow even without increasing the work performed by the myocardium.

Neural Mechanisms in Coronary Control. Stimulation of the vagus nerves to the heart produces severe bradycardia and reduces the work performed by the heart. However, section of the vagus and stimulation of its peripheral end does not affect coronary flow so long as the heart rate and blood pressure remain unchanged. Stimulation of the sympathetic nerves to the heart profoundly affects the contractility, oxygen consumption and coronary flow. Some of the increase in flow might result from the more vigorous myocardial contraction, the reduced duration of systole and the relative increase in the duration of diastole (Fig. 16, Chap. 3). All of these factors would tend to increase coronary flow. The increase in coronary flow from sympathetic stimulation is always

accompanied by an increase in the work of the heart. Whether the sympathetic nerves have any direct effect on the caliber of the coronary vessels remains conjectural. According to Berne,[12] intracoronary administration of sympathetic transmitter substances (epinephrine and norephineprine) in a beating, fibrillating or potassium-arrested dog heart indicates that their primary action is vasoconstriction. The coronary dilation they produce must be related to their effects on myocardial metabolism. In fact, stimulation of sympathetic nerves to the heart when cardiac work is reduced by obstructing inflow of blood still increases the myocardial oxygen consumption. Since oxygen extraction from the coronary blood is so complete under resting conditions, any increase in myocardial oxygen consumption must be closely related to an increase in coronary blood flow. Thus we return to the starting place as indicated in the introduction to this chapter.

II. Myocardial Ischemia

All too frequently, myocardial ischemia is considered solely as a manifestation of coronary arterial disease. Actually, the coronary flow must be viewed in relation to the myocardial oxygen requirements and the total energy release of the heart. The coronary blood flow is only one factor which may limit the cardiac reserve (see Chap. 15). Myocardial ischemia results from relative coronary insufficiency during both normal and abnormal conditions, primarily from increased oxygen consumption by the myocardium rather than from decreased coronary blood flow. Such increased consumption occurs in normal persons during strenuous exertion. When the myocardium receives an adequate blood flow, it can accomplish prodigious amounts of work. A critical stage in heart disease is most often reached

when oxygen delivery is insufficient for the oxygen consumption during normal activity. Even in advanced stages of cardiac disability, the cardiac output and oxygen delivery may be entirely adequate at rest. In such circumstances, the cardiac reserve capacity diminishes to the point that it reduces the maximum activity the individual can sustain. The status of a patient should be evaluated in terms of the relationship between the load on the heart and the factors which might interfere with the transportation of oxygen into the myocardial cells.

GENERAL CAUSES OF MYOCARDIAL ISCHEMIA

Many types of cardiovascular disease impose an increased load on the heart and, at the same time, interfere with the delivery of oxygen to the myocardium (see Chap. 15). A few additional examples are cited.

Pressure Loads

Arterial hypertension increases the work of the heart and leads to hypertrophy of the muscle fibers which, in turn, increases the diffusion distance between the coronary capillaries and the center of the myocardial cells (see Fig. 8, Chap. 15). Since arterial hypertension is usually associated with some degree of arteriosclerosis, blood flow through the coronary arteries may be impeded. Whenever a load on the heart is compensated by an increase in the myocardial mass in the cardiac walls, the efficiency of oxygen delivery to the heart is diminished to some extent.

Similarly, aortic valvular stenosis imposes a serious pressure load on the left ventricle and simultaneously diminishes the pressure gradient from the root of the aorta to the coronary capillaries (see Fig. 7, Chap. 12). Blood flow through the coronary arteries may cease completely during ventricular systole.

Volume Loads

Abnormally great ventricular output results from a number of conditions. In any form of valvular insufficiency, the stroke output increases to compensate for the volume of blood which regurgitates (see Chap. 12). Aortic regurgitation produces a pernicious volume load on the left ventricle because the low diastolic pressure in the root of the aorta reduces the pressure driving blood through the coronary arteries. A similar functional disturbance results from arteriovenous shunts or from patent ductus arteriosus (see Chap. 14).

Diminished Oxygen Transport

Primary pulmonary disease may interfere with oxygenation of the blood in the lungs, so that arterial blood contains reduced quantities of oxygen to supply both the tissues and the myocardium. At the same time, pulmonary arterial hypertension may impose a pressure load on the right ventricle.

Clearly, the principles indicated by these few examples could be extended to encompass most forms of cardiovascular disease. Thus, myocardial hypoxia is an important factor to be considered in evaluating the condition of any patient with cardiovascular disease. This discussion is devoted primarily to myocardial ischemia produced by functional and organic disturbances in the coronary vessels.

CORONARY ATHEROSCLEROSIS

The principal cause of restricted coronary flow results directly or indirectly from atherosclerosis. Although its cause has not yet been determined, atherosclerosis is no longer considered a degenerative process to be expected with advancing age. It is now regarded as a metabolic disturbance of lipid metabolism, for which specific therapy may be ultimately developed.[13] This change in attitude is a most important development for future progress.

The Nature of Coronary Atheromata

Atherosclerosis occurs with greatest frequency in the aorta and in the cerebral and coronary arteries. In Figure 4, the pathogenesis of atherosclerotic lesions in the coronary arteries is illustrated schematically in accordance with the sequence of events described by Moon and Rinehart.[14] In early lesions the intima is diffusely thickened by accumulated mucoid ground substance and a proliferation of subendothelial fibroblasts. The internal elastic membrane is fragmented by focal areas of degeneration. Accumulation of lipids is not always demonstrable in early lesions, and its localization—in the intima, in the media or in both—is somewhat unpredictable.

When coronary atherosclerosis is well

PATHOGENESIS OF CORONARY ATHEROSCLEROSIS

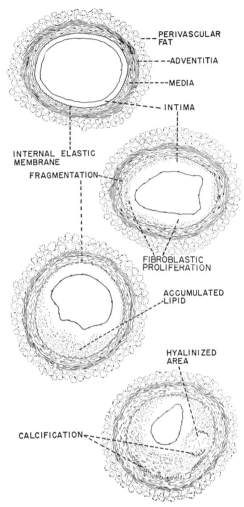

PERIVASCULAR FAT

ADVENTITIA

MEDIA

INTIMA

INTERNAL ELASTIC MEMBRANE

FRAGMENTATION

FIBROBLASTIC PROLIFERATION

ACCUMULATED LIPID

HYALINIZED AREA

CALCIFICATION

FIGURE 4. In the normal coronary artery, the intima is uniformly thin and composed of collagenous connective tissue. The early stages of coronary atherosclerosis are characterized by fragmentation of the internal elastic membrane and thickening of the intima due to fibroblastic proliferation associated with accumulation of mucopolysaccharide. In the early phases of the process, accumulation of lipid may or may not be demonstrable.[14] As the intima becomes thickened, lipids (e.g., cholesterol) tend to accumulate at the junction of the intima with the media. Finally, areas of the atherosclerotic plaque degenerate and become hyalinized. Calcium is deposited predominantly at the edges of hyaline areas and at the junction of intima and media. The lumen of the vessel is greatly restricted, and may even become completely occluded, by progressive expansion of the atheroma.

developed, the intima is thickened by fibrous proliferation, the advancing borders of the plaques being composed of loosely arranged fibroblasts and mucoid ground substance (mucopolysaccharide) resembling the early lesions. Lipid accumulates as fine and coarse droplets, principally at the base or center of the plaque and least along the endothelial border. The intimal plaques often encroach upon the media.

Advanced stages of atherosclerosis are characterized by hyaline degeneration at the base or center of the plaques where the concentration of lipid is greatest. Calcification usually begins at the junction of the intima and media, or in the hyalinized areas. The elastic tissue suffers extreme degeneration and fragmentation. Infiltration of the adventitia with lymphocytes is frequently observed. The histologic appearance of atherosclerotic lesions is illustrated by the photomicrographs in Figure 5.

Incidence of Coronary Atherosclerosis

The initial stages of coronary atherosclerosis are observed in nearly all adults. If rigid criteria are used, only very young children are completely free of any stigmata. The incidence and severity of atherosclerotic lesions in the coronary arteries increases with age. White, Edwards and Dry[15] tabulated the degree of coronary atherosclerosis observed during 100 consecutive autopsies on men whose ages were distributed through the six decades between 30 and 89 years. Some results of this study are summarized in Figure 6. The average severity of the lesions increased very rapidly from age 30 through 49 years. The lesions in the right main coronary artery and in the two main branches of the left coronary artery (anterior descending and circumflex) were comparable. On the average, the plaques were less extensive in the smaller branches of the right coronary artery (posterior descending and right marginal). This study

HISTOLOGY OF CORONARY ATHEROSCLEROSIS

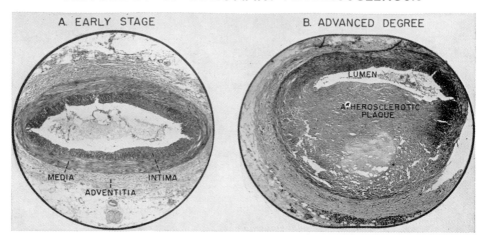

FIGURE 5. Two photomicrographs of a main coronary artery (on the right) and a small branch of the same vessel (on the left) illustrate the histologic appearance of early and advanced coronary atherosclerosis.

A, The intima is irregularly thickened to a very slight degree. Slight fragmentation of the internal elastic media is present, but not effectively reproduced in this photomicrograph. In other respects the vessel is normal.

B, The lumen of this large coronary artery is greatly reduced by a large atherosclerotic plaque. Fusiform vacuoles in the intima remain where lipids were dissolved away. The intima is grossly thickened by processes illustrated in Figure 4. A hyalinized area appears in the basilar portion of the plaque. Lymphocytes have infiltrated a region around the periphery of the adventitia at the bottom of the photomicrograph.

DEVELOPMENT AND DISTRIBUTION OF CORONARY ATHEROSCLEROSIS

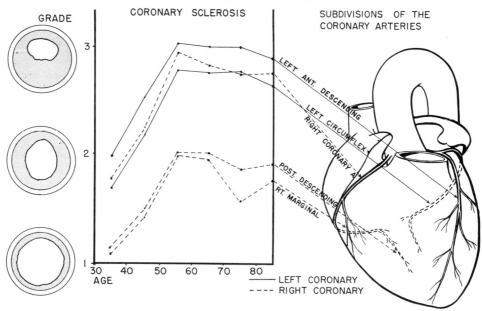

FIGURE 6. The most severe atherosclerotic lesions in each subdivision of the coronary arteries were determined in 100 consecutive postmortem examinations on men in each decade from 30 through 89 years. The average grade of the most severe lesion was plotted for each decade of life in each segment of the arterial tree. Similar degrees of atherosclerotic changes were noted in the right main coronary artery and in the anterior descending and circumflex branches of the left coronary artery. Smaller branches of the right coronary artery had less severe lesions. (After White, Edwards and Dry.[15])

222

indicates that the severity of atherosclerotic lesions tends to remain fairly constant after the fifth decade. About 70 per cent of the men who had passed their fifth decade had sclerosis of grade 3 or more somewhere in the distribution of the coronary arterial system.

Functional Effects of Coronary Obstruction

Expanding atheromatous plaques seriously restrict the lumen of the coronary arteries (Figs. 4 and 5). The diminished lumen increases the resistance to the flow of blood past the site of atherosclerotic lesions. Thus, the pressure drop along the vessel is greater than normal and the perfusion pressure in the distal branches is diminished. Since the pressure gradient is

HYDRAULIC EFFECTS OF VASCULAR OBSTRUCTION

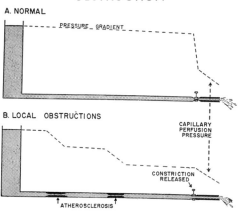

FIGURE 7. *A*, Fluid is propelled rapidly through vessels of large caliber by shallow pressure gradients. Pressure declines steeply wherever the caliber is greatly diminished. In the coronary vessels, the pressure gradient steepens as the vessels ramify to smaller and smaller caliber, but the greatest pressure drop occurs at the terminal vessels where peripheral resistance is controlled.

B, Atherosclerosis produces local obstructions consisting of segments in which the lumen is greatly restricted, as indicated schematically in the drawing. Steep pressure gradients at each restricted segment of vessel may dissipate much of the total pressure head before the blood reaches the terminal branches. Peripheral vasodilatation compensates for the increased resistance upstream, but the reserve coronary flow is depleted in the process.

very shallow in large arteries, their lumen can be considerably diminished without a significant reduction in the pressure head beyond the obstruction. In small arteries, the same reduction in the lumen produces a much greater pressure drop. Coronary atherosclerosis is usually not an isolated lesion, but a number of lesions scattered throughout the coronary arterial tree. Some of the arterial pressure head is lost as the blood passes each obstruction (Fig. 7). Vasodilatation of the small coronary vessels[11] helps compensate for increased resistance upstream. However, the compensatory dilatation of the coronary bed is limited, so that encroachment on the lumen of an artery beyond some critical degree will produce progressive diminution in blood flow.

Atherosclerosis develops gradually and may completely occlude a large branch of a coronary artery without causing destruction of the myocardium because collateral channels from adjacent branches expand and carry additional blood to maintain the viability and function of the affected area.[16] Widespread coronary atherosclerosis is occasionally observed in postmortem examination of patients who had no previous disability attributable to insufficient blood flow to the heart. Experimental coronary occlusion has clearly indicated the importance of the rate at which obstruction develops.

Experimental Coronary Obstruction. If a major branch of the coronary arteries in a dog is gradually occluded over a period of weeks or months, neither histologic evidence of myocardial damage nor reduced ventricular performance may be demonstrable.[17] Progressive occlusion of two main coronary branches may also be well tolerated. Dogs which survived this procedure ran at 3 m.p.h. on a grade of 25 degrees for 30 minutes without difficulty. One animal survived successive ligation of all three major branches of the coronary arteries. The septal and conus arteries must have been the principal remaining source of blood to the ventricles. A similar degree of coronary obstruction has been seen in man.[18] In about half of human hearts, an artery arises from a separate ostium near the right coronary artery to supply the pulmonary conus.[18] This artery may provide substantial collateral flow when the other vessels are more seriously afflicted with atherosclerosis.

Even moderate degrees of atherosclerosis presumably limit the cardiac reserve. Since coronary venous blood contains very little oxygen, a reduction in the arteriovenous oxygen difference would do little to remedy the deficiency (see Chap. 15). Complete occlusion of one or more major branches of the coronary arteries must diminish the total coronary reserve even though collateral channels dilate to serve myocardium deprived of its blood supply. Since atherosclerotic plaques are usually not restricted to one or two coronary branches (Fig. 6), collateral channels generally connect vascular networks with varying degrees of sclerosis.[19] In view of the fact that atheromata usually appear in several coronary trunks, the degree of coronary sclerosis which can develop without seriously limiting the exercise tolerance is almost unbelievable.[18, 19] The disparity between the extensive pathologic involvement of the coronary arteries and the limited degree of functional disability is difficult to explain. However, such discrepancies between organic disease of the heart and its powers of compensation are not only commonplace, but a constant source of difficulty in predicting the course of cardiovascular disease. This fact indicates that undetected factors play a role in these compensatory reactions.

ANGINA PECTORIS

The most common symptom of impaired coronary flow is precordial pain. Patients with coronary atherosclerosis may develop a syndrome consisting of a fairly specific, constricting type of pain, which seems to originate behind the sternum and frequently radiates over the left precordium and along the inner surface of the left arm. The term "angina pectoris" is applied to this particular type of pain. It characteristically occurs in paroxysms of relatively brief duration, brought on most commonly by exertion or any other activity which increases the cardiac output. Walking rapidly uphill against a cold wind is perhaps the most frequently cited set of circumstances precipitating an attack. The discomfort is often accompanied by a sensation of impending doom, causing the patient to stop in his tracks until the pain recedes.

Etiology of Angina Pectoris

Myocardial ischemia is the logical precipitating cause of angina pectoris. Anginal pain is usually compared to the pain produced by exercising the muscles of the forearm when their blood supply is cut off by an inflated cuff. Acid metabolites tend to accumulate in contracting muscles receiving too little oxygen, and these substances may stimulate pain endings directly or through changes in pH.

Inadequate blood flow through the coronary arteries is the principal underlying feature of the disease and may result from (a) increased resistance to coronary flow, (b) reduced perfusion pressure, (c) increased oxygen requirements of the myocardium or (d) a combination of these factors. Increased resistance to coronary blood flow stems from coronary atherosclerosis, coronary spasm or both. Coronary spasm is generally assigned an important role in angina pectoris because of its brief duration, and because of the facts that strong emotions may precipitate an attack, the pain disappears with rest, and clinical signs may be absent between attacks. The relief of pain after administration of nitroglycerin also indicates that coronary spasm existed during attack.

In general, angina pectoris can be produced by any set of conditions which simultaneously impose a load on the heart and impede coronary blood flow. However, the picture is not as clear as this statement implies. Many patients have severe angina, apparently without sufficient changes in coronary vessels, and others have no angina even after attacks of acute coronary occlusion. Furthermore, not all patients have the typical retrosternal pain with radiation to the left arm. The pain may be referred to different regions over the precordium or back and to more distant sites. These deviations from the typical response must be related to the perception and radiation of pain from the heart.

Characteristics of Visceral Pain from the Heart

The pain of angina pectoris is described variously as a constriction, a burning sensation, a fullness or tightness in the chest, a choking sensation, or an uncomfortable aching discomfort. Most commonly, the pain seems to be centered just behind the mid-portion of the sternum, radiating predominantly to the left precordium, but occasionally extending to the epigastrium, the root of the neck, the jaw, the shoulder, the back, and down the arms (usually the left). In contrast with somatic sensations of touch or pain evoked from the skin, visceral sensation is characteristically poorly localized. Somatic pain in many regions of the body is recognized as coming from a very discrete area; this can be easily demonstrated by pricking the finger or tongue with a pin. Nerve endings are very close together in these regions and are stimulated with sufficient frequency that localization is learned at an early age. On the skin of the back the point of stimulation cannot be as accurately recognized, apparently because the sensory nerve endings are farther apart. Nevertheless, the site of the stimulus is perceived as being within a circumscribed area on the skin. Con-

versely, pain produced by a needle thrust through the skin into skeletal muscles or into a blood vessel may produce a diffuse, deep, aching sensation which involves a large area, even an entire arm or leg. Inaccurate localization and diffuse distribution of pain from viscera are the basis for the radiation of pain in angina pectoris.

Radiation of Anginal Pain

The frequent radiation of cardiac pain from the precordium to other regions (Fig. 8A) indicates that visceral afferent fibers must have central connections in common with the somatic afferent system.

In 1893, MacKenzie[20] suggested that sensory impulses from the viscera have no direct connection with the brain, but act as an "irritable focus" in the segment at which they enter the spinal cord. He postulated that afferent impulses from viscera reinforce or facilitate impulses from the somatic afferent nerves producing perceptible pain. On the other hand, Ruch[21] has suggested that visceral afferent and somatic afferent fibers may converge on the same neurons in the spinal cord, or at higher levels, so that painful sensations from a viscus are perceived, on the basis of experience, as coming from the distribution of the somatic nerve. If convergence can exist between the somatic and visceral afferent systems, it is not surprising that pain from the heart is referred to distant regions served by the somatic afferent nerves. According to Wyburn-Mason,[22] cardiac pain is usually referred to the left side of the body because nerves supplying the left ventricle enter the spinal cord from the left. Anginal pain distributed over the right side may indicate involvement of the right side of the heart. In patients with dextrocardia, angina may be referred almost exclusively to the right of the midline. In some patients, pain from the heart has been referred to the left upper or left lower quadrants in the abdomen, to the epigastrium or even to the teeth or sinuses.

SITE AND RADIATION OF ANGINA PECTORIS

A. DISTRIBUTION OF ANGINAL PAIN

B. CONVERGENCE OF VISCERAL
AND SOMATIC AFFERENTS

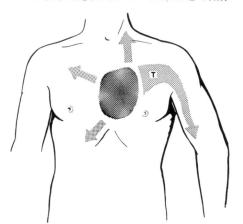
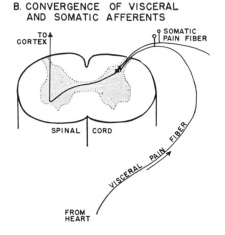

FIGURE 8.   A, Precordial pain or angina pectoris, associated with myocardial ischemia, usually seems most severe just beneath the sternum, but often radiates to more distant regions such as the left arm, right arm, upper abdomen, neck, jaw or back. According to Rinzler,[24] pressure on trigger zones (T) may produce the same kind of pain with a similar distribution. Blocking of the trigger areas with local anesthetics may alleviate angina pectoris.

B, Both visceral and somatic afferent nerves probably impinge upon the same spinothalamic cells in the spinal cord. Thus, one explanation of radiation of visceral pain is based on the subjective interpretation of impulses from visceral nerves as arising in somatic pain endings in the skin. (After Ruch.[21])

Travell[23] reported that anginal pain could be promptly alleviated by spraying the precordium with an ethyl chloride spray. Rinzler[24] reviewed evidence that coronary occlusion may produce "trigger" areas in chest muscles from a "visceromotor" reflex similar to the spasm of abdominal musculature associated with acute inflammatory disease within the abdomen (e.g., appendicitis). Spasm persisting in the thoracic musculature after the original pain in the heart has abated may also produce referred pain. Trigger areas frequently develop in the pectoralis major, pectoralis minor and serratus anterior muscles of patients with persistent cardiac pain. Stimulation of the trigger areas by pressure or by inserting a needle produces pain which is referred to the same general areas as the original angina pectoris (Fig. 8). Angina pectoris following acute myocardial infarction may be alleviated by local block of the trigger areas.

Radiation of anginal pain may raise problems in the differential diagnosis of coronary atherosclerosis and diseases in other viscera such as the gallbladder. In patients with cholecystitis or peptic ulcer, angina may be ameliorated by eliminating the source of irritation in the gallbladder or the stomach, but it rarely disappears. Since most attacks of angina pectoris are transient, differentiation between this condition and chronic cholecystitis or peptic ulcer should not be difficult. It is important to keep in mind the fact that pain in these distant regions may be associated with disease of the coronary arteries.

Even relatively slight intensities of visceral pain are peculiarly distressing and intolerable. Not only is the pain subjectively disagreeable, but stimulation of visceral afferents is prone to elicit powerful autonomic reflex activity often resulting in profuse sweating, epigastric uneasiness, bradycardia, hypotension and sycope.

A diagnosis of angina pectoris is not complete until the other sources of precordial pain are excluded and the etiology of myocardial ischemia has been determined as accurately as possible. For example, similar precordial pain occurs with pulmonary hypertension.[25] All conditions which may produce an abnormal load on the heart and restrict coronary blood flow should be included in the differential diagnosis. The characteristic signs of many of these disease entities will be considered in subsequent chapters. Bean[26] listed more than one hundred different conditions which had been improperly diagnosed as angina pectoris or coronary occlusion. If the angina results from coronary atherosclerosis, acute massive myocardial infarction with sudden death could conceivably occur at any time.

MYOCARDIAL INFARCTION

Acute Coronary Occlusion

Coronary arteries are most frequently occluded abruptly by thrombi formed in the lumen of the vessel. Roughening of the endothelial surface over atheromatous plaques and encroachment on the arterial lumen produce eddy currents beyond the obstruction and contribute to thrombus formation (Fig. 9A). Fragments of atheromatous plaques may break off and lodge at some point farther on. Inflammatory processes in the arterial wall theoretically might play a role in some cases. In recent years formation of hematomas within atheromatous plaques has received considerable attention (Fig. 9B). Paterson[27]

MECHANISMS OF CORONARY OCCLUSION

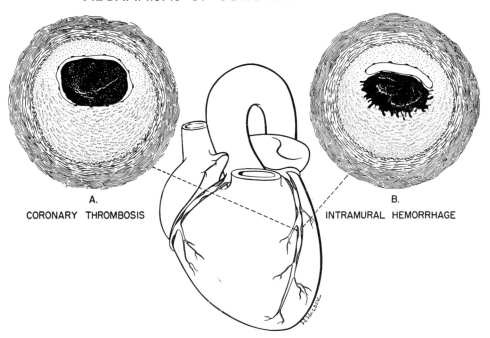

A.
CORONARY THROMBOSIS

B.
INTRAMURAL HEMORRHAGE

FIGURE 9. Two mechanisms have been postulated to account for acute coronary occlusion in patients with coronary atherosclerosis.

A, The most common cause is probably a thrombus which develops within the lumen of a sclerotic vessel.

B, In some specimens, coronary arteries appear to be occluded by hemorrhage into atherosclerotic plaques. Such intramural hemorrhages are believed by some investigators to originate from capillaries growing into the atherosclerotic plaque from the lumen of the coronary artery rather than from vasa vasorum.

suggested that hemorrhage into atheromatous plaques may predispose to thrombus formation in the lumen of the vessel. Sudden expansion of the hematoma may occlude the arterial lumen without rupture of the intimal lining.[28] Differentiating between such a condition and a mural thrombus at postmortem examination is difficult, but the evidence for intramural hemorrhage is becoming more convincing. Embolic obstruction of coronary arteries has been reported, but is a rare phenomenon.[29]

Infarction Without Recent Coronary Occlusion

In a series of 143 patients dying of acute myocardial infarction, 49 had no known recent coronary occlusion.[30] The ventricles in three-fourths of this puzzling group were hypertrophied to more than 50 per cent above normal. The degree of coronary sclerosis was similar in all patients regardless of the occurrence of coronary occlusion. However, occlusion usually produced transmural infarcts while the infarcts without occlusion were more frequently subendocardial. Littman and Barr[31] reported 207 consecutive cases of acute coronary insufficiency of which 59 (28.5 per cent) were not attributed to coronary occlusion. In these atypical cases, the nature of the coronary insufficiency can be described only in general terms.

Changes in the Myocardium During Infarction

Experimental coronary ligation in the dog first produces an irregular area of cyanosis in the region supplied by the vessel. Myocardium suddenly deprived of its blood supply contracts less vigorously. Within a minute the muscle loses so much contractile power that it stretches during isometric contraction, remains stretched during systole, and shortens during isometric relaxation.[32] Oxygen tension, measured directly in the muscle, decreases rapidly to less than 25 per cent

of the baseline values. In the border areas, the diminution in oxygen tension is less profound and beyond these borders there is no change.[33] The border areas represent regions where the collateral circulation is not adequate for normal function, but is sufficient to maintain viability in the myocardium. In the center of the ischemic tissue, congestion, hemorrhage and edema form in the connective tissue stroma, and cloudy swelling, fatty degeneration and necrosis occur in the myocardial fibers. Within two days fibroblasts concentrate in the borders of the infarct and by five days, a well defined zone of fibroblasts

Table 1. Incidence of Signs and Symptoms of Myocardial Infarction*

	FIRST ATTACK PER CENT	SECOND ATTACK PER CENT
1. Dyspnea	95	96
2. Enlarged heart	83	85
3. Weak heart sounds	85	82
4. Rales	83	82
5. Cyanosis	77	86
6. Cough	70	84
7. Pallor	69	79
8. Pain	75	66
9. Orthopnea	68	63
10. Sweating	60	60
11. Vomiting	59	59
12. Ankle edema	55	54
13. "Shock"	57	45
14. Restlessness	44	49
15. Tachycardia (rate over 100)	42	39
16. Systolic murmur	38	71
17. Cheyne-Stokes respiration	24	42
18. Ascites	26	33
19. Cloudy sensorium	26	23
20. Enlarged liver	18	27
21. Gallop rhythm	12	4
22. Prodromal phenomena	21	15
23. Bradycardia (rate below 80)	16	20
24. Angor animi	12	11
25. Pericardial friction rub	15	14
26. Pulsus alternans	9	8
27. Precordial hyperesthesia	8	10

* From Bean, W. B.: Infarction of the heart. II. Symptomatology of acute attack. *Ann. Intern Med.*, 11:2086–2108, 1938.

divides necrotic from living muscle. After about three weeks, the infarcted area consists of a well formed scar much smaller than the original area of cyanosis, indicating that increased collateral circulation restored some of the border areas.

The sequence of events during infarction in human hearts reconstructed by Mallory, White and Salcedo-Salgar is similar to that described for the dog. The principal differences are the delayed onset of fibroblast proliferation (four days) and delayed scar formation (two to three months) in man (see Bayley[34]).

Diagnosis of Myocardial Infarction

Any particular patient with acute myocardial infarction may present either no definitive symptoms or, more frequently, a combination of a great many complaints. The incidence of various symptoms in a group of cases studed by Bean[35] is indicated in Table 1. These signs and symptoms can be arranged in a functional grouping which provides a rational approach to responses of different patients (Table 2).

Table 2. Functional Grouping of Signs and Symptoms of Myocardial Infarction

I. Pain

II. Autonomic Effects

A. Pallor	E. Syncope
B. Sweating	F. Tachycardia
C. Vomiting	G. Shock
D. Bradycardia	H. Disturbed Sensorium

III. Diminished Myocardial Contractility

A. Congestive Heart Failure

1. Left ventricular failure	2. Right ventricular failure
a. Dyspnea	a. Peripheral congestion
b. Orthopnea	b. Enlarged liver
c. Cough	c. Edema
	d. Cyanosis

B. Cardiac Signs

1. Weak heart tones	6. Paradoxical pulsation
2. Gallop rhythm	
3. Systolic murmur	7. Pericardial friction rub
4. Pulsus alternans	
5. Ventricular enlargement	8. ECG alterations

Pain with Myocardial Infarction. The origin of pain in myocardial infarction is presumably the same as that in angina pectoris. Pain from infarction is usually more severe and persists for longer periods of time, being unrelieved by cessation of physical exertion. Indeed, many attacks occur when the patient is at rest or even asleep. A wide variety of descriptive words is used by different patients to indicate the type of pain they experienced (Table 3). In general, these terms are the

Table 3. Types of Pain in Myocardial Infarction*

	PER CENT
Crushing pressure	44
Squeezing, constricting, vise-like	29
Choking, smothering, suffocating	18
Sharp, stabbing, knife-like	11
Sore, aching, dull	11
"Excruciating"	7
Burning	5

* From Bean, W. B.: Infarction of the heart. II. Symptomatology of acute attack. *Ann. Intern. Med.*, 11:2086–2108, 1938.

same as those used to describe anginal pain, to which about half of the patients have been subject prior to their first attack of acute myocardial infarction.

In some patients, acute myocardial infarction may not be accompanied by any pain, but there is disagreement on how often this occurs. Bean[35] reported 28 per cent of attacks without pain while Kennedy[36] found only 4 per cent. In reviewing the literature, Pollard and Harvill[37] found the reported incidence of painless myocardial infarction to vary from 61 per cent to 4 per cent. The actual incidence probably lies somewhere between these figures, but no value can be stated with confidence. When myocardial infarction occurs without pain, some combination of the other possible symptoms and signs can generally be discovered (Table 2). These "substitution symptoms" are particularly important in the absence of the typical precordial pain.

Autonomic Responses to Myocardial Infarction.

Syncope. Pallor, sweating, epigastric uneasiness and vomiting, bradycardia, hypotension and syncope result from a powerful autonomic response initiated by a wide variety of stimuli including (*a*) powerful emotions, (*b*) unpleasant sights, (*c*) moderate venesections, (*d*) vasodilating drugs, (*e*) stimulation of visceral afferent nerves as in the carotid sinus syndrome and (*f*) visceral pain. A precipitous reduction of arterial blood pressure results primarily from a lowering of total peripheral resistance without a corresponding increase in cardiac output. Bradycardia in the presence of arterial hypotension is an inappropriate autonomic response indicating the extent to which the regulatory controls have been unbalanced. The bradycardia may be an important factor in the failure of the cardiac output to increase in the face of reduced total peripheral resistance. In other words, the compensatory mechanisms responsible for the maintenance of arterial blood pressure are thrown out of balance by an overriding autonomic reflex response. However, as soon as the stimulus is removed, the normal equilibrium between peripheral resistance and cardiac output is rapidly restored. Syncopal attacks of this sort generally occur when the individual is erect and are promptly terminated when he lies down. If the patient is reclining, the same stimuli rarely induce syncope. In acute myocardial infarction, the stimulus is very powerful and is not promptly relieved. Severe hypotension may persist in reclining patients with coronary occlusion.

Shock. Shock is characterized by a progressive reduction in blood pressure due to persistent deficiency of cardiac output in spite of tachycardia and intense peripheral vasoconstriction. Thus, the principal deficiency is a reduction in stroke volume. This condition is classified under autonomic responses in Table 2, in view of the evidence that the diminished cardiac output is probably not caused solely by a disorder of myocardial contractility and the fact that many patients with extensive myocardial infarction fail to develop shock. For these and other reasons, the fundamental disturbance in shock is more appropriately considered a disturbance of autonomic controls. Despite a tremendous volume of research on the experimental forms of shock, the exact mechanisms remain controversial. The extent to which diminished contractility and distensibility contribute to the picture is not known. All in all, the factors which produce such a profound disturbance of autonomic or humoral mechanisms remain to be elucidated. They must be very powerful because they override the compensatory mechanisms which normally maintain the equilibria in the cardiovascular system.

It has been suggested that the fall in arterial blood pressure during shock from myocardial infarction is beneficial because it reduces the load on the ventricle. This observation overlooks the drop in coronary perfusion pressure which accompanies any significant decrease in arterial blood pressure. Indeed, myocardial infarction is sometimes precipitated by shock produced during surgery. For this reason, it is imperative that the shock which accompanies acute myocardial infarction be combated as promptly and effectively as possible.

Diminished Myocardial Contractility

When a portion of the left ventricular wall is suddenly deprived of its blood supply, the involved myocardium soon loses its ability to shorten during systole. Its contractile power is so diminished that it becomes stretched as the remainder of the ventricular wall contracts. Thus, the infarcted region not only fails to contribute to systolic ejection but places an added volume load on the remainder of the myocardial fibers. Bulging of the infarcted region during systole is caused by the displacement of blood which would otherwise have been ejected into the aorta. Thus, the myocardial fibers which are still actively contracting must release more energy and also shorten to a greater extent to make up for the bulging of the ischemic region. Clearly, the extent of effective compensation by the remaining myocardial fiber depends upon the location and size of the infarcted region. Interruption of the blood supply to a large portion of the deep constrictor fibers in the left ventricle generally produces sudden death. On the other hand, an infarct of similar size at the apex is more frequently survived. The condition of the myocardium and the coronary arteries also plays an important role in the immediate survival of the patient. The symptoms of diminished myocardial contractility due to myocardial infarction are the same as those of congestive heart failure from any cause (see Chap. 16).

There may be signs of left ventricular failure during and after acute infarction of the left ventricle. Right ventricular failure may also develop following acute left ventricular myocardial infarction and lead to peripheral congestion, edema, ascites, enlarged liver and cyanosis (see Chap. 16). However, this must not be interpreted as an infarction in the right ventricular wall. Although the right coronary artery is frequently involved in atherosclerotic processes, isolated infarction of the right ventricular wall is very rare.[38] Signs of right ventricular failure developing after myocardial infarction usually mean that left ventricular failure has imposed an increased load on the right ventricle, presumably through pulmonary hypertension. The right ventricular wall may occasionally be involved by extension of an infarct across the interventricular groove. The relative rarity of right ventricular infarction suggests that the blood supply to the right ventricle is great in relation to its load, which is usually much less than that of the left ventricle.

Auscultatory Signs

Although precordial pain and the peripheral vascular signs tend to dominate the clinical picture of myocardial infarction, auscultatory examination of the heart may reveal a number of helpful clues.

The heart sounds are often weak or muffled. The cause of this change in heart sounds is not known. The third heart sound often becomes audible near the apex producing a gallop rhythm (see Chap. 11). A systolic murmur is frequently heard and has been attributed to relative mitral insufficiency following dilatation of the left ventricle. Local regions of pericarditis over the infarcted area may produce a friction rub which is audible within the first two days after an infarction and persists or recurs over a period of four or five days.

The arterial blood pressure is generally reduced below the level sustained before the infarction, particularly if the patient had been hypertensive. For obscure reasons, the blood pressure tends to remain low for a long time. The force of left ventricular contraction may be reduced on every second cycle, so that the systolic pressure fluctuates 4 to 10 mm. Hg on altenate beats. This is called *mechanical alternans* and may be demonstrated during sphygmomanometry. Only half of the pulses may pass under a cuff inflated to a pressure between the two systolic pressure levels. Premature contractions or short bouts of paroxysmal tachycardia are frequently encountered during the first few hours or days after infarction. They may herald the development of ventricular fibrillation and sudden death.

Roentgenography

Roentgenography frequently reveals an enlarged heart, but it must be remem-

Table 4.　Causes of Myocardial Ischemia in Metabolic Disease

Disease	Mechanism	Restricted Coronary Flow	Reduced Myocardial Efficiency	Hypertension	Increased Cardiac Output
1. CORONARY ATHEROSCLEROSIS		X			
2. THYROID DISEASE					
A. HYPOTHYROIDISM	ATHEROSCLEROSIS	X			
B. HYPERTHYROIDISM	TACHYCARDIA		X		
	REDUCED EFFICIENCY		X		
	INCREASED BLOOD FLOW				X
3. GOUT	ATHEROSCLEROSIS	X			
	HYPERTENSION			X	
4. OBESITY	ATHEROSCLEROSIS	X			
	HYPERTENSION			X	
	VOLUME LOAD				X
5. ADRENAL DYSFUNCTION					
A. CORTICAL HYPERFUNCTION (CUSHING SYNDROME)	HYPERTENSION			X	
B. MEDULLARY HYPERFUNCTION (PHEOCHROMOCYTOMA)	EPINEPHRINE		X	X	X
6. HYPERINSULINISM	HYPOGLYCEMIA ↓ EPINEPHRINE		X	X	X
7. DIABETES	ATHEROSCLEROSIS	X			
	HYPERTENSION			X	
8. BERIBERI	IMPAIRED CONTRACTILITY		X		
	TACHYCARDIA		X		
	PERIPHERAL VASODILATATION				X

Table header structure: CAUSES OF MYOCARDIAL ISCHEMIA → RESTRICTED CORONARY FLOW / INCREASED MYOCARDIAL REQUIREMENTS → REDUCED MYOCARDIAL EFFICIENCY / INCREASED ENERGY RELEASE → HYPERTENSION / INCREASED CARDIAC OUTPUT

bered that a majority of these patients had systemic arterial hypertension or organic heart disease before the infarction. Fluoroscopy occasionally discloses a portion of the ventricular silhouette which bulges outward during systole. This paradoxical pulsation corresponds to the bulging of the weakened myocardial wall described above. Electrokymographic tracings may substantiate the reversal of pulsation,[39] but rarely disclose a change which could not be recognized during fluoroscopy.

Electrocardiographic Signs

Acute myocardial infarction produces sequential changes in the electrocardiographic patterns which are often the most obvious diagnostic signs. In Chapter 10 changes in the configuration of the various electrocardiographic complexes will be described in terms of alterations in the rate and course of depolarization and repolarization.

MYOCARDIAL ISCHEMIA IN CERTAIN METABOLIC DISEASES

The basic causes of myocardial ischemia involve restricted coronary blood flow and increased myocardial requirements due to (a) diminished myocardial efficiency or (b) increased myocardial energy release (e.g., from arterial hypertension or increased output). As indicated in Table 4, a wide variety of metabolic diseases are potential causes of myocardial ischemia through one or both of these mechanisms. This type of analysis reveals the fallacy of considering myocardial ischemia solely in terms of restricted coronary blood flow from coronary atherosclerosis. For example, *hypothyroidism* not only causes cardiac enlargement (myxedema heart), apparently involving impaired myocardial metabolism, but also fosters the development of atherosclerosis. *Hyperthyroidism* not only interferes with myocardial efficiency by inducing persistent tachycardia and by direct metabolic effects on the myocardium, but also imposes a sustained volume load on the heart to support the increased level of metabolism. These effects are discussed in greater detail below. Patients with *gout* often develop unusually severe atherosclerosis as well as systemic arterial hypertension. *Obesity* is frequently accompanied by atherosclerosis and mild or moderate degrees of arterial hypertension with some potential increase in the volume load on the heart due to the proliferation of capillary beds into newly formed adipose tissue. Systemic arterial hypertension is a prominent feature of adrenal cortical hyperfunction (*Cushing's syndrome*). Since epinephrine reduces myocardial efficiency and increases systemic arterial blood pressure and cardiac output, excessive release of epinephrine (e.g., from pheochromocytomas) imposes a severe load on the heart which may seriously tax coronary blood flow and induce myocardial ischemia. Similarly, the hypoglycemia produced by excessive insulin in the blood appears to stimulate release of abnormally large amounts of epinephrine. On the other hand, *diabetes* is characteristically associated with severe atherosclerosis and some degree of systemic arterial hypertension. In *beriberi*, the heart enlarges very greatly and myocardial contractility diminishes, apparently as a result of impaired thiamine metabolism by heart muscle. Tachycardia, which also impairs myocardial efficiency, is a prominent feature of the disease. Finally, a severe volume load is imposed on the heart through extensive peripheral vasodilatation. Cardiac catheterization in a patient with beriberi disclosed a cardiac output of 16.1 liters per minute, an oxygen consumption of 355 cc. per minute and an A-V oxygen difference of 2.2 cc.[40] Thus, the increase in cardiac output was not in proportion to the body's oxygen requirements as evidenced by the diminished A-V difference (see Chap. 15). Two

hours after thiamine administration, the cardiac output was reduced to 12 liters per minute, the oxygen consumption increased to 415 cc. per minute and the A-V oxygen difference was 3.45 cc. The sustained elevation of cardiac output in both beriberi and hyperthyroidism is equivalent to uninterrupted physical exercise continuing day and night so far as the heart is concerned. The functional effects of thyroid dysfunction are discussed in greater detail for reasons set forth below.

Thyroid Dysfunction

Abnormal thyroid activity has been selected for particular attention in this section for two reasons: (*a*) Excessive thyroid secretion impairs myocardial efficiency while greatly increasing the load on the heart. (*b*) In recent years, considerable attention has been directed toward the induction of hypothyroidism to provide symptomatic relief of patients with advanced heart disease, particularly those diseases which produce myocardial ischemia.

Hyperthyroidism. The precise chemical structure of the hormone released by the thyroid gland is not known, although it certainly contains amino acids in which iodine is incorporated. Functional disturbances resulting from deficiency in the thyroid hormone can be corrected by the administration of thyroxin, thyroid extracts, thyroglobulin, or iodinated casein. One function of the thyroid hormone is to accelerate oxidative processes in many tissues, since it increases the oxygen consumption of excised pieces of heart, liver, kidney and brain.[41] The metabolism of other substances such as carbohydrate, fat, electrolytes, and vitamins is influenced primarily by the generalized increase in metabolic rate.

Effects of Thyroid Hormone on the Heart Rate. Priestley *et al.*[42] administered thyroxin to rabbits and dogs for several days. Even when the hearts of these animals were excised and used in heart-lung preparations, the heart rates were significantly faster than the rates for hearts from normal animals. A heart transplanted into the neck of a donor animal developed tachycardia when thyroxin was administered to the host. Thyroxin administered to fragments of embryonic hearts, excised before nerve elements appeared, produced progressive acceleration of the heart and occasional irregularities in rhythm. The fragments also ceased pulsating sooner than the controls.[43] This was attributed to exhaustion of the muscle cells and accumulation of metabolic waste products. Irrigation of the specimen with Tyrode solution to wash away metabolic products restored pulsation at rapid rates. Tachycardia is also induced by thyroxin administered to dogs with denervated hearts.[44] The evidence seems clear that the tachycardia from excess thyroid hormone represents a direct effect on the pacemaker activity of the myocardium.

One important aspect of the action of thyroid hormone is the reduction in the efficiency with which work is performed, both by skeletal muscle and by myocardium. The oxygen consumption at rest is elevated (increased basal metabolic rate), and a given quantity of muscular work causes an abnormally great increase in oxygen consumption, peripheral blood flow, cardiac output and heart rate. Perhaps thyroxin inhibits certain enzymes involved in the anaerobic synthesis of high-energy phosphate bonds, and the alternative aerobic reactions increase the the oxygen consumption[45] and diminish efficiency. Be that as it may, hyperthyroidism imposes a heavy load on the myocardium, which must put out more useful work to supply the augmented metabolic requirements of the body while the efficiency of its contraction is diminished by tachycardia and by direct action of thyroid hormone on the myocardial fibers.

Functional Effects of Hyperthyroidism. The circulatory response to hyperthyroidism resembles that of a normal person to strenuous exercise.[46] The cardiac impulse is diffuse and forceful, the heart is accelerated, the pulse pressure is widened and the skin capillaries are dilated. When the metabolic rate of a resting patient is 35 per cent above normal, the cardiovascular response is equivalent to that of a normal individual continuously performing moderate exercise day and night. When a patient with hyperthyrodism undertakes physical exertion, the circulatory reaction is extravagant when compared to that of normal individuals performing the same task.

In young persons, the heart may compensate for this excessive load, but in older individuals, cardiovascular reserves may become exhausted and heart failure supervenes. Clearly, a degree of coronary sclerosis which would not produce symptoms in an otherwise normal person may produce myocardial ischemia on effort in the presence of hyperthyroidism. When the nature of the disease is recognized, a high incidence of angina pectoris in older patients with this condition is not surprising. Atrial fibrillation also is quite common, presumably because the irritability of the myocardium is increased.

It is unnecessary to postulate that increased thyroid hormone directly induces organic cardiac disease. The excessive load on the heart accentuates the effects of other disease processes and this is sufficient to explain the clinical manifestations of the disease.

Hypothyroidism. Hypothyroidism usually results from either spontaneous atrophy or surgical excision of thyroid tissue. The principal signs are weakness, fatigability, somnolence, slowed mental reactions, poor appetite and loss of weight,[41] puffiness of the skin (particularly around the eyes), diminished perspiration and generalized loss of hair.

These signs and symptoms develop insidiously over many years. As the clinical course progresses, the puffiness around the eyes spreads to include the entire body (myxedema), mental retardation becomes severe, and the voice is hoarse and low pitched. The heart rate is slow, and the P and T waves have low voltage. Cardiac enlargement, principally dilatation, develops during the final stages in the disease. The cardiac silhouette closely resembles that produced by pericardial effusion. In many patients, fluid in the pericardial sac, as well as the cardiac enlargement, contributes to the large cardiac silhouette. Extreme atherosclerosis is likely to develop in patients with severe hypothyroidism, and may lead to myocardial infarction. Myxedema is a rare condition, and current interest in the subject is largely directed toward the therapeutic induction of hypothyroidism to ameliorate intractable angina pectoris.

SUMMARY

Myocardial ischemia occurs whenever the coronary blood flow is insufficient in relation to the oxygen requirements of the myocardium. Many types of cardiac disease simultaneously increase the requirements for myocardial energy release and interfere with delivery of oxygen to the myocardium. For this reason, myocardial ischemia can be an important limitation on the cardiac reserve in virtually all types of heart disease.

Direct interference with the coronary blood flow most commonly results from coronary atherosclerosis, which develops to a significant degree in more than 70 per cent of men over 50 years of age. Moderate coronary sclerosis can be compensated for by peripheral vasodilation in the terminal coronary arterial tree and by expansion of collateral vessels. Progressively increasing coronary obstruction usually affects several branches of the coronary tree, and the coronary flow reserve is depleted. Characteristic pain in the precordium (angina pectoris), often radiating to other regions, occurs during exertion in some patients with coronary atherosclerosis and disappears quite promptly with rest. Spasm of the coronary vessels is probably important in the production of this type of precordial pain.

Gradual occlusion of coronary vessels provides time for collateral circulation to develop, and destruction of myocardial tissue is thereby avoided. However, a sudden occlusion of a coronary artery produces both dysfunction and death of myocardium deprived of its blood supply. A surprisingly large proportion of hearts showing infarction at postmortem examination have no obvious signs of recent coronary occlusion. The principal signs and symptoms of myocardial infarction can be considered in terms of (a) intense radiating precordial pain, (b) severe autonomic responses, (c) heart failure from diminished ventricular contractility, (d) changes in heart sounds and blood pressure, (e) roentgenographic findings and (f) electrocardiographic signs. Although interpretation of the electrocardiographic signs of myocardial infarction is somewhat empirical, serial records coupled with careful clinical studies usually indicate the diagnosis. Since the electrocardiographic changes are rather nonspecific, a number of other conditions can produce similar patterns (e.g., ventricular strain patterns). For this reason, the diagnosis must depend upon sound judgment applied to the total clinical picture.

REFERENCES

1. WAGNER, A., and POINDEXTER, C. A. Demonstration of the coronary arteries with nylon. *Amer. Heart J.*, 37:258–266, 1949.
2. BAROLDI, G., MANTERO, O., and SCOMAZZONI, G. The collaterals of the coronary arteries in normal and pathologic hearts. *Circulat. Res.*, 4:223–229, 1956.
3. SCHLESINGER, M. J. Relation of anatomic pattern to pathologic conditions of the coronary arteries. *Arch. Path.*, 30:403–415, 1940.
4. PRINZMETAL, M., SIMKIN, B., BERGMAN, H. C., and KRUGER, H. E. Studies on the coronary circulation. II. The collateral cir-

culation of the normal human heart by coronary perfusion with radioactive erythrocytes and glass spheres. *Amer. Heart J.*, 33: 420–442, 1947.

5. PRINZMETAL, M., BERGMAN, H. C., KRUGER, H. E., SCHWARTZ, LOIS L., SIMKIN, B., and SOBIN, S. S. Studies on the coronary circulation. III. Collateral circulation of beating human heart and dog hearts with coronary occlusion. *Amer. Heart J.*, 35:689–717, 1948.

6. WIGGERS, C. J. The functional importance of coronary collaterals. *Circulation*, 5:609–615, 1952.

7. PROVENZA, D. W., and SCHERLIS, S. Demonstration of muscle sphincters as a capillary component in the human heart. *Circulation*, 20:35–41, 1959.

8. GREGG, D. E. Regulation of the collateral and coronary circulation of the heart. Pp. 163–186 in *Circulation*, J. McMichael, ed. Oxford, Blackwell Scientific Publication, 1958.

9. GREGG, D. E., and SABISTON, D. C., JR. Current research and problems of the coronary circulation. *Circulation*, 13:916–927, 1956.

10. WIGGERS, C. J. The interplay of coronary vascular resistance and myocardial compression in regulation of coronary flow. *Circulat. Res.*, 2:271–279, 1954.

11. GREGG, D. E. *Coronary Circulation in Health and Disease.* Philadelphia, Lea & Febiger, 227 pp., 1950.

12. BERNE, R. M. Effect of epinephrine and norepinephrine on coronary circulation. *Circulat. Res.*, 6:644–655, 1958.

13. ALLEN, E. V., KATZ, L. N., KEYS, A., and GOFMAN, J. W. Atherosclerosis. A symposium. *Circulation*, 5:98–100, 1952.

14. MOON, H. D., and RINEHART, J. F. Histogenesis of coronary arteriosclerosis. *Circulation*, 6:481–488, 1952.

15. WHITE, N. K., EDWARDS, J. E., and DRY, T. J. The relationship of the degree of coronary atherosclerosis with age, in men. *Circulation*, 1:645–654, 1950.

16. ECKSTEIN, R. W., GREGG, D. E., and PRITCHARD, W. H. The magnitude and time of development of the collateral circulation in occluded femoral, carotid and coronary arteries. *Amer. J. Physiol.*, 132:351–361, 1941.

17. BURCHELL, H. G. Adjustments in the coronary circulation after experimental coronary occlusion. Pp. 139–144 in *Blood, Heart and Circulation.* Publication No. 13, F. R. Moulton, ed. Washington, D. C., American Association for the Advancement of Science, 1940.

18. ZOLL, P. M. Normal and pathological anatomy of the coronaries. *Trans. Amer. Col. Cardiol.*, 1:29–43, 1951.

19. BLUMGART, H. S., SCHLESINGER, M. J., and DAVIS, D. Studies on the relation of the clinical manifestations of angina pectoris, coronary thrombosis, and myocardial infarction to the pathologic findings. With par-

ticular reference to the significance of the collateral circulation. *Amer. Heart J.*, 19:1–91, 1940.

20. MACKENZIE, J. Some points bearing on the association of sensory disorders and visceral disease. *Brain*, 16:321–354, 1893.

21. RUCH, T. C. Pathophysiology of pain. Ch. 15 in *Medical Physiology and Biophysics*, 18th ed., T. C. Ruch and J. F. Fulton, eds. Philadelphia, W. B. Saunders, 1960.

22. WYBURN-MASON, R. Significance of the reference of anginal pain to the right or left side of the body. *Amer. Heart J.*, 39:325–335, 1950.

23. TRAVELL, JANE V. Early relief of chest pain by ethyl chloride spray in acute coronary thrombosis. *Circulation*, 3:120–124, 1951.

24. RINZLER, S. H. *Cardiac Pain.* Springfield, Ill., Charles C Thomas, 139 pp., 1951.

25. VIAR, W. N., and HARRISON, T. R. Chest pain in association with pulmonary hypertension. Its similarity to the pain of coronary disease. *Circulation*, 5:1–11, 1952.

26. BEAN, W. B. Coronary artery disease. Some aspects of the natural history of ischemic heart disease. Ch. 30 in *Diseases of the Chest, Including the Heart*, J. A. Myers, ed. Springfield, Ill., Charles C Thomas, 1960.

27. PATERSON, J. C. Factors in the production of coronary artery disease. *Circulation*, 6:732–739, 1952.

28. WARTMAN, W. B. Occlusion of the coronary arteries by hemorrhage into their walls. *Amer. Heart J.*, 15:459–470, 1938.

29. MORAGUES, V., BAWELL, M. B., and SHRADER, E. L. Coronary embolism: review of the literature and report of a unique case. *Circulation*, 2:434–437, 1950.

30. MILLER, R. D., BURCHELL, H. B., and EDWARDS, J. E. Myocardial infarction with and without acute coronary occlusion. A pathologic study. *Arch. Intern. Med.*, 88:597–604, 1951.

31. LITTMAN, D., and BARR, J. H., JR. Acute atypical coronary artery insufficiency. Incidence and clinical course. *Circulation*, 5:189–200, 1952.

32. TENNANT, R., and WIGGERS, C. J. The effect of coronary occlusion on myocardial contraction. *Amer. J. Physiol.*, 112:351–361, 1935.

33. SAYEN, J. J., SHELDON, W. F., HORWITZ, O., KUO, P. T., PEIRCE, G., ZINSSER, H. F., and MEAD, J., JR. Studies of coronary disease in the experimental animal. II. Polarographic determinations of local oxygen availability in the dog's left ventricle during coronary occlusion and pure oxygen breathing. *J. Clin. Invest.*, 30:932–940, 1951.

34. BAYLEY, R. H. An interpretation of the injury and the ischemic effects of myocardial infarction in accordance with the laws which determine the flow of electric currents in homogeneous volume conductors, and in ac-

cordance with relevant pathologic changes. *Amer. Heart J.*, 24:514–528, 1942.

35. BEAN, W. B. Infarction of the heart. II. Symptomatology of acute attack. *Ann. Intern. Med.*, 11:2086–2108, 1938.

36. KENNEDY, J. A. The incidence of myocardial infarction without pain in 200 autopsy cases. *Amer. Heart J.*, 14:703–709, 1937.

37. POLLARD, H. M., and HARVILL, T. H. Painless myocardial infarction. *Amer. J. Med. Sci.*, 199:628–635, 1940.

38. MYERS, G. B., KLEIN, H. A., and HIRATZKA, T. Correlation of electrocardiographic and pathologic findings in infarction of the interventricular septum and right ventricle. *Amer. Heart J.*, 37:720–770, 1949.

39. DACK, S., PALEY, D. H., and SUSSMAN, M. L. A comparison of electrokymography and roentgenkymography in the study of myocardial infarction. *Circulation*, 1:551–563, 1950.

40. LAHEY, W. J., ARST, D. B., SILVER, M., KLEEMAN, C. R., and KUNKEL, P. Physiologic observation on a case of beriberi heart disease with a note on the acute effects of thiamine. *Amer. J. Med.*, 14:248–255, 1953.

41. WINKLER, A. W. Disorders of the thyroid gland. Ch. 17 in *Diseases of Metabolism: Detailed Methods of Diagnosis and Treatment. A Text for the Practitioner*, 2nd ed., G. G. Duncan, ed. Philadelphia, W. B. Saunders, 1947.

42. PRIESTLEY, J. T., MARKOWITZ, J., and MANN, F. C. The tachycardia of experimental hyperthyroidism. *Amer. J. Physiol.*, 98:357–362, 1931.

43. MARKOWITZ, C., and YATER, W. M. Response of explanted cardiac muscle to thyroxine. *Amer. J. Physiol.*, 100:162–166, 1932.

44. MCINTYRE, M. The effects of thyroid feeding on the heart rate in normal dogs and in dogs with completely denervated hearts. *Amer. J. Physiol.*, 99:261–270, 1931.

45. MARTIUS, C., and HESS, B. The mode of action of thyroxin. *Arch. Biochem.*, 33:486–487, 1951.

46. BLUMGART, H. L., LEVINE, S. A., and BERLIN, D. D. Congestive heart failure and angina pectoris. The therapeutic effect of thyroidectomy on patients without clinical or pathologic evidence of thyroid toxicity. *Arch. Intern. Med.*, 51:866–877, 1933.

Chapter 10

ELECTRICAL ACTIVITY OF THE HEART

Electrical potentials associated with waves of excitation which spread through the heart can be recorded from electrodes applied to the surface of the body. The electrodes consist of curved metal plates firmly applied to areas of skin which have been coated with electrode paste and gently abraded to reduce skin resistance. Since the largest cardiac potentials recorded from the skin rarely exceed 2 mV., very sensitive recording equipment is needed to register them. String galvanometers, originally introduced by Einthoven for this purpose, have been almost completely replaced by direct-writing galvanometers powered by vacuum tube amplifiers.

Many physicians leave electrocardiographic interpretation to cardiologists and rarely see the original records. This attitude is unrealistic because considerable information can be gained from examining electrocardiographic records, even without specialized training. Since electrocardiograms represent potentials inscribed on paper moving at a constant speed, the records indicate the rate and sequence of cardiac excitation. Thus, heart rate can be accurately measured and abnormalities of rhythm and conduction can be readily identified. The principles involved in detecting changes in rate, rhythm and sequence of cardiac excitation can be mastered with little effort. Electrocardiography becomes more complicated when changes in the shape of the individual deflections are analyzed. Basic theories used to explain variations in the configuration of electrocardiographic complexes will be given consideration.

The sequence of cardiac excitation and the specialized conduction system of the heart were described in Chapter 2 (see Figs. 7 and 8). The normal sequence of excitation initiates myocardial contraction, and establishes the mechanical events of the cardiac cycle. If the sequence of cardiac excitation and contraction is not clearly understood, the reader would profit by a review of those sections before proceeding.

I. The Source of Cardiac Potentials

The changes in potentials, recorded as electrocardiograms, resemble electrical phenomena occurring in other excitable tissues such as skeletal muscle, smooth muscle and nerves (see Chap. 2). In the resting state there is a difference in potential between the inside and the outside of these cells. This potential difference can be detected only by inserting a microelectrode into individual muscle fibers (Fig. 1). The difference in potential between the inside and the outside of a resting myocardial fiber ranges around 75 mV.[1, 2] Its presence has been ascribed to a charged cell "membrane."

The Origin of Membrane Potentials

The cell membrane serves as a semipermeable barrier between two very different solutions. Outside the cell, the concentration of sodium is very high and the potassium level is very low. Within the normal resting cell, potassium is the predominant cation and the sodium concentration is very small. To attain a low concentration of sodium within the cells, sodium ions must be selectively transferred from regions of low concentration across the cell membrane to the extracellular spaces where the concentration is high. Since active transfer of Na^+ requires movement of a charged particle against a concentration gradient, energy must be expended by the oxidative metabolic processes of the cell. As Na^+ is removed from the cell, a potential difference develops across the cell membrane and drives K^+ into the cell until its outward diffusion pressure is balanced by the electrical potential. Thus, the only requirement for the development of a resting potential across a cell membrane is the selective transfer of sodium ions out of the cell.

Action Potentials

If the membrane potential is diminished to some critical level in a local area, either spontaneously or by an external electrical stimulus, the permeability of the membrane to sodium and potassium increases suddenly, permitting these ions to

POTENTIALS IN SINGLE MYOCARDIAL FIBERS

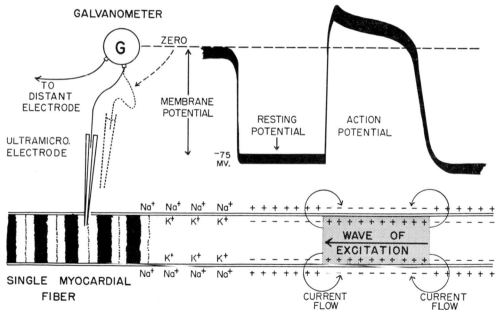

FIGURE 1.   Potentials between the inside and outside of myocardial cells can be measured directly with an ultramicroscopic electrode consisting of a thin glass tube drawn out to a very fine tip (less than 0.5μ) and filled with a solution of potassium chloride. The potential difference recorded when the electrode is inserted into the cell amounts to about 75 mV. This potential is due to a difference between the concentration of ions (mainly Na^+ and K^+) inside and outside of the cell, so that the inside of the cell is negative ($-$) in relation to the outside. As a wave of excitation passes over the fiber, an action potential is recorded; the potential rapidly approaches zero and overshoots (reversed polarity of the membrane). The resting potential is restored gradually at first and then very rapidly during the later stages of the repolarization process.

pass through the membrane.[3, 4] This process rapidly reduces and then reverses the membrane potential. At the same time, current flowing into the depolarized portion of the membrane passes out through adjacent regions of the cell membrane. This local current flow is sufficient to depolarize these adjacent regions and produce propagation of the impulse down the fiber. In this way, a wave of increased permeability (with its associated changes in membrane potential) spreads rapidly down the myocardial fiber. The fiber is restored to the resting state when membrane permeability to sodium and potassium returns to normal and the unequal ion distribution again becomes manifest.

The rapidly propagating area of increased membrane permeability produces a flow of electrical current and changes in potential which can be recorded from an intracellular electrode (Fig. 1). As the wave of excitation passes the electrode at a velocity of about 0.3 m. per second, the membrane potential decreases and reverses very rapidly (the inside of the cell becomes positive with respect to the outside). Thus, an active myocardial cell is not only "depolarized," but actually exhibits an overshoot to a positive potential. The membrane potential returns toward the resting value, slowly at first and then very rapidly.

Action potentials measured from single myocardial cells bear little resemblance to cardiac potentials recorded from the surface of the body. These differences must be resolved by considering the principles underlying the recording of external potentials from masses of myocardial tissue rather than from single cells.

Electrical Manifestations of Polarized Membranes

The changes in the concentrations of Na^+ and K^+ cannot be directly measured during the passage of an action potential. However, the changes in potential caused

CURRENT FLOW IN VOLUME CONDUCTORS

A. CURRENT FLOW IN WIRE

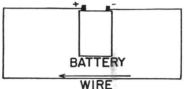

B. CURRENT FLOW IN SALINE

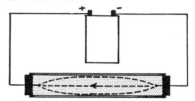

C. CURRENT FLOW IN VOLUME CONDUCTOR

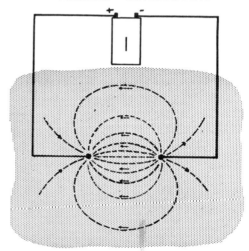

FIGURE 2. *A*, Electrical current in a wire is carried by electrons which travel from the negative to the positive terminals of a battery.

B, Electrical currents are carried through solutions by positive and negative ions which move in opposite directions through liquid media.

C, A volume conductor is a medium through which electrical current can flow in three dimensions, as in a large volume of an electrolyte solution. Current density is greatest on a line directly connecting the two electrodes and diminishes along the more circuitous routes.

by the movements of these charged particles can be amplified, recorded and studied. Thus, it is important to consider the electrical manifestations of the distribution of charged particles. To this end, it is necessary to be familiar with a few definitions.

The fundamental quantities in electricity are positive and negative *charges*, which are equal in magnitude and mutually attract each other. Electrical currents are defined in terms of the number of unit charges passing a cross section of conducting medium each second. *Current density* refers to the number of charges passing through a unit area each second. Electrical *potentials* are actually differences in potential between two specific points (e.g., electrode positions). The *potential difference* between two points is defined as the work necessary to carry a unit positive charge between these two points.

Potential differences and current flow in biologic systems occur in volume conductors instead of wires. A *volume conductor* is a medium, such as a large vessel containing an electrolytic solution (Fig. 2), which conducts electricity in three dimensions. Since all the body fluids contain electrolytes, the body is a volume conductor. Electrical currents flowing through volume conductors may traverse an infinite number of pathways (Fig. 2). If the solution is homogeneous, the current density is greatest along a direct path between the electrodes. Potential differences can be recorded between any two points along a current pathway, either on a wire or in a volume conductor (Fig. 3). On the other hand, if recording electrodes are placed at appropriate points on two comparable current pathways, no potential difference is present. The current flow progressively diminishes through the portions of the volume conductor at greater distances from the current source. The potentials diminish with the square of the distance, schematically illustrated by the greater separation of isopotential lines in Figure 4.

At a great distance from the current source, the potential may be nearly zero, so an electrode placed in such a region can be used as a zero reference (indifferent electrode). Since the potential actu-

POTENTIALS IN VOLUME CONDUCTORS

A. POTENTIALS ALONG WIRES   B. POTENTIALS IN A VOLUME CONDUCTOR

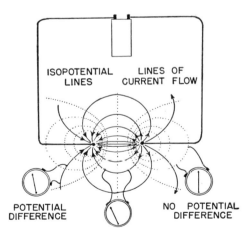

FIGURE 3.   *A*, Differences in potential can be recorded along a current pathway, as in a wire. Indeed, the potential difference is the cause of current flow. No potential is recorded from corresponding points on two identical wires and no current flows between these two points.

B, Potential differences can be recorded along the lines of current flow in volume conductors. No potential difference can be recorded along lines which are perpendicular to the lines of current flow (see *A*, above). The dotted lines indicate isopotential lines along which no potential difference can be recorded ˙

UNIPOLAR ELECTRODE

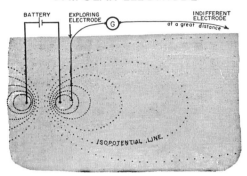

FIGURE 4.   A galvanometer records the difference in potential between two points. If absolute potential is to be measured, one side of the galvanometer must be connected to an electrode at zero potential. The potentials in a volume conductor diminish with the square of the distance from a current source, as indicated by the progressively increasing separation between isopotential lines. If one of the electrodes is placed at a sufficient distance in the volume conductor, the potentials become negligible for practical purposes. Using this distant (indifferent) electrode as a zero reference, the exploring electrode can be used to determine the "absolute" potentials at any point in the volume conductor. This process is called "unipolar" recording, since only one electrode is affected by the potentials.

ally becomes zero at an infinite distance, the indifferent electrode must be at a point where the potentials are too small to be significant. Whether a potential is significant depends upon the required accuracy of the measurements. If an indifferent electrode is connected to one side of a galvanometer, the electrode on the other side can be used as an "exploring electrode" to measure the potentials in any portion of the volume conductor. Measurement of potentials with an exploring and an indifferent electrode (termed unipolar recording) is simpler to visualize and to illustrate than bipolar recording, in which both electrodes are in regions of high current density (e.g., the standard limb electrodes in routine electrocardiography).

Dipoles.   The difference in potential on the two sides of a membrane can be represented by a positive charge (+) outside the membrane balanced by an equal

negative charge (−) on the inside (Fig. 1). Each pair of positive and negative charges is called a dipole (Fig. 5A). The potential produced by a single dipole is insignificant, but in biologic systems, many pairs of positive and negative charges are arranged on opposite sides of membranes.

Membrane Potentials.   When a membrane has positive and negative charges arranged symmetrically as a double layer on opposite sides of it, it is said to be "polarized" (Fig. 5B). A large number of charges symmetrically arranged on a membrane combine to produce a potential which can be recorded at some distance. A positive potential will be recorded whenever the electrode is closer to the positive than to the negative charges. In other words, when the positive charges on a membrane face the exploring electrode, a positive potential is recorded by that electrode. If the number of charges per unit area (charge density) is constant, the magnitude of the recorded potential will be determined by three factors: (a) the area of the membrane (total number of charges), (b) the orientation of the membrane with respect to the electrode and (c) the proximity of the electrode to the membrane. These three variables can be most easily described in terms of the solid angle subtended by the charged membrane (see Fig. 5C). The solid angle is greater when the area of the polarized membrane is increased or the radius is diminished according to the formula: Solid angle = Area/Radius^2 (Fig. 5C). The solid angle is maximal when a flat membrane is oriented perpendicular to a line drawn from its center to the electrode (Fig. 5D). If the membrane is tilted from this position, the solid angle is diminished, as is the potential recorded by the electrode. No potential is recorded when the distances from the electrode to the positive and negative charges are precisely equal (Fig. 5D).

By means of solid angles, the relative

magnitude and sign of potentials from polarized membranes of any size, shape, orientation or distance from the electrode can be predicted. For example, the two membranes (M_1 and M_2) illustrated in Figure 5E subtend the same solid angle and, individually, each would produce the same potential at an electrode. The

POLARIZED MEMBRANES

A. DIPOLE

B. POLARIZED MEMBRANE

C. SOLID ANGLE

$$SOLID\ ANGLE = \frac{AREA}{R^2}$$

D. ORIENTATION OF MEMBRANE

E. SIZE AND SHAPE OF MEMBRANES

basic mechanism by which two membranes with the same solid angle produce equal potentials at an exploring electrode is indicated in Figure 5E. On the other hand, the pairs of membranes illustrated in Figure 6A subtend the same solid angles, but positive charges on one membrane and negative charges on the other face the electrode. The potentials from these pairs of membranes counteract each other, and no potential can be recorded by the exploring electrode. By the same token, no potential can be recorded by an exploring electrode near a cell which is polarized equally over its entire surface Fig. 6B).

This principle is basic to electrocardiographic interpretation because it applies equally to collections of cells such as the heart. During the intervals when the myocardium is completely polarized or uniformly depolarized, no potentials are recorded by external electrodes and the galvanometer remains at the baseline. Electrocardiographic complexes are inscribed only when part of the myocardium is polarized and the remainder is depolarized (e.g., during excitation or return to the resting state).

When an area on a cell is depolarized, the charges on the membrane are reduced in number or reversed in sign and a potential can then be recorded. In the re-

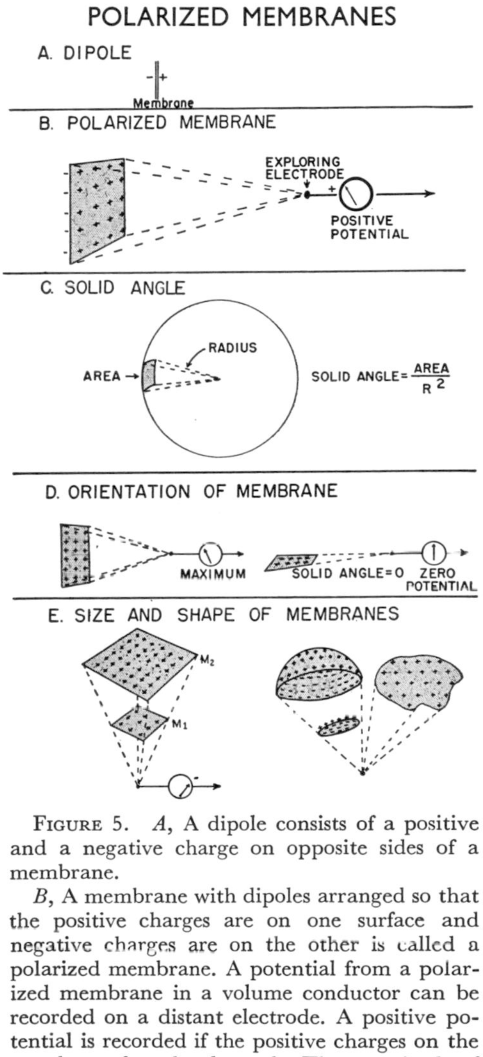

FIGURE 5.   A, A dipole consists of a positive and a negative charge on opposite sides of a membrane.

B, A membrane with dipoles arranged so that the positive charges are on one surface and negative charges are on the other is called a polarized membrane. A potential from a polarized membrane in a volume conductor can be recorded on a distant electrode. A positive potential is recorded if the positive charges on the membrane face the electrode. The magnitude of the potential depends upon the solid angle subtended by the polarized membrane.

C, A solid angle actually refers to the apparent size of a surface as viewed from a specific position (e.g., the site of an electrode).

D, When a polarized membrane is perpendicular to a line drawn through its center to the electrode it has maximum apparent size when

viewed from the electrode position and it produces its maximal potential in this orientation. No potential is recorded if only the edge of the membrane is presented to the electrode because the distances from it to the positive and negative charges of each dipole are exactly equal.

E, The potential recorded from a charge decreases with the square of the distance, but the number of charges on a uniformly charged membrane increases with the square of the distance. Thus, if M_2 is twice as far from the electrode as M_1, the potential recorded from each charge on M_2 is one-quarter as great but there are four times as many charges as on M_1. Thus, each of these membranes would develop the same potential at the electrode. So long as polarized membranes subtend the same solid angle, they will produce equal potentials at the electrode regardless of their size or shape.

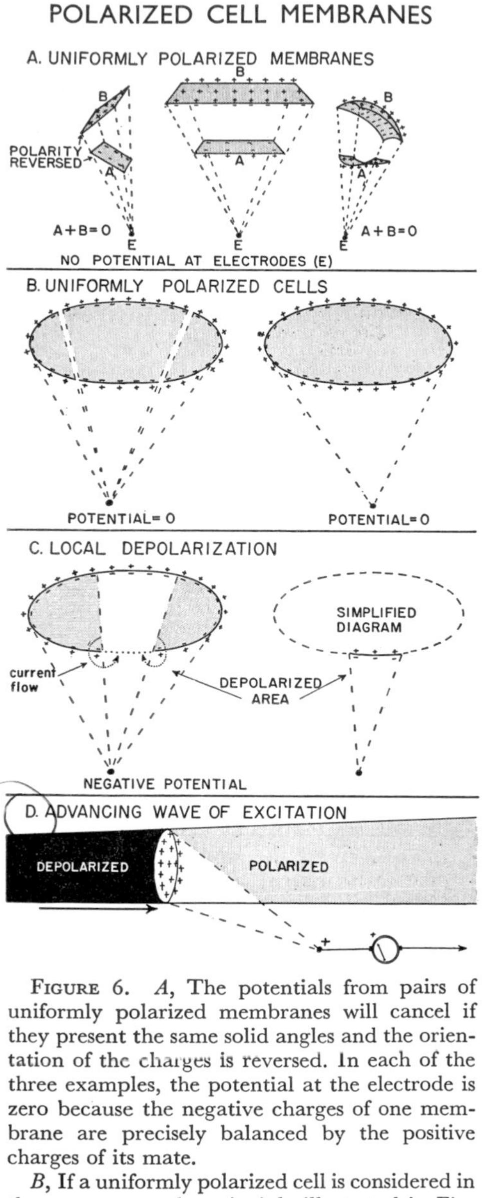

POLARIZED CELL MEMBRANES

A. UNIFORMLY POLARIZED MEMBRANES

POLARITY
REVERSED

A+B=0　　　　　　　　　　　　A+B=0

NO POTENTIAL AT ELECTRODES (E)

B. UNIFORMLY POLARIZED CELLS

POTENTIAL= 0　　　　　　　POTENTIAL= 0

C. LOCAL DEPOLARIZATION

SIMPLIFIED
DIAGRAM

current
flow

DEPOLARIZED
AREA

NEGATIVE POTENTIAL

D. ADVANCING WAVE OF EXCITATION

DEPOLARIZED　　　　POLARIZED

FIGURE 6. *A*, The potentials from pairs of uniformly polarized membranes will cancel if they present the same solid angles and the orientation of the charges is reversed. In each of the three examples, the potential at the electrode is zero because the negative charges of one membrane are precisely balanced by the positive charges of its mate.

B, If a uniformly polarized cell is considered in three segments, the principle illustrated in Figure 6*A* applies. In each of the three solid angles, the proximal portion of the membrane has positive charges and the more distant portion has negative charges facing the electrode. Since the near and distant portions of the membrane subtend the same solid angle and the charges are oriented in opposite directions, their effects cancel and the potential at the electrode is zero. Thus, a uniformly polarized (or uniformly depolarized) cell produces no potential which can be recorded by an external electrode. In other words, if the membrane is uniformly polarized, there is no potential difference and no flow of electrical current, and no potential can be recorded.

gion outlined by the solid angle in Figure 6*C*, a portion of the membrane facing the electrode is illustrated as completely depolarized and the portion of the membrane immediately behind has negative charges facing the electrode. Current flows from the surrounding polarized membrane into the depolarized zone and, as soon as current flows, a potential can be recorded at the electrode. Under these conditions, the electrode records a negative potential with a magnitude proportional to the solid angle drawn to the junction of the polarized and depolarized areas (Fig. 6*C*). This rather complicated picture can be simplified schematically by substituting a suitably charged membrane conforming to the zone of transition between the polarized and the depolarized membrane. Such a hypothetical membrane precisely reproduces the electrical effects illustrated in the more complicated drawing. Thus, a wave of excitation produces a negative potential when it is moving away from an electrode and a positive potential when it approaches an electrode (Fig. 6*D*). In the same way, a wave of excitation passing through a mass of myocardial tissue can be outlined by a solid angle which indicates the relative magnitude and sign of a potential re-

C, When a region of a polarized cell becomes partially or completely depolarized, electrical currents flow from the polarized regions into the depolarized zone. A potential can then be recorded by a distant electrode; the magnitude of the potential is determined by the solid angle subtended by the depolarized area. On the far side of the cell, negative charges are not balanced by opposite charges in the depolarized region, so the electrode records a negative potential. On the right, a suitably charged membrane conforming to the depolarized area is comparable to the more complicated picture on the left, since the solid angle is the same.

D, The advancing wave of excitation can be visualized as though a suitably charged membrane were placed at the junction between polarized and depolarized regions (as in *C*, above). Since the outside of the polarized area is positive in relation to the inside, an electrode records a positive potential when a wave of excitation advances toward it and a negative potential when a wave of excitation is moving away.

corded from an electrode at a specific site in relation to the electrical disturbance.

In summary, myocardial cells produce no external potentials so long as they are either completely polarized or completely depolarized, because the equal and opposite charges in each fiber precisely counteract each other. Potentials are recorded only from a transition zone between the polarized and depolarized regions where the charged surfaces are not cancelled. Stated another way, potentials can be recorded only when electrical current flows in response to potential differences (e.g., between polarized and depolarized regions). This is the essence of electrocardiography.

SEQUENCE OF CARDIAC EXCITATION
by ALLEN M. SCHER

Atrial Excitation and Repolarization

The wave of excitation originates in the sinoatrial node, at the junction of the superior vena cava and the right atrium (see Fig. 2, Chap. 3). The area that is initially depolarized is somewhat elliptical, and activity spreads from it toward the inferior borders of the atrium. The wave pattern has been compared to that produced when a stone is dropped into still water. The velocity of conduction is about 1 m. per second and does not appear to involve any specialized conduction system. As atrial conduction progresses, the area of the boundary between resting and active tissue waxes and then wanes and disappears.

Viewed from a unipolar electrode on the left leg, the advancing ring of excitation has positive charges facing the recording electrode, and the recorded P wave* is an upward deflection (Fig. 7). A

---

* The three major deflections in the electrocardiogram are termed (in order of appearance) the P wave, the QRS complex and the T wave (see Figs. 11 and 12). These waves are recorded during atrial depolarization, ventricular depolarization and ventricular repolarization, respectively.

negative potential is recorded from an electrode at the right shoulder because the wave of excitation is moving away from this point. The wave of excitation travels toward the left shoulder at first, and during the last stages it may pass beyond this position, producing first a positive, then a negative (diphasic) deflection (Fig. 7).

The wave of repolarization normally follows the same course as the wave of excitation, but the polarity is reversed. The myocardial fibers in advance of the wave of depolarization are relatively negative (the outside is negative in relation to the inside of the cell), and the repolarized tissue is relatively positive. This condition is the reverse of that existing during depolarization, and can be represented by a charged membrane with negative charges oriented in the direction of the wave's

EXCITATION OF THE ATRIA

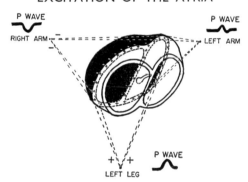

FIGURE 7. As a wave of excitation spreads concentrically through the atrial musculature, different patterns are recorded by unipolar electrodes placed on the extremities. For example, the wave of excitation is advancing toward the left leg which therefore responds to the positive charges facing this electrode and inscribes an upward deflection (see Fig. 6D). In contrast, the wave of excitation moves away from the right shoulder, so a downward deflection is recorded from the right arm. If the wave of excitation first advances toward the left shoulder and then recedes from this position, a diphasic deflection is recorded from a unipolar electrode on the left arm. In each case the magnitude of the deflection at any instant is determined by the solid angle subtended by the wave of excitation as viewed from the effective electrode position (right and left shoulders and symphysis pubis).

movement. Thus, the wave of repolarization (T_a wave) causes a deflection in the opposite direction to that of the P wave. The T_a wave has longer duration and smaller amplitude than the P wave because repolarization is a slower process. It is generally obscured by the QRS complex, which normally occurs during inscription of the T_a wave. However, even if the T_a wave is not coincident with the QRS complex, the potentials developed during atrial repolarization are so small that they may be invisible in the electrocardiogram.

Transmission Through the Atrioventricular Node

In the electrocardiogram a "silent" period appears between atrial excitation (P wave) and ventricular excitation (QRS complex). This P-R interval ordinarily shows a flat baseline, i.e., no potentials are recorded at the body surface during this period. Actually, activity has been recorded from the region of the A-V node with both intracellular and extracellular electrodes, but the potentials generated by the node and by the Purkinje fibers are far too small to influence electrodes on the skin or to be recorded by extracellular electrodes which are farther than a few millimeters from these tissues. Intracellular records from this region show resting and action potentials smaller than those in ordinary myocardium. The rate of change of potential during the depolarizing phase is also less rapid. With an extracellular electrode, conduction can be shown to be continuous through the A-V node, but the velocity of conduction is extremely slow. It appears that the region which blocks most easily along the atrioventricular conduction pathway is immediately above the A-V node, where many anatomists have seen extremely small cells. These cells, like those of the A-V node, are separated from one another by much connective tissue. The conduction velocity in this area appears

to be as low as 0.05 m. per second, and that within the A-V node itself as low as 0.1 m. per second.

The term "delay" has often been used to refer to the A-V node, but it does not appear that there is any time when conduction is not taking place. It further appears that A-V nodal excitation involves no mechanisms which are dissimilar from those seen elsewhere in the myocardium; i.e., conduction takes place from one cell to the adjacent cell because of current flow. Approximately half of the silent period between the end of the P wave and

RECORDING POTENTIALS WITHIN VENTRICULAR WALLS

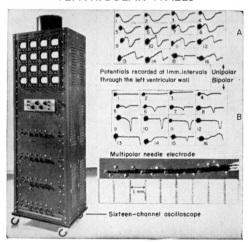

FIGURE 8. A multipolar electrode is illustrated at the bottom on the right. Small bubbles have been formed at the tip of each electrode by electrolysis. The 16-channel oscilloscope is shown at the left. A and B show unipolar and bipolar records taken with this equipment from electrodes inserted through the left ventricular wall. The upper set of unipolar records (A) shows cavity potentials on channels 1 to 4; channel 14 was at the ventricular surface. Progression of the wave of excitation through the wall is indicated on channels 5 through 13. The bipolar records show the difference in potential between adjacent unipolar electrodes. In other words, channel 1 of the bipolar leads shows the difference between the first two unipolar electrodes. The recording convention provides a downward deflection if the endocardial terminal of a bipolar lead is excited first. As can be seen, excitation proceeds from inside out along this electrode. In both unipolar and bipolar records, a fixed time reference potential appears on channel 15 and a lead II electrocardiogram is presented on channel 16.

the beginning of the QRS complex is consumed by events within the common bundle and its branches, the right and left conduction bundles. Cells in these structures have a high conduction velocity, but, like the A-V node, these bundles subtend too small a solid angle to cause potentials at any distant electrode.

Ventricular Excitation

The normal sequence of excitation has been investigated in the dog heart. The same general pattern apparently occurs in all other mammals except the ruminants. The pathway of excitation has been plotted with multipolar electrodes consisting of 15 fine tungsten wires on a central shaft with their tips staggered at small (1.0 mm. or 0.5 mm.) intervals (Fig. 8). These electrodes can be inserted into the right or left wall of the heart, or pushed into the interventricular septum. The recording system used in conjunction with these electrodes consists of a 16-

tube cathode ray oscilloscope which permits simultaneous recording from all points on the electrode, as well as the recording of a fixed time reference potential and a conventional electrocardiogram (Fig. 8). A switching system permits recording of a unipolar potential (each terminal against an indifferent electrode) or bipolar potentials (difference between adjacent terminals).

Activity usually begins a few milliseconds earlier in the left ventricle than in the right (Fig. 9). In both ventricles, activity commences in the regions supplied by the most proximal terminations of the right and left bundles. On the left, activity occurs first in an apical portion of the septum and then in the region of the anterior and posterior papillary muscles; on the right, in the region of the anterior papillary muscle, which lies on the right septal surface. Early in QRS, activity moves from left to right across the septum for a few milliseconds, i.e., there is a pre-

WAVE OF EXCITATION IN DOG VENTRICLE

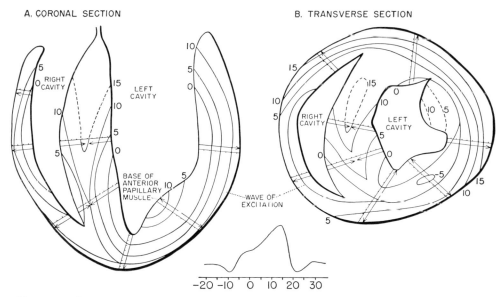

FIGURE 9. The normal sequence of activation within the ventricles is illustrated on a coronal and a transverse section of a dog's heart. The position of the electrodes used to gather the data is indicated. Successive positions of the wavefront are indicated by lines joining corresponding levels on the electrodes. Each of these is labeled with the time before or after the fixed time-reference potential. General features of excitation are described in the text.

SEQUENCE OF VENTRICULAR DEPOLARIZATION

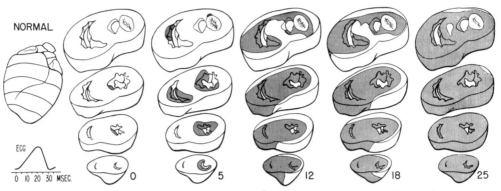

FIGURE 10. Pathway of normal ventricular excitation in dog as discerned by noting extent of depolarization at 0, 5, 12, 18 and 25 milliseconds after beginning of QRS complex. Small drawing of heart indicates positions of planes in which records were taken. Lead II electrocardiogram is labeled to indicate total duration of electrical activity.

At 0 millisecond, small amount of muscle bordering left cavity is active. Apparently this volume of muscle is too small to give a deflection in peripheral electrocardiogram at this amplification. At 5 milliseconds after beginning of QRS, an incomplete and irregular cone of activity surrounds left cavity, mostly on septal aspect, and a smaller cone surrounds right cavity. By 12 milliseconds after beginning of QRS, these two cones have united in lower three sections and have joined slightly in upper section. Heart now contains a cone of depolarized muscle within an incomplete cone of muscle which is still in resting state. Notice break-through of electrical activity anteriorly on right. This leaves activity in posterior and leftward portion of ventricles unopposed. This pattern of excitation continues during next 6 milliseconds. Picture at 18 milliseconds is generally unchanged, although amount of muscle depolarized is, of course, larger; fraction of posterior and left portions in resting state has become smaller. At 25 milliseconds after beginning of QRS complex, only a small amount of muscle in posterior and lateral portion of left wall and of basal septum remains to be excited. (From Scher, Chap. 27 in Medical Physiology and Biophysics, 18th ed., T. C. Ruch and J. F. Fulton, eds., 1960.)

ponderance of left-to-right over right-to-left activity. The Purkinje terminations, however, send numerous branches to the free walls of both ventricles in the apical region. A large portion of the apical endocardium and peri-endocardial region is simultaneously activated by these Purkinje branches and this activity, plus the bilateral septal activity, produces two irregular cones of depolarized tissue which surround the apical cavities on both sides (Fig. 10).

Since the endocardium has been widely excited, the wave of activity has really only one direction in which it can proceed, i.e., toward the surface of the ventricles. It does so at a velocity of about 0.3 to 0.4 m. per second. The two irregular cones around the two cavities move outward in the walls and toward the center of the septum. Shortly after the beginning of the QRS complex the boundary between resting and active tissue reaches the surface of the free wall on the right and there ceases to be a boundary in this region. On the left, however, boundary still exists within the wall, and the impulse has not progressed entirely to the base of the heart, either in the septum (bilaterally) or in the left wall. Thus, after the wave breaks through to the surface of the right ventricles, other portions are still moving from the inside out in the apical, anterior and posterior left wall and toward the center of the septum from both septal surfaces. Because of the predominance of Purkinje fibers in the apical region, even the left apical wall is completely depolarized before the wave reaches the basal epicardium. The wave of activity thus swings leftward and posteriorly, the latter because the posterior portions of the right and left walls are also activated late. The final portion of the electrocardiogram is occupied by the depolarization of a small region of the posterior wall and a larger region in the basal septum. The last region to be activated lies in the basal septum bordering the atrium.

As a simple summary, we may say that the excitation consists of three phases: the first from left to right in the septum, the second from endocardium to epicardium in the mid and apical free walls (with activity proceeding centripetally from both septal endocardial surfaces), and the third toward the base of the walls and septum.

The S-T Segment

When ventricular excitation is complete, the degree of membrane polarization is normally uniform throughout the myocardium (Fig. 9B). Under these conditions, no potentials are recorded by external electrodes (see Fig. 6B), and the galvanometer returns to the baseline, where it remains until the effects of repolarization are manifest in the inscription of the T wave.

The T Wave

The normal sequence of ventricular repolarization is unknown. Since a wave of repolarization should produce potentials opposite in sign from those developed during depolarization, the QRS and T waves would deflect in opposite directions if these two processes followed the same course. On the contrary, the QRS and T waves usually deflect in the same direction, so the process of repolarization does not follow the same sequence as depolarization. Experimentally, repolarization can be delayed by applying pressure to the myocardium. Repolarization may be delayed in the subendocardial layers of myocardium owing to high intraventricular pressure affecting the inner layers more than the external layers. On this basis, repolarization is frequently visualized as beginning in the outer layers of myocardium and progressing toward the endocardial surface, in general following a path opposite in direction to the one pursued by the wave of excitation. This traditional view will be followed in the present discussion, although it has not been adequately established by direct experimental evidence.

The T waves are generally of smaller amplitude and longer duration and have a more rounded contour than the QRS complex because repolarization is a slower process than depolarization. The delay in repolarization is illustrated in the monophasic action potential from a single myocardial fiber (see Fig. 1) in which the upward deflection (depolarization) occurs much more rapidly than the return to the baseline (repolarization). Complexes with precisely the same shape could be produced by many different sequences of ventricular excitation. The only way to determine the exact course of the spreading waves of excitation is to measure their arrival at electrodes inserted into the ventricular walls.

II. Interpretation of the Sequence of Excitation

The electrical activity of the heart is routinely recorded in a standardized manner on graph paper moving at a constant speed. Such electrocardiograms are graphic representations of the sequence of the excitation of the heart. For this reason, any change in this sequence should be readily visible on the records. Even without extensive experience in interpretation of electrocardiograms, changes in the rate or rhythm of the heart beat or in the conduction of the wave of excitation can be analyzed on a purely logical basis. Only a few principles and a few simple rules are

THE STANDARD LIMB LEADS

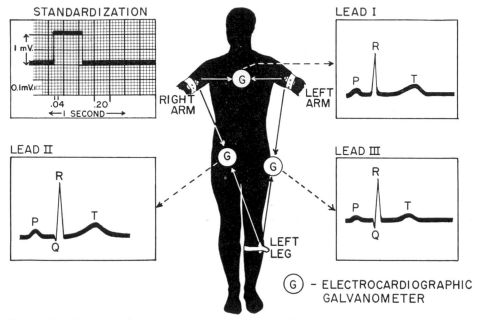

FIGURE 11. Electrocardiograms are recorded on paper divided into 1 mm. and 5 mm. squares. Standardization of the electrocardiograph is accomplished by adjusting its sensitivity until a potential of 1 mV. produces a vertical deflection of 1 cm. The paper moves at a standard rate of 25 mm. per second, so 5 mm. along the horizontal axis represents an interval of 0.20 second and 1 mm. indicates 0.04 second.

The standard limb leads are lead I, lead II and lead III. Lead I records the differences in potential between electrodes on the right and left arms. In lead II the galvanometer is connected to electrodes on the right arm and left leg. Lead III refers to connections between the left arm and left leg.

required for this type of interpretation. Additional information of great value can be obtained by more detailed analysis of the changes in the shape of the electro-cardiographic deflections, which will be considered in Section III of this chapter.

Standardization

The sensitivity of the recording equipment is adjusted until a calibrating potential of 1 mV. produces a vertical deflection of precisely 1 cm. Thin horizontal lines on the paper are 1 mm. apart and represent 0.1 mV., and the thick lines indicate 0.5 mV. The recording paper routinely moves at a constant rate of 25 mm. per second (approximately 1 in. per second). The thin vertical lines demarcate intervals of 0.04 second (1/25 second) and the broad vertical lines indicate intervals

of 0.20 second (1/5 second). Routine electrocardiography includes records obtained by registering potential differences between the extremities as indicated in Figure 11.

THE NORMAL PATTERN OF EXCITATION

On typical electrocardiograms, P waves are followed, after an interval, by the electrical signs of ventricular excitation (QRS) and recovery (T). The duration of the various waves and of the intervals between them usually varies within fairly definite ranges in normal individuals. Average values rounded to the nearest 0.04 second are indicated in Figure 12. The duration of the P wave ranges around 0.08 second. During the interval between the end of the P wave and the beginning of the ventricular excitation (Q or R wave) the galvanometer remains at the baseline for about 0.08 second because no external potentials are recorded during the A-V nodal delay and the passage of the wave of excitation to the ventricular myocardium. The QRS interval (0.08 second) represents the time required for waves of excitation to spread through the ventricular walls. The flat segment between the end of the QRS complex and the beginning of the T wave (S-T interval, 0.12 second) represents the period during which the ventricles are more or less uniformly excited, and the T wave occurs during the restoration of the ventricular myocardium to the resting or excitable state.

VARIATIONS IN HEART RATE

The heart rate is determined normally by the frequency with which the sino-atrial node emits excitatory impulses. The frequency at which the S-A node discharges is influenced by activity of nerve

DURATION OF WAVES AND INTERVALS

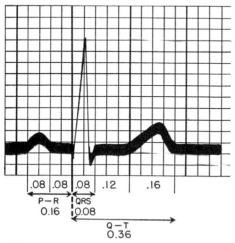

FIGURE 12. The average durations of electrocardiographic waves and intervals are rounded to the nearest 0.04 second so they are easier to remember. The P-R interval, QRS interval and Q-T interval are among the most common values measured during routine electrocardiographic interpretation (see Figs. 18, 19 and 0).

fibers from the autonomic nervous system (see Fig. 3, Chap. 3).

Measurement of Heart Rate

Since the electrocardiogram contains an accurate representation of the intervals between successive cardiac cyles, atrial and ventricular rates can be easily measured. The simplest method is to determine the number of cycles (and fractions thereof) occurring in 3 seconds and multiply this number by 20 to give the number of cycles in one minute (60 seconds) (Fig. 13). At the normal paper speed (25 mm. per second), 1 second is represented by five large squares; 3 seconds by fifteen large squares (3 in.). The QRS complexes, easily identified because of the rapid deflections, are tallied over a 3 in. distance. If exactly four ventricular cycles occur during 3 seconds, the ventricular rate is 80 per minute (see Fig. 13). If the P waves can be identified, the same process can be used to determine the atrial rate. P waves can usually be differentiated from T waves, which always follow QRS complexes at a fairly characteristic interval (see Fig. 12).

Abnormalities of Heart Rate

Variations in the intensity of the sustained vagal tone have greater influence on the S-A node than does altered sympathetic activity. The slow heart rates found in certain athletes and during sleep, and the tachycardia found in fever, emotion and exercise, are attributed largely to variations in vagal tone. Respiratory activity also may produce variations in vagal tone leading to phasic changes in heart rate with acceleration near the end of inspiration and slowing at the end of expiration. This condition (*sinus arrhythmia*) is frequently encountered in normal individuals, particularly when the heart rate is relatively slow.

A heart rate faster than some arbitrary value (e.g., 100 beats per minute) is termed *sinus tachycardia* if the impulses

MEASUREMENT OF VENTRICULAR RATE

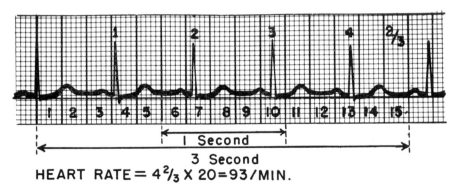

3 Second

HEART RATE $= 4\frac{2}{3} \times 20 = 93$/MIN.

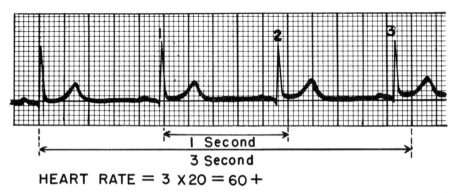

3 Second

HEART RATE $= 3 \times 20 = 60 +$

FIGURE 13. The heart rate in beats per minute can be computed by counting the number of cycles in 3 seconds and multiplying this value by 20 (3 × 20 = 60 seconds). At standard paper speed, 3 seconds is represented by 15 large squares. In the first example, there are $4\frac{2}{3}$ cycles in 3 seconds so the heart rate is about 93 per minute. In the second example, there are slightly more than 3 cycles in 3 seconds so the heart rate is a little over 60 per minute.

originate in the S-A node. By the same token, a heart rate of sinus origin below some value (e.g., 60 beats per minute) is called *sinus bradycardia*. Intense vagal stimulation (e.g, from carotid sinus pressure) may transiently interrupt impulse formation by the S-A node. If such *sinoatrial arrest* is sufficiently prolonged, some other site in the heart may begin to discharge conducted impulses. The fact that excitation of the heart can be initiated at any site in the myocardium or conduction system is the basic cause of cardiac arrhythmias.

ABNORMAL RHYTHMS

Since abnormal rhythms of the heart usually result from variations in the site

and frequency of impulse formation, the nature of pacemaker activity deserves special consideration.

Pacemaker Activity in Myocardial Fibers

The functional differences between smooth muscle, skeletal muscle and myocardium lie in the mechanisms for excitation and control (see Fig. 2, Chap. 2). Under appropriate conditions, all forms of muscle may exhibit myogenic excitation originating within the muscle itself. For example, the visceral smooth muscle in the ureter rhythmically contracts to produce peristaltic waves in response to myogenic impulses originating at a "pacemaker" near the pelvis.[5] If the ureter is sectioned below the normal pacemaker, a new pacemaker is established below the transection and impulses are produced rhythmically at a somewhat slower rate. Another transection lower down brings into play still another site of pacemaker activity with an even slower inherent rate. Occasionally a pacemaker region in the ureter exhibits impulse formation at a rate four or five times faster than the normal. This phenomenon is reminiscent of the rapid rates of discharge in ectopic foci during paroxysmal tachycardia (see below).

If the heart of a chick embryo is sectioned between the common atrium and ventricle, these two segments of myocardium may continue to contract rhythmically but the rate of ventricular contraction is slower than that of the atrium.[6, 7] Similarly, excised myocardial tissue from mammalian hearts may contract repeatedly and, again, the inherent rhythmicity of atrial tissue exceeds that of ventricular myocardium. Every portion of the myocardium and conduction system can assume the role of pacemaker and initiate impulses conducted to contiguous regions. At any moment, the pacemaker of the heart abides in the region with the fastest inherent rate of impulse formation, which is normally the sino-atrial node. If impulses from the atria are blocked at the atrioventricular node, the atria continue to contract at their characteristic rate and another pacemaker in the ventricles emits impulses at a slower rate (30 to 60 beats per minute). When the pacemaker is situated in the ventricles, impulses may be conducted in a retrograde direction to the atria or they may be blocked at the A-V node.

The functional and electrocardiographic characteristics of arrhythmias are dependent upon four factors: (a) All portions of the myocardium and conduction system are capable of originating waves of excitation. (b) Functionally the heart consists of two double shells of myocardial fibers (atria and ventricles) joined by the common bundle of Purkinje fibers (Fig. 14). (c) Owing to the syncytial arrangement of myocardial fibers, these waves of excitation spread to all contiguous myocardial cells. (d) The wave of excitation pursues an abnormal course through some parts of the myocardium.

Premature Contractions

The inherent capacity of all the myocardial fibers to rhythmically generate conducted impulses is not apparent so long as the _sino-atrial_ node retains its position as pacemaker. However, impulses are generated in regions other than the S-A node fairly often in both normal individuals and patients with organic heart disease. Changes occurring in regions of increased irritability (ectopic foci) have been the subject of considerable speculation with little or no direct experimental evidence. It is fairly well established that myocardial fibers returning to their resting state after a cardiac contraction pass through a stage of increased excitability which appears to correspond to a similar state during the negative after-potential in nerve fibers.[8] Conducted impulses originating at various sites in the ventricles tend to occur just after the T wave and the abnormal contractions follow closely behind the preceding beat. Such premature contractions per se have little or no clinical significance because they occur in so many normal persons. Frequent premature contractions from multiple sites often occur with various types of heart disease. The general location of the ectopic focus giving rise to these premature contractions can usually be determined electrocardiographically.

Atrial* Premature Contractions. If an

* The word *auricle* has been widely used as though it were a synonym for *atrium*. Anatomically, *auricle* refers to an atrial appendage and is not appropriate for indicating the main atrial chamber. To avoid inconsistency, the correct term will be used in spite of traditional usage in such familiar conditions as "auricular" premature contractions, "auricular" fibrillation, etc.

TYPES OF PREMATURE CONTRACTIONS

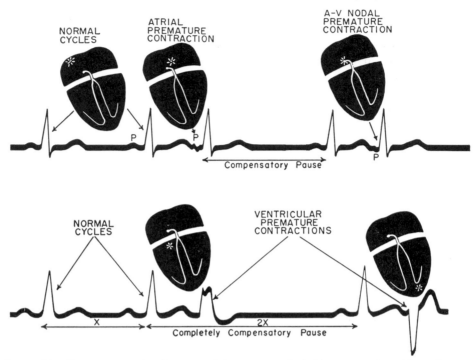

FIGURE 14. Premature contractions can originate at ectopic foci in any portion of the atria or ventricles. A few examples are illustrated schematically.

Atrial premature contractions begin with a deformed P wave shortly after the T wave of the preceding normal cycle. The P-R interval is usually shortened but the QRS complex is characteristically unchanged in configuration. The interval between the premature contraction and the next normal cycle is somewhat prolonged (compensatory pause).

Premature contractions originating at the A-V node are similar to atrial premature contractions except that the P wave is largely buried within the QRS complex since the atria and ventricles are excited more or less simultaneously.

Ventricular premature contractions are characterized by markedly deformed and prolonged QRS complexes with no definite S-T segment and with the T wave deflected in a direction opposite to the major deflection of the QRS. P waves are not visible.

irritable focus in the atrium generates a conducted impulse very soon after the preceding contraction, the wave of excitation spreads out concentrically from this new site (Fig. 14). The course of this wave is different from that of an impulse arising in the sino-atrial node and, therefore, the shape of the P wave is altered. The time required for the atrial wave of excitation to engulf the atrioventricular node is different, so the P-R interval also varies from that of the preceding normal beat. The QRS and T waves are generally unchanged because the excitatory impulse follows a normal course from the A-V node through the ventricular myocardium and repolarization of the ventricles is usually not affected. However, in some cases, slight changes in the configuration of QRS and T waves are produced, probably because the impulse follows the previous excitation so closely that some portion of the conduction system has not fully recovered. This is called *aberrant ventricular conduction*. The abnormal wave of excitation in the atrium envelops the S-A node, which cannot discharge another impulse until it has passed through its complete recovery cycle. Thus, the interval between an atrial premature contraction and the next normal beat is prolonged (compensatory pause in Fig. 14). The salient features of atrial premature contractions are: altered configuration of the P wave which closely follows the T wave of the preceding normal contraction, altered P-R interval (usually diminished), normal or nearly normal QRS and T complexes and a compensatory pause. The extent of the changes in P wave configuration and in the P-R interval varies with location of the ectopic focus in relation to the S-A node. If the wave of excitation originates from the region of the A-V node, the P waves are inverted and the P-R interval is very brief (Fig. 14).

A-V Nodal Premature Contractions.

Premature contractions may be initiated from an irritable focus in or near the atrioventricular node. The wave of excitation passes immediately down the Purkinje system to the ventricles, so a QRS complex closely follows the preceding normal T wave (Fig. 14). Usually, conduction into the atria is blocked and no P waves appear. Occasionally a P wave begins just before the onset of QRS or is buried in the QRS complex, indicating retrograde conduction into the atrial musculature. Usually the ventricular excitation occurs in its normal sequence and the form of the QRS complex is similar to the patterns displayed during normal cycles. In the absence of retrograde conduction into the atria, the rhythm of the S-A node is undisturbed and the interval between the normal cycles preceding and following the premature contraction is equal to that of two normal cycles. In other words, the short interval before the premature contraction is precisely balanced by the greater delay following the abnormal beat (completely compensatory pause). The characteristic signs of A-V nodal premature contractions are normal or relatively normal QRS complexes appearing just after the

preceding T wave, with P waves absent, buried in the QRS complex or beginning just before the premature QRS.

Ventricular Premature Contractions.

If a focus within the ventricular musculature discharges prematurely, the course of the wave of excitation and the sequence of ventricular depolarization are abnormal and the configuration of the QRS complex is correspondingly distorted. Since such ectopic foci can develop anywhere in the ventricles, an infinite variety of complexes may result.

The typical electrocardiographic picture consists of slurred, prolonged QRS complexes, beginning without a P wave just after the termination of the preceding normal cycle. Repolarization occurs in an abnormal sequence and the T waves are also deformed, tending to deflect in a direction opposite to the major QRS deflection (Fig. 14). When an ectopic focus is located near the base of the heart, at some distance from the conduction system, the general course of the wave of excitation extends from base to apex, and the major QRS deflections are upward in all standard limb leads as in a normal cycle. If, in contrast, a premature ventricular contraction originates near the apex, excitation spreads from the apex toward the base of the heart and the major QRS deflections are downward in all standard limb leads (Fig. 14). A completely compensatory pause follows the typical premature ventricular contraction, just as in the A-V nodal ectopic beats.

Premature ventricular contractions, recurring regularly after every normal cycle, may persist for extended periods of time. These premature contractions are termed *coupled* beats and the resulting rhythm is called *bigeminy* because two pacemakers alternate in discharging excitatory impulses to the ventricular myocardium. In a few patients with slow heart rates, premature ventricular contractions are regularly interposed between normal

TYPES OF PAROXYSMAL TACHYCARDIA

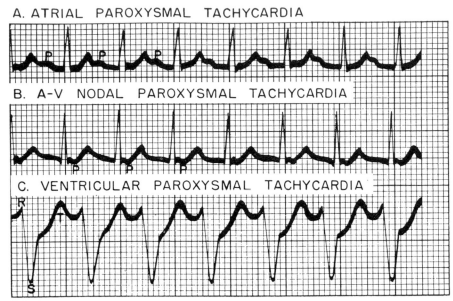

FIGURE 15.   The fact that paroxysmal tachycardia actually represents a series of premature contractions is clearly indicated by comparing atrial, A-V nodal and ventricular paroxysmal tachycardia with corresponding isolated premature contractions in Figure 14.

beats without a compensatory pause. These ectopic beats are called *interpolated* premature ventricular contractions.

Paroxysmal Tachycardia

A burst of three or four ectopic impulses is generally classed as multiple premature contractions. However, an ectopic focus may discharge a long series of premature contractions in rapid succession at rates higher than 140 per minute (Fig. 15). Such sustained ectopic pacemaker activity lasting minutes or days is called paroxysmal tachycardia. This arbitrary distinction between premature contractions and paroxysmal tachycardia indicates the close functional relation between them. Ectopic foci producing either isolated premature contractions or paroxysms of tachycardia may develop anywhere in the heart. In a typical attack of paroxysmal tachycardia, the heart rate is abruptly elevated to levels of 140 to 240 beats per minute, most commonly around 160 per minute. Once attained, this rapid

rate is exceedingly regular, and is essentially unaffected by respiratory activity, exercise, or other controlling mechanisms until the attack is abruptly terminated.

Clinical diagnosis of paroxysmal tachycardia depends upon a history of a very fast, extremely regular heart rate which begins abruptly and does not change until it suddenly reverts to normal. Paroxysmal tachycardia originating from sites in the atria or A-V node is often terminated promptly by inducing intense vagal discharge (pressure on the carotid sinus, deep inspiration with mild Valsalva maneuver, induced vomiting, pressure on the eyeballs, etc.). These procedures generally have no effect on an ectopic pacemaker in the ventricular walls; this fact suggests that parasympathetic distribution to the ventricular myocardium is scanty or absent. Successful therapy by carotid sinus pressure or other procedures producing vagal discharge represents a diagnostic test for atrial or A-V nodal tachycardia. It may be difficult to differentiate atrial and nodal paroxysmal tachycardia because P waves may be obscured by T waves when the cycle length is short. This poses no practical problem, since the functional significance and therapy of these two conditions are similar. The prolonged and bizarre QRS complexes which occur with ventricular paroxysmal tachycardia simplify its recognition (Fig. 15).

The deleterious effects of tachycardia on cardiac efficiency and on coronary blood flow have been discussed in Chapter 9. It is not surprising that patients developing persistent ectopic tachycardia of this type suffer limitation in exercise tolerance and may even develop acute congestive failure when the heart is diseased. For example, Grant[9] described an episode of paroxysmal auricular tachycardia in a 20-year-old army private who had previously shown "average" exercise tolerance in tests at the Harvard University Fatigue Laboratory. About four months later he noted "pounding of the heart" during a routine 30-mile hike. Tachycardia at a rate of about 200 per minute persisted until the next day, when he had definite signs of congestive heart failure. In spite of numerous attempts to interrupt the attack of tachycardia, the patient died after 40 hours. Postmortem examination revealed unsuspected mitral stenosis.

Atrial Flutter

Very rapid regular atrial excitation can be caused experimentally by inducing a wave of excitation which continuously follows a circular pathway in the atrial musculature around some obstruction (e.g., around the roots of the superior and inferior venae cavae). This "circus movement" can be produced by damaging the atrial myocardium between the superior and inferior venae cavae and electrically stimulating the atrium to induce a wave of excitation which circles the obstruction at a rate determined only by the conduction velocity of the myocardium and the circumference of the circle.[10]

From this circular pathway, excitation spreads to the remainder of the atrium and to the A-V node (Fig. 16B). Thus, the atria are excited at rates of 150 to 350 times per minute. Apparently the A-V node cannot respond to repetitive excitation at these high rates and transmits alternate impulses (2:1 block), every third impulse (3:1 block) or every fourth impulse (4:1 block), depending upon its recovery time. The concept that the atrial flutter observed in patients was due to a circus movement in the atria held sway for many years but a large body of subsequent evidence indicates that atrial flutter is due to rapid, repetitive excitation from a single ectopic focus (Fig. 16A). This conclusion, discussed in detail by Scherf and Schott[11] and by Prinzmetal et al.,[12] implies that atrial flutter must be considered comparable to paroxysmal tachycardia except that the atrial waves of excitation occur at a rate which is faster than the A-V node can transmit impulses. The electrocardiographic signs of atrial flutter can be predicted from either of these descriptions even though the etiology of the condition remains controversial.[13] The ventricular rate is usually regular although a shift from one degree of block to another may occur. The major difficulty in interpreting the records stems from the fact that the P waves tend to be superimposed upon the T waves. If this fact is not recognized, half of the P waves may be overlooked and erroneous conclusions drawn. P waves hidden in T waves or in other complexes can generally be detected by carefully inspecting the record at a point just half-way between the clearly defined P waves. A pair of calipers adjusted until the distance between the points is just half the distance between obvious P waves is often helpful in the procedure.

The functional significance of atrial flutter depends ultimately upon the ventricular heart rate. If the A-V node transmits alternate atrial impulses (2:1 A-V

ATRIAL FLUTTER

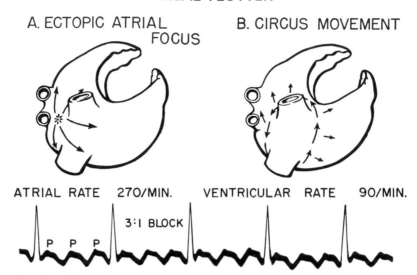

FIGURE 16.   Atrial flutter is characterized by repetitive atrial excitation occurring at such a rapid rate that all waves of excitation are not transmitted through the A-V node into the ventricles. Thus, there may be two P waves for each QRS complex (2:1 block), three P waves to one QRS (3:1 block) or even 4:1 block.

A, According to one theory, the rapid atrial rate results from the rapid firing of an ectopic focus in the atrial musculature, similar to atrial paroxysmal tachycardia except for the failure of the A-V node to transmit all the impulses.

B, According to another theory, atrial flutter occurs when a wave of excitation encircles the roots of the superior and inferior vena cava at a rate determined by the conduction velocity of the myocardium. Waves of excitation spread from the circular pathway to the remainder of the atrial musculature. Circus movements of this type can be produced experimentally (see text).

block), the ventricular rate is very rapid (e.g., 150 beats per minute). Under these conditions, the diastolic filling interval for the ventricles is seriously curtailed and the resulting condition closely resembles paroxysmal atrial tachycardia (see above). If 3:1 or 4:1 block persists during various levels of activity, the heart rate remains relatively fixed at levels of 70 to 100 beats per minute at rest and the cardiac reserve is curtailed during exertion because tachycardia does not occur.

Atrial Fibrillation

If more than one wave of excitation were moving over the atrium at all times, coordinated atrial contraction could not occur and individual P waves could not be identified on electrocardiograms. Instead, the P waves would be replaced by irregular oscillations of the baseline: "fibrillation" waves. A similar situation would result if multiple ectopic atrial foci were discharging asynchronously at rates. Here again, a number of postulates have been advanced (Fig. 17) but the ultimate answer must await further evidence. In any event, waves of excitation arrive at the A-V node at random intervals. Only a portion of these excitatory waves are transmitted to the ventricles. Some excitatory waves are too weak or diffuse to invade the A-V node and others arrive during its refractory period. By this mechanism, the ventricular rate is absolutely irregular since the A-V node receives its excitation in a completely random sequence. The complete lack of ventricular rhythm can be readily perceived by palpation of the radial pulse or auscultation over the precordium. The electro-

graphic diagnosis of defective intraventricular conduction is readily made, its clinical significance requires analysis of the type and location of the disturbance. The nature and extent of abnormal ventricular conduction can be assessed only by an analysis of the configuration of the QRS complexes in various leads.

The Duration of Electrical Systole (Q-T Interval). The interval occupied by the QRS-T complex represents the time required for excitation and repolarization of the ventricular myocardium. The so-called Q-T interval is measured from the beginning of the QRS complex (Q or R wave) to the end of the T wave (Fig. 12). As the Q-T interval varies somewhat with heart rate, age and sex, it is generally necessary to refer to a table to determine if a particular value is within normal limits or exceeds the upper limit of normal (Table 2). Accurate measurement of the

Table 2. Upper Limits of the Normal
Q-T Interval*

HEART RATE PER MIN.	MEN AND CHILDREN	WOMEN
	sec.	sec.
40	0.491	0.503
43	0.479	0.491
46	0.466	0.478
48	0.460	0.471
50	0.453	0.464
52	0.445	0.456
54.5	0.438	0.449
57	0.430	0.441
60	0.422	0.432
63	0.413	0.423
66.5	0.404	0.414
70.5	0.395	0.504
75	0.384	0.394
80	0.374	0.384
86	0.363	0.372
92.5	0.351	0.360
100	0.338	0.347
109	0.325	0.333
120	0.310	0.317
133	0.294	0.301
150	0.275	0.282
172	0.255	0.262

* From Ashman, R., and Hull, E.: Essentials of Electrocardiography. 2nd ed. New York, The Macmillan Co., 1945.

Q-T interval is more complicated than it appears. For this reason, Kossmann[14] pointed out the futility of listing normal values to three significant figures when errors of 5 to 12.5 per cent occur even when 3 to 12 cycles are measured. He recommended that the maximum normal Q-T interval (corrected for heart rate) for any age or sex be set at 0.425. Any value above this level should be "described as a prolonged Q-T$_c$ but may not necessarily be abnormal." A large number of factors are known to alter the Q-T interval.

SUMMARY

Electrocardiographic signs of abnormal heart rate, rhythm and conduction were summarized briefly to illustrate the kind of logic which can be applied to an analysis of electrocardiograms. Electrocardiographic interpretation was introduced in this way to demonstrate that information can be gleaned from electrocardiographic tracings on logical grounds. It is not considered appropriate to attempt an exhaustive discussion in a text of this sort. Additional details should be sought in standard textbooks of electrocardiography.[20-22] With a little experience, following a simple routine will disclose most of the common types of abnormal heart rates, arrhythmias and conduction disturbances.

Procedure for Detecting Abnormalities of Heart Rate, Rhythm and Conduction

Analysis of electrocardiograms should begin with the following steps:

1. Determine ventricular rate and atrial rate
2. Examine the record for variations in rhythm
3. Examine the complexes to detect changes in configuration
4. Measure P-R interval and compare with Table 1
5. Measure QRS interval

Determining the ventricular rate is the first step in analyzing an electrocardiogram. If a P wave precedes each QRS complex by a constant interval, the atrial rate is the same as the ventricular rate. The P-R interval is measured in several complexes. If this value is relatively constant and within the range of normal, the rhythm is probably of sinus origin. In adults, heart rates below 60 can be termed sinus bradycardia and those above 100 are labeled sinus tachycardia. If the heart rate is absolutely constant at levels above 140 at rest and the QRS complex is normal, the diagnosis is atrial paroxysmal tachycardia when P waves precede the QRS complexes by a normal interval. If P waves cannot be distinguished, the term supraventricular (atrial or A-V nodal) paroxysmal tachycardia is applied. Premature contractions are identified while scanning the records by noting two cycles in rapid succession followed by a slightly prolonged interval or compensatory pause. A P-R interval in excess of the maximal normal values presented in Table 1 means a first degree A-V block or increased A-V nodal delay. Regularly recurring cycles consisting of a P wave without a QRS-T complex signify partial A-V block (second degree A-V block). A continuously variable P-R interval suggests complete A-V block.

The QRS interval is measured as indicated in Figure 12, and if this value exceeds 0.10 second in adults with normal heart rates, an interventricular conduction disturbance is present. When P waves precede the prolonged QRS complexes by normal intervals, conduction within the ventricles is delayed or blocked. If P waves are absent and the ventricular rate is very regular at rates in excess of 140 per minute at rest, and if the QRS complexes are prolonged and bizarre, the diagnosis is ventricular paroxysmal tachycardia. Very slow ventricular rates (less than 60), with P waves absent or buried in a prolonged, bizarre QRS complex, imply sinus block with an ectopic pacemaker in the ventricles.

If the process of cardiac excitation can be clearly visualized and the P, QRS and T waves can be identified on the records, most of the common disturbances of rhythm and conduction can be recognized with little effort. More complete analysis, particularly as it involves interpretation of the changes in shape of the various waves, can best be approached with an understanding of the basic principles of electrocardiographic theory.

III. Interpreting Differences in Wave Form of Electrocardiographic Complexes

The shape of the various electrocardiographic deflections is altered by many different factors including: the position of the recording electrodes on the body surface, the orientation of the heart within the thorax, the thickness of the walls of the heart, the course of the excitation through the myocardium, the rate of depolarization and repolarization, and the extent of polarization and depolarization. The changes in wave form due to the electrode position and to the orientation of the heart in the thorax must be distinguished from changes in these patterns produced by various disease states. Certain changes observed on electrocardiograms are frequently associated with specific abnormal functional states of the myocardium (e.g., myocardial ischemia, myocardial infarction and the effects of varying electrolyte concentrations and drugs). The altered electrical activity of the heart under these conditions can be assessed by two very different approaches:

(a) empirically or (b) by theoretical analysis. Empirical interpretation involves matching certain electrocardiographic patterns with specific disease states. Such correlations require considerable experience since they involve learning and applying a vast quantity of detailed information collected over the years. Comprehensive coverage of this material cannot be achieved in a text of this scope. Instead, the theory underlying the production, distribution and recording of potentials from the heart is used to describe factors which may affect the form of electrocardiographic complexes.

THE EFFECTS OF ELECTRODE POSITION ON ELECTROCARDIOGRAPHIC PATTERNS

The potentials developed in a volume conductor were described in terms of a unipolar exploring electrode and an in-

different electrode so distant from the source of potentials as to be unaffected. The most distal portions of the arms and legs are not sufficiently distant to be truly indifferent because electrocardiograms can be readily recorded by placing electrodes on the wrists or ankles. Thus, there is no point in or on the body which could serve as an indifferent electrode. With the body immersed in a large tank of salt water the indifferent electrode can be placed at a great distance from the heart,[23] but this is impractical. However, if wires from three electrodes, equidistant from each other and from the heart, are joined at a single terminal, the potentials developed at the electrodes tend to cancel each other (Fig. 21). This principle has been utilized in the central terminal of Wilson,[24, 25] to provide an acceptable indifferent electrode for unipolar recording.

Wilson's central terminal is connected

CENTRAL TERMINAL OF WILSON

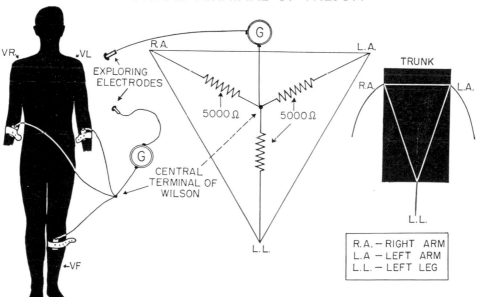

FIGURE 21. Accurate unipolar recording of cardiac potentials requires an indifferent electrode which is unaffected by potentials developed by the heart. If electrodes on all three extremity leads are connected through 5000 ohm resistors to a single terminal (the central terminal of Wilson) the potentials at the extremities almost completely cancel out to provide a fairly reliable indifferent electrode. The heart is not exactly equidistant from each electrode, since it is situated toward one end of a roughly rectangular volume conductor, but the resulting errors have not proved too serious for practical purposes.

VENTRICULAR EXCITATION

A. VENTRICULAR DEPOLARIZATION (QRS)

VENTRICULAR RECOVERY

B. UNIFORM DEPOLARIZATION (ISOELECTRIC S-T)

C. REPOLARIZATION (T WAVE)

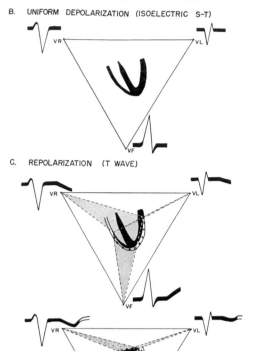

FIGURE 22. *A*, The origin of the potentials recorded by unipolar extremity electrodes during ventricular depolarization is illustrated schematically. The sequence of excitation has been distorted for simplification of analysis (see Figs. 9 and 10). The initial wave of excitation is presented as originating on the left side of the interventricular septum and moving toward the right ventricle. This area of excitation would produce an upward deflection in both B_R and B_F because the positive charges face these electrodes. A downward deflection would be recorded from V_L because the wave of excitation is moving away from the left shoulder.

At a later stage, the wave of excitation conforms roughly to a cuplike shell progressing from endocardium to epicardium. Since the wave of excitation is moving toward V_F and away from V_R, the deflections in these two leads are in opposite directions.

If a wave of excitation invades the basilar portion of the left ventricular wall in the final stages, it is moving toward the left shoulder. A down-ward deflection is inscribed from V_R and V_F and an upward deflection from V_L.

B, When the ventricles are uniformly depolarized, no potentials are recorded from any of the external electrodes.

C, Since depolarized regions are negative with respect to polarized myocardium, a negative deflection is recorded when a wave of repolarization advances toward an electrode. Assuming that repolarization begins on the epicardial surface of the ventricles and progresses inward, a negative deflection would be recorded at V_R since the activity is moving toward the right shoulder. A positive deflection would be recorded at V_F, and, in the example illustrated, very little potential would be recorded by V_L because a very small solid angle would be subtended.

The endocardial region of the left ventricle may be the last portion to be repolarized. Here, as in the other examples, the cuplike configuration of the wave of excitation can be represented by a flat, polarized membrane at the junction between polarized and depolarized myocardium at the base of the heart.

to one side of the galvanometer and an exploring electrode to the other (Fig. 21). If the exploring electrode is placed on the surface of the body at the right shoulder (V_R), left shoulder (V_L) and left leg (V_F), the wave of excitation passing through the heart can be "viewed" from different angles (Fig. 22). These electrode positions are called the unipolar limb leads, and can be employed to illustrate the potentials developing during cardiac excitation and recovery, i.e., ventricular excitation.

Unipolar Limb Leads

As the wave of excitation passes down the conduction system, the solid angle subtended by this bundle of tissue is very small, and the resultant potentials are not sufficient to produce a deflection. The first recorded potential develops when a significant area of ventricular myocardium has been invaded by a wave of excitation. The configuration of the QRS complex will depend upon the sequence of ventricular excitation and the direction taken by the excitatory waves.

The QRS Complex. Ventricular excitation can be schematically illustrated by a simplified diagram as in Figure 22. The magnitude and sign of the potentials are indicated by the solid angles subtended by the margins of the transitional zone between the polarized and depolarized regions. The wave of excitation travels toward the left leg (V_F), producing a positive deflection, and moves away from the right shoulder as indicated by the negative deflection at V_R. The small solid angle subtended at V_L is associated with a small deflection which may be upward or downward depending upon the exact orientation of the spreading wave. In Figure 22 the largest deflections during the entire course of depolarization occur in V_R and V_F, since the solid angles from these electrode positions are greater than that from V_L. The patterns derived from V_L are very susceptible to variations in the orientation of the heart. They are generally diphasic; the downward deflection predominates when the heart is oriented more vertically and the upward deflection is more prominent if the long axis of the heart approaches horizontal.

Standard Limb Leads

When electrodes are applied to two extremities and connected to a galvanometer, the records indicate continuously the difference in potential between the two electrode positions. The standard limb leads can be recorded by measuring the potential difference between each pair of unipolar records, as in Figure 23. In accordance with the polarity indicated on Einthoven's triangle (+ and − signs), the complex at the negative end of the lead line is subtracted from the complex at the positive end. It is apparent that the standard limb leads are more complicated than unipolar leads, since the potentials fluctuate at both electrodes and the final record represents the difference in potential at each instant in time. Because it is difficult to visualize the result of subtracting one solid angle from another, this method is not widely used to describe the origin of the potentials recorded on standard limb leads. Instead, an electrical axis is usually employed for this purpose.

The Electrical Axis of the Heart. Although the amplitude and polarity of potentials recorded from unipolar electrodes can be predicted by knowing the solid angle subtended by an area of uniform charge density, the process cannot be reversed. In other words, the portions of the heart undergoing depolarization cannot be determined from externally recorded potentials such as the electrocardiogram. Areas of depolarization in an infinite variety of combinations can theoretically produce the electrocardiographic pattern recorded from any particular electrode position. For this reason, electrical activity in the heart is often represented by vectors which indicate the mag-

DERIVATION OF STANDARD LIMB LEADS

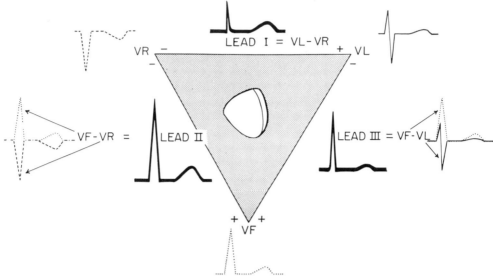

FIGURE 23. Each standard limb lead represents the difference in potential between two extremities. Since the unipolar limb leads record the potentials at the individual extremities, subtracting the potential recorded at the right arm (V_R) from the potentials at the left arm (V_L) should produce the patterns recorded from lead I. The process is more easily visualized in deriving lead II complexes by subtracting V_R (dashed line) from V_F (dotted line). An upward deflection is inscribed in lead II when V_F is positive with respect to V_L (note positive and negative signs on the Einthoven triangle). This schematic drawing indicates the complex origin of the standard limb leads as compared to the unipolar extremity leads.

nitude and mean direction of excitation without specifying the location of the activity. An arrow can be erected in the center of an area of spreading activity (see Fig. 24C) to indicate the mean direction of progression (the mean orientation of the charges), with the length of the arrow proportional to the solid angle (the magnitude of the recorded potential). Vectors can be derived from the electrocardiographic records obtained with the standard limb leads. Such vectors indicate the mean direction and magnitude of potentials developed within the heart as projected upon a frontal plane. However, they do not identify the specific regions of the heart being invaded by waves of excitation.

Instantaneous Electrical Axes. An electrical axis or vector can be determined for any instant during the cardiac cycle from simultaneously recorded standard limb leads (e.g., leads I and III). The method requires use of the Einthoven triangle, which is based on the concept that the heart lies in a large, uniform volume conductor at the center of an equilateral triangle with the limb electrodes at the apices. In spite of the rectangular configuration of the trunk (Fig. 21) and the lack of homogeneity of the body, these assumptions are more completely realized than would appear at first glance.[23] The positive and negative signs on Einthoven's triangle (Figs. 23 and 24) indicate that the limb electrodes are connected to the recording galvanometer in such a way that an upward deflection is recorded under the following conditions in each lead:

Lead I: When the left arm is positive in relation to the right arm.

Lead II: When the left leg is positive in relation to the right arm.

Lead III: When the left leg is positive in relation to the left arm.

The method of determining an instantaneous electrical axis at a particular moment in time is illustrated in Figure 24. The instantaneous axis indicates the mean direction in which the wave of excitation is traveling at a particular instant, and its length represents the relative magnitude of the externally recorded potentials developed at that time (Fig. 24*B*). If instantaneous electrical axes are determined at short intervals during the remainder of ventricular excitation, the series of instantaneous vectors change in length and orientation during the cardiac cycle (Fig. 24*C*). A series of instantaneous electrical axes constitutes a *vectorcardiogram*.

Vectorcardiograms. A line connecting the points of the instantaneous vectors describes a loop. Loops of this type can be inscribed on the face of a cathode ray oscilloscope, thus continuously indicating the instantaneous electrical axis from moment to moment.[26] The instantaneous electrical axes illustrated in Figure 24*C* actually represent three-dimensional vectors as projected on a frontal plane. Since the original potentials actually develop in three dimensions, a more complete picture of the shifting patterns of potentials can be derived from three-dimensional vectors: stereovectorcardiography.[27-30]

Although stereovectorcardiography has added little to our basic knowledge of electrocardiography, the graphic representation of vectors helps to visualize the process of ventricular excitation (see Fig. 25*B*). An average or mean electrical axis has proved useful in electrocardiographic interpretation even though it is not nearly as accurate or complete as a vectorcardiogram or a series of instantaneous vectors.

Mean Electrical Axis. Theoretically, a mean electrical axis should be the resultant of instantaneous vectors such as those illustrated in Figure 24*C*. The routine method of determining the mean electrical axis is a compromise based on the questionable assumption that the height of the Q, R and S deflections is proportional to the area under them. The net upward or downward deflection is determined for the typical QRS complex in two of the three standard leads (e.g., leads I and III). As indicated in Figure 25, the mean electrical axis is determined in much the same way as an instantaneous electrical axis (see Fig. 24). Note that in Figure 25 the mean electrical axis ap-

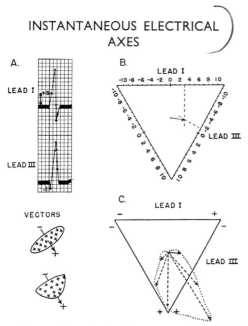

INSTANTANEOUS ELECTRICAL AXES

FIGURE 24. *A,* An instantaneous electrical axis can be derived from two standard limb leads recorded simultaneously. Simultaneous points on the two complexes are selected (e.g., 0.02 second after the beginning of the QRS complex). At this instant, the galvanometer had deflected upward 3 mm. in lead I.

B, From a point +3 units on the lead I line of Einthoven's triangle a perpendicular line is erected. Similarly, at this same instant, the deflection was 1 mm. below the bottom of the baseline in lead III. A perpendicular line is erected at −1 unit on the lead III line. An arrow drawn from the center of the triangle to the intersection of the perpendicular lines is the instantaneous electrical axis.

C, Such vectors indicate the mean direction in which the wave of excitation is advancing at a particular instant. If vectors are derived at intervals of 0.02 second during the remainder of the QRS complex (black dots on the QRS complexes), a series of instantaneous electrical axes can be derived. This series of vectors indicates the changing orientation and magnitude of potentials developing during ventricular excitation and is called a *vectorcardiogram.*

MEAN ELECTRICAL AXES

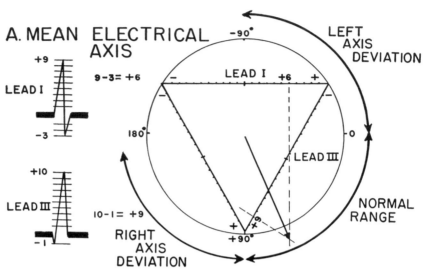

A. MEAN ELECTRICAL AXIS

B. MEAN SPATIAL AXIS

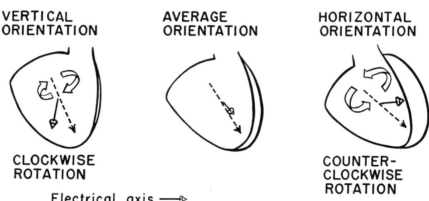

Electrical axis ——▷
Anatomic axis------▸

FIGURE 25.   *A*, The mean electrical axis is computed from two of the three standard limb leads (e.g., leads I and III). The sum of the downward deflections is subtracted from the sum of the upward deflections. For example, the vertical height of the R wave above the baseline is measured in millimeters (+9 mm. in lead I). The total amplitude of the downward deflections (−3 mm. in lead I) is added algebraically to the height of the R wave (+9) and leaves a net value of +6. At a point 6 units toward the plus sign on the lead I line of the triangle, a perpendicular is erected. The net amplitude of upward and downward deflections in lead III is +9 (+10 − 1). A perpendicular erected 9 units toward the plus sign on lead III is extended to intersect the perpendicular from lead I. An arrow drawn from the center of the triangle to the intersection of these two perpendicular lines is the *mean electrical axis*.

B, The mean electrical axis oriented in three dimensions (spatial vector) is directed rather strongly posteriorly. For this reason, rotation of the heart around a longitudinal axis produces large changes in the orientation of the mean electrical axis as projected on a frontal plane. This is the principal mechanism by which changes in the orientation of the heart produce changes in both the mean electrical axis and the configuration of patterns from the various electrocardiographic leads.

proximates the resultant of all the instantaneous axes illustrated in Figure 24C. Although the mean electrical axis is intended to represent the mean value for the instantaneous axes, serious discrepancies often occur, particularly in the presence of ventricular conduction disturbances (see Fig. 35).

The direction of the mean electrical axis is expressed in degrees on a circle drawn from the center of the equilateral triangle. In most normal subjects the mean electrical axis lies in the range from 0 to + 90 degrees (+100 degrees according to some authors). A mean electrical axis greater than +90 degrees is termed right axis deviation, while a shift of the electrical axis into the negative range is called left axis deviation. A large downward deflection in lead III and a tall R wave in lead I produces left axis deviation. A number of factors influence the orientation of the mean electrical axis, including the position of the heart within the thorax, the rotation of the ventricles around their longitudinal axis (Fig. 25B), the thickness of the ventricular walls (e.g., hypertrophy), and the rate and sequence of ventricular conduction. For example, left axis shift occurs when the heart is horizontally oriented, as in short, stocky individuals with high diaphragms. Vertical orientation of the heart tends to shift the mean electrical axis toward the right (Fig. 25B). So long as the heart is normal, these axis shifts are generally confined to the normal range. More extreme axis deviation may result from predominant enlargement of one ventricle (e.g., left ventricular preponderance produces left axis deviation).

Unipolar Precordial Leads

The anterior and posterior aspects of the heart can be explored by means of electrodes applied directly to the surface of the thorax (Fig. 26). This is important because the limb leads respond primarily to potentials developed on the lateral,

PRECORDIAL LEADS

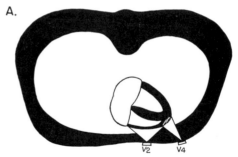

PRECORDIAL LEADS

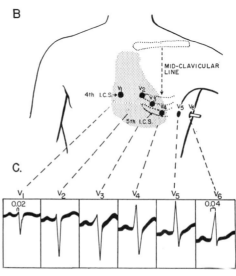

FIGURE 26. A, Electrodes placed at prescribed positions on the precordium are influenced to a greater extent by the myocardium directly beneath than by more distant regions. For this reason they are termed "semi-direct" precordial leads. A local region of depolarization at the apex would have a greater effect on V_4 than on V_2, illustrating the utilization of these leads for detecting altered potentials from local areas under the electrodes.

B, Unipolar precordial electrodes are routinely placed on six positions. V_1 is in the fourth intercostal space (I.C.S.) at the right sternal edge. V_2 is in the fourth I.C.S. just to the left of the sternum. V_4 is in the fifth I.C.S. in the mid-clavicular line with V_3 midway between V_2 and V_4. On a horizontal line drawn from V_4, V_5 is located at the anterior axillary line and V_6 at the mid-axillary line.

C, Electrocardiographic patterns recorded from the six precordial electrode positions are schematically presented. In V_4 the amplitude of R and S are approximately equal. This is termed the *transitional zone*, which is believed to lie over the interventricular septum.

superior and inferior regions of the heart. Electrical activity on the anterior and posterior surfaces subtends very small solid angles from the limb electrodes and produces relatively small potentials. For these reasons, records of cardiac potentials from unipolar electrodes, positioned at specific points on the thoracic wall over the heart, have become a part of the routine electrocardiographic examination.[25] The myocardium immediately under these precordial electrodes contributes more to the recorded deflections than do myocardial walls farther away. A small area of altered polarization in the proximal zone subtends a relatively large solid angle (see V_4 in Fig. 26A), and appears as a large deflection from that particular electrode. The central region of the solid angle has the greatest influence on the recorded potentials. Around the periphery of the solid angle, the membranes approximate a radius of the solid angle and contribute very little to the recorded potentials.

Changes in the functional state of small myocardial areas can be detected by an electrode placed sufficiently near the defect (e.g., local myocardial ischemia). Unfortunately, unipolar electrodes can be placed close to the myocardium only over the precordium. In some cases it is desirable to explore additional areas on the surface of the thorax. For example, unipolar electrodes placed on the back provide an appreciable degree of localization over the posterior surface of the heart,[31] even though these points are farther from the electrodes. An electrode in the lower esophagus has a fairly high degree of specificity for certain regions on the posterior aspect of the atria[32] and ventricles.[33] Small areas of myocardial destruction caused by occlusion of coronary arteries may produce characteristic signs at these various electrode positions when no indication appears on records from the more distant standard limb leads. Electrocar-diographic changes during myocardial infarction are discussed below.

The precordial leads are also used to assess the orientation of the heart within the thorax and the presence of ventricular enlargement. These applications require an understanding of two characteristics of the precordial electrocardiograms: (a) the intrinsicoid deflection and (b) the transitional zone.

Intrinsicoid Deflection. If a unipolar exploring electrode is placed directly on the surface of the right ventricle, the time during which the wave of excitation passes from the endocardial surface to the epicardial surface under the electrode can be measured. As the wave of excitation moves toward the electrode, a positive potential is recorded. When the excitatory process breaks through the surface under the electrode, the positive potential is suddenly replaced by a negative potential because excitation in other parts of the heart is moving away from this electrode. The abrupt transition between increasing positivity and increasing negativity (the peak of the R wave) occurs at the moment the excitatory process breaks through the surface immediately under the electrode and is called the *intrinsic* deflection. The interval between the beginning of the QRS complex and the intrinsic deflection (peak of the R wave) is a measure of the time in which the wave of excitation traveled through the myocardial wall lying under the electrode (ventricular activation time). The remainder of the complex represents activation in more distant portions of the ventricular walls. The intrinsic deflection occurs earlier in records from the epicardial surface of the right ventricle than in those from the left ventricle. Although exploring electrodes cannot be placed directly on the surface of a patient's heart, precordial leads record very similar electrocardiographic patterns. These leads are often called semidirect leads, and the downward deflection recorded following the peak of the R wave is called the *intrinsicoid* deflection.[34]

The routine use of precordial leads includes recording from points overlying the right ventricle (V_1 and V_2 in Fig. 26). Complexes from these leads usually have small R waves, a short interval between the onset of QRS and the intrinsicoid deflection (e.g., 0.02 second), and a deep S wave. In lead V_1 the small R wave represents the rapid penetration of the thin-walled right ventricle by the wave of excitation, and the large S wave indicates the spread of excitation away from the electrode in the more distant portions of the heart (primarily the left ventricle). Precordial leads V_5 and V_6 normally lie over the left ventricle and their records are characterized by large R waves, a more delayed intrinsicoid deflection (e.g., 0.04 second), and a small S wave (Fig. 26C). This configuration denotes that the wave of excitation in the left ventricle advances toward the electrode during a greater proportion of the QRS interval than in the right ventricle, presumably because the left ventricular wall is much thicker. If the left ventricular wall is abnormally thick, ventricular activation time is even more prolonged, so the intrinsicoid deflection tends to be delayed (0.05 second or longer). In the same manner, right ventricular hypertrophy is associated with larger R waves and a delayed intrinsicoid deflection (longer than 0.03 second) in the right precordial leads (V_1 and V_2). There is some controversy whether ventricular activation time should be measured from the beginning of the QRS to the peak of the R wave, or from the beginning of the R wave to the point at which the downward limb of the R wave crosses the baseline. Furthermore, accurate measurement of such very brief intervals is difficult. For these and other reasons, there are wide differences of opinion concerning the value of the intrinsicoid deflection in analyzing electrocardiograms.

The Transitional Zone. In Figure 26 it should be noted that there is a transition from a large S wave on the right side of the precordium to a large R wave on the left. The R and S waves in V_4 have almost equal amplitude. The precordial positions at which R and S are equiphasic indicate the "transitional zone," and are believed to overlie the interventricular septum.[35] If the position of the heart within the thorax changes, the transitional zone tends to shift to one side or the other. The precordial localization of the transitional zone is particularly affected by rotation of the ventricles around their longitudinal axis. For this reason, the configuration of the QRS complex in the precordial leads is useful in estimating the orientation of the heart within the thorax (see below).

Augmented Extremity Leads

In 1942, Goldberger[36, 37] described a simplified technique for recording electrocardiographic patterns from the extremities. Instead of connecting all three extremity leads to a central terminal and positioning an exploring electrode, Goldberger connected two extremity leads to a single terminal and recorded the potential difference between that combination and a third extremity electrode. Thus, he achieved a compromise between standard limb leads and unipolar extremity leads. Goldberger leads record deflections of greater amplitude than appear from unipolar leads connected to the Wilson terminal and, for this reason, have been called "augmented" extremity leads. To be more precise, when the Wilson unipolar lead is used, the deflection amplitude is a little more than 50 per cent (1:1.72) of that obtained with standard limb leads, while use of augmented extremity leads results in an amplitude about 86 per cent the size of that recorded through standard leads. Although the augmented extremity leads are not truly unipolar limb leads, they have been used in much the same way, and are desig-

EFFECTS OF HEART ORIENTATION ON UNIPOLAR LIMB LEADS

A. VERTICAL HEART   B. HORIZONTAL HEART

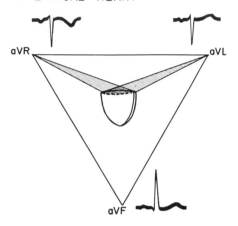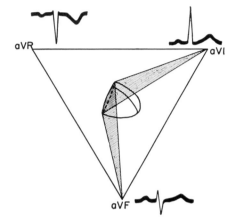

FIGURE 27.   *A*, When the heart is oriented vertically, the QRS complexes are similar in leads aV$_R$ and aV$_L$.

B, In the horizontal heart, aV$_R$ and aV$_L$ are essentially mirror images, a phenomenon which suggests that the wave of excitation actually progresses from right to left. This is confirmed by the diphasic QRS in aV$_F$.

nated aV$_R$, aV$_L$, and aV$_F$ to distinguish them from the unipolar leads illustrated in Figure 21. A principal advantage to the Goldberger leads is that they can be recorded by adjusting the lead selector switch on standard electrocardiographs and do not require the use of an exploring electrode. The augmented extremity leads are frequently used in lieu of the unipolar limb leads for indicating the "electrocardiographic position" of the heart (Fig. 27). Currently, routine electrocardiography includes records from the three standard limb leads, the three unipolar or augmented extremity leads, and the six precordial positions (see Fig. 29). Many more electrode positions have been advocated, but they will not be considered here.

THE ELECTROCARDIOGRAPHIC POSITION OF THE HEART

The orientation of the heart within the thorax has important bearing on the interpretation of electrocardiograms, just as it influences roentgenographic interpretation (see Chap. 13). For example,

electrocardiographic patterns which suggest enlargement of the left ventricle can result solely from a horizontal orientation of the heart. However, the electrocardiographic indications of cardiac orientation do not correspond to the anatomic position, so we may speak of the "electrocardiographic position" of the heart. For instance, the mean electrical axis of a horizontal heart may be directed toward the left shoulder. This obviously does not imply that the long axis of the heart is rotated until the apex lies above the base of the heart (see Fig. 25*B*).

Analysis of the electrical position of the heart has been extended in recent years to include rotation around three axes: the anteroposterior, the transverse and the longitudinal (see Fig. 25*B*). In view of the transitional stages of rotation around any or all of three axes, the heart can occupy innumerable electrical positions. For example, electrocardiographic patterns of 45 different orientations of the heart have been presented by LaDue and Ashman.[38] Such an approach is far too comprehensive for the present discussion. Instead, examples of electrocardiographic patterns in normal hearts oriented vertically or horizontally are presented (Figs. 27 and 28). Goldberger[37] discussed the subject more extensively. The electrical position of the heart must be considered in evaluating electrocardiographic evidence of ventricular enlargement.

ELECTROCARDIOGRAPHIC SIGNS OF CHAMBER ENLARGEMENT

For many years, routine electrocardiographic interpretation was based almost exclusively on the standard limb leads. Ventricular preponderance or hypertrophy was recognized by those changes in QRS configuration which cause the mean electrical axis to deviate beyond the range of normal (see Fig. 25). The basis for these changes in QRS configuration could be convincingly rationalized in accordance with accepted electrocardiographic theory. More recently, the widespread utilization of unipolar precordial and limb leads has greatly broadened the scope of electrocardiographic interpretation to include more complete information concerning the orientation of the heart, the intrinsicoid deflection and changes in the S-T, T complex. The criteria for predominant hypertrophy of each ventricle have become diversified, more empirical and more controversial.

Left Ventricular Hypertrophy

Selecting a "typical" series of electrocardiograms to illustrate left ventricular hypertrophy is extremely difficult because such diverse records are obtained from patients with apparently similar degrees of ventricular enlargement. Signs of left ventricular hypertrophy appear in the ex-

HEART ORIENTATION ON ROUTINE E.C.G. LEADS

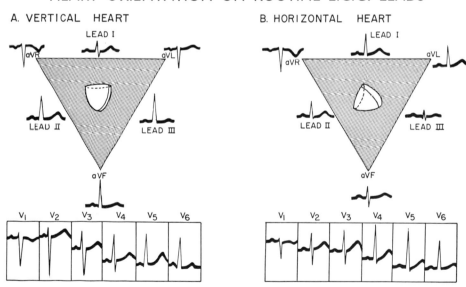

FIGURE 28.   *A,* When the heart is oriented vertically within the thorax, the potentials viewed from the right and left shoulders are similar, so the patterns obtained from aV_R and aV_L are also similar. The QRS in lead I has low potentials and is diphasic, since it represents the difference between aV_R and aV_L (see Fig. 23). The transitional zone between V_3 and V_4 indicates a slight shift of the interventricular septum toward the right. The intrinsicoid deflections are within normal limits throughout, indicating that these changes are not due to ventricular conduction disturbances or hypertrophy.

B, The horizontal heart has a small diphasic lead III which may be slurred or notched. The augmented extremity leads are similar to those illustrated in Figure 27 and the V leads show a transitional zone at about V_3, which indicates a counterclockwise rotation of the ventricles around their longitudinal axis (Fig. 25*B*).

LEFT VENTRICULAR HYPERTROPHY OF HORIZONTAL HEART

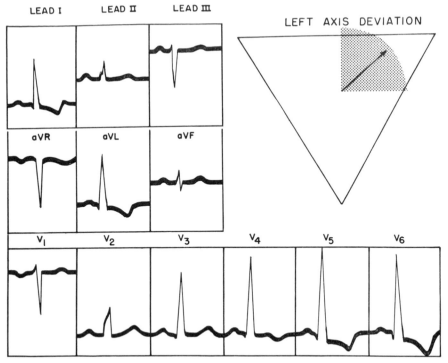

FIGURE 29.   Electrocardiographic signs of left ventricular hypertrophy in this patient with a horizontal heart consist of a tall R_I, small R_{III} and deep S_{III}. These changes in the standard limb leads produce deviation of the mean electrical axis to the left beyond the normal range. The presence of a horizontal heart is affirmed by the tall R wave in aV_L and the diphasic deflection in aV_F (see also Fig. 28). The R wave predominates in V_2 through V_6, indicating that the transitional zone has been shifted to the right. The intrinsicoid deflection (peak of R) occurs more than 0.05 second after the beginning of the Q in $V_{5, 6}$. Inversion of T waves and depression of the S-T segment (strain patterns) occur in leads I, aV_L, $V_{4, 5, 6}$. (From a record obtained through the courtesy of Dr. Samuel Aronson.)

ample presented in Figure 29. This is a rather extreme case, chosen to show clues which may be useful in recognizing the condition.

In Figure 29 the R wave is tall in lead I and very small in lead III. The very deep S_{III}, combined with a tall R_I, is responsible for the deviation of the mean electrical axis to the left beyond the normal range. The QRS interval is less than 0.10 second, so the altered QRS configuration is presumably due to hypertrophy rather than to a ventricular conduction disturbance (see below). The augmented extremity leads (aV_R, aV_L and aV_F) indicate that the electrocardiographic position of the heart is horizontal. In the precordial leads, R waves predominate in V_2

through V_6, so the transitional zone has shifted strongly toward the right. In this example, the horizontal position of the ventricles is accompanied by marked counterclockwise rotation around the longitudinal axis. The T waves are inverted in leads I, aV_L, V_4, V_5 and V_6; this situation is frequently described as a ventricular "strain pattern."

Left Ventricular Strain Patterns.   The T wave may become flattened or inverted under a wide variety of conditions in which an abnormally severe load is imposed upon a ventricle. If the "strain" is transient, the changes in T wave configuration are reversible. In general, the T waves tend to deviate in a direction opposite to the main deflection of the QRS complex (e.g., leads I, aV_L, V_4, V_5, V_6 in Fig. 29). The mechanisms which produce changes in the S-T, T complex are not understood, but will be considered in relation to abnormalities of repolarization (see below). The term "strain pattern" has been criticized because it implies that mechanical features of cardiac function are indicated by the electrical activity, which is clearly impossible. No widely acceptable substitute for the term has been offered thus far.

Strain patterns appearing with other clinical and electrocardiographic signs of left ventricular hypertrophy add weight to the diagnosis. When the QRS and T waves deviate in opposite directions, the typical left axis deviation of QRS is often accompanied by a deviation of the T axis to the right. This phenomenon is graphically illustrated by a frontal vectorcardiogram in Figure 30. Clearly, the additional signs of ventricular hypertrophy disclosed by means of unipolar and extremity leads, plus greater attention to changes in the

S-T, T complex, have increased the frequency with which left ventricular hypertrophy is diagnosed. Many patterns result from variations in the orientation and rotation of the heart. The pattern resulting from left ventricular hypertophy in a patient with vertical orientation of the heart is an excellent example of this problem.

Left Ventricular Hypertrophy in a Vertical Heart. A vertical orientation of the heart tends to produce right axis deviation, while left ventricular hypertrophy tends to shift the mean electrical axis to the left. When the two conditions are combined, these effects may cancel out, and the mean electrical axis may be well within the normal range. Such a condition is illustrated in Figure 31. Here the QRS complexes in the standard limb leads and the mean electrical axis appear entirely normal. The configuration of aV_L and aV_F indicate a vertical orientation of the heart (see Figs. 24 and 25). The precordial leads reveal a transitional zone at

FRONTAL VECTORCARDIOGRAM IN LEFT VENTRICULAR HYPERTROPHY

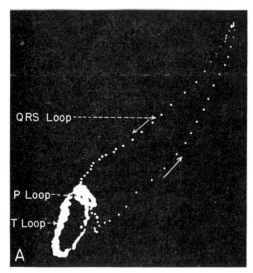
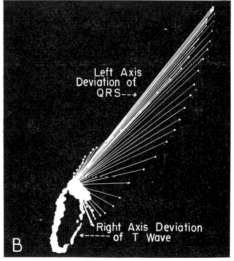

FIGURE 30. *A*, A frontal vectorcardiogram from a patient with extreme left ventricular hypertrophy illustrates the marked deviation of the QRS and T loops.

B, The many instantaneous axes (and mean electrical axis) are clearly deviated to the left and upward (left axis deviation beyond the normal range). The rightward deviation of the T wave indicates that the T waves deflect in a direction opposite to the main QRS vectors: a sign of left heart strain.

LEFT VENTRICULAR HYPERTROPHY OF VERTICAL HEART

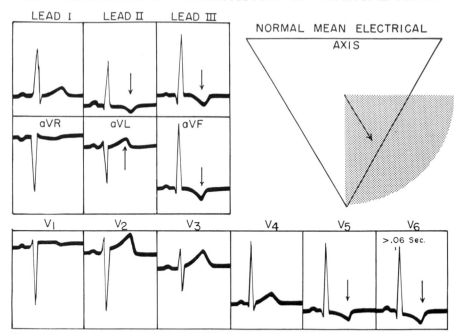

FIGURE 31.   Electrocardiographic signs of vertical orientation of the heart may be counteracted by left ventricular hypertrophy in the QRS complexes of the limb leads (see Fig. 25*B*). Thus, the mean electrical axis may be well within the normal limits when these two conditions are coincident. The principal signs of ventricular hypertrophy in this example are the inverted T waves (strain pattern) in those leads indicated by the arrows (lead II, lead III, aV$_L$, aV$_F$, and V$_{5,\,6}$). The intrinsicoid deflection in V$_6$ exceeds the normal limits (0.05 second). The transitional zone is at V$_3$, which is normal. (From a record obtained through the of courtesy Dr. Samuel Aronson.)

V$_3$. The clues to left ventricular hypertrophy in these records are the strain patterns exhibited in a number of leads (Fig. 31). The intrinsicoid deflection is greater than 0.05 in lead V$_6$, indicating a prolonged activation time in the left ventricle, presumably due to the thickened wall.

The examples illustrated in Figures 29 and 31 obviously do not form an adequate basis for attempting to detect left ventricular hypertrophy in the general run of patients. A comprehensive list of criteria for this diagnosis, used by Sokolow and Lyon,[39] is presented in Table 3. Evaluating a given record in terms of these criteria requires judgment derived from considerable experience with routine electrocardiographic interpretation. Kossmann[40] discussed some of these problems in relation to a patient with left ventricular hypertrophy and rightward deviation of the mean electrical axis, and another with right ventricular hypertrophy and left axis deviation. Since ventricular hypertrophy tends to prolong the QRS interval, patterns resulting from ventricular conduction disturbances are often so similar that differentiation is extremely difficult.

Right Ventricular Preponderance

The electrocardiographic signs of right ventricular enlargement approximate the reciprocal of those described for left ventricular enlargement. The S wave in lead I becomes much deeper at the expense of R$_I$ while R$_{III}$ tends to become abnormally tall (Fig. 32). The mean electrical axis is usually shifted toward the right beyond the upper limits of normal. Right ven-

Table 3.   The Criteria for the Diagnosis of
Left Ventricular Hypertrophy*

---

1. Standard Limb Leads

(a) Voltage $R_1 + S_3 = 25$ mm. or more.

(b) RS-T_1 depressed 0.5 mm. or more.

(c) T_1 flat, diphasic, or inverted, particularly when associated with (b) and a prominent R wave.

(d) T_2 and T_3 diphasic or inverted in the presence of tall R waves and (b).

(e) T_3 greater than T_1 in the presence of left axis deviation and high-voltage QRS complex in leads I and III.

2. Precordial Leads

(a) Voltage of R wave in V_5 or V_6 exceeds 26 mm.

(b) RS-T segment depressed more than 0.5 mm. in V_4, V_5 or V_6.

(c) A flat, diphasic, or inverted T wave in leads V_4 through V_6 with normal R and small S waves and (b).

(d) Ventricular activation time in V_5 or $V_6 = 0.06$ sec. or more, especially when associated with a tall R wave.

3. Unipolar Limb Leads

(a) RS-T segment depressed more than 0.5 mm. in aV_L or aV_F.

(b) Flat, diphasic, or inverted T wave, with an R wave of 6.0 mm. or more in aV_L or aV_F and (a).

(c) Voltage of R wave in aV_L exceeds 11.0 mm.

(d) Upright T wave in aV_R.

---

* From Sokolow, M., and Lyon, T. P., *Amer. Heart J.*, 37:161–186, 1949.

tricular hypertrophy is most commonly encountered in children, in whom the vertical orientation of the heart is far more common than it is in adults. For this reason, right ventricular hypertrophy in the presence of a horizontal heart is rarely encountered.

Right ventricular hypertrophy with strain is illustrated in Figure 32. The mean electrical axis is shifted toward the right beyond the normal range. The S-T, T complexes, which indicate the presence of right ventricular strain, are indicated by arrows. Many other electrocardiographic patterns may be encountered among patients with right ventricular hypertrophy. Myers et al.[41] have discussed these patterns in detail.

Explanations for the Electrocardiographic Signs of Ventricular Enlargement

The electrocardiographic signs of ventricular enlargement could be caused by: (a) rotation of the heart around its longitudinal axis (see below), (b) a thicker ventricular wall or (c) delayed conduction within the myocardium (e.g., ventricular conduction disturbances). Distinguishing between these explanations is difficult. Indeed, each of them has been invoked to explain the signs of ventricular hypertrophy.

Kossmann et al.[42] presented electrocardiographic evidence that clockwise rotation around the longitudinal axis plays an important role in the production of both the deviation of the mean electrical axis and the changes in the precordial leads associated with right ventricular hypertrophy. The same type of reasoning applies to left ventricular hypertrophy except that the heart rotates counterclockwise around its longitudinal axis as viewed from the apex (see Fig. 25B).

Grant[43] has directly compared the electrical and anatomic positions of normal hearts, and has found the expected relation between left axis shift and the horizontal position of the heart. However, the left ventricle and interventricular septum had remarkably similar positions in the body whether the heart was normal or displayed evidence of ventricular hypertrophy. In short, he found no evidence that left ventricular hypertrophy produced rotation of the heart around its longitudinal axis, and concluded that the criteria for detecting rotation of the heart by means of unipolar electrodes have little or no validity. He explained the shift in the mean electrical axis as a result of delayed transmyocardial progression of excitation through the thickened ventricular wall. The potentials from the basilar portion of the left ventricle are large,

RIGHT VENTRICULAR HYPERTROPHY

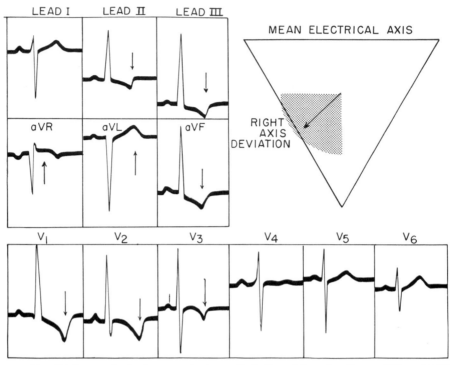

FIGURE 32.   Right ventricular hypertrophy is usually indicated by a deep S_I, small R_I and tall R_{III}. The mean electrical axis deviates toward the right beyond the normal range. Vertical orientation of the heart is indicated by aV_R, aV_L and aV_F (see also Fig. 27). The transitional zone is between V_3 and V_4. Right heart strain is indicated by inversion of T waves in leads I, II, III, aV_R, aV_L, aV_F, and $V_{1, 2, 3}$. This record represents severe right ventricular hypertrophy to illustrate the types of changes which may be observed. Lesser degrees of right ventricular hypertrophy may present no strain patterns and less distinctive changes in the limb leads.

being unopposed by excitation elsewhere, and the terminal QRS vectors are directed more leftward and posterior in hypertrophied ventricles than in normal hearts. In 1929, Wilson and Herrmann[44] presented evidence that the average QRS interval increases with both the weight of the ventricles and the thickness of the left ventricular wall. In no case did they find QRS intervals longer than 0.10 second, so they concluded that greater prolongation of the QRS interval must be due to some other factor (e.g., ventricular conduction disturbance). In 1931, Wilson MacLeod and Barker[45] pointed out the similarities between ventricular conduction disturbances and left ventricular hypertrophy. They concluded that many electrocardiographic patterns attributed to hypertrophy of a ventricle are partly, if not entirely, due to conduction defects such as "bundle branch block." Since the effects of the factors suggested by Grant and by Wilson are similar to those of abnormal ventricular conduction, there may be little functional distinction between ventricular hypertrophy and intraventricular block. Segers *et al.*[46] presented eight cases in which electrocardiographic curves, ordinarily indicative of ventricular preponderance, appeared or disappeared spontaneously and were apparently caused by a peculiar intraventricular block. Indeed, all electrocardiographic evidence of ventricular preponderance is seriously obscured in the presence of defective ventricular conduction. Although severe ventricular conduction disturbances can occur when there is no other evidence of cardiac disease (Fig. 35), they are usually associated with ventricular hypertrophy. Thus, deviations of the mean electrical axis beyond the expected range should stimulate a search for other signs of ventricular hypertrophy, regardless of the cause of the axis shift.

Although ventricular preponderance is one of the most common electrocardiographic interpretations, the criteria used by various authorities are remarkably diverse. Dimond[47] quoted the answers given by eight authorities in response to the simple question "What are the electrocardiographic evidences of left ventricular hypertrophy?" No two answers were alike, and the divergence of opinion was extreme. Of five authorities asked the normal limits of the intrinsicoid deflection, three stated they did not use this measurement. It is very important to recognize that interpreting configurational changes in deflections remains a highly

ATRIAL ENLARGEMENT

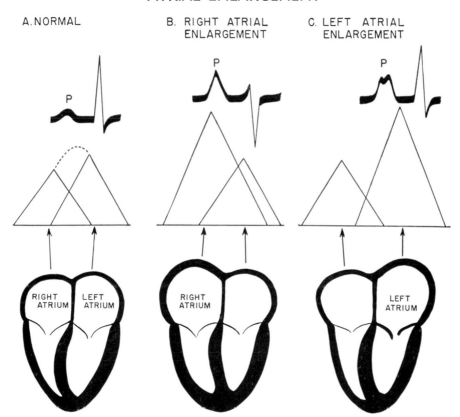

FIGURE 33. *A,* Direct recording of electrical potentials from the surface of the atria in human patients confirms the fact that the right atrium is excited before the left. The P wave can be regarded as a summation of potentials from the two atria.

B, Right atrial dilatation produces larger right atrial potentials of longer duration leading to tall peaked P waves, particularly in lead II. P waves with this configuration are most frequently encountered among patients with congenital malformations of the heart (see Chap. 14).

C, Broad, notched P waves occur most often among patients with mitral stenosis, but may also occur during attacks of acute rheumatic myocarditis. Prolongation of the P waves with notching or flattening of the summit has been related to delay in left atrial excitation and the larger potentials produced by the increased left atrial muscle mass. (After Reynolds, G.: The atrial electrogram in mitral stenosis. *Brit. Heart J.,* 15:250–258, 1953.)

subjective process which depends in large measure on the experience and attitudes of the individual.

Right Atrial Dilatation

Enlargement of the right atrium tends to increase the total mass of atrial musculature, and a larger solid angle is subtended during depolarization (Fig. 33). Tall, peaked P waves, particularly in lead II, frequently occur in conditions which produce right atrial dilatation. The P wave pattern illustrated in Figure 33B is commonly called "P pulmonale" because it is often associated with pulmonary hypertension from primary disease of the lungs. Similar changes are also encountered in many congenital malformations of the heart.

Left Atrial Dilatation

Distention of the left atrium prolongs its depolarization, and the P waves become broad, flattened and notched, particularly in leads I and II (Fig. 33C). This P wave pattern occurs with rheumatic mitral valvular stenosis and has been called "P mitrale."

ELECTROCARDIOGRAPHIC SIGNS OF ABNORMAL VENTRICULAR CONDUCTION

Whenever a portion of the specialized conduction system in the ventricles is nonfunctional, the excitatory process must traverse the slowly conducting myocardial fibers. Thus, excitation is delayed in the myocardium served by the affected portion of the conduction system. If excitation of a sufficient mass of myocardium is delayed, the QRS interval is prolonged and the configuration of the QRS complexes is altered.

Intraventricular Block

Grossly prolonged and distorted QRS complexes are generally attributed to a block in the main branches of the bundle of His (right and left bundle branches).

INTRAVENTRICULAR CONDUCTION DISTURBANCES

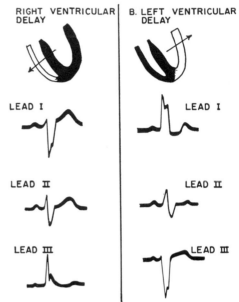

FIGURE 34. A, A ventricular conduction disturbance which delays the arrival of the wave of excitation to the right ventricle produces prolongation of the ventricular depolarization and wide QRS complexes, an example of which is shown. The mean electrical axis deviates to the right, beyond the normal limits in this case (arrow). The T waves tend to deflect in a direction opposite to the direction of the mean QRS deflection. This type of conduction disturbance is generally called right bundle branch block.

B, Delayed conduction to the left ventricular myocardium produces abnormal electrocardiographic patterns in the standard limb leads with the deformed portion of QRS predominantly upward in lead I and downward in lead III. The mean electrical axis tends to deviate to the left. However, the mean electrical axis is usually not equivalent to the resultant of the instantaneous electrical axis when severe conduction disturbances are present (see Fig. 35).

Interference with conduction along the right bundle branch would delay the arrival of excitation in the right ventricular wall (Fig. 34A). In this case, the following sequence is postulated: (a) atrial excitation beginning at the sino-atrial node follows a normal course, so the P wave and P-R interval are essentially normal; (b) excitation of the left side of the septum and the left ventricular wall proceeds at normal speed; (c) the right ventricular wall is invaded after considerable delay by a wave of excitation along the slowly conducting myocardial fibers or by way of Purkinje bundles excited below the region of the block. Although the proximal portions of the bundle branches are generally indicated as the site of blocked conduction, a widespread interference with conduction in the peripheral distribution of the Purkinje fibers (e.g., at the junction of the Purkinje fibers with the myocardium) could have similar functional and electrocardiographic effects. The initial deflections of the QRS complexes are sharp and brief, while the subsequent deflections are delayed, slurred and deformed. When the right ventricular wall is depolarized late, the mean electrical axis tends to be directed from the center of the chamber toward the right ventricle (right axis deviation). The prolonged and slurred deflections are directed downward in lead I and upward in lead III. Repolarization begins in the regions activated first and tends to follow the same general course as the depolarization. Thus, the T wave is deflected in a direction opposite from that of the most prolonged QRS wave. The segment between the QRS and T waves is usually displaced from the baseline. There is no period when the ventricles are completely depolarized, and there is no isoelectric S-T segment.

Conversely, in left bundle branch block, conduction to the left ventricular wall may be delayed while the endocardial surface of the right ventricular cavity is excited promptly (Fig. 34B). Under these conditions, waves of excitation spread more or less simultaneously through the free wall of the right ventricle and through the interventricular septum. By the time a wave of excitation reaches the left ventricular wall, depolarization of the right ventricle and the septum is largely complete. Thus, the final deflection of the QRS is prolonged, slurred and

deformed because it results from retarded activation of the left ventricular wall, unopposed by activity in the remainder of the heart (Fig. 34B). The prolonged QRS wave is generally downward in lead III and upward in lead I, and the T waves deflect in the opposite direction.

Clearly, alterations in the rate and sequence of excitation and repolarization can produce an unlimited variety of wave forms on the electrocardiographic records. All degrees of intraventricular conduction disturbance from simple slurring and notching of QRS deflections to grossly deformed and prolonged QRS complexes are encountered during routine electrocardiographic interpretation. As the correlation between pathologic lesions in the vicinity of the bundle branches and the electrocardiographic signs has been controversial, the rather complicated classification of such conduction disturbances has questionable value. For these reasons, it may be preferable to lump all the ventricular conduction disturbances into the single classification, intraventricular block.[48] A notation of right or left ventricular delay may be warranted when electrocardiographic signs are clear (Fig. 34).

The Mean Electrical Axis with Abnormal Ventricular Conduction

When the waves of excitation pursue abnormal courses through ventricular myocardium, the instantaneous and mean electrical axes generally deviate from their normal orientations. The mean electrical axis, determined in the routine manner (Fig. 25), approximates the resultant of the instantaneous vectors only *so long as the height of the individual deflections is proportional to the area under them.* If each deflection of the QRS complexes conformed to an isosceles triangle subtending the same apical angle, the height of the deflection would be proportional to its duration and would therefore be propor-

MEAN ELECTRICAL AXIS IN VENTRICULAR CONDUCTION DISTURBANCES

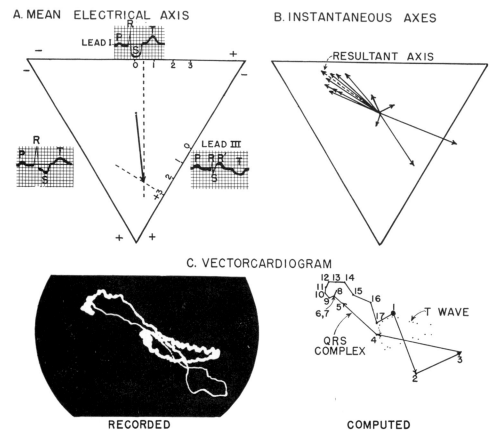

FIGURE 35.   Electrocardiographic records from a 24-year-old medical student with no history or evidence of cardiac disorder revealed a severe ventricular conduction disturbance. The P-R interval was 0.20 and the QRS interval was 0.16 second.

A, A mean electrical axis, determined in the routine fashion, was +85 degrees.

B, Instantaneous electrical axes, computed for each 0.01 second during the QRS complex, were directed primarily upward and toward the right shoulder so the resultant axis was approximately −140 degrees. The reason for the discrepancy between the mean electrical axis and the resultant of the instantaneous axes was the fact that the amplitude of the deflections failed to indicate the time during which the potentials were present, particularly when certain portions of the QRS were slurred and grossly prolonged.

C, Frontal vectorcardiograms drawn from the instantaneous vectors and directly recorded from a cathode ray oscilloscope are presented for comparison. (From Merrill, C. F., Minor, R. H., Paton, R. R., and Shields, J. R.: An analysis of some aspects of vectorcardiography. Student Project Reports, Department of Physiology and Biophysics, University of Washington.)

tional to the area under the deflection. When a deflection is markedly prolonged, its height is not related to the duration of the deflections and the mean electrical axis, and the instantaneous vectors usually point in entirely different directions. A rather extreme example of discrepancy between the mean electrical axis and the

instantaneous vectors is illustrated in Figure 35. Instantaneous electrical axes were computed at intervals of 0.01 second for comparison with frontal vectorcardiograms. The mean electrical axis was also computed and was found to subtend an angle of about +85 degrees. In contrast, most of the instantaneous axes were directed in quite another direction, so their resultant vector was directed at about −140 degrees. Mistakes of this type could be avoided by using the area under each deflection in the QRS complex to compute the mean electrical axis. This can be accomplished by counting the small squares and fractions thereof which lie inside the area bounded by the deflection and the baseline. Each square represents 4 microvolt seconds (sometimes called an Ashman unit). The mean area-axis of the QRS can then be computed by determining the net positive and negative QRS areas of leads I and III and entering them on an Einthoven triangle If this time-consuming procedure is used, the mean area-axis of QRS (designated ÂQRS) should conform closely to the resultant of the instantaneous vectors in the example illustrated in Figure 35. From ÂQRS and

the mean area-axis of the T wave, a resultant vector can be derived which is called the ventricular gradient. Changes in the ventricular gradient result from variations in the duration of the excited state in the myocardium as it is affected by changes in its functional condition. When a method is developed by which the ventricular gradient can be routinely determined, it will be possible to differentiate more readily between the alterations in the S-T, T complex due to changes in the *sequence* of repolarization (ventricular conduction disturbances) and those due to changes in the *rate* of repolarization.[49, 50]

Premature Ventricular Contractions

Ventricular excitation follows an abnormal course and sequence when a premature contraction is initiated at some ectopic focus in the ventricular myocar-

PREMATURE VENTRICULAR CONTRACTIONS

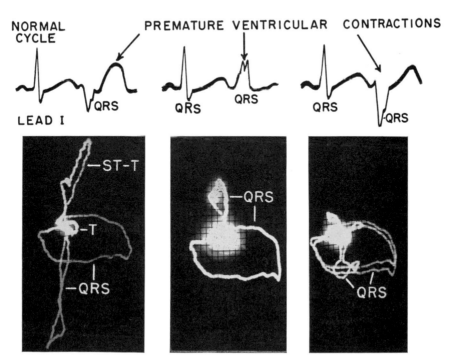

FIGURE 36.   In an electrocardiogram every normal cycle was followed by a premature ventricular contraction (coupling). However, at least three irritable foci in the ventricles were discharging impulses at one time or another. The frontal vectorcardiographic patterns were also produced by the abnormal ventricular conduction from three ectopic foci.

dium. Distorted QRS complexes of widely varying form are produced by this mechanism. Premature ventricular contractions generally begin, without a P wave, very shortly after the T wave of a preceding normal cycle. The QRS-T pattern varies with the origin and course of the wave of excitation. The configurations of complexes initiated by different ectopic foci are illustrated in Figure 36.

The patterns inscribed during normal cycles were very reproducible, while the premature ventricular contractions varied widely. The general direction taken by the wave of excitation as projected on the frontal plane is indicated by the QRS loops on the vectorcardiogram. Considerable discrepancy between the mean electrical axis and the resultant of the instantaneous vectors occurs with premature ventricular contractions just as with ventricular conduction disturbances (Fig. 35).

ABNORMALITIES OF VENTRICULAR REPOLARIZATION (S-T, T)

In contrast to the process of excitation, which is rapidly distributed by a specialized conduction system, the sequence of repolarization depends only on the duration of the depolarized state in the various myocardial fibers. The duration of the excited state is varied by temperature, pressure, electrolyte concentration (e.g., potassium, calcium) and other factors such as administration of various drugs and the oxygen supply, as they affect the "physiologic" condition of the myocardium. For this reason, the T wave has the most labile configuration of all the major deflections. Since the repolarization process occurs during the inscription of both the S-T segment and T wave, changes in the T waves are often but not always associated with changes in the duration of the S-T segment. It is not considered appropriate to embark upon a comprehensive discus-

sion of the many factors which can affect repolarization. Certain causes of altered S-T, T complexes are mentioned because they pertain to subjects covered in other chapters.

Abnormal Sequence of Repolarization

As indicated in the preceding section, ventricular conduction disturbances delay excitation of certain regions of the heart walls and correspondingly retard completion of repolarization in those areas. The abnormal sequence of excitation is reflected in an abnormal sequence of repolarization which changes the configuration of the S-T, T complex. Generally, the S-T, T complex and the main (prolonged) QRS deflection deviate in opposite directions (see Figs. 34–36). This signifies that in abnormal cycles the process of repolarization follows the sequence of excitation more nearly than it does in normal cycles. Thus, the changes in S-T, T complex coincident with an abnormal course of ventricular excitation result from an abnormal sequence of repolarization.

Abnormal Degrees of Polarization

Changes in the functional state of the myocardial fibers can change the extent of polarization. For example, whenever the S-T segment and the T-Q segment are isoelectric, the ventricular myocardium is uniformly depolarized during systole and uniformly polarized during diastole (Fig. 37A). If, during diastole, the depolarized state persisted in a region of myocardium sufficiently large to affect external electrodes, a potential difference would exist which would depress the T-Q interval below the S-T segment (Fig. 37B). If the same region remained partially polarized during both systole and diastole, precisely the same electrocardiographic pattern would be produced with the S-T segment elevated and the T-Q segment depressed

ABNORMALITIES IN THE EXTENT OF POLARIZATION AND REPOLARIZATION

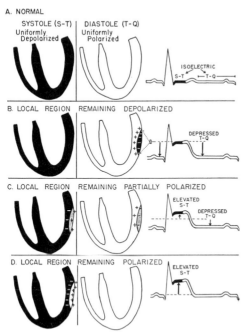

FIGURE 37. *A,* When the ventricular myocardium is uniformly polarized or depolarized, no potentials can be recorded by an external electrode. For this reason, the S-T and T-Q intervals are normally isoelectric.

B, If a local region in the left ventricle remained depolarized during diastole, a potential difference would exist between the polarized and depolarized regions. The junction between these two zones could be represented by a charged membrane with the negative charges facing the exploring electrode as indicated above. At this electrode, a negative potential would produce a downward deflection during diastole (T-Q interval) but not during systole. Thus, the T-Q segment would be displaced downward in relation to the S-T segment. If the local region became partially polarized, the T-Q segment would again be displaced but not quite so far.

C, If a region remained partially polarized to the same extent during both systole and diastole, the S-T segment would be somewhat elevated and the T-Q interval would be similarly depressed, producing a picture very similar to that indicated in *B,* above.

D, If a local region remained polarized through the cycle, the S-T segment would be elevated in relation to the T-Q segment. If the exploring electrode were placed on the opposite side of the heart, the S-T and T-Q segments would be displaced in the opposite direction. (Adapted from Kossmann.[51])

(Fig. 37*C*). Finally, if the same area remained polarized throughout the cycle, a potential difference during electrical systole would elevate the S-T segment (Fig. 37*D*). Whenever a region of myocardium retains the same degree of polarization through a cardiac cycle, identical patterns can be produced by any one of the three mechanisms illustrated in Figure 37. The only difference between the three patterns lies in the level of a "zero" potential, which cannot be distinguished on electrocardiographic records. This approach to understanding the electrocardiographic effects on myocardial injury was discussed in detail by Kossmann.[51]

Abnormal Rates of Repolarization

Although the myocardium might ultimately reach uniform polarization and depolarization, acceleration or retardation of these processes can affect the levels of the S-T and T-Q segments. For example, if a region of the myocardium remained depolarized for an abnormally long time, potential differences similar to those illustrated in Figure 37*B* would become manifest during the latter part of the S-T segment. The S-T segment would ascend and terminate in a tall T wave. This mechanism actually operates in causing the abnormal S-T and T complex associated with severe ventricular conduction disturbances in which delayed depolarization produces delayed repolarization. In contrast, therapeutic doses of digitalis accelerate the process of repolarization. If the rate of repolarization is not uniform throughout the ventricular myocardium, the S-T segment is displaced and the T wave is altered. Changes in the concentration of certain electrolytes in and about the myocardial cells also affect the repolarization process. For example, if the concentration of calcium in the blood is abnormally low, the process of repolarization is prolonged, which is evidenced by prolongation of electrical sys-

EXPERIMENTAL CORONARY OCCLUSION

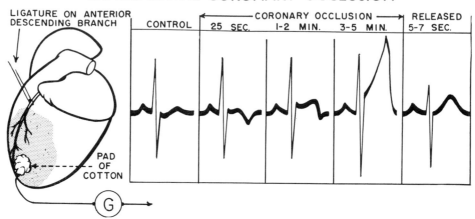

FIGURE 38. Experimental coronary obstruction rapidly produces dramatic changes in electrocardiograms recorded from cotton electrodes positioned over the ischemic area. The initial change is a marked inversion of the T wave (at about 25 seconds), followed by elevation of the S-T segment in about 1.5 minutes. After 3 to 5 minutes, the S-T segment and T waves are both displaced upward. These changes largely disappear in 5 to 7 seconds after release of the ligature.

tole (Q-T interval). High blood calcium levels have the opposite effect. Hypopotassemia also changes the duration of the Q-T interval and alters the S-T, T complex. Goldberger[37] proposed that the ventricular strain pattern is related to a loss of potassium from the myocardial fibers of a ventricle under stress. Inflammatory processes in the myocardium may produce widely diversified changes in all the electrocardiographic complexes including the S-T, T complex.

Direct information concerning the rate and sequence of repolarization is scarce. Not even the rate and sequence of repolarization of normal ventricles have been described, to say nothing of the changes which result from disease. For this reason, the interpretation of the configurational changes in the S-T complex is almost completely empirical.

RECOGNIZING CHANGES IN THE MYOCARDIUM

Acute Coronary Occlusion

Acute coronary obstruction produces characteristic changes in electrocardiograms; some of these changes are rarely observed during spontaneous attacks in patients but may be reproduced in experimental animals.

Bayley, LaDue and York[52] temporarily obstructed the anterior descending branch of the left coronary artery in dogs and recorded the following sequence of events with exploring electrodes on the surface of hearts (Fig. 38). Within 3 or 4 seconds after occlusion, the T waves, which had been positive, became sharply inverted, reaching maximal inversion in about 20 to 25 seconds. Thereafter the inverted T deflections diminished in amplitude as the S-T segment became elevated and rounded with the convexity upwards. The diastolic baseline (T-Q) was deflected in the opposite direction. After 3 to 5 minutes striking displacement of the S-T junction and upward peaking of T waves developed. When the occlusion was released after 2 to 5 minutes, S-T deviation and the large T waves vanished within 5 to 7 seconds, indicating that the procedure did no permanent damage to the myocardium. These striking electrocardiographic changes result from a functional change in the state of the affected myocardium rather than from demon-

ELECTROCARDIOGRAPHY OF MYOCARDIAL INFARCTION

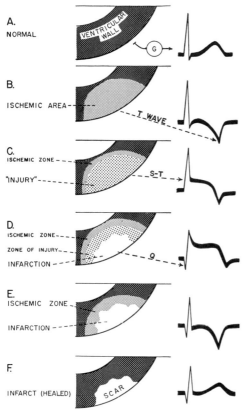

FIGURE 39. The sequence of electrocardiographic patterns recorded from unipolar electrodes over the site of a developing infarct is presented as reconstructed by Bayley.[53]

A, A normal electrocardiographic pattern recorded from a precordial electrode is illustrated for comparison.

B, Immediately after occlusion of a coronary artery, the myocardium served by the vessel becomes ischemic. A change in the rate of repolarization in the area produces a strongly inverted T wave (see also Fig. 38).

C, Within a short time myocardial hypoxia interferes with the repolarization process to the point that the affected myocardium fails to polarize to the normal extent. Incomplete repolarization produces an "injury" current by the mechanism illustrated in Figure 37. The S-T segment assumes a different level than the T-Q segment; this is generally described as a displacement of the S-T segment.

D, Within the center of the ischemic region, some of the myocardium dies and fails to contribute to the potentials during either systole or diastole. Under these conditions, a Q wave appears because the proximal tissue fails to balance the potentials in more distant regions where the

strable pathologic changes. The changes in the S-T segment and T waves develop very rapidly and are easily demonstrable by experiments like those illustrated in Figure 38 because the electrode is placed directly on the site of myocardial ischemia. They mimic the sequence of electrocardiographic alterations which develop over a much longer period of time following occlusion of coronary arteries in man.

Myocardial Infarction

Since the electrocardiographic patterns change progressively following the attack, it is important to obtain serial electrocardiograms at intervals dictated by the patient's progress. The evolution of the electrocardiographic patterns during myocardial infarction is illustrated in Figure 39.

Phase I. If the infarcted region includes the epicardial surface, ischemia of the affected myocardium apparently alters the process of repolarization. The T waves in various leads become either sharply inverted or very tall and peaked, depending upon the orientation of the electrodes in relation to the infarct. The patterns depicted in Figure 39 represent records obtained from a unipolar electrode facing the infarcted region. The changes in T waves are so transient that they are rarely recorded clinically [54] This initial phase of the sequence was first discovered following experimentally induced infarction in dogs (Fig. 38). Frequently, the rate of repolarization is sufficiently

wave of excitation is moving away from the electrode.

E, The myocardium in the zone of injury either dies or is incorporated in the ischemic zone, so the "injury" current disappears and the S-T segment returns to the baseline. The ischemic zone persists, as indicated by the sharply inverted T wave.

F, In a healed infarct, the ischemic zone is supplied by collateral vessels and returns to normal. The only residual sign is the Q wave, which is attributed to the presence of electrically inactive scar tissue.

changed locally so that the S-T segment also is displaced, generally in the same direction as the T wave (see Fig. 38). The changes in the S-T segment and T wave deflection in any particular lead depend upon the size, location and orientation of the affected area in relation to the particular electrodes involved.

Phase II. As ischemia continues, the rate of repolarization becomes progressively slower. This causes the T wave to reverse in direction. At the same time, the extent of polarization or depolarization diminishes, which causes displacement of the S-T segment. The T wave is deflected in a direction opposite to the deviation of the S-T segment, because the latter is a combined effect of an altered rate of repolarization (primary T wave changes) and changes in the extent of depolarization or repolarization (see the S-T segment shifts in Fig. 39). These two effects have different time courses, and are generally attributed to two different degrees of myocardial dysfunction. Probably the blood supply to the tissue at the periphery of the infarcted area is only slightly diminished because collateral channels of capillary size extend into this area from the normal tissue. Deeper within the infarct, a greater degree of myocardial ischemia would be expected as the distance from normal vessels increases. There is probably a gradient in the degree of ischemia from the normal tissue toward the central portion of the infract where the myocardium will ultimately die and be replaced by connective tissue. However, for the sake of convenience, this ill defined shell of damaged myocardium is divided into two zones: (*a*) a zone of ischemia, which lies near the normal tissue and is believed to be responsible for the primary T wave changes, and (*b*) a zone of injury with an abnormal extent of polarization or depolarization producing S-T segment deviations (see Fig. 39).

Phase III. Eventually, the myocardium near the center of the infarct becomes mechanically and electrically inactive. The spread of excitation does not invade the inactive myocardial tissue, which does not contribute to the QRS complex. Electrodes facing the infarct register a prominent negative deflection because the waves of excitation spreading through distal regions of the heart are moving away from the electrode. This negative potential appears early in the process of excitation and produces prominent Q waves in records from particular leads. Pardee[55] noted early that Q waves with an amplitude greater than 25 per cent of the R wave occurred in lead III records taken from a substantial proportion of patients with clinical or pathologic evidence of myocardial infarction. The Q waves become deeper as more and more myocardium in the center of the infarct dies. At the same time, the myocardium which has been "injured" either dies or recovers as collateral circulation is augmented, so the S-T segment deviation tends to dwindle as the Q wave becomes more pronounced. The T wave remains inverted, indicating continued ischemia in the fringe around the dead myocardium. The inverted, sharply peaked T wave with an upward convexity of the S-T segment was called a "coronary" T wave by Pardee[56] and is now frequently referred to as the "Pardee type" of T wave.

Phase IV. Over a period of months, the ischemic myocardium either fully recovers or dies. The inverted T waves may become upright, leaving Q waves as the sole remaining sign of the previous infarction.

If this sequence of electrocardiographic patterns appeared consistently in all patients with myocardial infarction, diagnosis would be very simple. Actually, these changes occur in only about two-thirds of patients. In the remainder, the typical patterns tend to be masked by such pre-existing conditions as bundle branch block, ventricular pacemaker, left heart strain or previous infarction. A very wide variety of electrocardiographic changes is encountered owing to differences in the extent and location of the infarcted region.[57] An intramural infarct produces no change in electrocardiograms for the same reason that a uniformly polarized cell

LOCALIZATION OF MYOCARDIAL INFARCTION

A. ANTEROLATERAL INFARCT

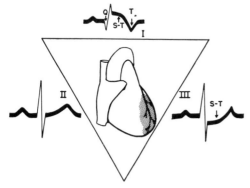

B. POSTERIOR INFARCT

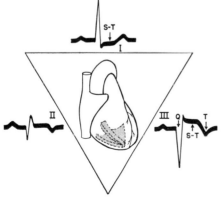

FIGURE 40. *A*, An anterolateral infarct produced by occlusion of the anterior descending branch of the left coronary artery produces a fairly characteristic pattern. In lead I, a prominent Q wave appears with elevation of the S-T segment and inversion of the T wave. This pattern resembles that presented in Figure 39*D*. During recovery, the S-T segment returns to the baseline, leaving a Q wave and an inverted T wave in lead I (the Q_1T_1 pattern). In lead III the S-T segment is depressed and the T wave is upright, so the pattern reverts to normal more quickly in lead III than in lead I.

B, A posterior infarct produces a prominent Q wave in lead III with an elevated S-T segment and an inverted T wave. During recovery, this infarct produces the Q_3T_3 pattern.

produces no external potential. At the same time, a number of other conditions may be associated with electrocardiographic patterns which closely resemble those characteristic of infarction. For example, right and left ventricular hypertrophy and strain may produce QRS-T patterns which can easily be confused with those of myocardial infarction.[58-60] The reasons for the similar patterns resulting from different functional states are obvious, since the electrocardiographic patterns change only because the course, rate and extent of polarization and depolarization are affected.

In spite of its recognized limitations, electrocardiographic interpretation is a valuable adjunct in the diagnosis of myocardial infarction. By utilizing the various standard electrode positions one can determine the location and extent of most myocardial infarctions. Sample electrocardiograms from two common types of infarction are illustrated schematically in Figure 40. An infarct on the anterolateral surface of the heart results from occlusion of the anterior descending branch of the left coronary artery. A prominent Q wave develops in lead I, the S-T segment is elevated and the T wave is deeply inverted. A unipolar precordial electrode placed over the affected region produces a similar pattern, illustrated in Figure 39*D*. As the infarct heals, the S-T segment returns to the baseline, leaving a prominent Q wave and an inverted T wave in lead I. This produces the well known Q_1T_1 pattern of anterior (or anterolateral) infarction.

Conversely, an infarct on the posterior or diaphragmatic aspect of the heart usually results from occlusion of a posterior descending branch. In this case, the Q wave appears in lead III, where the S-T segment is elevated and the T wave inverted. As the infarct heals, a Q_3T_3 pattern develops. Infarction in different regions of the heart changes the patterns in the various leads. Additional details can be obtained from standard texts on electrocardiographic interpretation.

Acute Rheumatic Carditis

Reflecting the widely diversified nature of rheumatic myocarditis, changes in the electrocardiographic complexes follow no specific pattern during the disease. In some patients, the electrocardiograms may not change significantly. In any particular case, any or all aspects of cardiac electrical activity may be modified. Disturbed conduction through the atria, atrioventricular node, and ventricles may alter the P wave, P-R interval and QRS complex and cause secondary alterations in the S-T, T complex. Prolongation of the P-R interval is an expression of retarded atrioventricular conduction and can be more easily detected and evaluated than any other alteration in the complexes. If the established criteria for the upper limits of normal P-R interval are used, first degree atrioventricular block appears at some time during the course of acute rheumatic carditis in about 80 per cent of patients. However, the P-R interval tends to vary widely and may exceed normal limits only on a single day, so serial electrocardiograms must be taken at frequent intervals to demonstrate significant changes in many individuals.

Changes in P Waves. Alterations in the P waves may take many forms, including depression or inversion, notching or diphasic form, widening or increased amplitude. The exact type of configuration assumed is not nearly as important as the fact that a significant change occurs within relatively brief intervals on serial electrocardiograms.

Changes in QRS Complex. If one examines a large series of electrocardiograms obtained from unselected school children, the predominance of sharp clean QRS complexes of brief duration is very striking. In contrast, electrocardiograms obtained from patients with histories of acute rheumatic fever often display more prolonged QRS complexes with a fairly high incidence of slurring or notching of the individual deflections. Cardiologists dealing principally with adults tend to class slurring and notching of QRS complexes among the normal variants. In the early stages of acute rheumatic carditis, QRS complexes of low amplitude (less than 0.5 mV.) are frequently observed in lead I, without evidence of pericardial effusion. These low-potential deflections persist for varying periods, but in many cases the QRS interval may increase on serial electrocardiograms or the amplitude of the waves may become progressively higher as slurring and notching develop on the various components of the complex.

Changes in S-T and T Complex. Perhaps the most common electrocardiographic alteration during acute myocarditis is a change in the amplitude and configuration of T waves. Since the form of the T wave is somewhat labile even in normal individuals, variations should be interpreted with caution. In serial electrocardiograms, the T waves may become elevated, depressed, notched, diphasic or inverted during the course of acute myocarditis. Deviation of the S-T segment is uncommon but has greater significance than changes in the form of the T waves. In general, the S-T segment tends to be displaced in the same direction as the T wave, presumably due to inflammatory processes in the subepicardial region. In some patients, changes in S-T and T complex may simulate those of myocardial ischemia or infarction.

The Q-T Interval. The total duration of electrical activity in the ventricles during systole is indicated by the interval between the beginning of the QRS complex and the end of the T wave (Q-T interval). Some clinicians consider prolongation of this interval an important sign in acute rheumatic fever. Because it is greatly influenced by tachycardia, the Q-T interval is frequently corrected for heart rate. This corrected value (QT_c) may be divided by the "ideal" Q-T interval for the particular patient, producing the Q-T ratio. If the Q-T ratio exceeds an arbitrary value (1.08 for men and children), the Q-T interval is considered prolonged. This process can be facilitated by using appropriate nomograms, but will not be discussed further because the measurement has doubtful value in the recognition of acute rheumatic fever. For example, Pokress and Goldberger[61] found prolongation of the Q-T ratio beyond the maximal normal value in only 28 of 100 patients with acute rheumatic fever. The variability in the Q-T interval among 517 normal infants and children[62] was compared to that in the Q-T interval in 143 rheumatic

ACUTE RHEUMATIC FEVER (FIFTH ATTACK)

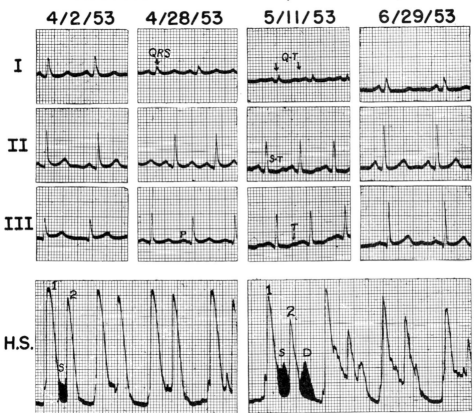

FIGURE 41. In a patient admitted during her fifth attack of acute rheumatic fever, the electrocardiogram on 4/2/53 revealed slight prolongation of the QRS complex and slight elevation of S-T segment in leads II and III. A systolic murmur, detected by auscultation and sonvelography, was the only residual sign from the preceding four attacks. After 26 days (4/28/53), the amplitude of QRS_1 was definitely diminished and the configuration of P waves was altered in all standard limb leads. After 39 days the heart rate was faster and configurations of the P, QRS and T deflections had altered from the preceding record. The Q-T interval was within normal limits during the entire attack. The systolic murmur had increased in intensity, and an early diastolic murmur was barely audible on auscultation but clearly demonstrated sonvelographically. By 6/29/53 the electrocardiogram had reverted to its previous condition and the diastolic murmur had disappeared. A systolic murmur persisted, only slightly louder than on admission. Although this attack can be considered fairly typical, wide variability in the signs and symptoms of acute rheumatic fever is its most important characteristic. (Figures 41 and 42 are presented through the courtesy of the Cardiac Clinics, Children's Orthopedic Hospital, Seattle, Washington.)

ACUTE RHEUMATIC FEVER (FATAL ATTACK)

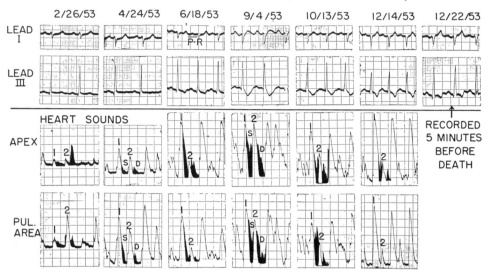

FIGURE 42.   Electrocardiograms (leads I and III) and sonvelograms, taken at approximately two-month intervals, were selected from a large number of serial records obtained during a fatal attack of acute rheumatic fever which began eight months before the first record. The amplitude and configuration of P, QRS and T deflections were significantly altered. Often one or more of these patterns were changed on serial records taken only a few days apart. On admission, the heart sounds were distant, but both systolic and early diastolic murmurs were heard and recorded. The sounds became progressively louder and the murmurs more intense. Perhaps the most dramatic changes in the electrocardiographic patterns were the deep S waves in lead I and the marked inversion of the T waves in lead III. In a record taken less than 5 minutes before the patient expired, the principal change was a slight depression of S-T segment in lead III. Comparing these records with those in Figure 41, it is apparent that virtually any type of electrocardiographic change may occur during the course of acute rheumatic fever.

children between the ages of 7 and 14 years.[63] Twenty-nine patients with fatal pancarditis had Q-T intervals within the normal range. Changes in the Q-T interval paralleled changes in the clinical conditions in two-thirds to three-quarters of the cases, but obvious discrepancies were also noted. The frequency distribution curve of Q-T intervals in patients with rheumatic fever was confined within that for normal children.

Evaluation of Electrocardiographic Changes. The diverse electrocardiographic patterns which occur during acute rheumatic myocarditis signify that a single electrocardiographic tracing has relatively little value. On the other hand, careful comparison of serial electrocardiograms will bring to light progressive changes in patterns in virtually all pa-

tients with acute rheumatic fever (Figs. 41 and 42) plus a large number of patients with a wide variety of other febrile illnesses. If one assumes that significant changes in electrocardiographic patterns indicate changing functional conditions in the myocardium, this test becomes exceedingly sensitive.

SUMMARY

The fundamental difficulty in electrocardiographic interpretation stems from the fact that the changes in configuration of the complexes are rather nonspecific and limited in number. For example, the QRS and T waves can have major deflections upright, downward or deformed. The S-T segment can be isoelectric, elevated, depressed or curved. Since a vast number of disease states may directly or indirectly affect the electrocardiographic complexes, certain electrocardiographic patterns must be common to many different pathologic conditions. The theoretical approach which has been followed in this chapter emphasizes the fact that interpreting changes in the configuration of individual waves and complexes frequently involves recognizing rather subtle differences which have been discovered empirically. Contrary to the usual discussion of electrocardiography, the points of similarity between complexes and mechanisms have been emphasized rather than the differences which can be demonstrated by selected examples. This attitude is not intended to depreciate or cast doubt upon electrocardiographic interpretation, but to help place it in a proper perspective. Although certain characteristic differences can be described to distinguish the patterns produced by ventricular conduction disturbances, ventricular hypertrophy and strain, myocardial infarction, and myocarditis, the basic similarities in the patterns must not be overlooked. In less extreme examples, the differences may be difficult to distinguish, particularly when more than one of these conditions is present in one patient. While a truly remarkable amount of important information can be gleaned from a routine electrocardiographic examination by a competent cardiologist, his interpretation must always be viewed in relation to all other sources of information concerning the patient under consideration. By correlating the electrocardiographic patterns with other signs and symptoms, a large number of disease states can be excluded from the differential diagnosis and a specific diagnosis often can be made. Serial electrocardiograms taken at appropriate intervals and accompanied by parallel clinical studies during the progress of a disease state will frequently establish a diagnosis when the cardiac status is in doubt at the initial examination.

Since electrocardiographic interpretation has been approached on a theoretical basis, the empirical approach has been neglected. To illustrate the kinds of patterns commonly encountered in electrocardiographic interpretation, a few examples have been presented. However, for a comprehensive discussion of electrocardiographic interpretation, the reader is referred to standard texts on the subject.

REFERENCES

1. WOODBURY, L. A., WOODBURY, J. W., and HECHT, H. H. Membrane resting and action potentials of single cardiac muscle fibers. *Circulation*, 1:264–266, 1950.
2. DRAPER, M. H., and WEIDMANN, S. Cardiac resting and action potentials recorded with an intercellular electrode. *J. Physiol.*, 115:74–94, 1951.
3. HODGKIN, A. L., and HUXLEY, A. F. The components of membrane conductance in the giant axon of Loligo. *J. Physiol.*, 116:473–496, 1952.
4. HODGKIN, A. L., and HUXLEY, A. F. Currents carried by sodium and potassium ions through the membrane of the giant axon of Loligo. *J. Physiol.*, 116:449–472, 1952.
5. BOZLER, E. The activity of the pacemaker previous to the discharge of muscular impulse. *Amer. J. Physiol.*, 136:543–552, 1942.
6. PATTEN, B. M., and KRAMER, T. C. The initiation of contraction in the embryonic chick heart. *Amer. J. Anat.*, 53:349–375, 1933.
7. PAFF, G. H. Conclusive evidence for sinoatrial dominance in isolated 48-hour embryonic chick hearts cultivated in vitro. *Anat. Rec.*, 63:203–210, 1935.
8. HOFF, H. E., and NAHUM, L. H. The supernormal period in the mammalian ventricle. *Amer. J. Physiol.*, 124:591–595, 1938.
9. GRANT, R. P. Congestive heart failure and death in a case of paroxysmal auricular tachycardia. Case report. *Amer. Heart J.*, 33:121–123, 1947.
10. ROSENBLUETH, A., and RAMOS, J. G. Studies on flutter and fibrillation. II. The influence of artificial obstacles on experimental auricular flutter. *Amer. Heart J.*, 33:677–684, 1947.
11. SCHERF, D., and SCHOTT, A. *Extrasystoles and Allied Arrhythmias*. New York, Grune & Stratton, 1953, 531 pp.
12. PRINZMETAL, M., CORDAY, E., BRILL, I. C., OBLATH, R. W., and KRUGER, H. E. *The Auricular Arrhythmias*. Springfield, Ill., Charles C Thomas, 1952, 387 pp.
13. HECHT, H. H., KATZ, L. N., PICK, A., PRINZMETAL, M., and ROSENBLUETH, A. The nature of auricular fibrillation and flutter: a symposium. *Circulation*, 7:591–613, 1953.

14. KOSSMANN, C. E. The normal electrocardiogram. *Circulation*, 8:920–936, 1953.

15. WOLFF, L., PARKINSON, J., and WHITE, P. D. Bundle-branch block with short P-R interval in healthy young people prone to paroxysmal tachycardia. *Amer. Heart J.*, 5:685–704, 1930.

16. KENT, A. F. S. The right lateral auriculoventricular junction of the heart. *J. Physiol.*, 48:xxii–xxiv, 1914.

17. KOSSMANN, C. E., BERGER, A. R., BRILLER, S. A., RADER, B., and BRUMLÍK, J. Anomalous atrioventricular excitation produced by catheterization of the normal human heart. *Circulation*, 1:902–909, 1950.

18. PRINZMETAL, M., KENNAMER, R., CORDAY, E., OSBORNE, J. A., FIELDS, J., and SMITH, L. A. *Accelerated Conduction. The Wolff-Parkinson-White Syndrome and Related Conditions.* New York, Grune & Stratton, 1952, 110 pp.

19. WOLFF, L. Syndrome of short P-R interval with abnormal QRS complexes and paroxysmal tachycardia (Wolff-Parkinson-White syndrome). *Circulation*, 10:282–291, 1954.

20. BURCH, G. E., and WINSOR, T. *A Primer of Electrocardiography.* 2nd ed. Philadelphia, Lea & Febiger, 1949, 245 pp.

21. SCHERF, D., and BOYD, L. J. *Clinical Electrocardiography.* 4th ed. New York, Grune & Stratton, 1953, 490 pp.

22. LEWIS T. *Electrocardiography and Clinical Disorders of the Heart Beat: a handbook for practitioners and students.* London, Shaw & Sons Ltd., 1949, 285 pp.

23. DOLGIN, M., GRAU, S., and KATZ, L. N. Experimental studies on the validity of the central terminal of Wilson as an indifferent reference point. *Amer. Heart J.*, 37:868–880, 1949.

24. WILSON, F. N., JOHNSTON, F. D., MacLEOD, A. G., and BARKER, P. S. Electrocardiograms that represent the potential variations of a single electrode. *Amer. Heart J.*, 9:447–458, 1934.

25. WILSON, F. N., JOHNSTON, F. D., ROSENBAUM, F. F., ERLANGER, H., KOSSMANN, C. E., HECHT, H., COTRIUM, N., MENEZES DE OLIVERIA, R., SCARSI, R., and BARKER, P. S. The precordial electrocardiogram. *Amer. Heart J.*, 27:19–85, 1944.

26. WILSON, F. N., and JOHNSTON, F. D. The vectorcardiogram. *Amer. Heart J.*, 16:14–28, 1938.

27. GRISHMAN, A., and SCHLERIS, L. *Spatial Vectorcardiography.* Philadelphia, W. B. Saunders Co., 1952, 217 pp.

28. CRONVICH, J. A., BURCH, G. E., and ABILDSKOV, J. A. Some requirements in equipment and technics for vectorcardiography. *Circulation*, 8:914–919, 1953.

29. DUCHOSAL, P. W., and SULZER, R. *La Vectocardiographie; méthode d'exploration du champ électrique créé dans le corps humain pars les courants d'action du coeur dans les conditions normales et pathologiques.* Basel, S. Karger, 1949, 172 pp.

30. FRANK, E. A direct experimental study of three systems of spatial vectorcardiography. *Circulation*, 10:101–113, 1954.

31. ELEK, S. R., HERMAN, L. M., and GRIFFITH, G. C. A study of unipolar left back leads and their application to posterior myocardial infarction. *Circulation*, 7:656–668, 1953.

32. NYBOER, J., and HAMILTON, J. G. M. Oesophageal electrocardiograms in auricular fibrillation. *Brit. Heart J.*, 2:263–270, 1940.

33. MYERS, G. B., and KLEIN, H. A. The relation of unipolar limb leads to precordial and esophageal leads. *Amer. Heart J.*, 35:727–755, 1948.

34. KOSSMANN, C. E., and JOHNSTON, F. D. The precordial electrocardiogram. I. The potential variations of the precordium and of the extremities in normal subjects. *Amer. Heart J.*, 10:925–941, 1935.

35. ROSENBURG, M. J., and AGRESS, C. M. Position of precordial leads. An anatomical study. *Amer. Heart J.*, 38:593–603, 1949.

36. GOLDBERGER, E. The aVl, aVr, and aVf leads. A simplification of standard lead electrocardiography. *Amer. Heart J.*, 24:378–396, 1942.

37. GOLDBERGER, E. *Unipolar Lead Electrocardiography and Vectorcardiography: including the standard leads, the aV and V leads, the cardiac arrhythmias and the principles of vectorcardiography,* 3rd ed. Philadelphia, Lea & Febiger, 1953, 601 pp.

38. LaDUE, J. S., and ASHMAN, R. Electrocardiographic changes in acute glomerulonephritis. *Amer. Heart J.*, 31:685–701, 1946.

39. SOKOLOW, M., and LYON, T. P. The ventricular complex in left ventricular hypertrophy as obtained by unipolar and precordial limb leads. *Amer. Heart J.*, 37:161–186, 1949.

40. KOSSMANN, C. E. Electrocardiograms of deceptive form in ventricular hypertrophy. *Circulation*, 8:403–416, 1953.

41. MYERS, G. B., KLEIN, H. A., and STOFER, B. E. The electrocardiographic diagnosis of right ventricular hypertrophy. *Amer. Heart J.*, 35:1–40, 1948.

42. KOSSMANN, C. E., BERGER, A. R., BRUMLÍK, J., and BRILLER, S. A. An analysis of causes of right axis deviation based partly on endocardial potentials of the hypertrophied right ventricle. *Amer. Heart J.*, 35:309–335, 1948.

43. GRANT, R. P. The relationship between the anatomic position of the heart and the electrocardiogram: a criticism of "unipolar" electrocardiography. *Circulation*, 7:890–902, 1953.

44. WILSON, F. N., and HERRMANN, G. R. Relation of QRS-interval to ventricular weight. *Heart*, 15:135–140, 1929.

45. WILSON, F. N., MacLEOD, A. G., and BARKER, P. S. The interpretation of the initial deflections of the ventricular complex of

the electrocardiogram. *Amer. Heart J.*, 6: 637–664, 1931.

46. SEGERS, M., REGNIER, M., and DELATTE, E. L'installation brusque de l'image éléctrocardiographique de prépondérance. *Acta cardiol. Brux.*, 7:63–75, 1952.

47. DIMOND, E. G. *Electrocardiography*. St. Louis, C. V. Mosby Co., 1954.

48. ROSENMAN, R. H., PICK, A., and KATZ, L. N. Intraventricular block. Review of the literature. *Arch. Intern. Med.*, 86:196–232, 1950.

49. WILSON, F. N., MacLEOD, A. G., BARKER, P. S., and JOHNSTON, F. D. The determination and significance of the areas of the ventricular deflections of the electrocardiogram. *Amer. Heart J.*, 10:46–61, 1934.

50. ASHMAN, R., GARDBERG, M., and BYER, E. The normal human ventricular gradient. III. The relation between the anatomic and electrical axes. *Amer. Heart J.*, 26:473–494, 1943.

51. KOSSMANN, C. E. The electrocardiographic effects of myocardial and pericardial injury. Chap. 11 in *Disorders of the Circulatory System*, R. L. Craig, ed. New York, The Macmillan Co., 1952.

52. BAYLEY, R. H., LaDUE, J. S., and YORK, D. J. Electrocardiographic changes (local ventricular ischemia and injury) produced in the dog by temporary occlusion of a coronary artery, showing a new stage in the evolution of myocardial infarction. *Amer. Heart J.*, 27:164–169, 1944.

53. BAYLEY, R. H. On certain applications of modern electrocardiographic theory to the interpretation of electrocardiograms which indicate myocardial disease. *Amer. Heart J.*, 26:769–831, 1943.

54. DRESSLER, W., and ROESLER, H. High T

waves in the earliest stage of myocardial infarction. *Amer. Heart J.*, 34:627–645, 1947.

55. PARDEE, H. E. B. The significance of an electrocardiogram with a large Q in lead 3. *Arch. Intern. Med.*, 46:470–481, 1930.

56. PARDEE, H. E. B. Heart disease and abnormal electrocardiograms. With special reference to the coronary T wave. *Amer. J. Med. Sci.*, (N.S.) 169:270–283, 1925.

57. LEVY, L., II, and HYMAN, A. L. Difficulties in the electrocardiographic diagnosis of myocardial infarction. *Amer. Heart J.*, 39:243–262, 1950.

58. MYERS, G. B. QRS-T patterns in multiple precordial leads that may be mistaken for myocardial infarction. I. Left ventricular hypertrophy and dilatation. *Circulation*, 1:844–859, 1950.

59. MYERS, G. B. QRS-T patterns in multiple precordial leads that may be mistaken for myocardial infarction. II. Right ventricular hypertrophy and dilatation. *Circulation*, 1:860–877, 1950.

60. BENCHIMOL, A. B., and SCHLESINGER, P. Electrocardiographic changes in a case of left ventricular and septal hypertrophy resembling anterior myocardial infarction. *Circulation*, 1:970–974, 1950.

61. POKRESS, M. J., and GOLDBERGER, E. A study of the Q-T interval in rheumatic fever. *Amer. Heart J.*, 38:423–432, 1949.

62. ALIMURUNG, M. M., JOSEPH, L. G., CRAIGE, E., and MASSELL, B. F. The Q-T interval in normal infants and children. *Circulation*, 1:1329–1337, 1950.

63. CRAIGE, E., ALIMURUNG, M. M., BLAND, E. F., and MASSELL, B. F. The Q-T interval in rheumatic fever. *Circulation*, 1:1338–1344, 1950.

Chapter 11

CARDIOVASCULAR SOUNDS

I. Heart Valves and Heart Sounds

The contracting ventricles supply the energy for a unidirectional flow of blood around the circulatory system. Efficient pumping action of the ventricles depends upon the effectiveness of heart valves in preventing retrograde flow. To serve this function adequately, the cardiac valves must conform to a number of stringent requirements. The valves must open easily and widely to offer minimal impedance to blood flowing at a high velocity. Otherwise, excessive pressure energy will be dissipated and wasted in propelling blood through restricted orifices. The valves must close completely with minimal leak and minimal displacement because any blood passing in the retrograde direction must be pumped forward again. Thus, the valves must close abruptly and seal promptly. Since the closed valves represent a diaphragm between regions of very high and very low pressure, the valve structure must be able to withstand large stresses. The valve cusps shut and are subjected to stress by these pressures roughly 48,000 times a day for as long as 100 years without interruption for repairs or replacement. Thus, the cardiac valves must be extremely flexible, very strong and highly durable to function during the lifetime of an individual. These requirements are so difficult to meet that no reasonable substitute for natural valves has been devised in spite of our tremendous technological advances of the last half century.

FUNCTION OF ATRIOVENTRICULAR VALVES

The tricuspid and the mitral valves are interposed between the ventricles and atria on the right and left sides of the heart, respectively. Their structural charactertistics were summarized in a preceding chapter (see Fig. 6, Chap. 2). The valve cusps are firmly attached around the circumference of the fibrous valve rings. The two main valve cusps and the small accessory cusps which make up a tricuspid or a mitral valve are not separated at the commissures all the way to the valve ring. Around the circumference of the valves, the cusps are continuous to form an uninterrupted diaphragm which is shaped like a shallow funnel. According to Brock,[1] the area of the orifice at the small end of the mitral "funnel" is not significantly greater than the aortic orifice. The main valve cusps extend quite deeply into the ventricular cavity and their combined area is about twice the area of the orifice they must occlude.

In spite of their large area, the atrioventricular valves do not function effectively if the chordae tendineae are ruptured or sectioned. The chordae tendineae extend from the papillary muscles to the edge of the valve cusps and continue into

300

the substance of the valve (Fig. 1). These tough strands of collagenous fibers contribute much to the strength of the valve cusps. The chordae tendineae appear to function like clew lines fastened to the edges of square sails. They act to prevent flapping and eversion of the valve cusps that would render the valves incompetent or unable to seal the atrioventricular orifice. Some of the chordae (first order) insert on the edges of the valve cusps; others (second order) insert just beyond the free edge of the cusp; and a few (third order) originate directly from the ven-

tricular wall near the valve ring and insert on the ventricular surface of the valves. The chordae are of unequal length but are so arranged that tension is exerted on all strands when the valve is closed. The valve substance between the insertions of the first-order chordae is very thin and flexible and thus produces a completely watertight seal as soon as the valve edges come into apposition.

Concepts of Valve Closure

In 1912, Henderson and Johnson[2] reported a series of most ingenious demon-

ANATOMY OF THE MITRAL VALVE

FIGURE 1. These normal human mitral valves are presented in a postulated position of rest with slight tension being exerted by the chordae tendineae. From this position, slight separation of the valves could admit a rapid flow from the atria or slight movement toward apposition would produce rapid closure with little or no regurgitation.

CLOSURE OF ATRIOVENTRICULAR VALVES

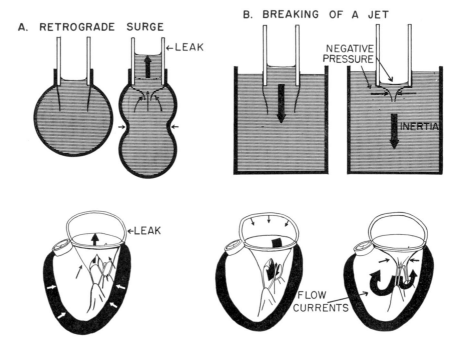

FIGURE 2. Two mechanisms for closure of A-V valves are indicated by simple models and by schematic drawings.

A, A valve, consisting of a section of thin-walled rubber tubing mounted within a rubber bulb, could be closed by a surge of fluid only after considerable leakage past the closing valve. Similarly, if the mitral valves gape wide at the beginning of ventricular contraction, considerable blood would regurgitate into the left atrium during closure of these valves.

B, If the flow of fluid through a model valve ceases rather abruptly, the inertia of the moving fluid carries it onward, leaving a wake of negative pressure which could close the valve with no regurgitation whatever. Cessation of flow into the ventricle after atrial systole may produce partial closure of the A-V valves by this mechanism, facilitated by currents of flow upward and behind the closing valve cusps (after Henderson and Johnson[2]).

strations of two different mechanisms for closure of heart valves. The first mechanism is a retrograde flow of blood toward the atria as the ventricles begin to contract, catching the valves like a pair of sails and flinging them into apposition (Fig. 2*A*). Imagine a door being slammed by a gust of wind. Clearly, this mechanism inevitably involves a large leak before the orifice is closed. The occurrence of such regurgitation is widely acknowledged when the atrioventricular valves are closed by ventricular systole which is not preceded by an atrial contraction, i.e., premature ventricular contraction. If the mitral valve normally closes without regurgitation, flow of blood through the mitral orifice during atrial systole must bring the valves into partial or complete apposition. Henderson and Johnson[2] also demonstrated that when flow of fluid through an orifice is suddenly arrested, the inertia of the moving blood produces in its wake a negative pressure which closes either simulated or real heart valves (Fig. 2*B*). The portion of the valves nearest their base is the first to move inward and the edges of the flaps are the last to make contact. In this way, the valves close without the slightest regurgitation. Such inrolling during valve closure "invariably occurred under conditions simulating the movements of blood in the normal heart."

Dean[3] connected the edge of a mitral valve cusp to a delicate lever by means of a human hair and recorded the valve movements in isolated, perfused hearts (Fig. 3). When the interval between atrial and ventricular systole was less than 0.147 second, the valve cusps opened wider at a time when blood was flowing through the orifice and, near the end of atrial contraction, moved quickly and markedly toward the atrium but did not close completely. The onset of ventricular contraction at this moment completed closure of the valves as a single movement. A longer interval between atrial and ventricular systole (greater than 0.272 sec.) allowed the valves to move toward apposition and then separate again before ventricular contraction ensued. These observations are clearly consistent with the concepts of Henderson and Johnson.[2]

The concepts proposed by Henderson and Johnson and by Dean promptly achieved wide acceptance and have served as the basis for most interpretations of both valve function and heart sounds. Direct observation and motion picture recording of the action of atrioventricular valves[4, 5] in isolated hearts have revealed that during systole the valve cusps tend to bulge upward toward the atrium. Displacement of the valves toward the atrium is basically equivalent to a retrograde leak through the valves so far as the ventricular myocardium is concerned. When it was learned that the exposed or excised heart tends to shrink and function at abnormally small dimensions (see Fig. 5, Chap. 3), it seemed probable that valve mechanics are somewhat distorted under these conditions. The ventricular myocardium shortens as the cardiac chambers shrink, but the fibrous valve rings, valve cusps and chordae tendineae retain their same dimensions. Under these conditions, the valves and their attachments might have a great deal more slack than normal and thus could execute wider excursions. For this reason, the motion of the mitral valves in the intact dog was studied by

MOVEMENTS OF THE MITRAL VALVE

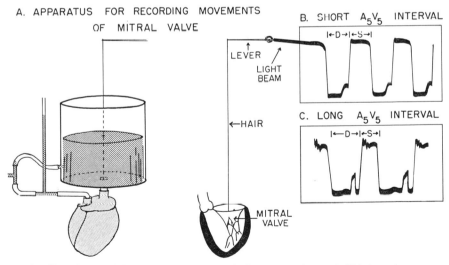

A. APPARATUS FOR RECORDING MOVEMENTS OF MITRAL VALVE

B. SHORT A_5V_5 INTERVAL

C. LONG A_5V_5 INTERVAL

FIGURE 3.   Dean's records indicated that during the later part of diastole (D) the valve cusps moved toward a position of closure after atrial systole and before ventricular systole (S). If the interval between atrial systole and ventricular systole was short, valve closure was initiated before ventricular systole and was completed by the rising ventricular pressure. If this interval was sufficiently long, the valves closed partially and then gaped wide before ventricular contraction ensued (lower record).

means of motion pictures of the images produced by x-rays on fluorescent screens (cinefluorography).

Cinefluorographic Studies of Mitral Valve Function

To study the displacement of the valves in intact dogs, a probe applicator was devised which could be inserted through the left atrial wall and into the left ventricular cavity. When a plunger was activated, tiny silver clips were crimped to the edges of the valve cusps or to the chordae tendineae near the valve attachments. The location of the mitral valve ring was marked by suturing a delicate silver chain to the atrioventricular groove. The animals recovered from this operation promptly and lived indefinitely. Motion pictures of the movements of the metal markers were obtained days or weeks after the operation.[6]

In such experiments, the excursion of the valves was surprisingly small. Certainly, the valve cusps did not gape wide at any phase of the cardiac cycle. At no time did the valve edges ascend to the plane described by the mitral valve ring. In other words, the valve edges were apparently held well down within the ventricular cavity during all phases of the cardiac cycle. To be sure that large valve excursions were not occurring in some other plane, stereoscopic cinefluorographic equipment was developed to study valve motion in three dimensions.[7] These studies merely confirmed that the valve edges moved very small distances.

Both the restricted lateral movement during diastole and the limited motion toward the atrium during systole point to more or less continuous restraint by the chordae tendineae.

The valve action was also studied when the heart was functioning at abnormally small dimensions (either immediately after the operation or after induction of pneumothorax). Under these conditions, the excursion of the valve edges was consistently much wider than that observed when the heart had regained its normal large dimensions.

Mechanisms of Mitral Valve Closure

During the final stages of ventricular filling, the ventricular cavity is well distended with blood. The roots of the papillary muscles are correspondingly displaced toward the apex and away from the atrioventricular valve ring (Fig. 4). The chordae tendineae and valve cusps are probably under some tension, drawing the valve edges toward apposition. This is the period of slow filling or diastasis, when little or no blood is flowing through the valve. At the onset of atrial contraction, blood is propelled through the cleft formed by the valve cusps. The valve cusps are then approximated by the negative pressure following the interrupted stream of blood, supplemented by eddy currents flowing back behind the valves (see Fig. 2). The wave of excitation, rapidly propagated by Purkinje fibers, first enters the ventricular myocardium at the roots of the papillary muscle and over the endocardial surface. The early contraction of papillary muscles and trabeculae carneae simultaneously draws the valve edges and valve rings toward the apex and produces a lateral displacement of ventricular walls (see Fig. 15, Chap. 2). The valves are tightly sealed by the rising ventricular pressure. As ventricular ejection proceeds, the shortening of the ventricular myocardium is accompanied by shortening of the papillary muscles, taking up any slack in the valves that might otherwise develop (Fig. 4). At the end of systole the relaxation of the ventricular myocardium (and papillary muscles) releases the tension on the valves, and they can gape open freely as blood pours rapidly from the atrium into the ventricle. At the end of the rapid-filling interval, the ventricle is well distended and the valve cusps are again drawn toward apposition by the traction exerted by the stretched papillary muscles, and the cycle repeats (Fig. 4). Although corresponding studies have not been conducted on the tricuspid valves, the similarity in structure and function of the two atrioventricular valves (Fig. 6, Chap. 2) suggests that they both utilize the same basic mechanisms.

FUNCTION OF SEMILUNAR VALVES

The pulmonary and aortic valves are each composed of three cusps of equal size which resemble flexible cups attached symmetrically around the circumference of the valve orifice (Fig. 5). Two valve cusps of equal size would be equally effective in completely closing and sealing off the opening in the valve ring. However, such a bicuspid valve would not open widely, and would necessarily obstruct the flow of blood. Occasionally a bicuspid valve develops as a congenital deformity, characteristically producing functional changes corresponding to stenosis of the valve. The normal aortic and pulmonary valves close completely and when open have a triangular orifice which is considerably smaller than the cross-sectional area of the artery (Fig. 5). This opening is sufficiently large that the pres-

ATRIOVENTRICULAR VALVE ACTION DURING THE CARDIAC CYCLE

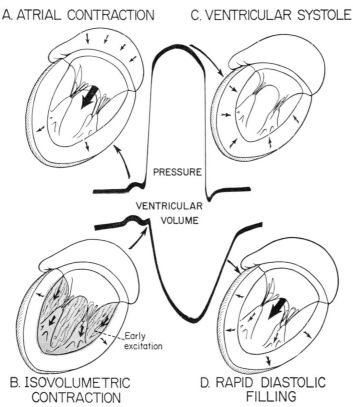

FIGURE 4. At the end of diastole, the distended ventricle applies traction through the chordae tendineae to the valve cusps, drawing them toward apposition. At the end of atrial systole, the jet of flow through the valves is arrested and the valve cusps close, aided by the swirling currents. Ventricular systole seals the valves together by the high internal pressure. The valves gape open promptly as the ventricular myocardium relaxes at the end of systole.

SEMILUNAR VALVES

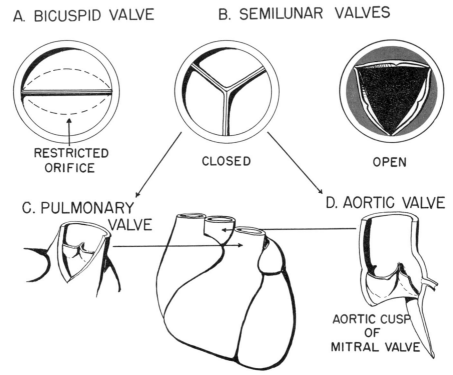

FIGURE 5. *A,* Bicuspid valves can close completely but they will not open fully.

B, A valve with three symmetrical cusps can close completely and theoretically could open to the full dimensions of the artery. However, motion pictures of aortic valve action have demonstrated that even normal valve cusps are only partly displaced during systolic ejection, opening a triangular orifice very much smaller in area than the cross section of the artery (see also Fig. 1, Chapter 11). (From McMillan, I. K. R., and Daley, R.: The action of human mitral and aortic valves studied postmortem by cinematography, presented at the Second World Congress of Cardiology, Washington, D. C., September 16, 1954.)

C, The pulmonary valve is situated at the junction of the conus region and the pulmonary artery.

D, The aortic valve cusps are in close relation to the orifices of the coronary arteries. The sinuses of Valsalva behind the valve cusps, coupled with the incomplete opening of the cusps, prevent obstruction of the coronary orifices during ventricular systole.

sure gradient required to force blood through it is negligible even at the highest velocities attained during ejection.

Behind the aortic valve cusps are three outpouchings, the sinuses of Valsalva, which help prevent obstruction of the coronary ostia. If a valve leaflet came in contact with the coronary orifice, shutting off the blood flow from the aorta, the pressure in the coronary artery would fall rapidly as blood passed out of the coronary capillaries. The coronary arterial pressure would approach coronary venous pressure during each diastolic interval while the aortic pressure was continuously maintained at high pressure. Under these conditions, a valve cusp sealing a coronary orifice even momentarily would remain sealed because there appears to be no mechanism which could release it. The sinuses of Valsalva provide a space behind the valve cusps and apparently prevent this unfortunate accident. Flow through hydraulic models suggests that turbulent eddies circle back behind the valve cusps during systolic ejection, holding the valve edges out away from the walls of the sinuses of

Valsalva (Fig. 6). At the end of ventricular systole, ejection ceases for a brief interval before ventricular relaxation becomes manifest. At that moment, a slight retrograde surge of blood toward the ventricle is abruptly arrested as the valve cusps snap shut. The closure of both atrioventricular and semilunar valves is associated with the development of vibrations or heart sounds which are easily heard by listening over the surface of the chest.

HEART SOUNDS

Auscultation is the most sensitive test of the functional integrity of the heart. Frequently, murmurs or alterations in the heart sounds are the only definite signs of organic heart disease, appearing long before the stress on the cardiovascular system is sufficient to produce other signs and symptoms. As in any sensitive test of physiologic function, the distinction between normality and abnormality is difficult in many borderline cases. Nevertheless, characteristic murmurs and changes in heart sounds may direct attention to-

ward the heart as the site of disease processes. In a few conditions, a distinctive murmur provides a definite diagnosis of an anatomic lesion at an early stage in its development. Clinicians learn to recognize well developed, characteristic murmurs by training and experience. However, the significance of murmurs and the subtle changes in heart sounds can be more fully appreciated with a fairly clear understanding of the nature of the sounds, the mechanics of sound transmission and the characteristics of auditory perception.

The Nature of Sounds

Production of Sounds. Sounds are subjective interpretations of the sensations produced by the vibrations reaching the auditory apparatus. Sound waves are produced and transmitted by the vibratory motion of particles or bodies which are repetitively displaced from their position of equilibrium and then restored by a force of restitution toward their position of rest (Fig. 7A).

Characteristics of Sounds. Consider a tuning fork with its prongs vibrating

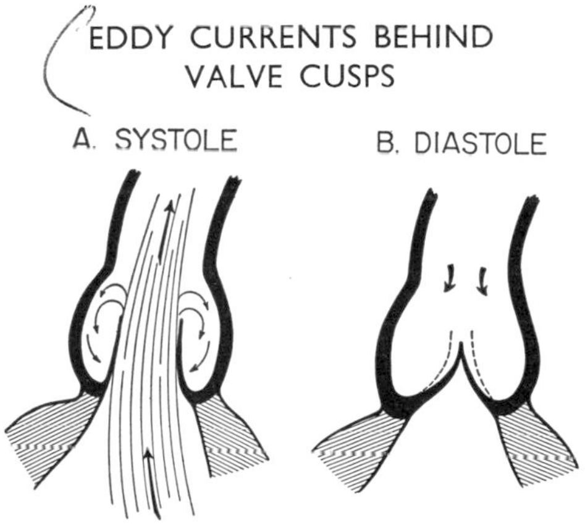

EDDY CURRENTS BEHIND VALVE CUSPS

A. SYSTOLE   **B. DIASTOLE**

FIGURE 6. Hydraulic models, simulating the aortic valve, demonstrate eddy currents that swirl behind the flexible cusps during rapid flow through the valve orifice. These currents tend to prevent the cusps from sealing off the coronary orifices and stagnation of blood behind the valves. (Derived from studies by Dr. K. A. Merendino, Department of Surgery, and Mr. Wayne Quinton, Medical Instrument Shop, University of Washington.)

THE NATURE OF VIBRATIONS

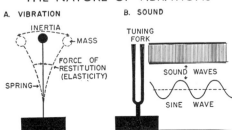

A. VIBRATION   B. SOUND

FIGURE 7. *A*, Vibration occurs when a mass, held in position by elastic support, is displaced from its position of rest. The spring tension acts to return the mass toward the equilibrium position but momentum carries it beyond the position of rest. An oscillatory motion of the mass back and forth past the position of rest persists until the energy instilled in the system is dissipated by friction.

B, Sound waves produced by a tuning fork are waves of alternating compression (increased pressure) and expansion (reduced pressure) of the air. The fluctuating pressures from a vibrating tuning fork are recorded from a microphone as a sine wave, indicating that the sound is a pure tone.

CHARACTERISTICS OF VIBRATIONS

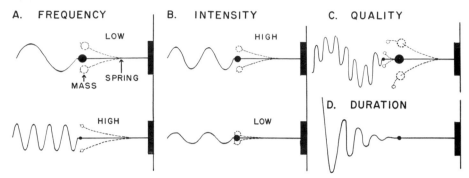

FIGURE 8.   *A,* The frequency of vibration (cycles per second) is determined by the relation between the mass and the elasticity of its support; a large mass on a weak spring produces a slow vibration; a small mass on a stiff spring vibrates rapidly.

B, The amplitude of vibrations depends on the amount of displacement from the position of rest (the energy imparted to the system).

C, The quality of vibrations refers to the number of overtones or harmonics, which are schematically represented by two vibrating systems connected in series. When responding to complex sounds, a single structure (e.g., the cone of a loudspeaker) may be simultaneously vibrating at more than one frequency.

D, The duration of a vibration after the source of energy is cut off depends upon the rate at which the energy is dissipated. The greater the frictional resistance to motion, the faster the energy is used up, and the greater the "damping."

simultaneously (Fig. 7*B*). During the time that the right prong moves toward the tube, the air molecules are compressed at the orifice. A wave of compression moves through the tube with the velocity of sound in air (1100 ft. per second). When the prong moves back, the air molecules rush back to fill the void and a wave of rarefaction follows the compression wave at that same velocity down the tube.

Frequency. The frequency at which a system vibrates depends upon the mass in motion in relation to the restoring force (elasticity). A small mass fastened to a stiff spring vibrates rapidly (Fig. 8*A*). In general, the mass of body tissues is large in relation to their elasticity, so they tend to vibrate at low frequencies. Exceptions to this rule are bones and connective tissue structures under high tension (e.g., arterial walls).

Intensity. The intensity of the sound depends upon the amplitude of the vibrations, which is determined by how far the vibrating body is displaced. In other words, the intensity of the sound depends

upon the amount of energy imparted to the vibrating body as it is displaced from its position of rest (Fig. 8*B*).

Quality. A tuning fork is an instrument that produces a pure tone, a sound with but one frequency which is recorded as a sine wave (Fig. 7*B*). Most natural sounds are composed of various frequencies or overtones which combine to determine the quality of the sound (Fig. 7*C*). Distinctive combinations of tones and harmonics allow recognition of different musical instruments, of familiar voices, and characteristic heart sounds. The vibrations emitted by the heart should be classed as noises since they are composed of unrelated frequencies with very brief durations.

Duration. Vibrations tend to die out as the energy originally imparted to the system is dissipated in the form of heat from friction. If the frictional resistance is increased, the vibratory motion persists for a shorter period of time because it is "damped" (Fig. 8*D*). The soft tissues of of the body very effectively damp the vibrations of internal structures. For example, heart sounds consist of relatively few vibrations, but sounds of longer duration may persist as long as energy is supplied to the vibrating system (murmurs).

Components of the Heart Sounds

The heart sounds must be considered in relation to the mechanical events of the cardiac cycle. The temporal relationships of vibrations produced during the cardiac cycle are most easily established by examining objective records (Fig. 9). Many vibrations are inaudible because of their slight intensity. For example, low-frequency vibrations associated with atrial contraction can be recorded phonocardiographically from the precordium or from the esophagus even though they cannot be heard (Fig. 9). The first sound, associated with the beginning of ventricular systole, is frequently divided into four components. One or two "introductory vibrations" occur before the ventricular pressures begin to rise (i.e., be-

fore the A-V valves are closed). The exact cause of these initial vibrations has been controversial.[8-11] The second component of the first heart sound consists of more intense vibrations beginning just as the ventricular pressure starts to rise, signaling the closure of atrioventricular valves. The third component resembles the second component in frequency and intensity[12, 13] and occurs as the ventricular walls begin to contract. However, contraction of myocardial fibers is probably not the immediate cause of these vibrations.[5, 14] The fourth component of the first sound occurs during rapid ejection of blood from the ventricles into the corresponding arteries. Only the second and third components of the first sound are consistently audible.

The second heart sound has also been divided into four components,[15] although they may not all appear on a single phonocardiogram. The initial vibrations have slight intensity and are inaudible. The second component consists of a few

THE TIMING OF HEART SOUNDS

A. HEART SOUNDS

B. COMPONENTS OF HEART SOUNDS

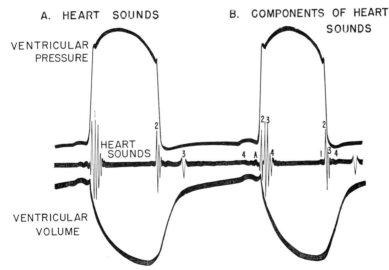

VENTRICULAR PRESSURE

HEART SOUNDS

VENTRICULAR VOLUME

FIGURE 9. *A*, Four heart sounds may be recorded during each cardiac cycle in some subjects. The audible vibrations of the first heart sound appear at the beginning of ventricular systole, coincident with the rise in ventricular pressure. The second heart sound is associated with the dicrotic notch on the pressure curve (closure of the semilunar valves). The third heart sound occurs at the end of the rapid-filling phase during ventricular diastole. The fourth heart sound is associated with atrial contraction.

B, Both the first and second heart sounds are sometimes divided into four components, the causes of which are discussed in the text (see also Fig. 11).

high-amplitude vibrations which represent the audible portion of the second sound. These vibrations are clearly associated with closure of the semilunar valves. The third and fourth components are small and unimpressive.

The third heart sound consists of a few low-frequency vibrations occurring in early diastole. Although such deflections can be recorded consistently,[16, 17] the third heart sound is heard rarely in normal adults. It is perceived somewhat more frequently in children. The third heart sound occurs at the end of the rapid-filling phase and its intensity is affected by the rate of ventricular filling.[18]

A recent monograph by McKusick[19] contains an excellent historical review and discussion of the causes of heart sounds and murmurs.

Origin of Heart Sounds

As many as 40 different theories have been proposed to explain the first heart sound.[5] Wide divergence of opinion also characterizes the theories regarding the origin of other heart sounds and murmurs. This chaotic condition appears to stem from the type of investigation which has been applied to the problem. Virtually every possible mechanical event occurring during the cardiac cycle has, at one time or another, been ascribed a role in the production of heart sounds. For example, different components of the first sound are attributed variously to vibrations of numerous structures including valves, muscular walls and arteries. Since the chambers of the heart are filled with blood, none of these structures can vibrate independently without producing movements of the blood. Similarly, vibrations in the blood must be transmitted to the surrounding structures. If the sounds can be picked up from the external surface of the body, all structures between the heart and the thoracic wall must be vibrating. It is futile to consider vibrations of the heart walls, valves, arterial

walls and blood individually when in fact they constitute an interdependent system and all vibrate at the same time. A more realistic approach to the problem results from considering those conditions which lead to vibrations of cardiohemic systems composed of the blood, heart walls and valves.

Vibrations in Fluid-Filled Elastic Systems. Vibrations in the cardiovascular system are caused by two general mechanisms: (*a*) acceleration or deceleration of blood and (*b*) turbulence developing during rapid blood flow. In the subsequent discussion, vibrations or sounds due to acceleration or deceleration of blood will be classified as heart sounds. Vibrations or sounds due to turbulence in flowing blood will be considered as murmurs (see below).

Earlier in this chapter, the characteristics of vibrations were described in terms of a mass supported by a spring (Fig. 7). In an elastic chamber completely filled with fluid, the elasticity of the walls is analogous to the spring, and the fluid plus the supporting walls is analogous to the vibrating mass. Imagine a fluid-filled balloon in which any sudden movement (acceleration or deceleration) throws the entire system into vibration (Fig. 10). Clearly, no portion of the balloon could vibrate independently, without affecting all other portions of the system. A sharp tap in a very small area produces vibrations affecting all parts of the fluid and the walls. The vibrations result from the momentum of the fluid producing an overstretch of the elastic wall, which recoils and displaces the fluid in the opposite direction. This sequence is repeated until the residual energy in the system is dissipated. The intensity of the vibrations is determined largely by the rate of change of velocity (the amount of acceleration or deceleration). Their frequency depends upon the relation between the vibrating mass and the elasticity of the walls. In the heart, the combined mass of the blood and the walls of the chambers is very large in relation to the elasticity of the walls, so the vibrations usually have a low frequency. When the ventricles are contracting, the elasticity of the walls should be greater and the vibration frequency increased. Vibrations due to acceleration and deceleration of blood tend to consist of only a few cycles, indicating that they are promptly damped.

Cardiohemic Systems in Heart Sound Production. From a knowledge of the mechanical events of the cardiac cycle, the regions where acceleration or deceleration of blood is occurring at any particular phase should be readily identifiable. The character of the vibrations is influenced by the nature of the specific *cardiohemic system* which is vibrating. The term *cardiohemic system* has been coined to cover any combination of blood and heart

VIBRATIONS IN A FLUID-FILLED BALLOON

A. ACCELERATION OF FLUID SYSTEM

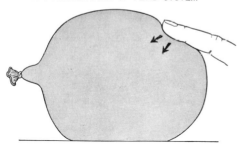

B. GENERALIZED VIBRATION

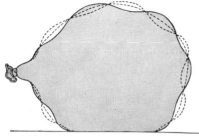

FIGURE 10. Tapping a balloon filled with water throws the entire system into vibrations. Although the deformation was applied at a single point, the vibrations involve all parts of the fluid and walls.

walls which is the primary site of vibrations produced by changes in velocity of the blood. The vibrations induced within any cardiohemic system may be transmitted in all directions and may be audible if they are transmitted to the thoracic walls with sufficient intensity and at a high enough frequency. From the concept of cardiohemic systems, the etiology of heart sounds can be described logically.

Atrial Sounds. In the latter part of diastole, the ventricles are well filled with blood and in direct communication with the atria through the partially open atrioventricular valves. When atrial contraction displaces blood through these valves, the ventricular walls become more distended and stretched, as indicated by the slight increase in the intraventricular pressure. The recoil of the distended ventricles sets the stage for vibrations back and forth between the atria and ventricles. This recoil may also contribute to transient valve closure. Since this cardiohemic system consists of the thin-walled right and left atria and relaxed ventricular walls, it is not surprising that these vibrations consist of a few low-frequency oscillations.

First Heart Sound. At the onset of ventricular contraction, blood is accelerated in the ventricle, surging toward the atrioventricular valves. This acceleration of blood, occurring before the valves are sealed and taut, is responsible for the introductory vibrations of the first heart sound (first component) which precede elevation of the intraventricular pressure. Their frequency is very low and their intensity is slight, presumably because the ventricles remain largely relaxed and the acceleration of blood is not rapid. However, this movement of blood must be sufficient to close, seal and apply tension to the atrioventricular valves before ventricular pressure rises. When this movement of the blood is suddenly arrested, the valves become tense. The second

THE ETIOLOGY OF HEART SOUNDS

A. COMPONENTS OF FIRST HEART SOUND

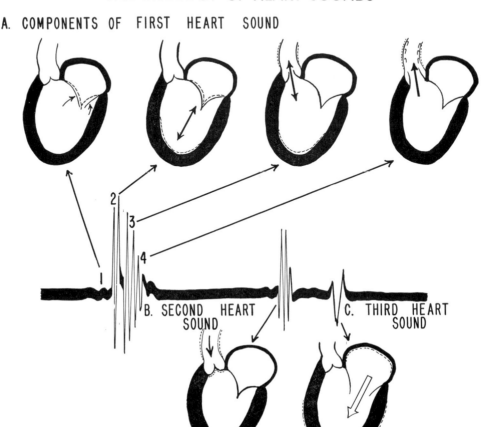

FIGURE 11. Schematic drawings of the causes of various components of the heart sounds based on the concept that the vibrations are induced by acceleration or deceleration of the blood within elastic chambers.

A, The first sound can be divided into four components (see Fig. 9). The initial vibrations occur when the first myocardial contractions in the ventricle shift blood toward the atrium to approximate and seal the atrioventricular valves. The second component begins with abrupt tension of closed atrioventricular valves decelerating the moving blood (Fig. 9). It may represent oscillation of blood initiated by overdistention of the atrioventricular valves, countered by recoil of the contracting ventricular myocardium. The reaction would be similar to tapping a balloon filled with water. The third component may involve oscillations of blood between the distending root of the aorta and the ventricular walls. The fourth component probably represents vibrations due to turbulence in blood flowing rapidly through the ascending aorta and pulmonary artery (see also Fig. 15).

B, The second heart sound is introduced by a few low-frequency vibrations which may accompany the deceleration and reversal of flow through the aorta and pulmonary artery prior to the closure of the semilunar valves. The audible portion of the second sound begins with closure and tensing of the semilunar valves. Although the primary vibrations occur in the arteries, they are also transmitted to the ventricles and atria by movements of the blood, valves and valve rings.

C, The third heart sound occurs at the end of the rapid filling phase. Sudden termination of the rapid-filling phase may throw the entire atrioventricular system into vibrations which have very low frequency because the walls are relaxed.

component of the first sound begins as the momentum of the moving blood produces sufficient valvular overstretching to cause a recoil back toward the ventricles (Fig. 11*A*). In this case, the cardiohemic vibrating systems consist primarily of the two ventricular cavities, completely enclosed by valves and contracting myocardium. Thus, the vibrations generated at the onset of ventricular systole have a higher frequency and a greater amplitude than those produced by atrial contraction.

The intensity of the vibrations depends upon the velocity attained by the blood and the abruptness with which it is decelerated. Thus, the sound would be greater if the valves gaped wide at the onset of the ventricular contraction than if they were approximated at this moment, because the blood would attain a higher velocity before complete closure occurred. This concept appears consistent with the observations of Henderson,[2] Dean,[3] Shearn *et al.*[20] and others.[21-23]

The third component of the first heart sound begins as ventricular contraction elevates the intraventricular pressure above that in the corresponding artery and blood begins to move toward the semilunar valves. The inertia of the long columns of blood in the arterial trunks opposes acceleration just as though there were an obstruction a short distance beyond the semilunar valves. Therefore, the first portion of the blood moving out of the ventricles distends the proximal portions of these arteries. Sudden distention of the proximal arterial segments may induce a rebound of blood toward the ventricles. Oscillation of the blood back and forth between the arterial roots and the ventricular chambers would result from a mechanism similar to that associated with closure of the atrioventricular valves (Fig. 11*A*). Since the cardiohemic systems producing the second and third components of the first sound are very similar, their frequencies, intensities and

qualities are also similar. Indeed, these two components are usually merged into a single set of vibrations which cannot be differentiated. Splitting or reduplication of the first sound is usually ascribed to asynchronous closure of the tricuspid and then the mitral valves in rapid succession.[24] *or vice versa? or click*

The fourth component of the first heart sound is probably the result of turbulence in the blood flowing rapidly through the arterial trunks and for this reason will be considered under murmurs (see below).

Second Heart Sound. Near the end of systole, the rate of ejection slows as the ventricular and arterial pressures begin to diminish. Ventricular pressure drops precipitously at the onset of ventricular relaxation. Blood in the roots of the aorta and in the pulmonary artery rushes back toward the ventricular chambers, but this movement is abruptly arrested by closure of the semilunar valves. The momentum of the moving blood overstretches the valve cusps, and the recoil initiates oscillations in both the arterial and the ventricular cavities (Fig. 11*B*). The pitch of the second sound seems higher than that of the first sound. The intensity of the sound, again, depends upon the velocity attained by the blood gushing back toward the ventricle and the abruptness with which the motion is arrested. In systemic or pulmonary hypertension, the velocity should be great and the sounds intensified. In the presence of semilunar valvular stenosis, on the contrary, the amplitude of the second sound should be reduced if the valves are largely approximated before the retrograde flow is well established.

Third Heart Sound. When intraventricular pressure drops below atrial pressure, the atrioventricular valves swing open before a mass movement of blood into the relaxed ventricular chambers. Inflow is arrested rather suddenly, as is manifest in the rapid transition from the rapid-filling phase to the plateau which indicates slow filling or diastasis.[25, 26] The momentum of the moving mass of blood produces low-frequency vibrations because the chamber walls are all relaxed. Such vibrations would be more likely to occur when the rapid-filling phase terminates abruptly. Because of their low frequency, the vibrations must have considerable amplitude to reach the auditory threshold, particularly if the loss of energy during transmission is great. Third heart sounds are more frequently heard in children with thin chests.

Gallop Rhythms. When three audible heart sounds occur in rapid succession, followed by a pause, the subjective impression is similar to the sounds produced by a galloping horse. Several combinations of heart sounds can produce this impression. The most common form of gallop occurs when the third heart sound is clearly audible. In such instances the three heart sounds occur in sequence and are followed by a relatively silent interval during the remainder of diastole. This type is frequently called the "protodiastolic" gallop, which is a misnomer because the third sound follows the protodiastolic interval. For no very good reason, third heart sounds, commonly heard in normal children, are usually not included among gallop rhythms. A gallop rhythm which develops in the course of heart disease (e.g., myocarditis, congestive failure) signifies alterations in the myocardium. The third heart sound is so rarely audible in aged individuals that the protodiastolic gallop often indicates a serious prognosis. The nature of the myocardial change which accentuates the third heart sound is not clear, but presumably the rapid-filling phase is terminated more abruptly.

If the sounds accompanying atrial systole are intensified and precede the first sound by a sufficient interval to be distinguished, a gallop rhythm is produced which consists of the fourth, first and second heart sounds in succession. Since the abnormal sound occurs in late diastole, this rhythm is called a "presystolic" gallop.

If the heart rate is rapid, the diastolic interval becomes shorter and the third and fourth heart sounds may occur almost simultaneously. The combined intensity of the two sets of vibrations may become audible and the resulting rhythm is called a *summation* or mid-diastolic gallop.

Transmission of Sounds. The factors that influence the transmission of vibrations are the same as those involved in their production (see Fig. 8). The elasticity or restoring force of the transmitting media is very important. Since the mass of vibrating material (the heart, blood and tissues) is great in relation to tissue elasticity, low frequency sounds predominate in both production and transmission. This is most unfortunate because the human auditory mechanism is particularly insensitive to low-pitched sounds (see *Auditory Perception of Heart Sounds*, below).

Since the heart sounds are composed of vibrations with long wave lengths (low pitch), their transmission from the point of origin to the surface of the body differs materially from that of the waves illustrated in Figure 7. To produce four vibration cycles traveling at a rate of 1100 ft. per second within a length of tube 1 ft. long, the tuning fork must vibrate at about 4400 c.p.s. If the tuning fork oscillates at a rate of only 100 c.p.s., the cycle length is 11 ft., longer than the transmission distance through the tube. Under these conditions, the air in the tube would be alternately compressed and rarefied.

Vibrations in the heart are probably transmitted to the surface of the skin at the velocity of sound transmission through water (almost 5000 ft. per second). The maximum transmission distance from the heart to the surface of the chest is less than a foot, and the cycle length of the vibrations is greater than this distance. For this reason, all the structures involved in the transmission of these vibrations to the surface tend to oscillate together. Under these conditions, sound waves are not reflected. The most important loss of heart sound energy occurs in compressible tissues (e.g., lung) interposed between the heart and chest wall. Vibrations of the heart wall may be so well damped while passing through a thick cushion of aerated lung tissue that they are poorly transmitted to the chest wall (e.g., in emphysema). Thus, the heart sounds have maximum intensity in those surface areas to which the vibrations are transmitted directly through solid tissues or through a minimal thickness of inflated lung. Layers of fat also attenuate heart sounds because of damping.

Surface Localization of Heart Sounds. Sounds emitted from the vicinities of the four valves have maximal intensities at four different surface areas. For example,

TRANSMISSION OF SOUNDS AND MURMURS

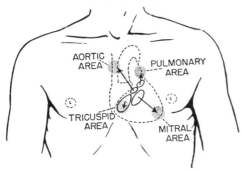

FIGURE 12. Although heart sounds are widely transmitted over the precordium, vibrations from the four valves tend to be of maximal intensity at the areas on the precordium indicated by the arrows above. The mitral area on the precordium is near the apex of the heart, the tricuspid area is in the fourth intercostal space on either side of the sternum. The pulmonary area is in either the second or the third intercostal space at the left parasternal line, and the aortic area is in the second right intercostal space but often extends obliquely across the precordium toward the apex (see Fig. 17).

murmurs from the region of the pulmonary valve are most intense in the *pulmonary area*, centered at the third left intercostal space at the left parasternal line (Fig. 12). The *aortic area* lies to the right of the sternum in the second right intercostal space. The *tricuspid area* is near the right sternal border in the fourth intercostal space, and the *mitral area* is near the apex of the heart. This particular localization of sounds on the surface probably represents the most effective transmission pathways from the original sites of vibration to the surface of the chest. The pulmonary and tricuspid valves are near the precordium and the corresponding auscultatory areas are close by. The aortic and mitral valves are situated farther from the precordium and their auscultatory areas do not overlie the valve rings (Fig. 12). In the region of the apex, the heart sounds are usually loud because the heart is in direct contact with the anterior wall of the thorax. Vibrations of the ventricular chamber, associated with mitral valvular disease, are frequently localized over the apex. The ascending aorta curves forward and most closely approaches the anterior chest wall near the aortic area. Sounds emitted from the region of the aortic valve may also traverse the right ventricular chamber to appear in the third or fourth intercostal space to the left of the sternum, or follow the left ventricular chamber to a point near the apex.

The fact that both the first and second heart sounds are generally audible at all four areas indicates that their production is not limited to vibrations in the regions of the valves. The wide distribution is consistent with oscillation of cardiohemic systems produced by mass movements of blood.

It is inaccurate to consider the second sound in the pulmonary area to be composed primarily or exclusively of vibrations from the pulmonary valve. In records taken from directly over the A-V valve rings on the surface of the heart, the contribution of one valve cannot be dissociated from that of another. The reason for this becomes apparent when it is recognized that the atria, ventricles, arterial trunks and valves are all firmly fastened to the fibrous skeleton of the heart (Fig. 3, Chap. 2) and must all be affected by vibrations at any point. Nevertheless, a loud second sound in the pulmonary area on the precordium is frequently a reliable indication of pulmonary hypertension and its localization permits its differentiation from a loud aortic second sound, which may occur with systemic hypertension.

Auditory Perception of Heart Sounds.
Under optimal conditions the ear can detect vibrations with an amplitude less than the diameter of a molecule. The energy of barely perceptible sound waves is so slight that it would have to be continued without loss or interruption for more than two million years to elevate the temperature of 1 gm. of water 1° C.[26]

Although the maximal range of audible frequencies normally lies between 20 and 16,000 c.p.s., the maximal sensitivity of human audition lies within the speech range, about 1000 to 2000 c.p.s.[27] To be perceived, sound with a frequency of 30 c.p.s. must attain energy levels thousands of times those needed by vibrations at 1000 c.p.s. (Fig. 13). Heart sounds extend above and below the threshold of hearing, so some are inaudible while others considerably exceed threshold levels. The frequencies of the audible vibrations of the heart probably range from below 20 c.p.s. to above 200 c.p.s. (The frequencies of murmurs may be as high as 600 to 1000 c.p.s.) Owing to extreme lack of sensitivity to low-frequency vibrations, the auditory mechanism may perceive relatively weak overtones of heart sounds more clearly than the more intense low-frequency fundamental vibrations.[28] Thus,

AUDIBILITY OF VARIOUS FREQUENCIES

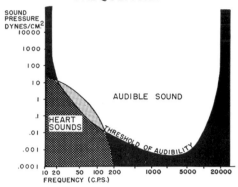

FIGURE 13.   The threshold of audibility varies for different sound frequencies. The auditory mechanism is far more sensitive to frequencies in the speech range (1000 to 2000 c.p.s.) than to sounds of either higher or lower pitch. The heart sounds are primarily low-frequency vibrations. Only a portion of the vibrations have sufficient intensity to reach the auditory threshold, the remainder being completely inaudible. Certain high-pitched murmurs reach frequencies of 1000 c.p.s. and can be perceived even when the sound energy is relatively slight.

the low-frequency vibrations, which are most easily recorded electronically, may constitute only a portion of the heart sounds which are heard during auscultation.

When listening to sounds of a particular frequency, the human hearing apparatus responds to sounds of very low and very high energy. At certain frequencies the energy level of the threshold for pain is more than three million times that for the threshold of audibility. This tremendous range of perceptible intensity is possible because the perceived "loudness" is proportional to the logarithm of the stimulus strength. In other words, if the sound intensity is doubled successively, the "loudness" of the sensation increases in equal steps. Thus, the auditory mechanism can respond to a tremendous range of sound energies while retaining sensitivity to sounds of very low intensity.

In complex sounds, the low-pitched tones often seem more prominent because the higher pitched tones become masked. This phenomenon is more marked when the intensity of the low tones is increased. Thus, the quality of sounds may be affected by any factor which alters the intensity. The higher frequencies found in diastolic murmurs can often be brought out by judicious use of the stethoscope, selectively attenuating the low frequencies.

Stethoscopes. Heart sounds can be readily heard by placing the ear directly on the chest of the patient. Stethoscopes are employed for the sake of convenience and propriety rather than to amplify the sound. Sounds are both damped and distorted by stethoscopes. When an open bell is applied to the chest, the skin forms a diaphragm while the underlying tissues act as a damping medium.[29] If the bell is held firmly against the skin, the low frequencies are attenuated more than the higher frequencies, which seem louder even though their actual sound energy is diminished. A similar effect can be produced by using a Bowles type stethoscope with a plastic diaphragm covering the air chamber. In any case, the presence of a taut diaphragm produces attenuation of the low frequencies which is useful in detecting the high-pitched diastolic murmurs, but undesirable in eliciting faint, low-pitched murmurs. A most complete analysis of the factors in the auditory perception of heart sounds and murmurs was presented by Rappaport and Sprague.[29] Included in their investigation was the influence of various types of stethoscopes on auscultation. For example, it is not generally recognized that properly fitting ear pieces on stethoscopes are extremely important since a leak with a diameter approximately five times that of a human hair may markedly reduce perception of heart sounds and murmurs.[30]

Lepeschkin[31] devised a most ingenious quantitative stethoscope with an adjustable orifice in the chest piece so that

sound intensity may be graded far more accurately than by purely subjective impression.

Phonocardiography. Verbal descriptions of sounds (e.g., harsh, coarse, ringing, etc.) are notoriously inadequate. For this reason, phonocardiography affords a common meeting ground for the discussion of heart sounds. The temporal relations between the heart sounds and the mechanical events of the cardiac cycle are of paramount importance in the interpretion of the significance of sounds and murmurs. In this sphere, phonocardiography makes its greatest contribution.

The heart sounds are so attenuated and modified by transmission through various media and by the vagaries of auditory perception that it is manifestly impossible to produce heart sound records which match the sounds heard during auscultation. Rappaport and Sprague[29] have discussed in detail the essential characteristics of heart sound recording equipment. In subsequent sections heart sounds and murmurs will be illustrated by two types of records: (*a*) standard phonocardiograms, from instruments with high frequency amplifiers and galvanometers, and (*b*) simplified heart sound recordings which indicate only sound intensity (sonvelograms).

Sonvelography. A device for recording heart sounds and murmurs as an envelope of the sound intensity was developed in the author's laboratory,[32] and has been called the sonvelograph (*son* = sound, *velo* = to envelope). The resulting records indicate timing and relative intensity of sounds during the various phases of the cardiac cycle. The amplifier has characteristics similar to those of the human auditory apparatus, so the records resemble the simple sketches that clinicians frequently draw to indicate the presence and timing of murmurs. Being designed for use with standard, direct-writing electrocardiographic equipment, the envelope of sound is a reliable indication of the logarithm of sound intensity, regardless of frequency. Although sonvelograms are not suited for research on heart sounds, they are useful in clinical diagnosis and as illustrations because their interpretation is so simple (see Figs. 41 and 42, Chap. 10).

II. Murmurs

In the preceding discussion, the origination of heart sounds has been ascribed to vibrations induced by sudden displacement of blood (acceleration) or by abrupt cessation of flow (deceleration). In contrast, heart murmurs are defined here as the result of turbulence developing in rapidly flowing blood. These definitions provide clear, functional and physical distinctions between the heart sounds and murmurs. Since the causes of turbulence are well known, the source of most murmurs should be explicable simply and logically. The pathologic conditions which predispose toward such turbulence are well established for most types of murmurs. Certain murmurs have no satisfactory explanation at present, simply because we lack essential information concerning conditions in the heart producing these vibrations.

CAUSES OF TURBULENCE IN FLOWING BLOOD

The flow of blood through virtually all vascular channels of the body is silent because the fluid exhibits laminar or streamlined flow (Fig. 7, Chap. 1). The conditions producing turbulence in fluid flowing through tubes of constant caliber are expressed in the formula $RVD/v =$ critical constant for turbulence (Reynolds' number),[33] where a fluid of viscosity v and density D flows with a mean velocity V through a tube of radius R. This formula indicates that turbulence occurs when fluids of low viscosity flow at high velocity through tubes of large diameter (Fig. 14A). Since the blood viscosity and the vascular diameter are relatively constant, the major variable is the velocity of blood flow. The critical level of Reynolds' number for turbulence in blood is reported as 970 ± 80.[34] Blood flows rapidly through the largest arterial channels, and at the highest velocity in the roots of the aorta and the pulmonary artery. According to Prec et al.,[35] the critical level for turbulence is normally exceeded at these sites during the rapid ejection phase of ventricular systole. On this basis, the vibrations usually classified as the fourth component of the first heart sound are probably caused by turbulence and are actually an early systolic murmur according to the definitions being used here. Thus, virtually all persons have an early systolic murmur, even though its duration is insufficient for its detection (see *Functional Murmurs*, below).

Turbulence tends to occur where the caliber of a channel enlarges abruptly. For example, when fluid must flow through a restricted orifice, eddy currents are apt to develop just beyond the obstruction (Fig. 14B). In such circumstances, turbulence will occur at a lower flow velocity than it will in a tube of constant bore. Similarly, when a narrow channel opens into a large cavity, turbulence is likely to develop at a relatively low flow velocity (Fig. 14C). When the two factors in B and C are combined, the tendency toward developing turbulence is greatly increased (Fig. 14D). Flow in either direction through such a restricted orifice will cause turbulence. This is a basic mechanism for the development of murmurs in organic valvular heart disease.

On the basis of this description, additional distinctions between heart sounds and murmurs can be drawn. Turbulence can develop in rather restricted areas and, for this reason, murmurs may be localized to relatively small areas on the precordium. Because the basic causes of murmurs are different, they usually have a longer duration, higher frequency and more discrete localization.

Functional Murmurs

Vibrations during the early ejection phase of ventricular systole occur in virtually all individuals, even though murmurs cannot always be heard (Fig. 15A). Early systolic murmurs can be heard in a large proportion of children,[36] particularly those with thin chest walls. In these individuals, all the heart sounds are loud because so little energy is lost in transmission to the surface. The "normal systolic murmur" can be recorded in prac-

tically all normal adults at rest if suitable equipment is used in a sound-damped room.[37] Such murmurs are classified as functional and are most commonly heard at the pulmonary area on the precordium.[38] Although the velocity of flow through both the pulmonary artery and the aorta is sufficient to produce turbulence in early systole, certain additional factors present in the outflow tract of the right ventricle are generally overlooked (Fig. 15B).

Audible, early systolic murmurs are usually produced by the increased velocity of flow in almost all normal persons following vigorous exercise, particularly if the subject leans forward and holds his breath after a forced exhalation. In patients with anemia, "hemic" murmurs develop because the viscosity of the blood is diminished while the flow velocity is accelerated owing to an increase in cardiac output.

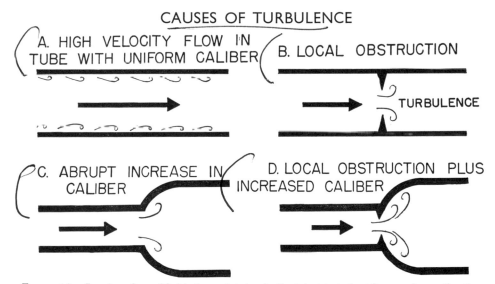

CAUSES OF TURBULENCE

A. HIGH VELOCITY FLOW IN TUBE WITH UNIFORM CALIBER

B. LOCAL OBSTRUCTION

TURBULENCE

C. ABRUPT INCREASE IN CALIBER

D. LOCAL OBSTRUCTION PLUS INCREASED CALIBER

FIGURE 14.   Laminar flow of fluids through tubes is silent, but turbulent flow produces vibrations.

A, Turbulence tends to occur in fluids of low viscosity flowing at high velocity through tubes of large caliber, in accordance with the formula for Reynolds' number (see text).

B, In a tube of uniform caliber, inserting a local obstruction produces turbulence at a much lower velocity of flow.

C, Turbulence also tends to occur at reduced velocity where fluid flows into a channel of much larger diameter.

D, When an obstruction occurs at the junction between a narrow channel and a wide one, relatively low velocity flow produces turbulence because the factors illustrated in B and C exert a combined effect.

FUNCTIONAL SYSTOLIC MURMURS

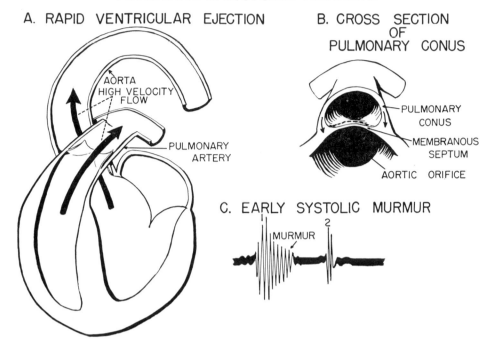

FIGURE 15. *A,* Under normal conditions, blood flows through the aorta and pulmonary arteries at sufficient velocity to produce turbulence during the rapid ejection phase of ventricular systole. Early systolic murmurs can be heard in many normal children at rest and in nearly any normal subject after exercise.

B, The right ventricular outflow tract has a roughly crescentic cross-sectional area, partly because the membranous portion of the interventricular septum bulges into the lumen. Bundles of myocardial fibers, encircling the conus region, tend to further diminish the cross-sectional area of this channel during systole. For these reasons, turbulence is more likely to develop in the pulmonary artery than in the aorta. Systolic murmurs in normal subjects usually have maximal intensity in the pulmonary area on the precordium.

C, An early systolic "functional" murmur may be regarded as an intensified fourth component of the first heart sound.

Production of Murmurs by Vortex Formation

Since the conditions of flow in the pulmonary artery and the aorta during early systole are adequate to induce turbulence by exceeding the critical value of Reynolds' number, an adequate physical basis for the production of such functional murmurs is generally recognized. This basic concept has also been applied to the generation of audible murmurs in relation to other murmur-producing conditions suggested by Figure 14. However, turbulence is a term which is used to cover a wide variety of nonlaminar or

unsteady flows. The mechanisms by which disturbances of flow can generate sound waves have been the subject of two interesting analyses.[39, 40]

At first sight, one might expect a fully turbulent region to produce more sound than one in which the turbulence is intermittent or is dispersed in different regions of the flowing stream. Although the energy content of wholly turbulent flow is very great, the particles move in all directions and might not induce powerful net movements or periodic vibrations of the enclosing walls to generate sound waves. Not only must there be enough energy within the fluid to produce vibrations, but these vibrations must be transmitted by the walls of vessels into the surrounding medium. For example, fluid passing out of a long glass tube through an orifice plate just beneath the surface of a body of water will display vortex formation. The sound waves could be picked up with a microphone immersed in the water, but no airborne sound could be heard.[40] The boundary between fluid (or vascular walls) and air is an effective barrier to sound transmission. Thus, vibrations within flowing fluid must have a very high energy if the resulting sounds are audible outside the fluid.

Fluctuating wakes or Aeolian tones have been suggested as mechanisms for the production of transmitted vibrations.[39] It is well known that fluid flowing around an obstacle (e.g., a cylinder) passes alter-

nately around its opposite side and produces a wake containing fluctuating pressures. Alternating vortex formation of this sort is illustrated schematically in Figure 16A. Such alternating or fluctuating vortices will also be produced as fluid flows past a local obstruction along the walls of a tube, or through a narrowed orifice. The alternating vortex formation in a fluctuating wake could easily transmit pressure to the enclosing walls and throw them into vibration. In one sense, lateral movement of the fluid in the formation of vortices would produce impacts against the walls owing to the inertia of the fluid. Computations have indicated that the sound energies developed by such a mechanism would be adequate to provide audible sound at a distance of 5 cm. from a source with flow velocities of 150 cm. per second. These values are reasonable for murmur production. A number of other properties of murmurs appear to be clarified by this concept.

Most studies of sound production in fluids are carried out under conditions of uninterrupted flow for reasons of simplicity in analysis. However, flow velocity which permits completely laminar flow may produce violent turbulence if it is rendered pulsatile. Such pulsatile flow is characteristic in all arteries and in some central veins. Inhomogenous turbulence occurs whenever the flowing fluid suddenly decelerates. These mechanisms may have a role in murmur production on the arterial side of the circulation.

Systolic Murmurs Due to Valvular Abnormality

Detection and recognition of heart murmurs is a valuable source of information concerning the function of heart valves. Although the mechanisms producing these sounds are very similar, certain types of valvular disease produce typical sound patterns which can be distinguished on the basis of frequency, transmission and timing.

TURBULENCE IN STREAMS OF FLUID

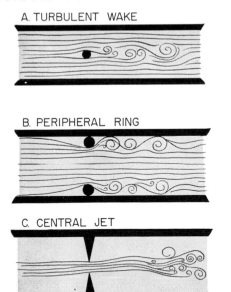

A. TURBULENT WAKE

B. PERIPHERAL RING

C. CENTRAL JET

FIGURE 16. A cylindrical obstruction in a stream of fluid causes eddy currents downstream which may produce sounds corresponding to Aeolian tones. Vibrations of similar origin may be produced by a circular obstruction around the periphery of a pipe. A smaller orifice produces a central jet which flutters downstream. These three mechanisms produce vibrations in flowing fluids which may be related to heart murmurs (see text).

SYSTOLIC MURMURS FROM VALVULAR DEFORMITY

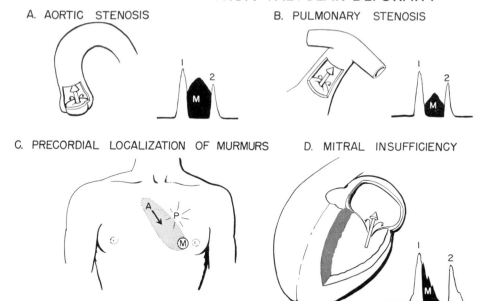

FIGURE 17. *A*, Aortic stenosis produces a membranous obstruction with a small orifice through which blood is ejected at high velocity during systole. The resulting systolic murmur tends to reach maximum intensity in mid-systole and is usually transmitted primarily to the aortic area. In different patients, the region of maximal intensity may occur anywhere in an area extending from the second left intercostal space toward the apex of the heart.

B, Pulmonary stenosis produces a loud systolic murmur extending through the systolic interval, although the intensity is often greatest immediately after the first sound and diminishes progressively The murmur is transmitted widely over the entire precordium.

C, The surface localization of systolic murmurs originating from various valves is indicated schematically (see also Fig. 12).

D, Mitral insufficiency produces systolic murmurs with maximum intensity near the apex of the het.ar

Aortic Stenosis. The aortic valve lies at a considerable distance from the precordium. Vibrations from this source reach the precordium after transmission directly from the ascending aorta (aortic area), through the pulmonary artery and conus (third left intercostal space) or through the ventricles toward the apex of the heart. Systolic murmurs of aortic origin have been clearly demonstrated in the broad area indicated in Figure 17C. Thus, aortic murmurs may be localized at various points on the precordium along a line paralleling the outflow tract of the left ventricle. Systolic murmurs of early aortic stenosis may be evidenced only in the pulmonary area and may be difficult to differentiate from functional murmurs. Levine[41] emphasized the fact that these murmurs tend to have maximum intensity in the mid-systolic period, and used this criterion to differentiate such murmurs from functional, pulmonary or mitral systolic murmurs.

Pulmonary Stenosis. Uncomplicated pulmonary stenosis, either congenital or acquired, is relatively rare. Fusion of the pulmonary leaflets produces a local constriction beyond which turbulence occurs during systolic ejection from the right ventricle (Fig. 17B). The resultant loud, harsh, systolic murmur usually resembles the murmur of aortic stenosis. Such murmurs are heard most loudly in the pulmonary area (see also Fig. 15, Chap. 14) and are widely transmitted over the precordium. Pulmonary stenosis is usually due to a congenital malformation.

Mitral Insufficiency. If for any reason the mitral valve cusps fail to occlude the mitral orifice completely, blood rushes through the defect during ventricular systole, propelled by the large pressure difference between the left ventricle and left atrium. The gap between the valve cusps acts as a local constriction through which the blood squirts at high velocity into the capacious atrial chamber (Fig. 17D). The resulting turbulence produces an apical systolic murmur which is ordinarily widely transmitted, particularly toward the left axillary region.

Diastolic Murmurs Due to Valvular Abnormality

Mitral Stenosis. The blood flows rapidly from the atria into the ventricles during the early filling period and during atrial systole. The fact that the diastolic period is normally quiet indicates that the velocity of flow is insufficient to induce significant turbulence, and that the mitral and tricuspid orifices do not constitute a local constriction. Thus, diastolic murmurs are rarely encountered unless there is some form of organic disease.

DIASTOLIC MURMURS FROM VALVULAR DEFORMITY

A. MITRAL STENOSIS

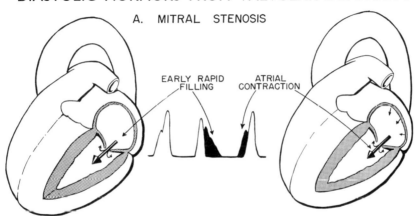

EARLY RAPID FILLING   ATRIAL CONTRACTION

B. PULMONARY VALVULAR INCOMPETENCE

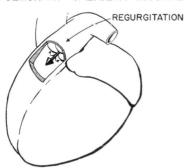

REGURGITATION

C. AORTIC VALVULAR INSUFFICIENCY

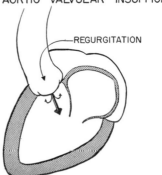

REGURGITATION

FIGURE 18.   *A,* Mitral stenosis produces murmurs occurring primarily during rapid flow through the mitral valve: during rapid ventricular filling in early diastole and during atrial systole. The murmur has a very low frequency and may be difficult to hear even though the sound intensity is great. The early diastolic murmurs tend to be localized fairly discretely at the apex of the heart.

B, Pulmonary insufficiency permits regurgitation of blood into the right ventricle during diastole. The resulting murmur tends to have maximum intensity in the pulmonary area, but is often transmitted over a wide area on the precordium.

C, Aortic insufficiency tends to produce high-pitched diastolic murmurs usually heard best in the aortic area but occasionally most intense in the pulmonary area or even near the apex of the heart.

Rheumatic valvulitis may convert the efficient, flexible mitral valves into a rigid funnel with a narrow elliptical orifice (see Fig. 8, Chap. 12). This local constriction between large chambers satisfies all the requirements for the production of turbulence if blood flow attains sufficient velocity (Fig. 18A). The sequence of events leading to advanced stenosis will be discussed in Chapter 12. A low frequency murmur which immediately precedes the first sound is the classic finding in mitral stenosis. In the early stages, this presystolic murmur can be easily missed since it is often localized to a very small area at or near the apical region on the precordium. The murmur may be audible only when the patient reclines in the left lateral position or after exertion. The low-pitched "rumble" seems to gather intensity and terminate in an accentuated first sound. Since this murmur frequently disappears in patients who develop atrial fibrillation, its presence has been attributed to rapid flow through the stenosed valve during atrial contraction.

In many cases of mitral stenosis, an early diastolic murmur predominates. This murmur occurs during the phase of rapid ventricular filling and attains maximum intensity shortly after the second sound. Thereafter, the murmur usually diminishes in intensity, frequently disappearing during the mid-diastolic period (see also Fig. 11, Chap. 12).

In many patients, the murmur appears to develop maximum intensity in mid-diastole. This is probably due to two factors: (a) A very slight interval between the second sound and the initial vibrations of the murmur gives a mistaken impression that the peak intensity occurs later than is revealed on heart sound records. (b) In some patients the rapid filling period may be prolonged because resistance is offered by the restricted orifice. The vibrations have such low frequency that they frequently escape detection by auscultation even when the recorded deflections appear large on phonocardiograms.

Pulmonary Insufficiency. Dilation of the pulmonary artery due to sustained pulmonary hypertension may render the pulmonary valves insufficient. When the pulmonary valves fail to approximate, a diastolic murmur becomes audible in the the pulmonary area.

Pulmonary valvular insufficiency permits the regurgitation of blood during the diastolic interval, which accounts for the diastolic murmur. The regurgitant stream flows rapidly through slits between the valve cusps and enters a large ventricular chamber (see Fig. 18B).

Aortic Insufficiency. Aortic insufficiency without stenosis generally results from cardiovascular syphilis (Fig. 18C; see also Fig. 5, Chap. 12). Systolic murmurs generally accompany the diastolic murmur because the regurgitation increases the rate and volume of ventricular ejection. Combined systolic and diastolic murmurs resemble the sounds produced by sawing wood with a hand saw, the systolic murmur representing the cutting stroke and the higher pitched diastolic murmur corresponding to the back stroke.

The Significance of Palpable Thrills

Vibrations produced by murmurs occasionally have such great intensity that they may be palpated on the surface of the chest. In comparison to auditory perception, the tactile vibratory sense is extremely insensitive. The palpation of a thrill indicates the great intensity of the vibrations, but provides no information of diagnostic significance that is not gained by auscultation.[42]

Variability in Detection of Heart Murmurs

Whenever a group of physicians gather beside a patient with cardiac disease, differences of opinion concerning the auscultatory findings almost invariably arise. Such controversies result from differences in auditory acuity, training and the technique of listening, complicated by the extreme difficulty of describing auditory sensations. When examiners are confronted with patients with advanced heart disease, the differences of opinion are lessened, but are by no means eliminated. Recognition of the limitations of auscultation is the first step toward its maximal effective use as a diagnostic tool. The most common deficiency is the inability to perceive certain low-frequency sounds. For example, many examiners consistently miss third heart sounds or low-frequency diastolic murmurs. Timing of murmurs by auscultation also presents problems to some clinicians. Although some of the difficulties may result from depressed auditory acuity, an improper approach to auscultation is frequently the source of the trouble.

A SYSTEMATIC APPROACH TO AUSCULTATION

The body is continuously bombarded by sensory stimuli of all kinds, but their entry into consciousness must be restricted to one at a time to make any order out of chaos. It is impossible to listen attentively and still be acutely aware of visual images, odors, proprioceptive stimuli or pain. If an attempt is made to concentrate on two things simultaneously, attention rapidly shifts from one to the other with little detailed information being gained from either source. Thus, the ability to concentrate on a single source of stimuli is an essential characteristic of human perception. Similarly, innumerable complex sound waves impinge continuously upon the ear, but most of these sounds fail to reach consciousness. While you read these words you are probably ignoring the sounds in your immediate environment.

However, undivided attention is insufficient for accurate auscultation. If an examiner listens to all the noises emitted by the heart, his attention is usually directed toward the most intense sounds, which may not be the most meaningful. It is necessary to utilize a high degree of "selective" attention to gain the maximum information from auscultation. Consider how many common sounds can be identified as coming from a specific source such as a nearby radio, a familiar voice, the sound of a car, the creak of a chair, or foot steps. Some of these vibrations are sustained, others are intermittent and still others may occur singly, but if they are familiar, their source can be immediately recognized. The ability to synthesize combinations of complex sound waves and overtones into patterns which can be identified represents an important attribute of audition. As an example, a symphony orchestra emits sound waves having a wide range of frequencies of almost inconceivable complexity. One can listen to the music as a harmonic entity made up of sounds from all the instruments On the other hand, the sounds produced by a single instrument may be extracted from this mass of complex sound waves by merely directing attention toward them. The conductor is constantly alert to tones which are off beat or out of tune. He can instantly fix the offender with a malevolent glance. By a similar process, heart sounds and murmurs can be analyzed individually and assigned their proper temporal relationship within the cardiac cycle. The following routine has proved valuable in this regard.

Selective Attention During Auscultation

The most convenient initial step is positive identification of the first heart sound. If the stethoscope is placed near the apex, the timing of the first sound can be correlated with the precordial thrust. When the identity of the first sound is definitely established, attention should be confined to this sound alone during several successive cycles. If the listener voluntarily blanks out all other sounds in the cycle, the first sound can be subjectively isolated. Several characteristics of the first sound should be noted individually and in sequence, including intensity, duration, relative frequency or pitch, splitting, etc. The loudness of the sound must be interpreted in light of judgment concerning the transmission characteristics and hemodynamic situation of the individual subject. For example, a loud first sound in an obese subject has far greater significance than one of a similar intensity in an asthenic adult or a thin-chested youth. The intensity of the vibrations is also affected by the vigor of the ventricular contraction, the heart rate, the cardiac output, the P-R interval and similar factors. The relative intensity of the first and second sounds provides an additional clue concerning these factors.

The next step is to direct attention solely to the second sound for a period sufficient to establish its characteristics. The loudness of the first sound and second sound can then be compared, but a final decision concerning this observation should be deferred until other areas of the precordium have been examined. At this stage, the first and second sounds at the apex should be so familiar that they can be recognized without reference to the apex beat.

A systematic search for murmurs is initiated by directing attention solely to the interval which follows each first sound. Little experience is required to focus on this interval without actually hearing the first sound. Listening first for low-pitched sounds and then for high-pitched sounds is a good policy because attention is so discrete that involuntary anticipation of low-frequency vibrations may cause one to overlook a high-pitched murmur. Having ascertained that the early systolic interval is either quiet or occupied by a murmur, attention is next directed toward the later portions of systole. If a murmur is present during either of these portions of systole, the attention can then

be spread to include the whole of the systolic interval to determine the time at which the murmur reaches maximum intensity. This technique is the best way to differentiate early systolic murmurs from mid-systolic and late systolic murmurs.

The diastolic interval is scanned in the same way. Attention is directed first to the interval immediately following the second sound. Focussing the attention on the early diastolic interval during a succession of beats is extremely important because it provides the only hope of detecting third heart sounds or early diastolic gallop, the "opening snap" of mitral stenosis and certain early diastolic murmurs. It is even more important to listen for both low-pitched and high-pitched sounds during this interval.

The period just preceding the first sound is then selectively analyzed. For many individuals this is the most difficult step of all because there is no specific stimulus for "turning on" the attention during each cycle. If the heart is beating regularly, this difficulty can be easily overcome because the rhythm is established. With practice, the presystolic interval can be scanned even in the presence of arrhythmia. Similarly, the process of directing selective attention to a particular interval while voluntarily blanking out all others is more difficult during tachycardia. This technique is not only applicable but absolutely essential when the heart is beating rapidly or irregularly.

When a detailed analysis of the heart sounds and murmurs at the apex has been completed, the same process is repeated in the pulmonary, the aortic and the tricuspid areas. If a murmur is recognized in any of the intervals, the region of maximum intensity and the extent of transmission should be established. By limiting attention only to the murmur in question, these characteristics can be determined very quickly by systematically listening over a sequence of points around the primary areas. It is frequently desirable to establish the relative intensities of the heart sounds and murmurs by going back over each area in quick succession, evaluating each sound in turn. This is accomplished rapidly if the sounds have become familiar during the more careful analysis in each area.

When this technique is recommended to medical students, they commonly express concern regarding their ability to accomplish this task. In most cases, these doubts can be alleviated by suggesting that they produce schematic drawings of what they hear. It is very helpful to compare such drawings with phonocardiograms or sonvelograms at first. Even experienced examiners agree that the process of schematically drawing subjective impressions of sounds and murmurs can be a valuable experience.

A second objection to systematic auscultation of the type described is the increased expenditure of time. There is no doubt that this technique is more time-consuming, particularly at first. However, routine use of the method rapidly improves proficiency. After a few weeks of concentrated effort, analysis of heart sounds and murmurs can become complete and accurate with little wasted time. With experience it is possible to scan each phase of the cardiac cycle in turn by listening to only a few cycles during each step. The time and effort spent are amply rewarded by striking improvement in accuracy of auscultatory diagnosis. After many years of unsystematic auscultation, many examiners begin to recognize certain types of murmurs for the first time by taking advantage of dormant ability to focus attention on specific intervals of time.

SUMMARY

Heart sounds and murmurs are audible vibrations emitted from the heart and great vessels. Since the walls of the heart cannot vibrate without setting the blood into vibration, and vice versa, the origin of heart sounds was described in terms of oscillations induced by abrupt changes in velocity of the blood (due to closure of valves, etc.). Heart murmurs occur in rapidly flowing blood and can be attributed to turbulence. Turbulence occurs in fluids of low viscosity flowing rapidly through tubes of large caliber. The velocity required to induce turbulence is greatly diminished by local obstructions in a tube, causing fluid to flow through a small orifice into a large channel or chamber. Most heart murmurs can be readily explained on the basis of high velocity flow or abrupt changes in caliber of the vascular channels. These mechanisms obviously apply to systolic and diastolic murmurs, produced by valvular deformities.

REFERENCES

1. BROCK, R. C. The surgical and pathological anatomy of the mitral valve. *Brit. Heart J.*, 14:489–513, 1952.
2. HENDERSON, Y., and JOHNSON, F. E. Two modes of closure of the heart valves. *Heart*, 4:69–82, 1912.
3. DEAN, A. L., JR. The movements of the mitral cusps in relation to the cardiac cycle. *Amer. J. Physiol.*, 40:206–217, 1916.
4. ESSEX, H. E., SMITH, H. L., and BALDES, E. J. Origin of the heart sounds (motion picture with sound recording). *Fed. Proc.*, 12:40, 1953.
5. SMITH, H. L., ESSEX, H. E., and BALDES, E. J. A study of the movements of heart valves and of heart sounds. *Ann. Intern. Med.*, 33:1357–1359, 1950.
6. RUSHMER, R. F., FINLAYSON, B. L., and NASH, A. A. Movements of the mitral valve. *Circulat. Res.*, 4:337–342, 1956.
7. RUSHMER, R. F., ELLIS, R. M., and NASH, A. A. Stereo-cinefluorography. Motion roentgenography in three dimensions. *Radiology*, 64:191–196, 1955.
8. WIGGERS, C. J., and DEAN, A. L., JR. The nature and time relations of the fundamental heart sounds. *Amer. J. Physiol.*, 42:476–497, 1917.
9. SMITH, J. R., EDWARDS, J. C., and KOUNTZ, W. B. The use of the cathode ray for recording heart sounds and vibrations. III. Total cardiac vibrations in one hundred normal subjects. *Amer. Heart J.*, 21:228–237, 1941.
10. LIAN, C., MINOT, G., HEBERT, J., and RAGER, N. Relations chronologiques entre les phenomenes mecaniques et electriques du coeur. *Arch. mal. coeur*, 46:39–45, 1953.

11. COUNIHAN, T., MESSER, A. L., RAPPAPORT, M. B., and SPRAGUE, H. B. The initial vibrations of the first heart sound. *Circulation*, 3:730–732, 1951.

12. SMITH, J. R., GILSON, A. S., and KOUNTZ, W. B. The use of the cathode ray for recording heart sounds and vibrations. II. Studies on the muscular element of the first heart sound. *Amer. Heart J.*, 21:17–24, 1941.

13. LUISADA, A. A., ALIMURUNG, M. M., and LEWIS, L. Mechanisms of production of the first heart sound. *Amer. J. Physiol.*, 168:226–233, 1952.

14. DOCK, W. Mode of production of first heart sound. *Arch. Intern. Med.*, 51:737–746, 1933.

15. RAPPAPORT, M. B., and SPRAGUE, H. B. The graphic registration of the normal heart sounds. *Amer. Heart J.*, 23:591–623, 1942.

16. SLOAN, A. W., CAMPBELL, F. W., and HENDERSON, A. S. Incidence of the physiological third heart sound. *Brit. Med. J.*, 2: 853–855, 1952.

17. KOUNTZ, W. B., GILSON, A. S., SMITH, J. R., and STURM, R. E. The use of the cathode ray for recording heart sounds and vibrations. I. Studies on the normal heart. *Amer. Heart J.*, 20:667–676, 1940.

18. SLOAN, A. W., and WISHART, M. The effect on the human third heart sound of variations in the rate of filling of the heart. *Brit. Heart J.*, 15:25–28, 1953.

19. McKUSICK, V. A. *Cardiovascular Sounds in Health and Disease.* Baltimore, The Williams and Wilkins Co., 1958, vii, 570 pp.

20. SHEARN, M. A., TARR, E., and RYTAND, D. A. The significance of changes in amplitude of the first heart sound in children with A-V block. *Circulation*, 7:839–846, 1953.

21. WOLFERTH, C. C., and MARGOLIES, A. The influence of auricular contraction on the first heart sound and the radial pulse. *Arch. Intern. Med.*, 46:1048–1071, 1930.

22. RYTAND, D. A. The variable loudness of the first heart sound in auricular fibrillation. *Amer. Heart J.*, 37:187–204, 1949.

23. LITTLE, R. C., and HILTON, J. G. Effect of ectopic ventricular contractions on the first heart sound. *Fed. Proc.*, 12:89, 1953.

24. LEATHAM, A. Splitting of the first and second heart sounds. *Lancet*, 2:607–614, 1954.

25. DUNN, F. L., and DICKERSON, W. J. Third heart sound: possible role of pericardium in its production. *Circulat. Res.*, 3:51–55, 1955.

26. FOLEY, A. D. *College Physics*, 3rd ed. Philadelphia, The Blakiston Co., 1941.

27. STEVENS, S. S., and DAVIS, H. *Hearing, Its Psychology and Physiology.* New York, John Wiley & Sons, Inc., 1938, 489 pp.

28. MANNHEIMER, E. Calibrated phonocardiography. A new technique for clinical use. *Amer. Heart J.*, 21:151–162, 1941.

29. RAPPAPORT, M. B., and SPRAGUE, H. B. Physiologic and physical laws that govern ausculation, and their clinical application. The acoustic stethoscope and electrical amplifying stethoscope and stethograph. *Amer. Heart J.*, 21:257–318, 1941.

30. RAPPAPORT, M. B., and SPRAGUE, H. B. The effects of improper fitting of stethoscope to ears on ausculatory efficiency. *Amer. Heart J.*, 43:713–715, 1952.

31. LEPESCHKIN, E. A quantitative stethoscope and its clinical applications. *Amer. Heart J.*, 43:881–888, 1952.

32. RUSHMER, R. F., BARK, R. S., and ELLIS, R. M. Direct-writing heart sound recorder. *Amer. J. Dis. Child.*, 83:733–739, 1952.

33. REYNOLDS, O. An experimental investigation of the circumstances which determine whether the motion of water shall be direct or sinuous, and of the law of resistance in parallel channels. *Phil. Trans.*, 174:935–982, 1883.

34. COULTER, N. A., JR., and PAPPENHEIMER, J. R. Development of turbulence in flowing blood. *Amer. J. Physiol.*, 159:483–491, 1949.

35. PREC, O., KATZ, L. N., SENNETT, R. H., FISHMAN, A. P., and HWANG, H. Determination of kinetic energy of the heart in man. *Amer. J. Physiol.*, 159:483–491, 1949.

36. STUCKEY, D. Innocent systolic murmurs in childhood. *Med. J. Austr.* 2:841–842, 1955.

37. GROOM, R., CHAPMAN, W., FRANCIS, W. W., BASS, ANNE, and SIHVONEN, Y. T. The normal systolic murmur. *Ann. Int. Med.*, 52:134–144, 1960.

38. SPITZBARTH, H. Klinische Studien zur Entstehung der akzidentellen systolischen Geräusche über der Auskultationsstelle der Pulmonkoppe. *Arch. Krislaufforsch.* 22:1–72, 1955.

39. BRUNS, D. L. A general theory of the causes of murmurs in the cardiovascular system. *Amer. J. Med.*, 27:360–374, 1959.

40. WISKIND, H. K., and TALBOT, S. A. Physical basis of cardiovascular sound; an analytical survey. U. S. Air Force Off. Sci. Res. Tech. Rep. No. TR. 58–160, 1958.

41. LEVINE, S. A., and HARVEY, W. P. *Clinical Auscultation of the Heart.* Philadelphia, W. B. Saunders Co., 1949, 327 pp.

42. COUNIHAN, T. B., RAPPAPORT, M. B., and SPRAGUE, H. B. Physiologic and physical factors that govern the clinical appreciation of cardiac thrills. *Circulation*, 4:716–728, 1951.

Chapter 12

RHEUMATIC VALVULAR DISEASE

In recent years the medical community has been faced with a serious problem in detecting and caring for patients with signs and symptoms of myocarditis. In 1940, Sosman[1] clearly expressed a widely accepted attitude of that period, as follows: "There is little of therapeutic value in the earlier diagnosis of mitral stenosis, as there would be in the early diagnosis of cancer or of pulmonary tuberculosis. The treatment would not be any different nor would it presumably have any different effect. The value in such studies must lie therefore in the difference in prognosis, with a possible change in our ideas as to the latent or inactive period in potential heart disease—that period between the first infection with rheumatic fever and the onset of symptoms or the discovery of physical signs of acquired valvular heart disease."

The "batting average" in diagnosing the early stages of acute rheumatic fever has not been particularly good. As a matter of fact, rheumatic heart disease in 40 per cent of patients is first recognized only after permanent damage to the valves has produced clinical manifestations. In other words, the original attacks of acute rheumatic fever must have been undetected. So long as there was no treatment which would ameliorate or prevent recurrent attacks, failure to diagnose the initial attack of rheumatic carditis made little difference in the course of the patient's subsequent illness.

More recently, the development of antibiotics has at last provided effective prophylaxis against recurrent attacks of acute rheumatic fever. Prevention of recurrences should greatly diminish the likelihood of permanent valvular damage but requires prolonged administration of antibiotic agents. For many reasons, programs of antibiotic prophylaxis must not be initiated indiscriminately so the accurate diagnosis of initial attacks of acute rheumatic fever has become exceedingly important. Recognition of acute rheumatic fever has been seriously complicated by the fact that inflammatory lesions in the heart from many different disease entities may produce signs closely simulating those of acute rheumatic fever.

Since antibiotic prophylaxis has been developed during a period when inflammatory lesions of the heart are being recognized very frequently, clinicians are rather suddenly faced with the necessity of distinguishing acute rheumatic carditis from nonspecific myocarditis with its diverse etiology, variable symptoms and vague signs. Thus, the importance of early and accurate diagnosis of the initial stages of rheumatic carditis places a heavy responsibility on physicians attending such patients. Unfortunately, the signs and symptoms of acute rheumatic fever are also frequently vague and widely variable. Two attacks in the same patient may produce entirely different responses. Not all patients with acute rheumatic fever develop permanent damage to the heart or valves.

329

I. Acute Rheumatic Fever

The pathology, etiology and extra-cardiac symptomatology of rheumatic fever are considered with reference to the general problems of diagnosis. Recognition of acute rheumatic fever depends in part upon the criteria which delineate that entity.

Definition. Acute rheumatic fever is a general systemic disease characterized by widely disseminated focal and diffuse inflammatory reactions in connective tissue or various other tissues of the body, frequently developing between one and three weeks after an infection involving group A hemolytic streptococci. The inflammatory process is more obvious when localized in the heart, joints, and central nervous system, but it may also affect skeletal muscle, synovial membranes in general, blood vessels, lungs, gastrointestinal tract, kidneys, etc.

ETIOLOGY OF ACUTE RHEUMATIC FEVER

The nature and origin of rheumatic fever remain controversial. Recently, Waksman[2] reviewed the subject and included an extensive bibliography. Before 1900, a wide variety of micro-organisms were cultured from patients with rheumatic fever. It is now widely accepted that the causative micro-organisms cannot be isolated from the blood stream, heart or joints of patients with this disease.

Streptococcal Infections

Since 1930, and particularly during World War II, an association between recrudescence of rheumatic fever and infection with certain strains of hemolytic streptococci (in the group A of Lancefield) has been established. For example, acute rheumatic fever in army camps accompanied epidemics of streptococcal sore throats. By eliminating streptococci from the nasopharynx in a group of susceptible individuals, the rate of rheumatic fever attacks can be greatly reduced. Many different types of hemolytic streptococci can be identified on the basis of immunologically distinct proteins in the bacterial cells. None of these types is specific for acute rheumatic fever. Certain strains of the organism produce substances which may be detected by the antibody responses in the host. For example, most strains of group A streptococci growing in cultures produce a substance called streptolysin O, capable of causing lysis of rabbit erythrocytes. Among individuals infected with streptococci, some 90 per cent produce an antibody (antistreptolysin O) at some time in the course of the disease. However, most individuals with streptococcal infections do not develop acute rheumatic fever.

Immunologic Sensitization

It is well established that widespread tissue and vascular lesions occur during the height of an allergic reaction (e.g., sensitization to horse serum). For this reason, great interest is currently directed toward immunologic reactions in the etiology of rheumatic fever. Evidence has been presented that individuals who develop post-streptococcal complications (e.g., rheumatic fever) tend to form larger amounts of various antibodies than do individuals who recover from the infection without complications. In other words, exaggerated antibody responses to streptococcal infections are believed to characterize individuals who are susceptible to rheumatic fever. Lesions in the skin, joints, and heart, superficially resembling rheumatic inflammatory reactions, have been produced experimentally by a bewildering array of injected antigens, including various types of living and dead bacteria or their products, foreign serum, egg albumin, and even the animal's own tissues. The concept that rheumatic fever is an allergic process is based in part upon the following points: (*a*) Recurrent attacks indicate an absence of immunity. (*b*) The fibrinoid degeneration of collagen is considered characteristic of allergic reactions. (*c*) A period of one to three weeks commonly intervenes between a streptococcal infection and the onset of rheumatic fever. Such an interval is characteristic of known allergic diseases. (*d*) The acute phase of rheumatic fever has clinical signs and symptoms which are frequently indistinguishable from known allergic diseases (e.g., serum sickness). On this basis, individuals susceptible to rheumatic attacks may produce excessive amounts of antibody in response to repeated infections, particularly with group A hemolytic streptococci.

The etiology of acute rheumatic fever has been considered for two reasons: (*a*) the wide variety of clinical manifestations of the disease reflects the widespread distribution of lesions in different tissues, and (*b*) current knowledge regarding the nature of acute rheumatic fever does not permit us to make a clear-cut distinction between this condition and myocarditis associated with other types of systemic disease.

SYSTEMIC EFFECTS OF ACUTE RHEUMATIC FEVER

A definitive diagnosis of rheumatic fever can be made with confidence only when a particular patient displays a number of the systemic manifestations of the disease. Until a specific test becomes universally accepted, the exact diagnosis of many patients will remain controversial. Without specific criteria for the diagnosis, data on the incidence of the disease and on the effectiveness of various therapeutic attacks are difficult to evaluate. For this reason, Jones[3] grouped the various common signs of the disease into major and minor manifestations for the purpose of standardizing the diagnosis for statistical purposes (Fig. 1). Patients exhibiting various combinations of these manifestations (two major manifestations or one major and two minor manifestations) are often regarded as having acute rheumatic fever. These relatively rigid criteria for controlled investigation have demonstrable value when applied to groups of patients, but they are no substitute for clinical judgment in the care of an individual patient. However, the classification of signs and symptoms proposed by Jones forms a convenient organization for a discussion of this complex disease entity.

Major Manifestations

Carditis. In the proper setting, the development of significant cardiac murmurs, pericardial friction rub, cardiac enlargement, alterations in electrocardiographic patterns and congestive heart failure represents evidence of active carditis. The clinical signs of carditis will be considered in more detail in a subsequent section.

Arthralgia. The rapid development of painful joints which are tender, warm, swollen and red is generally considered a classic sign of rheumatic fever. The arthritic process generally involves more than one joint, migrating from one to another over a varying period of time. The pain is sufficient to limit mobility of the affected joints and should be distinguished from myositis or vague muscular pains. Although there is reason to believe that myositis may occur with acute rheumatic fever, the symptoms are so nonspecific that their significance is difficult to evaluate. According to Jones, transient mild polyarthritis without other diagnostic features of acute rheumatic fever is not significant unless the patient is a likely candidate for the disease on the basis of known contact with hemolytic streptococci.

Chorea. The development of chorea is frequently heralded by personality changes. For example, a lively, obedient, good-natured child may become sulky,

CLINICAL MANIFESTATIONS OF ACUTE RHEUMATIC FEVER

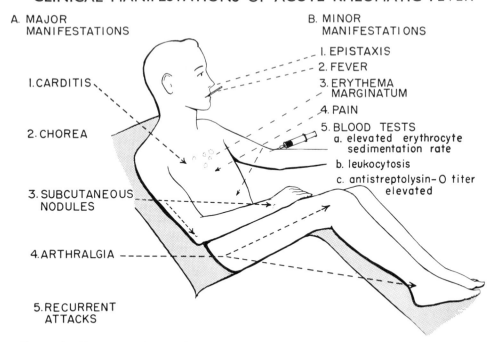

A. MAJOR
MANIFESTATIONS

B. MINOR
MANIFESTATIONS

1. EPISTAXIS
2. FEVER
3. ERYTHEMA
MARGINATUM
4. PAIN
5. BLOOD TESTS
   a. elevated erythrocyte
     sedimentation rate
   b. leukocytosis
   c. antistreptolysin-O titer
     elevated

1. CARDITIS

2. CHOREA

3. SUBCUTANEOUS
NODULES

4. ARTHRALGIA

5. RECURRENT
ATTACKS

FIGURE 1. The principal signs of acute rheumatic fever are illustrated schematically. According to Jones,[3] a diagnosis of acute rheumatic fever is made if a patient has two major manifestations or one major and two minor manifestations. These criteria are particularly valuable in gathering statistics for various types of research problems, but may not be applicable to an individual patient.

irritable and inattentive. Awkwardness and frequent emotional upsets are prone to occur. Finally, irregular, incoordinated, jerky and apparently purposeless movements appear. The involuntary movements of the extremities may become severe enough to interfere with walking. The condition is most likely to occur in children, frequently without signs of infection or any other manifestation of acute rheumatic fever. Nonetheless, a majority of children with chorea ultimately suffer from rheumatic heart disease, developing either insidiously or following recurrent attacks of more typical rheumatic fever.

Subcutaneous Nodules. Subcutaneous nodules, varying from the size of a pinhead to that of a pea or bean, are most commonly found near bony prominences over the back of the elbow, the wrists, the dorsum of the hand or foot, the ankles, the knees and the skull. Usually, these nod-

ules develop in cases with rather severe carditis and therefore suggest a relatively grave prognosis concerning both the acute attack and the subsequent development of organic valvular disease.

Previous History of Acute Rheumatic Fever. Although an occasional patient succumbs to an initial attack of rheumatic fever, most patients recover without evidence of residual damage even though the episode lasts for weeks or months. Murmurs and other signs of carditis usually diminish and may disappear completely. However, the incidence of recurrences is so great that once a patient has suffered an attack of rheumatic fever, subsequent attacks should be suspected whenever any of the other major or minor manifestations appear. In many cases, no evidence of valvular heart disease appears following the last known attack of rheumatic fever, yet years later well-developed mitral or aortic valvular lesions become apparent. The sequence of events in the interim is completely unknown, and it is frequently presumed that additional attacks occurred but were unrecognized.

Minor Manifestations

The minor manifestations of rheumatic fever represent the widespread involvement of a systemic disease (Fig. 1). None of them is at all specific for this condition; they are significant only when associated with one or more of the major manifestations. They often serve to stimulate a search for more definitive signs and a more prolonged observation of a patient.

Fever. Elevated body temperature is so frequently associated with infectious processes that this sign by itself is without value. Chorea may occur without fever, and acute rheumatic fever may produce a rise in body temperature no greater than that caused by a simple upper respiratory infection. When fever is of unknown origin, the possibility of acute rheumatic fever should be considered, but not accepted without definite indication.

Abdominal Pain. An initial attack of rheumatic fever may be indistinguishable from an attack of acute appendicitis. This phenomenon is unexplained but has been attributed to inflammatory reactions in splanchnic blood vessels and to a number of other mechanisms. Unnecessary appendectomies will continue to be performed on such patients until more specific diagnostic tests for rheumatic fever have been developed. In some patients the abdominal pain is mild and transient.

Precordial Pain. Although pain in the precordium is fairly common with acute carditis, it also occurs in other conditions, including myocardial ischemia, pulmonary hypertension, neurocirculatory asthenia, and aches or pains of nervous, muscular or skeletal origin.

Erythema Marginatum. Numerous types of skin rashes in patients with rheumatic fever have been described, including urticaria, erythema multiforme and petechiae. However, the most significant skin lesion is erythema marginatum. It usually begins on the trunk and consists of red or purplish macules which rapidly increase in area while clearing in the center to form circles or irregularly scalloped patterns. These lesions appear in crops, and are somewhat evanescent. They are commonly seen in patients with subcutaneous nodules, and have about the same clinical significance.

Epistaxis. Many patients with rheumatic fever frequently have nose bleeds without trauma. The bleeding often occurs at night, and is generally quite profuse and intractable. The exact cause is not known.

Pulmonary Lesions. Pleurisy with or without effusion occurs quite frequently and is often associated with pericarditis. This is one cause of precordial pain, but in this case, the discomfort is accentuated by respiratory activity. Diffuse inflammatory reactions in the lungs have been observed and called "rheumatic pneumonitis." There seems little doubt that these changes may occur, but controversy persists concerning their incidence and importance.

Laboratory Tests. Leukocytosis is common in active rheumatic fever, the leukocyte count being elevated from the normal range to levels above 10,000 per cubic millimeter. Anemia, principally microcytic, is frequently encountered, hemoglobin levels sometimes dropping to 7 or 8 gm. per cent. The erthrocyte sedimentation rate accelerates early in the disease process and often remains increased after other signs of infection (e.g., white blood count, body temperature) have returned to normal. This test is more valuable in following the course of rheumatic attacks which have been diagnosed than as a purely diagnostic aid.

The antistreptolysin titer is above normal levels following an infection with group A hemolytic streptococci. The principal value of this test lies in establishing the fact that a particular patient has had contact with this group of pathogenic organisms, but it may be misleading on two counts: not all strains of hemolytic streptococci produce acute rheumatic fever and, in some cases of rheumatic fever, the antistreptolysin titer does not exceed normal limits. Breese and Gray[4] reported that antistreptolysin titers in excess of 250 Todd units were found in 95 per cent of patients with rheumatic fever, 60 per cent of cases with other streptococcal infections, 42 per cent of patients with inactive rheumatic fever, and 24 per cent of controls.

The necessity for invoking a flexible and symptomatologic definition of this disease (major and minor manifestations) indicates the wide diversity of its clinical patterns. For example, a patient might exhibit chorea and no other signs whatever during the first attack. On a subsequent occasion, migrating polyarthritis might be the principal complaint, and a third attack might be overshadowed by abdominal symptoms simulating an acute abdominal emergency. Signs of cardiac involvement might appear during any or none of these attacks. On the other hand, carditis without specific extracardiac clues may appear. In a disease state of such manifold complexions, any set of criteria may be misleading in an individual case.

Most of the major and minor manifestations represent changes in tissues other than the heart. Although the diagnosis of acute rheumatic fever depends largely upon extracardiac signs, their severity is not a reliable index to the subsequent valvular damage. Special attention should be directed toward the signs of acute carditis.

Pathologic Manifestations

The initial phases of myocarditis consist of inflammation and edema of the connective tissue stroma and intense eosin staining of the gelatinous ground substance between the collagenous fibers. Later, a homogeneous, waxy appearance of the collagen bundles becomes so marked that individual fibers cannot be identified. This modified collagenous material superficially resembles fibrin. A "proliferative" reaction ensues, consisting of either diffuse accumulations of cells, particularly in the vicinity of blood vessels, or localized "granulomata" (Aschoff bodies) (Fig. 2D). Round cells, macrophages, fibroblasts and multinucleated giant cells accumulate in focal lesions. Typical giant cells have irregular outlines, slight basophilic staining of the cytoplasm, and two to seven round or oval nuclei near the center of the cell, often arranged like a fan (Fig. 2). Around the periphery of such lesions is an investment of polymorphonuclear leukocytes, lymphocytes, plasma cells, fibroblasts and occasional eosinophils. As healing progresses, this inflammatory process is replaced by spindle-shaped or triangular scars located between muscle layers and near blood vessels.

Inflammatory reactions also occur in other tissues. Subcutaneous nodules, varying in size from 1 mm. to 2 cm. in diameter, develop predominately over bony prominences. They develop rapidly, usually disappear quickly, and may be overlooked. Microscopically, these nodules are not identical with the focal processes in the myocardium. Subcutaneous lesions consist of aggregations of similar cells, but necrosis often develops in the center of the lesion. Similar diffuse and local inflammatory reactions occur in many tissues including tendons, skeletal muscles, joints, serous cavities in general, and the adventitia of arteries. Histologic evidence of meningoencephalitis in patients with chorea has been reported. During any particular attack, the pathologic changes may be localized in virtually any combination of the sites indicated above. Thus,

ACUTE RHEUMATIC CARDITIS

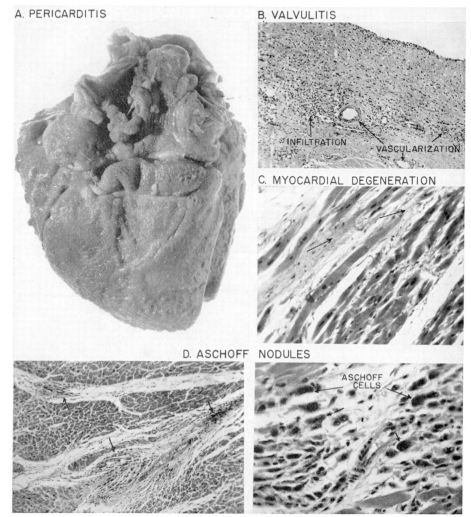

A. PERICARDITIS

B. VALVULITIS

INFILTRATION   VASCULARIZATION

C. MYOCARDIAL DEGENERATION

D. ASCHOFF NODULES

ASCHOFF CELLS

FIGURE 2. *A*, Pericarditis of extremely severe degree is illustrated by a specimen from a patient with fatal acute pancarditis. In the average attack of acute rheumatic fever, pericarditis appears to be a transient phenomenon as evidenced by evanescent friction rubs and precordial pain.

B, The valve cusps exhibit inflammatory reactions as evidenced by infiltrated leukocytes and vascularization by the proliferation of blood vessels.

C, Degeneration of myocardial fibers is generally postulated but is rarely demonstrable as clearly as indicated in the photomicrograph above. No doubt functional changes in the myocardium occur without such obvious histologic evidence.

D, Aschoff nodules in the myocardium are generally regarded as a pathognomonic sign of rheumatic fever. The typical nodule consists of a perivascular infiltration with leukocytes, including multinucleated giant cells (Aschoff cells). Healing of such a nodule usually produces triangular fibrous scars surrounding blood vessels in various portions of the heart walls. (These photomicrographs were obtained through the courtesy of Professor Stuart Lippincott.)

ACUTE RHEUMATIC VALVULITIS

A. MITRAL VALVE   B. TRICUSPID VALVE

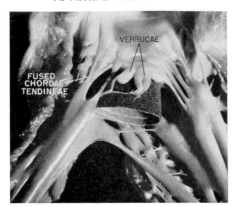 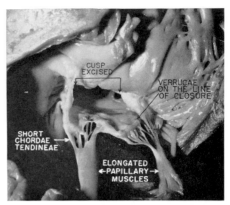

FIGURE 3.   Some effects of acute rheumatic valvulitis on the mitral and tricuspid valves are indicated by a specimen from a patient who expired in the course of her initial attack.

A, The mitral valve edges are greatly thickened with verrucae extending along filamentous chordae tendineae. Some of the chordae tendineae are fused together. All the chordae tendineae appear shorter and thicker than normal and the papillary muscles are unusually long, but at least part of this relation could have antedated the inflammatory process. The mitral orifice was only slightly diminished in area.

B, In the same patient a row of verrucae, up to 3 mm. thick, developed along the line of valve closure on all tricuspid valve cusps. The short, thick chordae tendineae are also associated with elongated papillary muscles. These diseased valves should be compared with the delicate, flexible normal valves and chordae tendineae illustrated in Fig. 1, Chap. 11. (This specimen is presented through the courtesy of Dr. S. A. Creighton, pathologist, Children's Orthopedic Hospital, Seattle, Washington.)

acute rheumatic fever is truly a systemic disease. It affects primarily the supporting structures of the body, collagen and elastica. Despite the widespread distribution of the lesions, most patients recover and little residual damage to vital organs persists, except in the valves of the heart. If valvular damage were not so frequent, this condition would be of no greater concern to cardiologists than is the nonspecific myocarditis associated with a tremendous number of other acute and chronic diseases.

Acute Rheumatic Valvulitis

Since the first attack of acute rheumatic fever is rarely fatal, pathologic changes during the typical initial attacks are not well established. Available descriptions of the initial pathology in rheumatic endocarditis and valvulitis are based on postmortem studies of patients overwhelmed by rheumatic attacks or of fortuitously

discovered endocardial inflammatory processes in accident victims. In neither instance can one be certain that the individuals would have ultimately developed typical rheumatic valvular heart disease. Until rheumatic valvular lesions can be reproduced experimentally, the reconstructed sequence of events must be accepted with some reservations.

Gross and Friedberg[5] concluded that the valve rings were the first portion of the valves to be involved in the rheumatic process. In patients who were believed to have succumbed during their first attack, the valve rings were the most common site of inflammatory reactions and in most cases all four valve rings were involved. Since the valve rings are closely related anatomically (see Fig. 3, Chap. 2), this widespread involvement has been explained as a direct extension of the process from one ring to another.[6] Swift[7] postulated that the mitral and aortic valves more frequently became deformed because of the greater "functional trauma" to which they are subjected. He presented observations on one fever-free patient who succumbed to an anesthetic on the nineteenth day of an apparently mild initial attack. The aortic and mitral valves were edematous and infiltrated with mononuclear cells. One small verrucous lesion with a very small necrotic focus underneath was found on the aortic valve. At later stages, the valve leaflets become thickened and are no longer transparent. Rows of gray or yellow wart-like vegetations develop along the line of closure of the aortic and mitral valves (Fig. 3). The valve edges become thick and newly formed blood vessels grow into the leaflets from the periphery. The structure and function of the valves frequently become essentially normal after initial attacks of rheumatic fever. Valvular deformities usually occur after repeated inflammatory assaults or protracted severe attacks of rheumatic fever.

During the healing process, the inflammatory lesions are replaced by fibrous tissue. Shrinkage of the collagen fibers usually causes shortening and retraction of the affected cusps. The chordae tendineae of the atrioventricular valves become shortened and fused, drawing the valve edges toward the papillary muscles. Fusion between the valve leaflets begins at the commissures and extends toward the center of the valve ring. As a result, the flexible mitral valve leaflets are finally converted into a rigid funnel with a narrow orifice held deep within the left ventricular cavity by the shortened, fused chordae tendineae (see Fig. 8 below). The semilunar valve leaflets are also thickened and shortened, with their edges rolled outward, and fusion of the commissures between the valve cusps restricts the valve orifices. Various types of valvular deformities and their functional effects are discussed below.

Sequelae of Recurrent Rheumatic Fever

If rheumatic fever and carditis were self-limited so that no further functional or organic damage followed a single attack, it would be a relatively small clinical problem. Most patients would recover completely with little residual sign except for soft apical systolic murmurs, some of which disappear in time. The principal therapeutic problem would center around supportive therapy to facilitate survival of the immediate attack. Unfortunately, this state of affairs bears little resemblance to the problem presented by rheumatic fever. For example, Bland and Jones[8] reported a follow-up study for 20 years on 1000 patients with rheumatic fever in childhood. The average age at onset for this group was eight years. From these data, the status of the group on discharge from the hospital, and after 10 and 20 years, has been plotted in Figure 4. Of 87 patients with systolic murmur at the apex, the murmur disappeared in about one-third, and remained unchanged in another third. Another group of about the same size developed a diastolic murmur indicative of mitral stenosis.

The ultimate effects of an attack of rheumatic fever are not established for many years (Fig. 4). In a large proportion of patients, signs of valvular damage disappear, while other patients acquire signs of organic valvular deformity with or without obvious recurrence of acute rheumatic fever. The tardy development of serious valvular disease suggests a very pertinent question. Does active myocarditis and valvulitis smolder undetected for many years after acute rheumatic fever? Recent evidence indicates that this can occur. During surgical correction of mitral valve deformities, the left atrial appendage is routinely excised, and about 50 per cent of these appendages contain Aschoff nodules.[9, 10] Such acute

TWENTY YEAR HISTORY OF RHEUMATIC FEVER

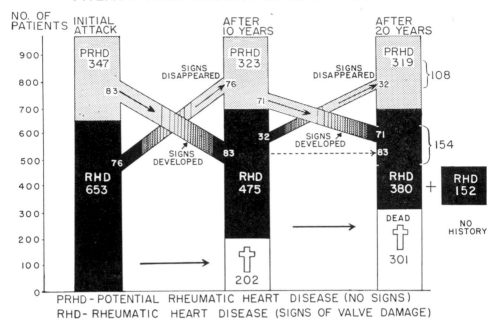

PRHD - POTENTIAL RHEUMATIC HEART DISEASE (NO SIGNS)
RHD- RHEUMATIC HEART DISEASE (SIGNS OF VALVE DAMAGE)

FIGURE 4.   A series of 1000 consecutive patients with rheumatic fever, chorea or rheumatic heart disease has been followed for 20 years. The original status of these patients on discharge from the hospital is indicated under the heading "Initial Attack." No clinical evidence of rheumatic heart disease was found in 347 patients who were therefore classified as potential rheumatic heart disease (PRHD). The remaining 653 had evidence of rheumatic heart disease (RHD), such as significant murmurs.

During the next 10 years, clinical evidence of rheumatic heart disease developed in 83 patients previously classified as having potential rheumatic heart disease, while signs of heart disease disappeared in 76 patients. Two hundred and two patients died.

At the end of 20 years, 71 more patients developed signs of rheumatic heart disease, making a total of 154 in whom evidence of heart disease developed at varying intervals after the initial attack. Among adult patients with rheumatic heart disease, about 40 per cent have no history of any attack of acute rheumatic fever. It is interesting that in this study about the same percentage developed signs of rheumatic heart disease at varying intervals after a definite rheumatic episode. In 32 additional patients, the signs of rheumatic heart disease disappeared and 99 more patients died (total 301). (From data presented by Bland, E. F., and Jones, T. D.[8])

inflammatory lesions appearing in the atrial appendage are generally accompanied by similar lesions in the remainder of the heart, particularly the left ventricle. Furthermore, there is evidence that rheumatic fever may be reactivated by mitral surgery in patients with no preoperative evidence of carditis.[11] These observations are extremely disturbing because cardiac surgery is not elected in the presence of any evidence of active carditis. Thus, a very large group of older patients with no history of active rheumatic fever for many years are found to have histologic evidence of rheumatic activity with-

in the heart muscle. Either the Aschoff nodule and the criteria for active rheumatic carditis are not as specific as previously believed, or these patients had subclinical rheumatic activity for many years. If active myocarditis and valvulitis can simmer undetected for 30 or 40 years, how long should prophylaxis continue? Will prevention of streptococcal infections by prophylactic administration of antibiotics eliminate external signs of rheumatic fever without suppressing the progressive development of valvular disease? It is too early to assess the implications of these questions.

In the meantime, entirely new concepts concerning the nature and development of acquired valvular disease are evolving from the rapidly expanding experience with cardiac surgery and cardiac catheterization. Direct knowledge of cardiac function and disease derived from living patients is exposing the inadequacy of previous physiologic, clinical and pathologic interpretations. This applies particularly to rheumatic mitral valvular disease, which will be considered in some detail in the next section.

Summary

A wide variety of disease states produces clinical signs closely resembling those associated with acute rheumatic fever. Such acute nonspecific myocarditis is not generally believed to produce chronic valvular lesions. About 40 per cent of patients with evidence of valvular disease are adults with no history of any previous attack of acute rheumatic fever. Until the causative factors in this large proportion of patients can be established, it seems unwise to ignore the possibility that at least some of these were originally among the very large number of patients who develop nonspecific carditis at some time during their life span. A specific test for acute rheumatic carditis is sorely needed to help solve both the theoretical and practical problems presented by this perplexing disease entity. In the meantime, each patient must be carefully considered individually in establishing both the diagnosis and the appropriate therapy. An incorrect diagnosis of acute rheumatic fever, followed by prophylactic treatment with prolonged courses of antibiotic therapy, involves both the expenditure of time and money and the possibility of producing a cardiac invalid from an essentially normal person. Alternately, failure to prevent recurrent attacks of rheumatic fever by adequate prophylaxis may lead to progressive valvular deformity and serious heart disease. Treading the narrow line between these dangerous alternatives requires balanced judgment.

II. Diagnosis of Valvular Disease

The ventricles can function as efficient pumps only if the inflow and outflow valves open adequately and close effectively. Deformities of the valves produce two main types of functional disturbance: stenosis and regurgitation. Valvular stenosis produces a restricted orifice through the valve. Valvular incompetence or insufficiency implies that the valves fail to close and seal, allowing blood to flow in a retrograde direction. Identifying the affected valve is important, particularly now that corrective surgery for valvular deformities is a practical reality. Each valve functions under different conditions and is more likely to be affected by one cause of deformities than another. Thus, the mitral valve is by far the most common site of rheumatic valvular heart disease, and the incidence of involvement is much lower in the aortic, tricuspid and pulmonary valves, in that order. Cardiovascular syphilis produces aortic incompetence as an isolated valvular lesion. The pulmonary valve is most commonly deformed during embryologic development (see also Chap. 14). Tricuspid valves are rarely affected by either acquired or developmental heart disease.

The necessity for accurate diagnosis of valvular disease will continue to increase as more specific types of therapy are developed for the various lesions. Recent developments in remedial surgery for valvular disease have not only stimulated interest in the problem of diagnosis but

INCOMPETENCE OF AORTIC VALVE

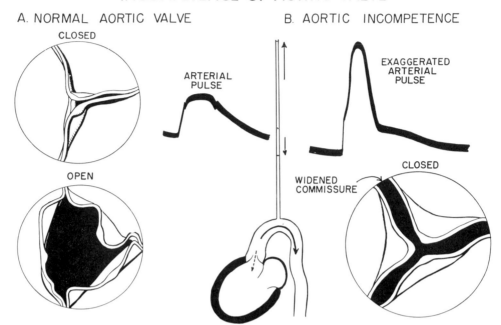

FIGURE 5.   *A*, The normal aortic valve completely seals off the aortic orifice during diastole and opens to expose a large triangular aperture during ventricular ejection (after McMillan, I. K. R., Daley, R., and Mathews, M. B.: The movement of aortic and pulmonary valves studied post-mortem by colour cinematography. *Brit. Heart J.*, 14:42–46, 1952).

B, Pure aortic incompetence usually results from dilatation of the aortic root due to syphilitic aortitis, which produces widening of commissures and incomplete closure of the valves. Free regurgitation of blood into the relaxed left ventricular chamber causes the arterial pressure to drop precipitously to low levels during diastole. The stroke volume is increased by the amount of the reflux and the systolic peak of pressure is greatly elevated to maintain a normal mean arterial blood pressure. Thus, the arterial pulse pressure is exaggerated. The abnormally great volume load produces dilatation of the left ventricle.

have also provided new dynamic information regarding the function of diseased valves in living hearts. In view of the recent drastic change in attitude toward these lesions, particular attention will be directed to the newer concepts. Although mitral valvular disease is the most common, the entire subject can be discussed more coherently by starting with lesions of the aortic valve.

INCOMPETENCE OF THE AORTIC VALVE

Rheumatic disease of the aortic valves usually produces both stenosis and insufficiency. However, a surprisingly high

incidence of rheumatic aortic insufficiency without functionally significant stenosis has been discovered during cardiac surgery. Pure aortic regurgitation is characteristically caused by dilatation of the aortic ring associated with syphilitic aortitis. The valve cusps may remain normal, but as the circumference of the aorta increases, the commissures between the valve cusps widen until they can no longer come into apposition (Fig. 5). Under these conditions, blood is freely ejected into the aorta during left ventricular contraction, but some of this blood regurgitates into the left ventricle during diastole. From the functional point of view, aortic incompetence represents a fairly clear-cut

commissures, which eventually causes stenosis of various degrees. The fibrotic valves may calcify as the patient grows older. Owing to shrinkage and retraction of the valve cusps with curling of the edges, the affected aortic valves are usually more or less incompetent. Thus, the typical case of rheumatic or calcific aortic valvular disease presents a picture of combined aortic stenosis and aortic insufficiency, with one or the other factor pre-dominating. Studying the appearance of signs and symptoms during the evolution of calcareous aortic stenosis over periods of 2 to 20 years, Boas[20] found that 7 of 15 patients had signs of aortic insufficiency as well.

Bailey et al.[21] described two principal patterns of rheumatic aortic stenosis. In one form, vegetations and inflammatory reactions developed uniformly along the lines of valve closure of each cusp so that

STENOSIS OF AORTIC VALVE

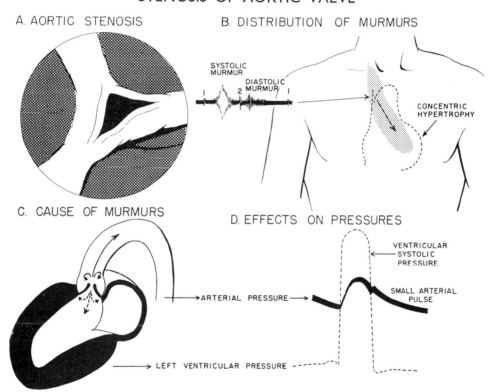

A. AORTIC STENOSIS

B. DISTRIBUTION OF MURMURS

SYSTOLIC MURMUR

DIASTOLIC MURMUR

CONCENTRIC HYPERTROPHY

C. CAUSE OF MURMURS

D. EFFECTS ON PRESSURES

VENTRICULAR SYSTOLIC PRESSURE

ARTERIAL PRESSURE

SMALL ARTERIAL PULSE

LEFT VENTRICULAR PRESSURE

FIGURE 7. A, Aortic stenosis usually results from rheumatic valvulitis which produces adhesions of the commissures. In advanced stages of this process the triangular orifice is rigid so that it impedes systolic ejection and allows regurgitation.

B, A murmur with maximum intensity in mid-systole usually results from the aortic stenosis. Incompetence of the aortic valve allows regurgitation, producing a diastolic murmur. These murmurs are generally distributed along a line connecting the aortic area with the apex of the heart, and may simulate the murmurs of pure aortic incompetence (see Fig. 6). However, the heart is not greatly enlarged unless heart failure supervenes. Instead, the left border of the cardiac silhouette is often rounded owing to concentric hypertrophy of the left ventricle.

C, The systolic and diastolic murmurs result from turbulence induced by high-velocity blood flow impelled by large pressure gradients across a restricted orifice.

D, The ventricular pressure pulse is abnormally elevated to provide a pressure head sufficient to force the normal increments of blood past the stenotic valve. The arterial pulse pressure is sometimes diminished when the aortic stenosis is severe. Clinical signs often fail to indicate whether stenosis or incompetence predominates in any particular patient with rheumatic aortic valvular disease.

the cusps adhered along the edematous commissures, beginning near the point of their insertion and progressing toward the lumen of the aorta. When the process involved the three commissures equally, the valve orifice was reduced to a small triangular area in the center of the aortic ring. Since the normal aortic valves do not open to the full caliber of the aorta, the functional difference between normal and stenotic valves may not be as great as the difference in their appearance at postmortem examination (compare Figs. 7A and 5A). Thus, moderate degrees of aortic stenosis may have relatively slight functional effects on the heart. Intense fibrosis makes the edges of the valve cusps so stiff that this orifice probably remains open during diastole. In these cases, slight degrees of insufficiency complicate the stenosis. If the aortic lumen is reduced to a small aperture, no serious degree of regurgitation occurs even if the valves are completely immobile. Thus, severe aortic stenosis precludes serious aortic regurgitation. Conversely, free aortic regurgitation cannot occur with significant aortic stenosis. In most patients with aortic valvular disease caused by rheumatic fever, either aortic stenosis or aortic insufficiency will tend to predominate. If aortic regurgitation is the principal functional effect, the signs and symptoms resemble those encountered in syphilitic aortitis. More frequently, the main functional disturbance is obstruction of blood flow from the left ventricle into the aorta.

Another common type of aortic stenosis is unequal fusion of the three commissures. Usually the two anterior leaflets are so completely fused together that the aortic valve is functionally bicuspid. The conjoined anterolateral valve cusps occupy two-thirds of the circumference of the aortic valve ring and act as an unyielding membrane partitioning most of the aortic orifice. So long as the posterior leaflet retains its flexibility and motility, the remaining aortic orifice opens fairly wide

and usually closes completely without regurgitation. For purposes of this discussion, attention will be directed primarily to aortic stenosis uncomplicated by functionally significant incompetence.

Functional Significance of Uncomplicated Aortic Stenosis

In the normal person, the systolic pressure in the left ventricle is but slightly greater than the pressure in the root of the aorta. Very small pressure gradients are required to propel large volumes of blood through large bore tubes. Aortic stenosis reduces the caliber of the channel at the junction between the left ventricle and the aorta. If the area of the aortic orifice is reduced by some 50 per cent, the normal quantity of blood can be ejected if the pressure drop between the left ventricle and the aorta is only slightly greater. However, if the size of the aortic orifice is reduced further, steep pressure gradients are needed to force the normal quantity of blood into the aorta. The mean systemic arterial pressure remains within normal limits under the influence of reflexes initiated by pressoreceptors while the cardiac output is also maintained within normal limits. Thus, the systolic pressure developed by left ventricular contraction must exceed the pressure in the aorta by an amount sufficient to maintain a normal stroke volume in spite of the increased resistance to outflow (Fig. 7D). This is the major functional effect of aortic stenosis.

Left Ventricular Response. So long as the area of the aortic orifice is more than half the normal, the increase in left ventricular pressure is functionally insignificant. The appearance of systolic murmurs in the aortic area from this cause precedes the development of significant stress on the left ventricle, often by many years (see below). As the aortic stensosis becomes more severe, the left ventricle responds to a sustained pressure load primarily by myocardial hypertrophy.

The myocardial fibers must generate greater tension to produce the higher intraventricular pressure during systole. Dilatation of the ventricle would be deleterious under these conditions because the myocardial tension would have to increase even more as the fibers described circles of larger and larger circumference. Thus, the myocardial fibers increase in diameter and the ventricular wall thickens. In the early stages of the disease, heart size usually remains within normal limits although the contour of the left border may appear rounded in roentgenograms of the posteroanterior view, presenting the picture of concentric hypertrophy (see Chap. 13). Left ventricular enlargement usually develops in advanced stages of the disease, indicating that the myocardium has suffered a loss of contractility. The greater the enlargement of the chamber, the higher the myocardial tension required. Impairment of myocardial function in the left ventricular wall results ultimately from the sustained load on that chamber and coincident myocardial ischemia. More than 90 per cent of the useful work of the normal left ventricle represents energy released in the form of pressure energy. Ventricular hypertension imposes a very great additional requirement for energy output by the contracting ventricular myocardium. The greater energy release requires more rapid delivery of oxygen to the myocardium when in fact aortic stenosis interferes with coronary blood flow.

Effects on Coronary Blood Flow. The quantity of blood perfusing the coronary arteries depends upon (*a*) the pressure gradient from the root of the aorta to the coronary veins and (*b*) the resistance to flow through these vessels, which depends upon the caliber of the vessels (see Chap. 9). In the normal heart, coronary blood flow is markedly diminished during ventricular contraction because the extravascular pressure compresses the coronary vessels. In advanced aortic steno-

sis, the intraventricular pressure greatly exceeds the pressure in the coronary arteries during each systolic interval. By this mechanism, intramural coronary vessels are emptied and systolic coronary flow is greatly retarded. Coronary blood flow should be normal or increased during diastole unless the coronary ostia are obstructed by an arteriosclerotic process. The increase in the diameter of the myocardial fibers increases the diffusion distance between the blood and the center of each cell, which would tend to retard the local delivery of nutrients and the elimination of metabolites. Thus, aortic stenosis requires an increase in the energy release of the left ventricular myocardium and simultaneously interferes with coronary blood flow while diffusion of oxygen is retarded by hypertrophy of the muscle fibers. Under these circumstances one would anticipate a high incidence of myocardial ischemia and infarction. Actually, precordial and anginal pain does occur, but the incidence is quite variable in reported statistics, ranging from 10 to 42 per cent of patients. About half of the patients with advanced aortic stenosis expire after one or more episodes of congestive heart failure. Relative myocardial hypoxia and ischemia no doubt play a role in diminishing myocardial contractility even though myocardial infarction occurs in a relatively small proportion of such cases.

Diagnosis of Aortic Stenosis

Auscultatory Signs. Forceful ejection of blood through a restricted orifice in the aortic valves produces turbulence and vibrations during systole. However, constriction of the orifice by only 15 to 30 per cent is enough to create audible vibrations.[14] A systolic murmur may be present for years before the aortic stenosis is sufficiently developed to impose any significant functional load on the left ventricle. The characteristic murmur of aortic stenosis is loud and rough and is

transmitted along the great vessels toward the neck and toward the apex of
the heart. These characteristics permit
differentiation of such murmurs from
the higher-pitched blowing murmurs of
"functional" origin which may be heard
in the aortic and pulmonary area. Pure
aortic stenosis does not produce a diastolic
murmur. However, many patients with
rheumatic aortic stenosis have both systolic and diastolic murmurs even though
regurgitation is not functionally significant.

Evidence of Left Ventricular Hypertrophy.
In its early phases, aortic stensosis usually
produces no roentgenographic signs of
left ventricular enlargement. Electrocardiographic signs of left ventricular preponderance appear in most cases. The
roentgenographic picture of concentric
left ventricular hypertrophy may be seen
in many such patients (see Chap. 13).
If the left ventricle becomes incapable of
effectively carrying the load, the outflow
tract of the left ventricle becomes elongated. When left ventricular dilatation
occurs in a patient with predominant
aortic stenosis, the clinical picture closely
resembles that of aortic insufficiency unless the characteristic changes in the peripheral arterial pulse can be demonstrated.

Changes in the Arterial Pulse. The arterial pressure pulse is normal until aortic
stenosis becomes sufficiently extensive to
seriously retard ejection of blood from the
left ventricle. When ejection into the
aorta is slowed, the amplitude of the pulse
wave is diminished. The pulse pressure
may be reduced so that the peripheral
pulse feels weaker than normal. The reduced pulse pressure and weak peripheral
pulse of aortic stenosis should be easily
differentiated from the opposite effects
observed with aortic regurgitation. Severe aortic stenosis and free aortic regurgitation can often be distinguished on this
basis. However, combined aortic stenosis
and regurgitation often results in a nor-

mal pulse pressure without distinctive
changes in the peripheral pulse.

Combined Aortic Stenosis and Insufficiency

Rheumatic valvulitis often produces
both stenosis and insufficiency. The functional significance of the stenosis or the
regurgitation cannot be estimated from
the intensity or character of the murmurs.

The systolic murmur of aortic stenosis
usually develops maximal intensity in
midsystole and the diastolic murmur is
loudest in early diastole (Fig. 7C). Free
aortic regurgitation without stenosis (lu-
etic aortic valvular disease) also causes
systolic and diastolic murmurs, but in
this disease the loudest vibrations often
occur early in the systolic interval. In
spite of theoretical differences, the murmurs of pure aortic insufficiency and of
aortic stenosis with slight regurgitation
often cannot be differentiated.

MITRAL STENOSIS

The clinical signs and symptoms of mitral valvular disease should be considered
in terms of the functional stresses imposed
by the deformed valves and the compensatory mechanisms evoked in response
to the load imposed on the circulatory
system. Although mitral stenosis and
regurgitation frequently occur together,
analysis is simplified by discussing them
individually.

Functional Anatomy of the Normal Mitral Valve

The anatomic relations of the mitral
valve were considered in Chapter 11. The
structure and functions of the mitral valve
in health and disease play such an important role in establishing the clinical
signs and symptoms of mitral valvular
disease that the specific functions of the
various component parts are currently receiving renewed attention.[22-25] Brock[25]
proposed a greatly simplified functional
description of the relation of the valves,

chordae tendineae and papillary muscles. The central portion of each mitral cusp is relatively unsupported by chordae tendineae. On either side of this central area (about 1 cm. from the midpoint) are the attachments of the thicker and stronger chordae tendineae which lie in the line of direct pull from the tip of the corresponding papillary muscles. These four sturdy tendons, two for each valve cusp, form the principal support for the central portion of the closed valve at the *critical areas of tendon insertion*. According to Brock, these critical areas have particular significance in the development of mitral stenosis (see below).

The Development of Mitral Stenosis

When the normal mitral valve is open, the valve cusps are separated and the chordae tendineae are spread out like a fan. During closure, the mitral cusps are held in firm apposition along their margins and the chordae tendineae become roughly parallel. The mitral aperture can become restricted either by adhesions developing along the areas of contact between opposing valve cusps or by fusion of the chordae tendineae. Both of these processes may play a role in the development of mitral stenosis. Rheumatic valvulitis most commonly produces thickening and fusion of the valve cusps from the region of the commissures toward the center of the mitral orifice. The edges of the cusps become thick, fibrotic and irregular. Viewed from the atrial side, the normally flexible valve is converted into a thickened funnel-shaped structure with a restricted orifice located eccentrically in the mitral ring (Fig. 8B). The degree of rigidity of the deformed mitral valve depends on the distribution of the thickening and fibrous proliferation. The restricted orifice caused by commissural adhesions impedes the flow of blood into the ventricles. The rigid, irregular valve margins probably fail to seal off the mitral orifice during systole, so that there is some regurgitation through the diseased valves. This general type of mitral stenosis occurs in about 85 per cent of such patients.

If the inflammatory process is concentrated in the chordae tendineae, they become fused together as indicated in Figure 8B. If the chordae tendineae are inseparably fused, the mobility of the mitral cusps is seriously restricted even if their flexibility is relatively unimpaired.[22, 25] This process may explain the development of "pure" mitral stenosis, with no regurgitation, since the mitral orifice could seal completely during systole. Fibrinous excrescences, such as those illustrated in Figure 3, may extend as webs or diaphragms down between chordae tendineae and later organize into fibrous tissue, lengthening the valve cusps. Both the valve cusps and the chordae tendineae may be involved to varying degrees by three processes: (*a*) fusion, (*b*) thickening and proliferation, and (*c*) retraction or shortening. A wide variety of end results can evolve from combinations of these three processes distributed unequally within the various portions of the valve and its adnexa.

In contrast to generally accepted concepts, Brock[25] suggested that fusion of the valve cusps begins near the insertion of the strongest chordae tendineae, at the two opposing "critical areas of tendon insertion." If adhesions developed at these areas, the hinge action of the valves would be immediately impaired since the central channel could not open widely. Even if the valve edges toward the periphery from these areas remained separate, they could not open widely and would probably become fused too.

Further evidence cited for this concept includes the fact that the mitral valve orifice is rarely greater than 1.5 by 0.75 cm. and rarely smaller than about 1 by 0.5 cm. The relative constancy of the valve aperture in mitral stenosis has been noted by Gorlin and Gorlin[27] and by Janton et al.,[28] but it could be explained on other

STENOSIS OF MITRAL VALVE

A. NORMAL MITRAL VALVE

OPEN

B. MITRAL STENOSIS

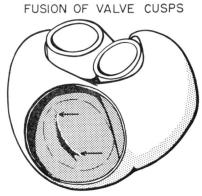

FUSION OF VALVE CUSPS

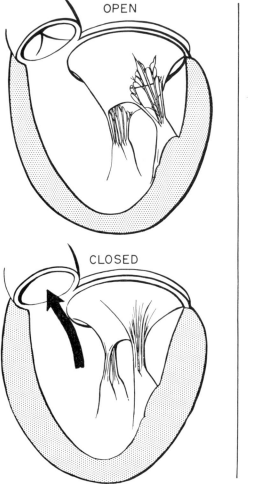

CLOSED

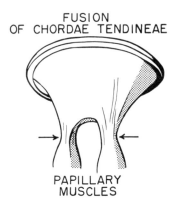

FUSION
OF CHORDAE TENDINEAE

PAPILLARY
MUSCLES

FIGURE 8.　*A,* When the normal mitral valve is open, the valve cusps gap and the chordae tendineae fan out. During ventricular systole, the valve cusps and chordae tendineae are forced together. Any process which holds the valve cusps or chordae tendineae in the closed position during ventricular filling produces mitral stenosis.

B, Mitral stenosis from recurrent rheumatic fever can result from either fusion of the valve cusps (above) or fusion of chordae tendineae (below). Generally, both processes occur in various degrees. The normally supple valve cusps tend to be converted into a thickened, rigid diaphragm when fusion along the commissures is the predominant deformity. If, on the other hand, adherence of the chordae tendineae is the primary pathologic process, the valve cusps may remain fairly flexible.

grounds (e.g., surgery is rarely indicated unless the mitral valve reaches 1.5 by 0.75 cm. and survival may not be common if the orifice is smaller than 1 by 0.5 cm.).

Functional Effects of Mitral Stenosis

The pressure gradient required to maintain a constant flow of fluid along a channel depends largely upon its caliber. The channel from the left atrium to the left ventricle is normally so spacious that the diastolic pressure gradient is difficult to demonstrate with available techniques. Since mitral stenosis is a local constriction at the mitral orifice, a greater pressure gradient is needed to sustain left ventricular filling. An increase in the pressure drop across a restricted mitral orifice represents a very large increase in the frictional energy loss in the flowing blood. Some of this energy loss is due to turbulence stemming from the high velocity with which the blood passes through the small aperture into the left ventricular chamber. The turbulence or vortex formation (see Fig. 16, Chap. 11) usually produces audible diastolic murmurs.

Since the work of the left ventricle is either normal or reduced, no ventricular compensation is required and the diastolic pressure is presumably normal. Gordon *et al*[29] found the mean left ventricular diastolic pressure to range between 3 and 11 mm. Hg, and the end diastolic pressures, between 2 and 15 mm. Hg. The pressure gradient from left atrium to ventricle through stenosed mitral valves varied from 4 to 20 mm. Hg before the orifice was expanded surgically, and diminished

thereafter in direct relation to the adequacy of the dilatation. An increased pressure gradient across the stenosed mitral valve requires an increase in left atrial pressure which is reflected back through the pulmonary veins, capillaries and arteries (see Fig. 10). Clearly, the principal functional disturbances produced by mitral stenosis are (*a*) increased blood pressure upstream from the site of the obstruction, resulting in pulmonary congestion and hypertension, and (*b*) turbulent flow through the mitral orifice, producing murmurs.

Gorlin and Gorlin[27] computed the magnitude of the pulmonary capillary or venous pressures required to provide a particular level of diastolic filling through mitral orifices with various areas (Fig. 9). As the area of the mitral valve orifice decreases below 2 sq. cm., pulmonary pressures must mount higher and higher to maintain a particular level of flow

PRESSURE DROP ACROSS STENOTIC MITRAL VALVES

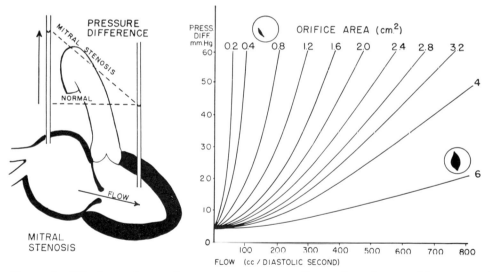

FIGURE 9.   Mitral stenosis necessitates a steep pressure gradient to force the normal increments of blood past the restricted orifice between the left atrium and ventricle. The magnitude of the pressure difference is related to the area of the effective mitral orifice, as indicated by the graph. If the mitral orifice is large, very rapid ventricular filling can result from a relatively slight increase in left atrial pressure. In contrast, the flow through extremely small orifices (0.2 or 0.4 cm.²) increases only slightly even when the pressure gradient reaches very high levels (after Gorlin and Gorlin[27]). Even though the computations are not universally accepted as quantitatively reliable (see text), this graph illustrates the important roles played by valvular orifice area and rate of blood flow in the production of pulmonary hypertension and congestion.

Table 1.   Relation of Valvular Cross-Sectional
Area to Clinical Symptoms in Patients
with Mitral Stenosis

CLINICAL CLASSIFI-CATION	MITRAL VALVE AREA (CM.^{2})	NUMBER OF PATIENTS	PHYSICAL ACTIVITY
I	2.5	1	Virtually unlimited
II	1.3-1.6	3	Some limitations
III	0.6-1.1	4	Very limited
IV	0.4-0.9	12	Bed and chair

through the valve. When the mitral orifice is smaller than 1 sq. cm., the blood flow is only slightly affected by pulmonary pressures ranging from 20 to 60 mm. Hg. Thus, at the smallest orifices illustrated in Figure 9, the flow is almost constant regardless of how steep the pressure gradients become. These investigators[27] also estimated the effective area of the mitral orifice from data obtained during cardiac catheterization and found a good correlation between the severity of the symptoms and the size of the mitral aperture (Table 1).

Considering the intimate relationship between pressure and flow through a restricted orifice, the functional effects of mitral stenosis should be predictable.

1. Progressive reduction in the area of the mitral orifice should be accompanied by higher and higher left atrial pressure.

2. More rapid blood flow (increased cardiac output) should be associated with a further increase in atrial pressure, e.g., during physical exertion. Severe mitral stenosis should limit the extent to which the cardiac output is increased during exercise.

3. Increased left atrial pressure must be accompanied by a corresponding increase in pulmonary venous and capillary pressure producing signs of pulmonary congestion which are accentuated whenever greater cardiac output is required.

4. After the pulmonary capillary pressure exceeds the osmotic pressure of the plasma proteins, the patients should develop pulmonary edema when the rate of capillary filtration exceeds the lymphatic drainage.[30]

5. Increased pulmonary capillary pressure calls for increased pulmonary arterial pressure since the normal pulmonary pressure gradient is very low. Such pulmonary hypertension imposes a severe pressure load on the right ventricle and produces right ventricular hypertrophy.

Some of the effects of mitral stenosis have been confirmed by direct measurements. When mitral stenosis becomes severe enough to produce symptoms, most patients have some elevation of pulmonary arterial pressure and low normal or subnormal cardiac output at rest. During exertion, the pulmonary hypertension tends to become greatly accentuated and the cardiac output fails to increase to the normal extent.[31-33] As so frequently occurs in clinical medicine, disturbing discrepancies are found between logical theory and direct observations. For example, Ball et al.[32] reported that intrathoracic blood volume in patients with mitral stenosis was no greater than normal even when the resting cardiac output was subnormal. Direct measurements of pulmonary arterial pressures by cardiac catheterization do not always correlate well with the severity of valvular lesions.[31] One cause of such discrepancies is the development of sclerosis in terminal arterial branches in the lungs (see below).

Response of the Left Atrium.   Contraction of the atrial wall reduces the capacity of the chamber and forces blood either into the left ventricle or into the pulmonary veins, depending upon which course offers less resistance. Myocardial fibers form an investment for the pulmonary veins extending some distance from the atrium. Contraction of these fibers should retard retrograde flow and promote forward flow into the left ventricle. The retrograde flow of blood into the pulmonary veins is further di-

minished by the high pressure in the pulmonary veins, which greatly reduces their distensibility. The atrial musculature must overcome a pressure load to which myocardial hypertrophy is the typical response.

Effects of Pulmonary Congestion. The pressure gradient from the pulmonary artery to the left ventricle is so slight that any elevation in left atrial pressure is reflected back through the entire pulmonary circuit. When the mitral orifice diminishes below some critical level, left atrial and pulmonary vascular pressures rise whenever the cardiac output increases. The increase in pulmonary pressure within a distensible vascular bed implies that the pulmonary vessels become engorged, simulating the effects of left ventricular failure (see Chap. 16).

Dyspnea. Quantitative measurements of circulatory and respiratory dynamics in patients with mitral stenosis indicate that the pulmonary congestion frequently decreases both vital capacity and maximal breathing capacity, but not to an extent which would account for the degree of respiratory disability.[34] From this type of information it can be inferred that the dyspnea associated with pulmonary congestion in mitral stenosis results predominantly from the mechanisms described in Figure 10, Chapter 16. As stenosis of the mitral valve progresses, pulmonary congestion follows smaller and smaller increases in cardiac output until dyspnea appears with mild physical exertion. Severe degrees of mitral stenosis result in elevated pulmonary pressures at rest, with very great pulmonary hypertension required to produce even slight increases in cardiac output (see Fig. 9). Limitation in cardiac output produces fatigue and dyspnea out of proportion to the degree of physical activity.

Pulmonary Sclerosis. Some of the discrepancies between the size of the mitral orifice and the severity of the symptoms may result from pathologic changes in the pulmonary vascular bed. Some patients with protracted severe mitral stenosis develop diffuse sclerotic changes in the terminal ramifications of the pulmonary arterial tree. The media also becomes thickened by a proliferation of smooth muscle which reduces the lumen of the vessels.[35] According to Henry,[36] such vascular changes occurred in 40 per cent of his patients with mitral stenosis and in none of his controls. The increased muscularity of the small pulmonary arteries is an expression of their sustained constriction, which produces a drop in the pressure of the blood just before it flows into the pulmonary capillaries. Under these circumstances, resistance is markedly increased in two different regions, in the pulmonary arteries and at the mitral valve. The pressure drop in the smaller pulmonary arteries diminishes the pulmonary capillary pressure, but also correspondingly diminishes the pressure gradient across the restricted mitral orifice (Fig. 10). Patients exhibiting this type of response to mitral stenosis have little or no dyspnea, but their physical activity is severely restricted since the cardiac output tends to remain fixed at the resting level. Oxygen consumption is increased almost exclusively by increased oxygen extraction, so intense fatigue on exertion is their principal complaint. Paul Wood[37] has described this type of response as a "protective pulmonary vasoconstriction" occurring in 12 per cent of his patients with mitral stenosis. Taquini *et al.*[38] found that 22 per cent of their patients with mitral stenosis followed a downhill course with early development of right ventricular failure which was associated with a very high pressure gradient between pulmonary arterial and pulmonary "capillary" pressure. In these patients, high arteriovenous oxygen differences and very low cardiac outputs were demonstrated.

Cyanosis. Visible cyanosis is commonly seen among patients with advanced

PULMONARY HYPERTENSION WITH MITRAL STENOSIS

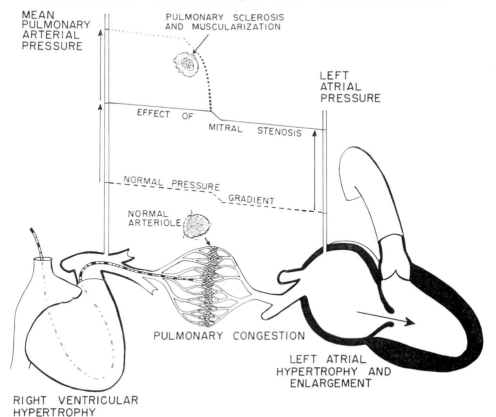

FIGURE 10. The resistance to flow through the normal pulmonary vascular tree is so slight that the gradient in mean pressures from pulmonary artery to left atrium ranges around 4 to 6 mm. Hg even at flow rates as high as 10 or 12 l. per minute. Mitral stenosis produces an elevation in left atrial pressure (see Fig. 9) which is reflected back along the entire pulmonary vascular bed. When pulmonary vascular pressure increases, pulmonary congestion usually follows. Sustained pulmonary hypertension appears to stimulate sclerosis and muscularization of the terminal pulmonary arteries and arterioles in about 40 per cent of patients with mitral stensosis (after Henry[36]), and greatly increases the resistance to flow through these narrowed channels in 12 to 20 per cent of such patients. The increased pulmonary arterial resistance produces severe hypertension in the pulmonary arteries, which imposes an even greater pressure load on the right ventricle. Under these conditions pressures recorded through a catheter wedged in a terminal pulmonary artery are much lower than in the main arterial trunk.

mitral stenosis. When the alveolar capillaries are distended with blood, the distance for diffusion of gases from the alveoli into the center of the blood stream is increased. Thickening of the alveolar walls and accumulation of extravascular fluid would also tend to retard oxygenation of the blood.[34] These factors presumably contribute to cyanosis appearing at rest. Limited increase in cardiac output requires an increased oxygen extraction and widened arteriovenous oxygen difference in the systemic capillaries during exertion. The increased oxygen extraction in the cutaneous capillaries may produce peripheral or "stagnant" cyanosis. A more comprehensive discussion of cyanosis will be presented in relation to congenital malformations of the heart (Chap. 14).

Hemoptysis. Acute, profuse hemoptysis occurs in some 10 per cent of patients with mitral stenosis.[39] It may appear at virtually any stage of the disease, but is more common when the disease process is advanced. The source of pulmonary hemorrhage probably lies in the rather unique relation between the bronchial and pulmonary circulations. The bronchial arteries are distributed to capillary beds in the walls of the bronchi. In most of the lung, the bronchial capillaries drain into the pulmonary veins. The elevated pulmonary venous pressure is reflected back into the bronchial capillaries, which also become congested. Rupture of small distended vessels in the bronchial mucosa is probably responsible for pulmonary hemorrhages and hemoptysis. The congestion of bronchial mucosa may also contribute to a productive cough occurring particularly after physcial exertion. Gilroy et al.[40] reported engorgement of pleurohilar veins, which drain into the systemic venous system, as well as distention of the true bronchial veins in some patients with mitral stenosis.

Right Ventricular Failure. The pulmonary arterial pressure is typically elevated by advanced mitral stensosis. Wood's[37] patients with mitral stenosis without significant pulmonary stenosis had mean pulmonary arterial pressures ranging around 35 mm. Hg and pulmonary "capillary" pressures about 20 mm. Hg at rest. Patients with the so-called "protective" hypertension had mean pulmonary arterial pressures of 50 to 60 mm. Hg. The right ventricle must pump against these increased outflow pressures, which constitutes a persistent pressure load. However, the right ventricle is poorly adapted for the role of a pressure pump. Thus, the terminal stage of mitral valvular heart disease is the advent of right ventricular failure with systemic venous congestion and peripheral edema by the mechanisms described in Chapter 16.

Diagnosis of Mitral Stenosis

Most patients are free of symptoms for many years after their final attack of acute rheumatic fever. During this per-

iod, the mitral orifice is presumably progressively restricted but exercise tolerance and physical well-being are not apparently affected. Among such patients are individuals with remarkable athletic prowess. The primary symptoms which ultimately develop are dyspnea on exertion and easy fatigability from pulmonary congestion and restricted cardiac reserve, respectively. Since subjective symptoms often appear late in the disease process, rheumatic valvular heart disease is frequently detected during routine examinations or protracted case studies of patients with known attacks of rheumatic carditis. For this purpose, auscultation is the most sensitive test.

Auscultatory Signs. The characteristic auscultatory manifestations of mitral stenosis are (a) accentuated first sound at the apex, (b) opening snap of the mitral valve, (c) accentuated second sound at the pulmonary area and (d) diastolic rumble at the apex. Not all of these signs are necessarily present in any one patient, and heart sounds and murmurs often change during recurrences of acute carditis.

Accentuation of the First Sound at the Apex. The apical first sound is frequently loud and snapping in the presence of mitral stenosis. The apparent increase in sound intensity may result from the higher frequency of vibration stemming from the more rigid valves.

Opening Snap. In some patients with mitral stenosis, a very brief, high frequency vibration is heard approximately 0.08 second after the principal elements of the second sound. This characteristic sound has been termed the "opening snap" of mitral stenosis because it seems to occur at the beginning of ventricular filling. The opening snap occurs slightly before the instant at which a third heart sound would be heard and can be distinguished from a third heart sound by its relatively high pitch.[41] The incidence of the opening snap varies according to

SIGNS OF MITRAL STENOSIS

A. ENLARGEMENT OF LEFT ATRIUM AND RIGHT VENTRICLE

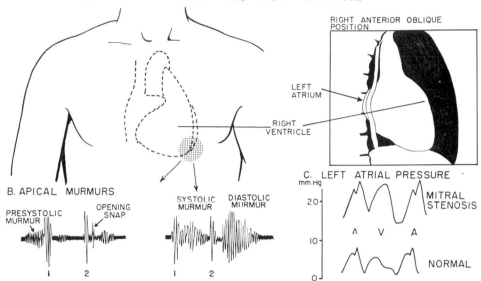

FIGURE 11.　*A*, The characteristic change in the cardiac silhouette produced by mitral stenosis is straightening of the left border viewed from the postero-anterior position (due to right ventricular hypertrophy). Left atrial enlargement, which occurs much earlier in the disease, can best be seen in the right anterior oblique position (see also Fig. 12, Chap. 13).

　　B, Ausculatory signs of mitral stenosis include presystolic murmurs which increase in intensity to end in a loud first heart sound; the opening snap, which is a brief high-frequency vibration occurring about 0.07 second after the second sound; a low frequency murmur during diastole; and often, a systolic murmur. (After Wells, B. G.: The graphic configuration of apical diastolic murmurs. *Brit. Heart J.*, 14:261–270, 1952.)

　　C, Direct pressure records from the left atrium demonstrate an elevated left atrial pressure. The form of the pressure waves is altered, producing a wide variety of patterns, but the taller pressure wave during ventricular systole (V) is frequently observed. (After Wynn, A., Matthews, M. B., McMillan, I. K. R., and Daley, R.[57])

different observers, but when present, is considered an important auscultatory sign of mitral stenosis. Mounsey[42] reported hearing an opening snap in 28 of 33 patients with mitral stenosis and finding phonocardiographic evidence in 4 more. This is a much higher incidence than is generally reported. The opening snap was heard best at a point just above and medial to the mammary region at the left sternal margin and at the mitral area. In 31 of 33 patients, Mounsey[42] found both splitting of the second sound and an opening snap. The two elements of a split sound occur within 0.07 second, which is very similar to the interval between a second sound and an opening snap. Acceleration of the heart rate tends

to reduce the interval between the second heart sound and the opening snap.[43] The typical diastolic murmur of mitral stenosis usually begins at about the time of the opening snap and the latter sound may persist when the diastolic murmur becomes equivocal or absent.

Accentuated Second Sound at the Pulmonary Area. The second sound in the pulmonary area is intensified when the pressure in the pulmonary artery is high, just as the aortic second sound tends to become louder during systemic hypertension. In most patients, other evidence of pulmonary hypertension and congestion can be elicited when the pulmonary second sound is accentuated.

Diastolic Murmurs. The turbulence re-

sulting from a rapid flow of blood through a stenotic mitral valve should produce an audible diastolic murmur. Theoretically, this murmur should be most intense during early diastole and during atrial contraction (presystole). Owing to the obstruction offered by the narrowed orifice, early diastolic filling is probably retarded so that flow persists throughout the diastolic interval. In other words, the period of slow filling or diastasis is utilized to permit more adequate ventricular filling. Thus, the diastolic murmur may persist throughout the entire ventricular filling period, being accentuated in early diastole and during atrial systole (Fig. 11). The resultant murmur is a low-frequency vibration or rumble, presumably because the relaxed left ventricular wall has a low natural frequency of vibration. The murmur usually is heard best in the vicinity of the precordial impulse, and may be accentuated when the patient lies on the left side. This position brings the apical portion of the left ventricle into better contact with the chest wall.

These characteristic murmurs of mitral stenosis may first appear many years after the last attack of acute rheumatic fever or, having once appeared, may regress and disappear completely.[8] According to Levine and Love,[44] 5 to 10 per cent or more of patients with mitral stenosis may have no audible diastolic murmur. There is little doubt that mitral stenosis may cause significant vibrations which are below the level of audibility. This can often be demonstrated by phonocardiographic equipment.[45]

In the past, mitral stenosis was rather confidently excluded if no apical diastolic murmurs were audible, and was diagnosed with some assurance if the typical apical diastolic rumble was detected. In view of recent evidence, neither of these attitudes is justified. Diastolic murmurs simulating those of mitral stenosis occur during initial or early attacks of rheumatic carditis and then disappear completely as the patient recovers. On the other hand, patients with definite mitral stenosis may have no audible diastolic murmurs.[44, 46] Incorrect diagnosis commonly results from excessive reliance on auscultatory signs of either mitral stenosis or mitral regurgitation.

Roentgenographic Signs. The changes in the size or shape of the cardiac chambers accompanying mild or moderate degrees of mitral stenosis are usually so slight that no evidence of chamber enlargement can be observed. In such patients, the cardiac silhouette appears normal from all angles in spite of the typical murmurs indicating mitral stenosis. Left atrial enlargement may not be demonstrable by roentgenographic examination even when it is marked. For example, Pariser et al.[47] reported that left atrial enlargement could not be demonstrated by fluoroscopy in 6 patients out of 30 who exhibited moderate to gross left atrial enlargement during postmortem examinations. In "pure" mitral stenosis, the left atrium may not be enlarged during the early stages,[48] presumably because this chamber compensates for the pressure load by hypertrophy. Similarly, mitral stenosis tends to retard left ventricular filling, so that the size of this chamber is usually normal or subnormal in the absence of heart failure, mitral incompetence or aortic disease, etc. Thus roentgenographic examination often fails to indicate enlargement of either the left atrium or the left ventricle in pure mitral stenosis. Jacobson et al.[49] preferred the left lateral to the right anterior-oblique position for the early detection of left atrial enlargement. Incompetence of the mitral valve accompanying mitral stenosis leads to dilatation of both the left atrium and the left ventricle (see Chap. 13). Persistent pulmonary hypertension causes right ventricular hypertrophy and accentuated pulmonary vascular markings in the lung fields, particularly in the hilar regions.

Intra-atrial Thrombosis.   Mural thrombi are a constant threat in patients with widely dilated atria, particularly when atrial fibrillation persists. The most immediate source of danger is systemic embolization, resulting from fragments of the clot lodging in vital organs. In some patients, the thrombus grows to progressively larger dimensions and, if strategically located, impedes blood flow through the atrium or through the already stenotic mitral orifice.

Atrial Fibrillation.   Fibrillation of the atria commonly develops when atrial chambers are enlarged, particularly from mitral valvular disease. Among patients with mitral stenosis, the resting cardiac output tends to be lower during atrial fibrillation than during normal sinus rhythm,[31] indicating that a coordinated atrial systole may contribute significantly to ventricular filling.

Electrocardiographic Signs.   When the left atrium becomes hypertrophied and dilated, the P waves usually are prolonged and have flattened or notched summits in lead I and to a lesser extent in lead II (see Chap. 10). This pattern is so typical that it is often termed P mitrale, even though it may occur in other conditions. Reynolds[50] recorded potentials directly from the atria during surgery on patients with mitral stenosis and found that the voltage from the left atrium was increased. Asynchronism of right and left atrial excitation was present in all tracings and was increased in patients with mitral stenosis. The initial peak is derived from the right atrium, and both the delay and the prolongation of left atrial excitation apparently produce the flattened or notched P waves.

Persistent pulmonary hypertension with right ventricular hypertrophy results in electrocardiographic evidence of right ventricular preponderance (see Chap. 10).

Cardiac   Catheterization.   Pulmonary hypertension can be detected by measuring the pressure through a cardiac catheter introduced into the pulmonary artery. Mean pulmonary arterial pressure is often elevated to 25 or 35 mm. Hg or more in patients with symptoms from mitral stenosis. Much higher pressures occur (over 55 mm. Hg) when sclerosis develops in the terminal branches of the pulmonary arterial tree (see Fig. 10). To determine the proportion of the pulmonary hypertension due to pulmonary sclerosis, the catheter is advanced until it wedges in a pulmonary arterial branch. Under these conditions, the pressure recorded through the tip of a wedged catheter is transmitted in a retrograde direction from contiguous vessels through which blood is flowing. Although such pressures are often termed "pulmonary capillary pressure," they are probably more closely related to pulmonary venous pressures.[51] Simultaneous measurements during cardiac surgery indicate that variations in the pressure in the pulmonary veins and left atrium are quite faithfully reflected in the wedged catheter. In some patients the vigorous atrial contraction produces an accentuated A wave on the records.

The resistance offered by the mitral orifice has been estimated by inserting the values for cardiac output and wedged catheter pressure in the formula: $R_{mv} = (PC_m \times 1.332 \times 60)/CO$, where R_{mv} is the resistance offered by the mitral valve, PC_m is mean "pulmonary capillary pressure" measured by a wedged catheter and CO is cardiac output. Formulae of this type are useful in summarizing data and making comparisons, but they are based on some assumptions which may introduce considerable error. For example, the true significance of the pressure recorded from a catheter wedged in a pulmonary artery is somewhat questionable. Further, the formula presented above implies that left ventricular pressure is zero. For such reasons, computed values using impressive formulae of this type are often purely qualitative and must not be taken too seriously.[52] More recently, techniques have been developed for inserting catheters into the left atrium and left ventricles. The pressure gradients across the mitral valve can be measured directly and the severity of the stenosis can be evaluated much more accurately.

MITRAL INCOMPETENCE

In the past, a diagnosis of mitral insufficiency was usually applied when an apical systolic murmur was too loud and persistent to be classified as "functional." Virtually all patients with acute rheumatic carditis develop systolic murmurs which persist for years. With no additional confirmatory evidence, such patients were labeled as having mitral insufficiency. Bland and Jones[8] reported the subsequent course of 87 patients with systolic murmurs on discharge from the hospital after their initial attack of rheumatic fever. Twenty years later, 7 had mitral stenosis, 16 had mitral stenosis with evidence of regurgitation, 35 had mitral regurgitation diagnosed primarily on the presence of the murmur, and 29 no longer had the systolic murmur. Clearly, the systolic murmurs so frequently discovered during initial attacks of acute rheumatic fever do not indicate significant mitral incompetence. Postmortem examinations on such patients are very rare and mitral incompetence cannot be reliably diagnosed by examining an excised heart unless the valvular deformity is severe. In most patients, the changes in the valves following acute rheumatic valvulitis are believed to heal quite completely although the systolic murmur often persists. On the basis of such evidence, the significance of apical systolic murmurs in rheumatic patients deserves reappraisal.

Types of Mitral Insufficiency

Mitral Misfit. Edematous thickening and verrucae, which develop along the valve margins during acute rheumatic fever (see Fig. 3), might prevent complete sealing of the valve cusps during ventricular systole. Spurts of blood between such vegetations theoretically could produce prominent systolic murmurs. Since reflux of such small quantities of blood would have no appreciable effect on cardiac function, it seems unwise to apply the ominous diagnosis of mitral incompetence; thus, the term "mitral misfit" is used above. However, these vegetations are largely resorbed after the acute phase of the disease has passed.

Functionally Significant Mitral Regurgitation. When mitral incompetence is encountered during cardiac surgery in adults, the valves have frequently become so fibrous and rigid that they resist both opening and closing. Even if the valves retain some flexibility, they may be rigidly restrained by grossly shortened chordae tendineae. In other patients, contraction of scar tissue in the valve cusps has so reduced their area that closure of the orifice would be impossible.

Some degree of mitral stenosis is almost always present unless the rigid orifice is extremely capacious. Extreme valvular incompetence does not coexist with serious stenosis. According to Brock,[25] mitral insufficiency is a more advanced stage of valvular deformity than mitral stenosis. Thus, "pure" rheumatic mitral insufficiency severe enough to have functional significance is probably a relatively rare lesion in which the heart functions as though there were no barrier between the left atrium and the left ventricle. On a theoretical basis, distinguishing between pure mitral stenosis and pure mitral insufficiency should be quite simple. In practice, this differentiation poses a most difficult diagnostic problem.

Functional Effects of Advanced Mitral Incompetence

In advanced mitral incompetence, filling of the ventricle is unimpeded, but during systole, blood is ejected simultaneously into the aorta and back into the left atrium. The rush of blood back through the mitral orifice into the capacious atrial chamber produces turbulence perceived externally as a widely transmitted systolic murmur usually with maximal intensity in the apical region. The stroke volume of the ventricle must be greatly increased to maintain arterial pressure and systemic blood flow. Under such a sustained volume load, the left ventricle should distend to much larger systolic and diastolic dimensions. The quantity of blood entering and leaving the left atrial cavity is correspondingly increased, so this chamber also labors under a volume load and should become dilated. Contraction of the dilated atrium might be expected to expel an abnormally large quantity of blood, increasing the terminal ventricular filling and also displacing a larger quantity of blood backward into the pulmonary veins. Furthermore, reflux of blood from the ventricle should exaggerate systolic expansion of the atrium, which would be associated with a second tall peak of pressure on the atrial pressure curve.

Based on this analysis, the principal signs of mitral incompetence should include (a) a loud systolic murmur in the mitral area, (b) dilatation of the left ventricle, (c) dilatation of the left atrium with augmented expansion during ventricular systole, (d) exaggerated pulmonary venous pressure waves during both atrial and ventricular systole, and (e) limited stroke volume and cardiac output reserve leading to fatigability. These symptoms may be clearly manifested in an occasional patient with functionally pure mitral incompetence. However, most patients with mitral insufficiency also have some stenosis, so the clinical picture becomes complicated.

Apical Systolic Murmur. Surprisingly enough, not all patients in whom a retrograde jet is palpated by the exploring finger of the surgeon during cardiac surgery have detectable systolic murmurs. For example, Elkin et al.[53] reported that 5

of 15 such patients had no systolic murmur. Venner and Holling[54] compared the clinical and surgical findings in 96 patients. Nine patients had widely incompetent mitral valves and systolic murmurs, but in one the intensity was no greater than that in persons with functional murmurs. Thirteen of 61 patients without palpable regurgitation had loud apical systolic murmurs. No distinguishing features between the systolic murmurs in patients with and in those without palpable regurgitation were noted. From these observations, systolic murmurs appear to be tenuous signs of mitral regurgitation, and other evidence must be sought.

Dilatation of the Left Ventricle. In the absence of aortic valvular disease, roentgenographic evidence of gross left ventricular enlargement facilitates differentiation of mitral insufficiency and mitral stenosis. In about half the patients with predominant mitral regurgitation, the left ventricular contour is not remarkable on either roentgenograms or fluoroscopic examination. Electrocardiograms provide evidence of left ventricular preponderance in about the same proportion, and in the remainder, right ventricular hypertrophy or combined ventricular hypertrophy may be indicated. Since rheumatic carditis often affects more than one valve, left ventricular enlargement can result from either mitral or aortic valvular disease. Other causes for left ventricular enlargement, such as heart failure, hypertension and myocardial infarction, must be kept in mind.

Dilatation of the Left Atrium. The atrium is dilated in a majority of patients with either mitral regurgitation or mitral stenosis. The force of a regurgitant jet of blood should exaggerate atrial expansion during ventricular systole. The expansile pulsation of the left atrium produced by ventricular systole seen during fluoroscopy is frequently cited as evidence of mitral insufficiency. When visualized, this sign is indeed highly suggestive of mitral insufficiency, but a word of caution seems warranted. The equivalent of mitral regurgitation occurs during early systole in normal individuals. During closure of the mitral valves, some blood probably leaks past the valve leaflets (see Chap. 11). As intraventricular pressure rises, the valves no doubt are displaced somewhat toward the atrium. The total effect should be a systolic expansion of the atrial chambers. For these reasons, abnormal systolic atrial pulsation may be mistakenly reported. Systolic pulsations are greatly damped by atrial distention because a very slight increase in circumference accommodates a relatively large volume. Indeed, increased systolic distention of the left atrium may not be seen by direct observation of the atrium during surgical exploration.[54] In spite of encouraging reports,[55] electrokymographic records are probably not greatly superior to fluoroscopic examination in eliciting this sign. For example, Soloff et al.[56] found that "plateau" curves, reported to be characteristic of left atrial border motion in organic mitral regurgitation, were obtained in 12 of 13 patients with an apical systolic murmur and also in 10 normal subjects.

Exaggerated Venous Pressure Waves.
A regurgitant jet of blood should produce a demonstrable increase in left atrial pressure which would facilitate diagnosis of mitral insufficiency. Unfortunately, direct measurements do not consistently demonstrate an abnormal pressure pulse.[54, 57] For example, Wynn et al.[57] directly recorded pressures in 14 patients with normal hearts and in 37 patients before and after mitral valvulotomy. In the 14 normal hearts, the atrial pressure rose 2 to 8 mm. Hg during atrial systole and 1 to 9 mm. Hg in late ventricular systole. In 8 patients with mitral stenosis and evidence of mitral incompetence, the form of the pressure pulse was not significantly different (Fig. 12). However,

the amplitude of the pressure peaks was somewhat greater in 7 patients with mitral stenosis and with mitral regurgitation, ranging from 3 to 19 mm. Hg; in one patient the systolic peak reached 25 mm. Hg.

An attempt has been made to differentiate between mitral stenosis and regurgitation by recording the pressures from a catheter wedged in a terminal pulmonary artery. Pressure contours diagnostic of mitral insufficiency were not found.[58] The elevations of pulmonary artery and wedged catheter pressures and exaggerations of waves are similar in mitral stenosis and mitral regurgitation.

Restricted Cardiac Output. Draper et al.[59] found that patients with both mitral stenosis and insufficiency had diminished cardiac output at rest. In response to exercise, the cardiac output remained essentially unchanged or even diminished slightly, the arteriovenous oxygen difference increased and a smaller proportion of oxygen was removed from the air exchanged in the lungs. The high pulmonary arterial pressure at rest rose further during exertion. They concluded that "physiological methods alone do not permit a clear differentiation between mitral stenosis and mitral insufficiency." Certain characteristic differences were noted. The resting cardiac output was lower and the arteriovenous oxygen difference was higher in patients with mitral regurgitation, who also more often displayed a reduction in cardiac output with exertion. These observations are consistent with the principal complaint of such patients: fatigue from very slight exertion.

The extent to which current diagnostic methods fail to evaluate correctly the nature and degree of mitral valvular disease was nicely summed up by Burchell and Edwards[60] as follows: "The exposure by the surgeon of the physician's incompetence in diagnosing mitral incompetence (insufficiency) has, in this era of mitral surgery, been more acutely em-

LEFT ATRIAL PRESSURE WITH MITRAL REGURGITATION

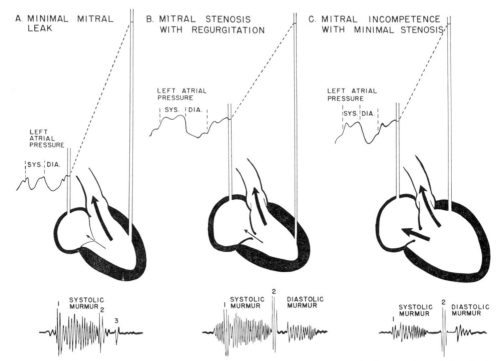

FIGURE 12. *A*, If the mitral valves fail to seal completely during ventricular systole, a high-velocity jet of blood regurgitates back into the atrium, because of the large pressure difference. Such a regurgitant stream may produce very loud systolic murmurs even though the amount of blood regurgitating is functionally insignificant. The pressure fluctuations in the left atrium retain the normal configuration under these circumstances. Since the circulatory load is minimal, the patient may have no symptoms or signs other than a loud systolic murmur maximally intense at the apex.

B, Many patients with mitral stenosis have some degree of mitral insufficiency even though the regurgitation is not functionally significant. Under these conditions, the left atrium tends to be enlarged, but the left ventricle remains small. The intensity of the systolic and diastolic murmurs is not a reliable indicator of the relative severity of regurgitation and stenosis of the valve.

C, Free mitral regurgitation imposes a severe volume load on both the left atrium and the left ventricle, which tend to become dilated. Elevated left atrial pressure tends to diminish the pressure gradient producing the regurgitation. The flow through a large mitral defect could theoretically produce less turbulence than could the high velocity jet flowing through a very small orifice. The left atrial pressure is elevated, and the pressure waves may indicate the presence of mitral valvular disease although they reveal no characteristic differences between patients with predominant stenosis and patients with serious incompetence.

barrassing to, and less easily forgotten by, the physician than the errors of diagnosis previously pointed out by pathologists. In the scramble to re-entrench themselves the internists have critically examined the traditional and new laboratory signs . . . "

PULMONARY VALVULAR INCOMPETENCE

The pulmonary valve is seldom affected by rheumatic valvulitis, and even then the functional effects are usually insignificant. The most common cause of pulmonary valvular incompetence is the dilation of the pulmonary artery which usually accompanies pulmonary hypertension. Patients with mitral stenosis or insufficiency characteristically have elevated pressures throughout the pulmonary vascular tree. Pulmonary arterial hypertension is greatly increased by pathologic changes in the lungs or by sclerosis in the terminal pulmonary arterial branches, as illustrated in Figure 10. Such pulmonary sclerosis is also caused by various congenital malformations of the heart which greatly increase pulmonary blood flow, including interatrial septal defects, patent ductus arteriosus and the Eisenmenger complex (see Chap. 14). Dilatation of the mainstem pulmonary artery may become sufficiently severe under these circumstances to induce widening of commissures between the pulmonary valve cusps and cause pulmonary valvular incompetence. The functional disturbances following dilatation of the pulmonary artery with commissural widening between the cusps correspond to those following syphilitic aortic insufficiency. The actual magnitude of the regurgitation is usually small even though the diastolic murmur may be prominent. The pulmonary arterial pressures are elevated. The right ventricle is generally hypertrophied by the antecedent pulmonary hypertension and assume some of the functional and anatomic characteristics of the left ventricle (thick wall and rounded chamber). Since murmurs both from pulmonary and from aortic valvular abnormalities may have maximum intensity in the third intercostal space to the left of the sternum, murmurs caused by pulmonary insufficiency cannot always be distinguished from those associated with aortic insufficiency or aortic stenosis with insufficiency. This is unfortunate, since they have very different significances. If pulmonary incompetence is mistaken for aortic insufficiency, a patient with stenosis of the mitral or aortic valves may be denied corrective surgery. The left ventricle should be greatly enlarged by aortic insufficiency, while the right ventricle is generally enlarged by pulmonary hypertension. The uncertainties of roentgenographic diagnosis are such that this distinction is not as clear-cut as it might seem (see Chap. 13). Ordinarily a dilated pulmonary artery can be clearly visualized as a prominent bulge on the left border of the mediastinum. Such a shadow should be considered carefully in evaluating the significance of systolic and diastolic murmurs heard at the base of the heart.

There is no need to dwell upon this condition beyond reiterating that its principal significance lies in identifying the cause of systolic and diastolic murmurs with maximum intensity at the base of the heart. Since pulmonary insufficiency frequently develops as a complication of pulmonary hypertension from other cardiac or pulmonary disease, an uncomplicated picture of simple pulmonary valvular incompetence is rarely encountered. The therapy consists of taking whatever measures are available to alleviate the pulmonary hypertension.

PULMONARY VALVULAR STENOSIS

Stenosis of the pulmonary valve is a rare condition, and most examples are found among patients with congenital malformations of the heart. Developmental defects in which pulmonary stenosis is associated with apertures in the septa of the heart are considered in Chapter 14.

TRICUSPID STENOSIS

The most common cause of tricuspid stenosis is rheumatic valvulitis. The incidence of tricuspid deformity associated with other valvular lesions is greater than is generally recognized. For example, O'Neill et al.[61] reviewed the literature and found that of 806 patients with valvular disease, 90 per cent had lesions in the mitral valve and 30 per cent had tricuspid deformities. The fact that mitral and tricuspid disease, without other valvular involvement, occurred in about 7 per cent of patients was considered important because of the similarity in the clinical signs of the two conditions. The diagnosis of tricuspid stenosis is rendered very difficult by the presence of mitral valvular disease, and may become evident only after mitral commissurotomy is followed by limited improvement in the patient's condition. Since the right atrium is not readily accessible through the surgical exposure used for mitral commissurotomy, lesions of the tricuspid valve cannot be detected and treated during routine operations on the mitral valve. For this reason, signs of functionally significant tricuspid valvular deformities should be ruled out as completely as possible preoperatively.

Functional Effects of Tricuspid Stenosis

A restricted tricuspid orifice impedes blood flow into the right ventricle and is compensated by elevated pressures in the right atrium and systemic veins. Thus, tricuspid stenosis produces elevated venous pressure and venous congestion upstream, but for reasons unknown, the splanchnic bed and liver are most seriously affected. Thus, ascites is more prominent than peripheral edema in patients with tricuspid valvular disease. The right atrium tends to become enlarged and hypertrophied. The powerful right atrial contraction produces very large atrial pressure waves which can often be directly observed in the jugular veins.

Diagnostic Signs of Tricuspid Stenosis

Patients with evidence of chronic valvular heart disease developing transient or constant ascites and peripheral edema with little or no sign of pulmonary congestion (e.g., dyspnea) should be carefully examined for tricuspid stenosis. The murmurs produced by mitral and tricuspid stenosis differ only in their distribution over the precordium. The diastolic murmurs of tricuspid stenosis tend to localize over the xiphoid process and toward the right of the lower sternum. However, the diagnosis is rarely made on the murmur alone. A vigorous pulsation of the jugular veins may be demonstrated as presystolic by palpating the carotid artery on the opposite side. Catheterization of the right atrium generally demonstrates the "giant" A wave, but since this occurs with pulmonary stenosis and tricuspid insufficiency as well, further exploration is required. A definite pressure drop between the right atrium and right ventricle is the most direct evidence of tricuspid stenosis. The therapy for this condition consists of commissurotomy just as in mitral stenosis.

TRICUSPID INSUFFICIENCY

Rheumatic tricuspid valvulitis is rarely severe enough to cause functionally significant incompetence and regurgitation. Thus, tricuspid insufficiency is generally the result of extensive right ventricular dilatation with expansion of the valve ring. Incompetence of the tricuspid valve is generally due to extensive disease in the heart and lungs, the signs or symptoms of which tend to overshadow the tricuspid lesion. It is often difficult to differentiate tricuspid insufficiency from tricuspid stenosis because they both accompany other cardiac disease states. Also, they both produce enlargement of the right atrium, increased atrial pressure waves, increased pressure and congestion in systemic veins and ascites. It may be possible to distinguish the two conditions on the basis of differences in the venous pulse,[62] but this is not absolutely reliable.

SUMMARY

In the past, a great deal of reliance has been placed on the character, timing and localization of murmurs to identify stenosis and insufficiency of the individual cardiac valves. Since the diagnosis generally could not be checked until a postmortem examination was performed, this method of valvular diagnosis was considered accurate. The advent of cardiac surgery has provided an opportunity to evaluate the diagnostic signs in the functioning heart. Since accurate preoperative diagnosis is exceedingly important in planning an optimal approach, the discovery of major or minor errors in diagnosis in 15 to 30 per cent of patients has prompted a re-examination of all possible diagnostic criteria.

Most disappointing of all has been the inconstancy of murmurs in the various valvular lesions. Murmurs may be completely absent or misleading in any of the different types of valvular deformities. It is now clear that all possible sources of information must be carefully evaluated to reach a judgment concerning the site and nature of valvular deformities. This situation results from two different factors: (a) rheumatic fever, the most common cause of valvular disease, usually affects more than one valve, and (b) individual valvular lesions are often difficult to differentiate from each other. For example, mitral stenosis is very often complicated by mitral insufficiency and the presence or degree of regurgitation cannot be accurately assessed even using every available technique including cardiac catheterization. Furthermore, the murmurs of mitral stenosis are easily confused with similar murmurs associated with aortic insufficiency and tricuspid stenosis. A marked pressure drop between the right ventricle and the pulmonary artery recorded during cardiac catheterization demonstrates a constriction in the outflow tract of the right ventricle due to either valvular or infundibular stenosis. In some patients, a distinction between these two types of pulmonary stenosis can be made. Techniques for inserting needles and tubes into the left atrium promise improved accuracy in diagnosing defects in the mitral and aortic valves.

REFERENCES

1. SOSMAN, M. C. Subclinical mitral disease. *J.A.M.A.*, 115:1061–1066, 1940.
2. WAKSMAN, B. H. The etiology of rheumatic fever: a review of theories and evidence. *Medicine*, Baltimore, 28:143–200, 1949.
3. JONES, T. D. The diagnosis of rheumatic fever. *J.A.M.A.*, 126:481–484, 1944.
4. BREESE, B. B., and GRAY, H. Antistreptolysin titer as an aid in the diagnosis of rheumatic fever. *New York J. Med.*, 51:389–391, 1951.
5. GROSS, L., and FRIEDBERG, C. K. Lesions of the cardiac valve rings in rheumatic fever. *Amer. J. Path.*, 12:469–493, 1936.
6. GROSS, L., and KUGEL, M. A. Topographic anatomy and histology of the valves in the human heart. *Amer. J. Path.*, 7:445–474, 4 pls., 1931.
7. SWIFT, H. F. Rheumatic heart disease. Pathogenesis and etiology in their relation to therapy and prophylaxis. *Medicine*, Baltimore, 19:417–440, 1940.
8. BLAND, E. F., and JONES, T. D. Rheumatic fever and rheumatic heart disease. A twenty year report on 1000 patients followed since childhood. *Circulation*, 4:836–843, 1951.
9. KUSCHNER, M., and LEVIEFF, L. Correlation between active rheumatic lesions in the left auricular appendage and elsewhere in the heart. *Amer. J. Med. Sci.*, 226:290–295, 1953.
10. SABISTON, D. C., Jr., and FOLLIS, R. H., Jr. Lesions in auricular appendages removed at operations for mitral stenosis of presumed rheumatic origin. *Johns Hopkins Hosp. Bull.*, 91:178–187, 1952.
11. SOLOFF, L. A., ZATUCHNI, J., JANTON, O. H., O'NEILL, T. J. E., and GLOVER, R. P. Reactivation of rheumatic fever following mitral commissurotomy. *Circulation*, 8:481–493, 1953.
12. WARNER, H. R., and TORONTO, A. F. Quantitation of backflow in patients with aortic insufficiency using an indicator technic. *Circulat. Res.*, 6:29–34, 1958.
13. GORLIN, R., McMILLAN, I. K. R., MEDD, W. E., MATTHEWS, M. B., and DALEY, R. Dynamics of the circulation in aortic valvular disease. *Amer. J. Med.*, 18:855–870, 1955.
14. WIGGERS, C. J. Dynamics of ventricular contraction under abnormal conditions. *Circulation*, 5:321–348, 1952.
15. ALEXANDER, R. S. Arterial pulse dynamics in aortic insufficiency. *Amer. J. Physiol.*, 158:294–302, 1949.
16. HEYER, H. E., POULOS, E., and ACKER, J. H. Electrokymographic studies in insufficiency of the aortic and pulmonic valves. *Circulation*, 1:1037–1048, 1950.
17. LUISADA, A. A. On the pathogenesis of the signs of Traube and Duroziez in aortic insufficiency. A graphic study. *Amer. Heart J.*, 26:721–736, 1943.
18. MAYNE, B. On aortic regurgitation. A new physical sign. *Irish J. Med. Sci.*, Ser. 6, No. 326:80–81, 1953.
19. GOULEY, B. A. The aortic valvular lesion associated with the Austin Flint murmur. *Amer. Heart J.*, 22:208–218, 1941.
20. BOAS, E. P. The evolution of calcareous aortic stenosis. *Geriatrics*, 8:142–150, 1953.
21. BAILEY, C. P., REDONDO-RAMIREZ, H. P., and LARZELERE, H. B. Surgical treatment of aortic stenosis. *J.A.M.A.*, 150:1647–1652, 1952.

22. RUSTED, I. E., SCHEIFLEY, C. H., EDWARDS, J. E., and KIRKLIN, J. W. Guides to the commissures in operations upon the mitral valve. *Proc. Staff Meet. Mayo Clin.*, 26:297–305, 1951.

23. RUSTED, I. E., SCHEIFLEY, C. H., and EDWARDS, J. E. Studies of the mitral valve. I. Anatomic features of the normal mitral valve and associated structures. *Circulation*, 6:825–831, 1952.

24. SOKOLOFF, L., ELSTER, S. K., and RIGHTHAND, N. Sclerosis of the chordae tendineae of the mitral valve. *Circulation*, 1:782–791, 1950.

25. BROCK, R. C. The surgical and pathological anatomy of the mitral valve. *Brit. Heart J.*, 14:489–513, 1952.

26. HARKEN, D. E., ELLIS, L. B., DEXTER, L., FARRAND, R. E., and DICKSON, J. F., III. The responsibility of the physician in the selection of patients with mitral stenosis for surgical treatment. *Circulation*, 5:349–362, 1952.

27. GORLIN, R., and GORLIN, S. G. Hydraulic formula for calculation of the area of the stenotic mitral valve, other cardiac valves, and central circulatory shunts. *Amer. Heart J.*, 41:1–29, 1951.

28. JANTON, O. H., GLOVER, R. P., and O'NEILL, T. J. E. Mitral commissurotomy in the older aged patient. An analysis of twenty patients over the age of fifty. *Circulation*, 8:321–327, 1953.

29. GORDON, A. J., BRAUNWALD, E., and RAVITCH, M. M. Simultaneous pressure pulses in the human left atrium, ventricle and aorta. Preliminary communication. *Circulat. Res.*, 2:432–433, 1954.

30. GORLIN, R., LEWIS, B. M., HAYNES, F. W., SPIEGL, R. J., and DEXTER, L. Factors regulating pulmonary "capillary" pressure in mitral stenosis. IV. *Amer. Heart J.*, 41:834–854, 1951.

31. FERRER, M. I., HARVEY, R. M., CATHCART, R. T., COURNAND, A., and RICHARDS, D. W., Jr. Hemodynamic studies in rheumatic heart disease. *Circulation*, 6:688–710, 1952.

32. BALL, J. D., KOPELMAN, H., and WITHAM A. C. Circulatory changes in mitral stenosis at rest and on exercise. *Brit. Heart J.*, 14:363–373, 1952.

33. GORLIN, R., HAYNES, F. W., GOODALE, W. T., SAWYER, C. G., DOW, J. W., and DEXTER, L. Studies of the circulatory dynamics in mitral stenosis. II. *Amer. Heart J.*, 41:30–45, 1951.

34. CURTI, P. C., COHEN, G., CASTLEMAN, B., SCANNELL, J. G., FRIEDLICH, A. L., and MYERS, G. S. Respiratory and circulatory studies of patients with mitral stenosis. *Circulation*, 8:893–904, 1953.

35. LARRABEE, W. F., PARKER, R. L., and EDWARDS, J. E. Pathology of intrapulmonary arteries and arterioles in mitral stenosis. *Proc. Staff Meet. Mayo Clin.*, 24:316–326, 1949.

36. HENRY, E. W. The small pulmonary vessels in mitral stenosis. *Brit. Heart J.*, 14:406–412, 1952.

37. WOOD, P. Pulmonary hypertension. *Brit. Med. Bull.*, 8:348–353, 1952.

38. TAQUINI, A. C., LOZADA, B. B., DONALDSON, R. J., D'AIUTOLO, R. E. H., and BALLINA, E. S. Mitral stenosis and cor pulmonale. *Amer. Heart J.*, 46:639–648, 1953.

39. THOMPSON, A. C., and STEWART, W. C. Hemoptysis in mitral stenosis. *J.A.M.A.*, 147:21–24, 1951.

40. GILROY, J. C., MARCHAND, P., and WILSON, V. H. The role of the bronchial veins in mitral stenosis. *Lancet*, 263:957–959, 1952.

41. ALIMURUNG, M. M., RAPPAPORT, M. B., and SPRAGUE, H. B. The auscultatory signs in rheumatic valvular disease. A phonocardiographic correlation. *New England J. Med.*, 244:1–9, 1951.

42. MOUNSEY, P. The opening snap of mitral stenosis. *Brit. Heart J.*, 15:135–142, 1953.

43. MESSER, A. L., COUNIHAN, T. B., RAPPAPORT, M. B., and SPRAGUE, H. B. The effect of cycle length on the time of occurrence of the first heart sound and the opening snap in mitral stenosis. *Circulation*, 4:576–580, 1951.

44. LEVINE, S. A., and LOVE, D. E. Mitral stenosis without murmurs. *Cardiologia*, 21:599–611, 1952.

45. JOHNSTON, F. D. The value of sound records in the diagnosis of mitral stenosis. *Amer. Heart J.*, 10:654–661, 1935.

46. BLAND, E. F., WHITE, P. D., and JONES, T. D. The development of mitral stenosis in young people. With a discussion of the frequent misinterpretation of a middiastolic murmur at the cardiac apex. *Amer. Heart J.*, 10:995–1004, 1935.

47. PARISER, S., ZUCKNER, J., TAYLOR, H. K., and MESSINGER, W. J. Mitral stenosis without clinically demonstrable left auricular enlargement. *Amer. J. Med. Sci.*, 221:431–439, 1951.

48. KUTTNER, A. G., and REYERSBACH, G. The value of special radiologic procedures in detecting cardiac enlargement in children with rheumatic heart disease. *Amer. Heart J.*, 18:213–227, 1939.

49. JACOBSON, H. G., POPPEL, M. H., HANENSON, I. B., and DEWING, S. B. Left atrial enlargement. The optimum roentgen method for its demonstration. *Amer. Heart J.*, 43:423–436, 1952.

50. REYNOLDS, G. The atrial electrogram in mitral stenosis. *Brit. Heart J.*, 15:250–258, 1953.

51. ANKENEY, J. L. Interrelations of pulmonary arterial, "capillary" and left atrial pressures under experimental conditions. *Amer. J. Physiol.*, 169:40–49, 1952.

52. Burton, A. C. Peripheral circulation. *Annu. Rev. Physiol.*, 15:213–246, 1953.

53. Elkin, M., Sosman, M. C., Harken, D. E., and Dexter, L. Systolic expansion of the left auricle in mitral regurgitation. *New England J. Med.*, 246:958–961, 1952.

54. Venner, A., and Holling, H. E. Comparison of operation and clinical findings in mitral stenosis and incompetence. *Brit. Heart J.*, 15:205–213, 1953.

55. Fleischner, F. G., Abelmann, W. H., and Buka, R. The value of the atrial electrokymogram in the diagnosis of mitral regurgitation. Observations on patients with rheumatic mitral stenosis before and after mitral valvuloplasty. *Circulation*, 10:71–80, 1954.

56. Soloff, L. A. Zatuchni, J., and Stauffer, H. M. The atrial border electrokymogram in mitral regurgitation. *Circulation*, 6:96–102, 1952.

57. Wynn, A., Matthews, M. B., McMillan, I. K. R., and Daley, R. The left auricular pressure pulse in normals and in mitral valve disease. *Lancet*, 2:216–219, 1952.

58. Connolly, D. C., Lev, R., Kirklin, J. W., and Wood, E. H. Pulmonary artery wedge pressures in mitral valve diseases; relationship to left atrial pressure. *Fed. Proc.*, 12:28, 1953.

59. Draper, A., Heimbecker, R., Daley, R., Carroll, D., Mudd, G., Wells, R., Falholt, W., Andrus, E. C., and Bing, R. J. Physiologic studies in mitral valvular disease. *Circulation*, 3:531–542, 1951.

60. Burchell, H. B., and Edwards, J. E. Rheumatic mitral insufficiency. *Circulation*, 7:747–756, 1953.

61. O'Neill, T. J. E., Janton, O. H., and Glover, R. P. Surgical treatment of tricuspid stenosis. *Circulation*, 9:881–885, 1954.

62. Messer, A. L., Hurst, J. W., Rappaport, M. B., and Sprague, H. B. A study of the venous pulse in tricuspid valve disease. *Circulation*, 1:388–393, 1950.

Chapter 13

THE SIZE AND CONFIGURATION OF THE HEART

I. Estimation of Heart Size

Most forms of organic heart disease produce a chronic load on the heart. If the stress is sufficiently intense and prolonged, the heart enlarges during the course of the disease. Massive enlargement of cardiac chambers can usually be recognized easily, but a diagnosis at this stage is of limited value to the patient since opportunities for preventive therapy have been lost. During the early stages of heart disease when accurate diagnosis has maximum value, the size and configuration of the heart generally remain within the "normal range." Detecting enlargement of a specific portion of the heart would be very simple indeed if its size, configuration and orientation were constant in all normal individuals. Unfortunately, there are many sources of variation in these factors. Small degrees of enlargement can be discovered only by considering whether the size and shape of the heart are normal for the particular patient. Such a judgment requires constant awareness of the sources of variation in cardiac size and configuration, supplemented by experience in evaluating the "normal range" encountered in patients of different habitus, age and sex. This decision must also be based on supplemental information derived from the clinical history, physical examination and laboratory tests. Since an incorrect diagnosis of heart disease may produce invalidism or cardiac neurosis, recogniz-

368

ing normality and detecting abnormality have equal importance. Therefore, the limitations of any diagnostic method must be fully understood.

Orientation of the Heart Within the Thorax

A major source of variation in apparent heart size is the fact that the heart occupies an asymmetrical position within the thorax. The septa which divide the atria and ventricles are oriented between the sagittal and frontal planes of the thorax. A frontal view of the heart (Fig. 1A) discloses the right atrium, right ventricle, pulmonary conus and aortic arch with a small portion of the left ventricle appearing on the left border. On the posterior aspect of the heart lie the remainder of the left ventricle, the left atrium and a portion of the right atrium. A transverse section through the thorax (Fig. 1B) indicates the relation of the heart and the thoracic walls. The cardiac chambers are separated from the anterior and lateral thoracic walls by varying amounts of lung tissue except near the apex of the heart. Here the right ventricle near the interventricular groove makes contact with the precordium.

THE POINT OF MAXIMAL IMPULSE

During early systole in most individuals, a circumscribed thrust appears in the fifth intercostal space near the left mid-clavicular line (Fig. 2). The origin of this impulse has long been attributed to the impact of the ventricles as the heart rotates during contraction. A more reasonable explanation was proposed in 1891 by Haycraft,[1] who observed that the flaccid ventricular chambers are easily deformed during diastole. At the beginning of systole, the contracting ventricular walls suddenly assume a more rounded contour and recoil away from the area of compression. The free wall of the right ventricle near the apex of the heart is in contact with the anterior chest wall (Fig. 1B). This portion of the ventricle is flattened during diastole, and abruptly becomes convex during the subsequent ventricular contraction. This action causes forward displacement of intercostal tissues near the apex of the heart—the so-called *apical thrust*. Burchell and Visscher[2]

THE ORIENTATION OF THE HEART WITHIN THE THORAX

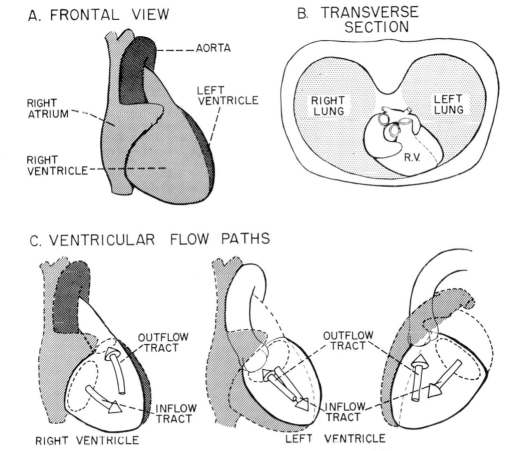

A. FRONTAL VIEW

AORTA

LEFT VENTRICLE

RIGHT ATRIUM

RIGHT VENTRICLE

B. TRANSVERSE SECTION

RIGHT LUNG

LEFT LUNG

R.V.

C. VENTRICULAR FLOW PATHS

OUTFLOW TRACT

INFLOW TRACT

RIGHT VENTRICLE

OUTFLOW TRACT

INFLOW TRACT

LEFT VENTRICLE

FIGURE 1. *A*, In the frontal view, the right atrium is situated on the right side with the right ventricle on the anterior surface. A small portion of the left ventricle appears on the left border. The superior vena cava, aorta and pulmonary artery are grouped above the heart in the upper mediastinum.

B, Viewed from above, the heart occupies an oblique position within the thorax with the right ventricle making contact with the anterior thoracic wall to the left of the midline.

C, Blood entering the ventricular chambers tends to flow from the atrioventricular valves toward the apex of the heart. This inflow tract in each ventricle is indicated by an arrow drawn from the center of the A-V valves to the apex. The outflow tract is described by an arrow extending from the apex of the ventricle to the center of the corresponding semilunar valve. In the right ventricle the inflow tract makes an angle of more than 45 degrees with the outflow tract. In contrast, the left ventricular inflow and outflow tracts are almost parallel owing to the cylindrical shape of the chamber.

DISPLACEMENT OF THE CARDIAC IMPULSE BY VENTRICULAR ENLARGEMENT

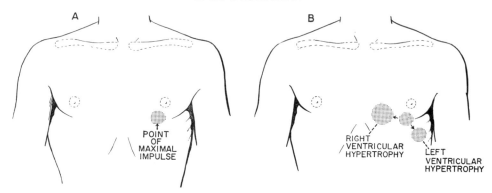

FIGURE 2.   *A,* During each cardiac contraction, a thrust can be observed and palpated in a small area on the precordium, located in the fifth intercostal space medial to the mid-clavicular line in the average normal individual.

B, The point of maximal impulse is displaced downward and to the left by elongation of the left ventricle. The right ventricle enlarges anteriorly toward the sternum and produces a diffuse impulse over a considerable area between the mid-clavicular line and the sternum (see Fig. 1*B*).

demonstrated by high-speed motion pictures that the inflow tract of the right ventricle contracts before the outflow tract, so that blood is first shifted from the inflow tract into the outflow channel and then ejected into the pulmonary artery.

It is generally stated that the point of maximum impulse is approximately 1 cm. to the right of the cardiac apex. However, it is clear that the distance between the point of maximal impulse and the apex of the heart must depend upon the site of contact between the anterior surface of the heart and the anterior thoracic wall (see Fig. 1*B*). Thus, the configuration of the heart and anterior thoracic wall must have an important bearing on the position of the cardiac impulse. The point of maximal impulse may be imperceptible in patients with emphysema or very thick chest walls.

It is frequently stated that whenever the point of maximal impulse lies to the left of the mid-clavicular line or more than 10 cm. to the left of the midline, the heart is probably enlarged. Actually, this is a sign of left ventricular enlargement. However, the point of maximal impulse does not bear a constant relation to the apex of the heart, so no rule of thumb can be safely used to describe the limits of normal. The location of the point of maximum impulse must be interpreted in terms of the individual's habitus as well as of other causes of variation in the orientation and size of the heart. These will be discussed below (see *Roentgenographic Examination of the Heart*). Massive ventricular enlargement may displace the apical impulse enough to provide a definite indication of abnormality. For example, a point of maximal impulse located at the left anterior axillary line or in the axilla is a reliable sign of left ventricular enlargement. Under these circumstances there should be other obvious signs of advanced heart disease. Lesser degrees of ventricular enlargement may be missed or overemphasized, and should be confirmed by roentgenographic examination. When the right ventricle becomes enlarged, it tends to protrude anteriorly toward the sternum. Under these conditions a diffuse precordial impulse may be palpated over a fairly wide area to the left of the sternal margin. Progressive enlargement of the right ventricle in young children often produces a protuberance of the left precordium.

PERCUSSION OF THE HEART

The technique of percussion was originated by Leopold Auenbrugger (1761) as a result of the observation that the quantity of wine in a barrel can be estimated by tapping the end and noting the resonance.[3] When a sharp tap is delivered to the thoracic wall, the underlying tissues are suddenly displaced. Due to their elasticity, they rebound and oscillate while the imparted energy is dissipated. The ensuing vibrations have four characteristics important in percussion: (1) frequency, (2) quality, (3) duration and (4) intensity (see Chap. 11). The frequency of vibration depends upon the elasticity of the structures in relation to the mass of tissue in vibration, which in this case includes tissues of varying density and elasticity (e.g., muscle, fat, bone, lung).

The vibrations produced by percussion over a well inflated lung appear to have

relatively high intensity (loudness), low frequency (pitch) and long duration (resonance). A region of "absolute dullness" may be outlined over the precordium (Fig. 3). The percussion note over this area has relatively low intensity, high pitch and short duration (reduced resonance). Extending beyond the region of absolute dullness is an area of relative dullness which approximately delineates the heart borders (Fig. 3). The area of relative dullness is not sharply defined. The rounded surfaces of the heart do not conform to the anterior thoracic wall (see Fig. 1B) and the heart borders outlined by percussion tend to be smaller than the silhouette observed on roentgenograms by 1.0 to 1.5 cm. or more.

Percussion combined with palpation of the point of maximal impulse has value as an adjunct in arriving at a clinical impression. They are not suitable for detecting early cardiac enlargement because their inaccuracy is superimposed upon the normal variability in cardiac size and configuration. Advanced enlargement of the left ventricle can often be detected with confidence. However, a patient with other signs of heart disease should not be denied roentgenographic examination just because the heart size seems normal from percussion of the precordium or palpation of the precordial impulse.

ROENTGENOGRAPHIC EXAMINATION OF THE HEART

When x-rays penetrate the chest, absorption of the radiation depends upon the effective radiodensity of the tissues lying in the path of each ray. The heart has greater radiodensity than the aerated lung. Roentgen rays which are not absorbed during penetration of the tissues can be used to illuminate a fluorescent screen (fluoroscopy) or to expose a photographic plate clamped between fluorescent intensifying screens in a cassette (Fig. 4). X-ray films are routinely exposed with the tube at a distance of 2 m.

PERCUSSION OF THE HEART BORDERS

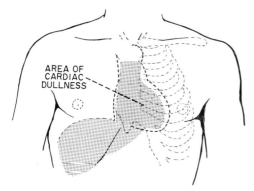

AREA OF CARDIAC DULLNESS

FIGURE 3. The size of the heart can be approximated by skilled percussion over the precordium. The region of dullness to percussion is always smaller than the actual size of the heart because of its rounded contour (see Fig. 1B). Severe cardiac enlargement consistently produces expansion of the area of dullness, but minor degrees of enlargement cannot be reliably detected.

METHODS OF ROENTGENOGRAPHY

A. TELEROENTGENOGRAPHY

B. FLUOROSCOPY   C. CINEFLUOROGRAPHY

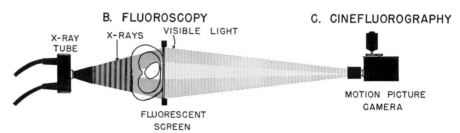

FIGURE 4.   As x-rays penetrate the body, the tissues absorb the rays in relation to their radiodensity. The rays which penetrate the body delineate the borders of internal organs on either x-ray films or the surface of a fluorescent screen.

A, Teleroentgenograms are x-ray plates exposed with the tube 6 ft. or 2 m. from the x-ray film. At this distance, the distortion of the heart size by the diverging rays is not misleading.

B, Fluoroscopy is accomplished by observing directly the visible light emitted by fluorescent screens exposed to x-rays. The tube is fairly close to the screen and the image of the heart is enlarged about 15 to 20 per cent by the diverging rays.

C, Cinefluorography involves motion picture photography of the images on fluorescent screens. Examples of cinefluorographic recordings have been presented in Chapter 2 (see Figs. 10 and 14).

from the film cassette and are identified as teleroentgenograms (*tele* = distance). The image of the cardiac silhouette on a fluorescent screen may be recorded by motion picture photography, cinefluorography.[4-6] Regardless of the technique, roentgenography serves to reveal the size and configuration of the cardiac silhouette as projected on a single plane.

Cardinal Positions for Cardiac Roentgenography

Since the heart appears as a silhouette on either roentgenographic plates or fluoroscopic screen, only those portions which appear on the borders can be observed. Obviously, not all the chambers can appear on the borders in any one view. For this reason a complete roentgenographic examination of the heart requires studying the cardiac silhouette from several views. Three standard positions are commonly used by cardiologists

—the postero-anterior, the left anterior oblique and the right anterior oblique positions. In each exposure the cassette or fluorescent screen is perpendicular to the central ray emitted by the tube. In the postero-anterior position, the patient stands squarely before the screen or cassette with the front of his chest pressed evenly and firmly against it (Figs. 5*B* and 6*B*). This is the most common position for cardiac and pulmonary roentgenography. The left anterior oblique view is attained by rotating the patient approximately 50 degrees so that his left shoulder is toward the screen or cassette (Figs. 5*A* and 6*A*). A patient facing the screen is rotated 45 degrees so that his right shoulder is toward the screen to view the heart in the right anterior oblique position (Figs. 5*C* and 6*C*). Rotating the patient 90 degrees from the postero-anterior position presents the lateral view, which is frequently employed by roentgenol-

THREE STANDARD POSITIONS FOR CARDIAC ROENTGENOGRAPHY

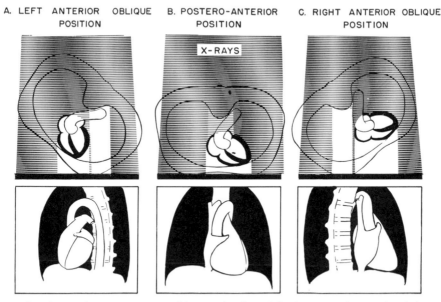

A. LEFT ANTERIOR OBLIQUE POSITION   B. POSTERO-ANTERIOR POSITION   C. RIGHT ANTERIOR OBLIQUE POSITION

FIGURE 5. A complete roentgenographic examination of the heart requires study of the cardiac silhouette in three positions. The orientation of the heart in each position is indicated schematically in a transverse section and on a teleroentgenogram. For labels see Figure 6.

A, To assume the left anterior oblique position, the patient turns with his left shoulder toward the x-ray cassette until the sagittal plane of his body makes an angle of 50 degrees.

B, In the postero-anterior position, the sagittal plane of the body is parallel with the cassette, which is in firm contact with the anterior thoracic wall.

C, In the right anterior oblique position, the patient rotates his right shoulder toward the cassette or screen until the sagittal plane of the body makes an angle of 45 degrees.

THE CARDIAC SILHOUETTE IN THREE STANDARD POSITIONS

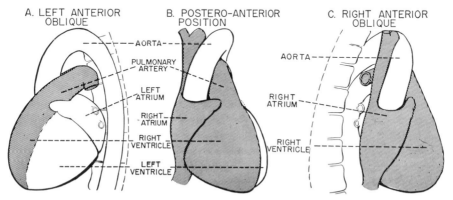

A. LEFT ANTERIOR OBLIQUE   B. POSTERO-ANTERIOR POSITION   C. RIGHT ANTERIOR OBLIQUE

FIGURE 6. *A,* The left anterior oblique position is best suited to determine the extent to which either the right or the left ventricle is enlarged, since they appear on opposite borders of the cardiac silhouette. The aortic arch is also best observed in this view.

B, In the postero-anterior position neither the right ventricle nor the left atrium is represented on the borders of the cardiac silhouette. However, enlargement of the left ventricle or right atrium is best seen in this view.

C, The right anterior oblique position provides the best view for demonstrating dilatation of the left atrium.

ogists but not as commonly used by cardiologists.

Postero-anterior Position. When the heart is viewed in the postero-anterior position (Figs. 5*B* and 6*B*), the rounded outline of the right atrium appears in the lower half of the right border of the heart. The junction between the right atrium and the superior vena cava is indicated by an obtuse angulation. Slight rotation of the patient to the right may expose the first portion of the ascending aorta just above the right atrial border. The upper half of the right border of the heart generally corresponds to the border of the superior vena cava and the brachiocephalic vessels. The ascending aorta, passing obliquely upward and to the right across the upper mediastinum, is not visible in the postero-anterior position. The uppermost portion of the aortic arch appears as a knob on the left border of the cardiac silhouette just below the level of the sternoclavicular junction. Below the aortic knob and extending to approximately the midpoint of the left border of the heart is the pulmonary artery. Along the lower half of the left border is the shadow of that portion of the left ventricle near the interventricular groove. There is usually a slight angulation at the junction between the pulmonary artery and the left ventricular shadow, which is called the cardiovascular angle. During systole, the segments above and below the cardiovascular angle tend to move in opposite directions because the pulmonary artery is distended as the ventricles contract. The point of opposite pulsation at the apex of the cardiovascular angle is an important landmark during fluoroscopy (see Fig. 8). In some cases the tip of the left auricle appears at the cardiovascular angle, but its position or movement is not apparent.

Left Anterior Oblique Position. When a patient is rotated to the left anterior oblique position (Figs. 5*A* and 6*A*), the right and left ventricles are on opposite sides of the silhouette and their relative sizes can be appraised. An angulation of the silhouette near the mid-point of the sternal margin of the heart represents the juncture of the right ventricular outflow tract with the root of the ascending aorta. The entire arch of the aorta is sometimes visible in this view although it may be obscured by such dense overlying structures as the scapula and the vertebral spine. The left atrium occupies a position between the base of the left ventricle and the bifurcation of the pulmonary artery. This portion of the border is also partially obscured by superimposed structures.

Right Anterior Oblique Position. In the right anterior oblique position, the outflow tract of the right ventricle appears on the sternal border of the heart. The ascending aorta appears in profile in the superior half of the cardiac shadow. The left atrium occupies a position near the center of the vertebral aspect of the cardiac silhouette with the right atrial border just below. If the patient is properly oriented, a region of low density appears between the posterior aspect of the heart and the vertebral spine, the retrocardiac space. The esophagus passes down the posterior mediastinum and is in apposition with the left atrium along its course. The esophagus filled with a radiopaque mixture of barium outlines the left atrial border and its motion can be clearly observed fluoroscopically. The right anterior oblique view is particularly useful for detecting early dilatation of the left atrium (see Fig. 13).

Sources of Variation in the Cardiac Silhouette

Roentgenographic interpretation is complicated by a number of factors which are not necessarily related to cardiac size or function. Certain of these conditions cause the normal heart to appear large. Others tend to cause an enlarged heart to appear normal in size. For this reason it is convenient to speak of the "apparent" size when considering the sources of variation in the cardiac silhouette. The sources of variation in the cardiac silhouette can be divided into two main categories: (*a*) individual variation and (*b*) technical variation. By careful standardization of the roentgenographic technique, technical variation can be largely eliminated. Individual variation must be recognized by the physician and evaluated in each case.

Individual Variation. The most important initial step in the roentgenographic examination of a patient is to visualize the "normal" range of cardiac size and configuration for a person with his particular habitus and extracardiac conditions. Proficiency in this essential feature of the examination is gained only through experience. Sound judgment can be developed simply by taking advantage of every opportunity to correlate the roentgenographic appearance of the heart with the habitus and cardiac condition of patients.

Habitus. In asthenic individuals, the thoracic cavity is long and narrow so that the long axis of the ventricles approaches a vertical orientation (Fig. 7). The cardiac silhouette is narrow and the left border may lie several centimeters inside the mid-clavicular line. Enlargement of the heart tends to restore the apparent cardiac size toward the normal configuration. In patients of this sort, a considerable degree of left ventricular enlargement is required to bring the left border of the heart to the mid-clavicular line, which is within the "normal" range for the average individual. For this reason, early ventricular enlargement is frequently overlooked in patients in whom the resting position of the diaphragm is lower than average.

In contrast, a patient with a stocky build characteristically has an elevated diaphragm (Fig. 7). When the longitudinal axis of the heart approaches a horizontal position, even a heart of normal size may appear enlarged. In such a patient the pulmonary markings are accentuated, the cardiovascular angle is more acute, and the apex of the heart is displaced toward the left. In short, such a normal individual could easily be mistaken for a patient with serious left ventricular enlargement and pulmonary congestion. Thus, an important step in roentgenographic interpretation is determining the habitus of the patient and the relative height of the diaphragm. For this purpose, it is convenient to establish the level of the dome of the diaphragm in relation to the costovertebral junctions (Fig. 7).

Variation in Patients with the Same Habitus. Individual variation is a constant problem in anatomy, physiology and clinical medicine. The cardiac silhouettes of different patients of similar age, sex, habitus and physical condition may vary rather strikingly. These changes may be explained in terms of the orientation of the heart within the thorax or of developmental variations of the heart, lungs or thoracic cage. Obviously, individuals in different age groups with the same type of habitus may have significantly different cardiac silhouettes. Again, wide experience is the most important factor in this type of evaluation.

The Phase of the Cardiac Cycle. Teleroentgenograms are generally exposed during a very brief period of time (e.g., one-fifth to one-sixtieth of a second). Since the diastolic interval is somewhat longer than the duration of systole, more than half of a series of teleroentgenograms will be exposed during diastole. However, more than one-third of the teleroentgenograms are exposed during some phase of systole. Fortunately, the change in the size and shape of the cardiac silhouette during the cardiac cycle is rarely sufficient to produce any serious error from this source (see Fig. 8).

The Pericardial Fat Pad. In many normal individuals, a triangular shadow

THE EFFECTS OF HABITUS AND POSITION ON THE CARDIAC SILHOUETTE

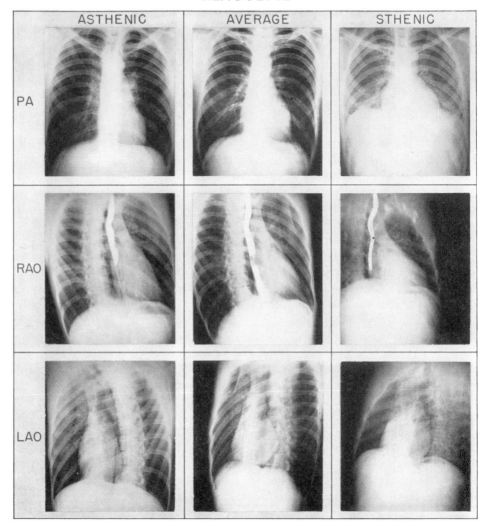

FIGURE 7.   Roentgenograms obtained on three normal individuals of different habitus in the three cardinal positions indicate the variation in the shape and apparent size of the normal cardiac silhouette.

In asthenic individuals the thorax is long and narrow so the heart assumes a vertical position. The cardiac silhouette is so narrow that severe enlargement of the heart may be overlooked in such patients.

If all patients had average habitus, criteria for enlargement of the individual chambers could be easily established and slight changes could be consistently detected.

In sthenic individuals, the high diaphragm supports the heart in a horizontal position. The wide cardiac silhouette gives the impression of left ventricular enlargement, and accentuation of the pulmonary vascular markings suggests pulmonary congestion. These factors must be constantly evaluated in analyzing roentgenographic images.

Note that the right dome of the diaphragm in the three individuals is at the level of the eleventh tenth and eighth costovertebral junctions, respectively.

appears at the apex of the heart which is due to the accumulation of fat in this region. Elongation of the left ventricular outflow tract and displacement of the apex downward and to the left might be erroneously suspected unless the region is carefully scrutinized. It is generally possible to detect the apical border passing through the shadow of the pericardial fat pad.

Displacement of the Heart. The heart does not always occupy its normal position within the thorax. For example, the heart may be displaced toward the left either by atelectasis in the left lung or pressure pneumothorax in the right pleural cavity. In either case, the left border of the heart moves toward the left and the right border may overlie the spine. If the pulmonary condition is unrecognized, cardiac enlargement may be incorrectly suspected.

Deformities of the Thorax. If the lower end of the sternum is depressed (funnel chest), the distance between the sternum and the vertebral spine is reduced. The heart may be compressed in its postero-anterior dimension and displaced toward the left. The left border of the heart may become rounded, giving the impression of ventricular enlargement.

In kyphoscoliosis, the abnormal curvature of the vertebral spine may produce cardiac displacement as well as a change in the "apparent" cardiac configuration. The border of the curved vertebral spine may be confused with the cardiac silhouette, giving an impression of cardiac enlargement.

Technical Variation. The technique of roentgenography must be carefully standardized to consistently produce films which can be reliably interpreted. The apparent size and shape of the heart may be seriously distorted by thoughtless or careless technicians.

Inaccurate Positioning of the Patients. If the patient is correctly placed in the postero-anterior position, the manubrium of the sternum should be centered over the vertebral bodies. If the patient is rotated even slightly from this position, the apparent configuration of the heart may be significantly altered (Figs. 6 and 7). Similarly, the configuration of the heart and its position in relation to the thoracic spine are seriously distorted by either inadequate or excessive rotation of the patient to obtain oblique views of the heart. Standardization of patient positioning is essential for accurate evaluation of teleroentgenograms. This problem need not arise during fluoroscopy because the examiner can view the heart from all angles and control the positioning during visualization.

Respiratory Activity. The level of the diaphragm is influenced by the phase of respiration in which the teleroentgenogram is exposed. If the x-ray technician instructs the patient to take a deep breath prior to exposing the x-ray plate, the level of the diaphragm is depressed and the longitudinal axis of the heart assumes a more nearly vertical position (Fig. 8). On the other hand, the patient may be instructed to press against the x-ray cassette, in which case he may forceably exhale, elevating the level of the diaphragm. Changes in the level of the diaphragm due to respiratory activity may seriously distort the apparent cardiac size (Fig. 8).

The Valsalva Maneuver. A patient instructed to hold his breath may inadvertently or unconsciously raise the pressure within the thorax—the Valsalva maneuver. The increased intrathoracic pressure impedes the blood flow into the thorax and causes a progressive reduction in the size of the heart. Under these conditions, the actual size of the cardiac silhouette may be significantly reduced.[7] The sources of variation due to respiratory activity and the Valsalva maneuver can be largely eliminated by well trained technicians.

THE EFFECTS OF RESPIRATION ON THE CARDIAC SILHOUETTE

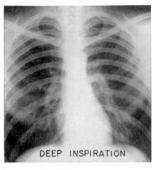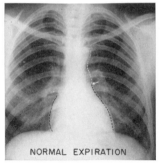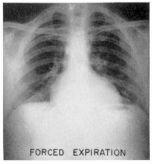

DEEP INSPIRATION   NORMAL EXPIRATION   FORCED EXPIRATION

FIGURE 8.   Three roentgenograms from a single normal subject illustrate the changes in shape and apparent size of the cardiac silhouette which can be produced by deep inspiration and forced expiration. In the center, the changes in the cardiac silhouette during a cardiac cycle are indicated by dotted lines based on cinefluorographic studies of normal human hearts. The arrow indicates the cardiovascular angle, at the junction of the left ventricle and the pulmonary artery on the left border. During systole the left ventricular margin moves in while the pulmonary artery expands. Since the upper and lower limbs of the cardiovascular angle move in opposite directions, the apex of this angle is often called the point of opposite pulsation, a prominent landmark during fluoroscopic examination.

The Relative Advantages of Rcentgenographic Techniques

All the sources of technical variations listed above apply to teleroentgenography and may be avoided during fluoroscopy. Furthermore, the roentgenograms are frequently interpreted without any information concerning the patient—a serious limitation indeed. In the course of fluoroscopy, the examiner has an opportunity to note the habitus of the individual and the presence of thoracic and spinal deformities. He is in a position to check his observations by inquiring into the clinical history, and to perform a physical examination when indicated. He can observe the changes in the size, configuration and position of the heart and great vessels throughout the cardiac cycle and view the heart from all aspects.

Standard fluoroscopy also has practical limitations. Because of radiation hazards, the illumination of the fluorescent screen should be maintained at an absolute minimum consistent with the adequate visualization of the image. The brightness and contrast of the images are barely adequate; the excellent definition of cone vi-

sion is sacrificed and the comparatively coarse rod vision must be used. For these reasons, much of the detail on the fluoroscopic image cannot be seen under routine conditions. The total duration of radiation exposure must be held at a minimum (e.g., 30 to 60 seconds if possible). This can be accomplished by relatively brief examination of the cardiac silhouette and by turning the machine off while the patient is positioned. The volume of tissue irradiated should be minimized by reducing the field of examination to include only the areas under scrutiny. Maximum information with minimal radiation can be attained only by training and experience. Fluoroscopy of patients should be undertaken only with complete understanding of the hazards of radiation and the methods of minimizing risks to both the patient and the examiner. The advent of screen-intensifying techniques promises to alleviate these difficulties in laboratories equipped with this apparatus.

The only permanent record obtained from routine fluoroscopy is a written description of the observations. Detection of changes during serial examinations is very difficult since a description of the cardiac silhouette in the various positions does not convey a complete or accurate impression of the image.

In spite of their limitations, teleroentgenographic films constitute a permanent record of the size and shape of the cardiac silhouette at the instant of the exposure. Films taken years apart may be compared for indications of change in contour or in chamber size. Teleroentgenograms may be viewed as long as desired under adequate illumination. The light intensity and the contrast between light and dark shadows greatly exceed those available during fluoroscopy. The quantity of radiation for a single x-ray exposure is significant, but not excessive. However, serial teleroentgenograms should not be ordered freely without considering the total radiation being administered to the patient.

Cinefluorography combines the advantages of fluoroscopy and teleroentgenography.[8-11] During projection, the films reveal the fluoroscopic images in motion with ample light intensity and good contrast. The principal disadvantages at present are that (1) the duration of the exposure is only about 10 seconds with radiation roughly equivalent to fluoroscopy for 1 minute, (2) it is difficult to obtain films in the three fundamental positions within 10 seconds' exposure time and (3) the films are more difficult to process and file. The first two disadvantages are greatly alleviated by fluoroscopic screen intensification.[12]

MEASUREMENTS OF THE CARDIAC SILHOUETTE

Detection of cardiac enlargement is generally a more or less subjective judgment in view of the numerous causes of variation described above. A more scientific approach to roentgenographic interpretation has been attempted by measuring various dimensions of the cardiac silhouette. Information concerning the length or width of the individual ventric-

ular chambers would be most helpful. However, the position occupied by the atrioventricular valve rings cannot be accurately identified, with the result that most of the measurements include both atrial and ventricular dimensions. Further, the dense shadows cast by abdominal organs largely obscure the inferior margin of the cardiac silhouette. The transverse diameter is the most common measurement in current use. To determine this dimension, a vertical line is inscribed over the vertebral spine on a teleroentgenogram exposed in the postero-anterior position. The point on the right border of the heart which is farthest from the midline is selected by inspection (in the midportion of the right atrial border). From this point a line is drawn perpendicular to the vertical reference line. In the same way a perpendicular is erected from the point on the left border of the heart which is most distant from the midline. The sum of the two horizontal segments is called the transverse diameter (Fig. 9).

In view of the extreme variation in different individuals, this measurement has no significance without reference to the habitus of the individual (Fig. 7). A fairly common practice is to divide the transverse diameter of the heart by the width of the thorax (the cardiothoracic ratio). It is frequently stated that a cardiothoracic ratio of more than 0.5 indicates cardiac enlargement. This assumption may have some validity among individuals of average body build. However, a vertically placed heart may be considerably enlarged before reaching a cardiothoracic ratio of 0.5. If the long axis of the heart approaches the horizontal, the cardiothoracic ratio may exceed 0.5 without any cardiac enlargement. The cardiothoracic ratio has little value and may be seriously misleading.

To overcome this deficiency, Ungerleider et al.[13, 14] measured the transverse diameter of a large group of "normal" individuals and devised tables by which it is

CARDIAC MEASUREMENTS

A. TRANSVERSE DIAMETER

B. CARDIOTHORACIC RATIO

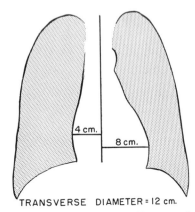

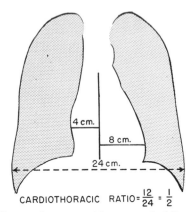

FIGURE 9.   *A*, The transverse diameter of the cardiac silhouette is measured from a vertical line along the vertebral spine. The maximum distances from this line to the right and left borders of the heart shadow are added to measure this dimension. Although neither of these points of measurement is particularly appropriate for detecting chamber enlargement, no other dimension has proved more revealing.

B, The quotient obtained when the transverse diameter is divided by the width of the thoracic cage at its widest point is termed the cardiothoracic ratio. This device is intended to correct for differences in habitus among patients. If the ratio exceeds 0.5, cardiac enlargement is said to be present. The extent to which this measurement can be misleading is indicated by a glance at Figures 7 and 8.

possible to predict the transverse diameter of an individual according to his weight, height, age and sex. If the measured transverse diameter of a patient exceeds the predicted dimension by more than 10 per cent, he "probably" has an enlarged heart.

Before using the transverse diameter as a criterion of cardiac enlargement, one must recognize the following limitations: (*a*) the measurement includes both the right atrium and the left ventricle; (*b*) the ventricular chambers do not enlarge primarily along a horizontal axis; (*c*) elongation of the outflow tract of the left ventricle would be detected but there is no representation by the right ventricle in this measurement; and (*d*) the application of the measurement presupposes that the sources of variation other than habitus, age and sex have been eliminated or controlled. It is more important to determine which chamber is involved than to establish that the heart is enlarged. If these restrictions are recog-

nized, the tables of Ungerleider and Clark may serve a useful purpose.

SUPPLEMENTARY ROENTGENO-GRAPHIC TECHNIQUES

Angiocardiography

Since the blood and myocardium absorb x-rays to a similar extent and the entire cardiac silhouette has relatively uniform density, the chambers cannot be differentiated from the walls. By rapid injection of suitable radiopaque substances the blood can be opacified to a very great extent. This technique is termed angiocardiography. Serial roentgenograms taken in rapid succession after the injection of a contrast medium reveal the course of the blood through the cardiac chambers. In the dog, the orientation of the heart within the thorax is well suited to angiocardiographic studies because each chamber of the heart may be visualized individually (see Figs. 10 and 14, Chap. 2). Human angiocardiography, on the contrary, is seriously complicated by the fact that in any position, the individual cardiac chambers overlap. Opacification of one area completely obscures all other structures superimposed upon it.

Occasionally there are unpleasant side reactions to the contrast media, including a hot flush, headache, vomiting, urticaria and syncope. According to Dotter and Jackson,[15] fatal reactions occur with an incidence of 0.38 per cent. Angiocardiography should not be employed unless the risks are outweighed by the necessity for specific information in formulating definitive therapy. This decision requires awareness of the types of cardiac lesions which are suitable for angiocardiographic study.

The clinical application of angiocardiography has been reviewed by Dotter and Steinberg.[16, 17] Widespread interest has been evoked in the diagnosis of congenital malformations of the heart and great vessels, including (a) coarctation of the aorta, (b) complete transposition of the great arteries, (c) aneurysm of the aorta as differentiated from mediastinal tumors, (d) anomalies in the course of the aorta and its branching, (e) anomalous drainage of pulmonary veins and (f) certain intracardiac defects (see Chap. 14). The technique has value in detecting specific pulmonary conditions (e.g., arteriovenous communications in the lungs).

The course of the radiopaque materials through the heart is generally recorded by the use of rapid cassette changers or roll film magazines.[18] Cinefluorographic angiocardiography is theoretically the method of choice because it provides a more complete coverage of the sequence of events. Repeated projection of the motion picture films reveals details which are entirely missed during examination of individual exposures.

Roentgenkymography

During systolic ejection, the area of the cardiac silhouette is reduced so slightly that it is difficult to visualize the movements of the heart borders during fluoroscopy. Movements of the heart borders have been recorded by means of the roentgenkymograph.[19] The roentgenkymograph consists of a lead plate with a series of horizontal slits 1 cm. apart. Behind this grid a roentgenographic plate moves down 1 cm. at a controlled rate. Movements of the heart borders produce serrated margins on the cardiac silhouette. This apparatus has failed to achieve wide application for several reasons:[20] (1) the amplitude of the recorded movements of the heart borders is very small, (2) the exposure is limited to 1.0 to 1.5 seconds, (3) the slits are not always perpendicular to the heart border and (4) the diaphragmatic aspect of the heart is obscured by dense abdominal structures. In recent years a technique— electrokymography—has been developed to amplify the movements of specific points on the borders of the fluoroscopic image.

Electrokymography

The sensitive element of the electrokymograph is a photoelectric cell which responds to the light emitted by a small fluorescent screen mounted behind a long narrow slit in a rectangular piece of lead.[21, 22] Movement of the cardiac border back and forth along the slit during each cardiac cycle reduces the total number of x-rays reaching the small fluorescent screen and the total quantity of light striking the photoelectric cell (see Fig. 10). This process can be compared to holding a photographic exposure meter toward a window and recording the movements of the needle as a semiopaque window shade is repeatedly raised and lowered. In this way, an objective record can be obtained which indicates the relative movements of the heart borders. It does not, however, distinguish between movements of the ventricular

ELECTROKYMOGRAPHY

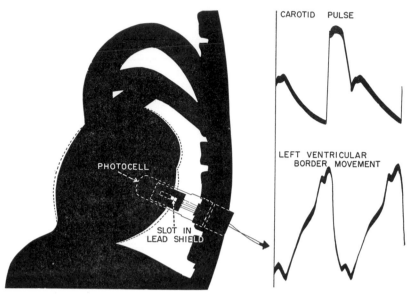

FIGURE 10.   Electrokymographic recording is accomplished by positioning a photoelectric cell over the borders of the heart under fluoroscopic control. Within the recording head is a piece of lead with a rectangular slit covered by a small fluorescent screen. Roentgen rays, striking the fluorescent screen, cause it to emit light in relation to the density of the intervening tissues. As the heart border moves back and forth across the slit, the quantity of light emitted by the fluorescent material varies, providing an objective record of the motion of that portion of the heart wall.

wall during contraction and changes in position of the heart within the thorax.

Electrokymography has been advocated for assessing a wide variety of clinical problems including the demonstration of paradoxical motion of the ventricular borders at the site of myocardial infarction. When a portion of the ventricular border moves outward during systole and inward during diastole, the presence of myocardial infarction is apparent. In constrictive pericarditis the filling is complete during early diastole, producing a pattern of very flat diastolic plateaus separated by V-shaped excursions due to systolic ejection and rapid filling. Varying degrees of success have been achieved in attempts to find distinctive patterns associated with myasthenia gravis, valvular disease and other forms of organic heart disease. The status of the method in 1950 was reviewed in detail in the proceedings of the first conference on electrokymography.[23]

Electrokymographs in current use were tested by Zinsser, Kay and Benjamin[24] and failed to produce instantaneous recordings which were directly proportional in magnitude to the dynamic event under study for three reasons: (a) the sensitivity of the phototubes was not uniform along the receptor slots, (b) a time lag (0.15 to 0.25 second) was observed and (c) the frequency response was inadequate. Morgan and Sturm[25] have described improved equipment which has sufficient stability and response to permit quantitative calibration. With apparatus of this sort, changes in the density at the central portion of the ventricular chambers may be recorded and related to stroke volume. Successfully accomplished, this would represent a significant step in cardiovascular analysis since it would afford a simple method for continuously recording a function which appears closely related to cardiac output (see Chap. 3).

SUMMARY

Changes in size and shape of the heart are important signs of heart disease. During early stages of heart disease, the heart usually remains normal in size. Detection of slight changes in the size of the cardiac chambers is extremely difficult because of variation in the size and shape of the normal heart due to the orientation of the heart within the thorax, the shape of the chest cage, habitus, age, respiratory activity and other factors. Extensive enlargement of the heart can be recognized with little difficulty by noting dislocation of the point of maximal impulse and by percussion. Enlargement of individual chambers alters the configuration of the cardiac silhouette. However, interpretation of roentgenograms requires experience in distinguishing individual variation of normal hearts from signs of chamber enlargement. In each patient, the cardiac silhouette must be considered in terms of the probable "normal" for that particular individual. Supplementary techniques, including angiocardiography and electrokymography, provide additional information under particular circumstances but are not applicable to routine diagnosis.

II. Enlargement of the Cardiac Chambers

It is impossible to illustrate here the characteristic changes in the heart shadow produced by enlargement of individual chambers under all possible circumstances. Teleroentgenograms in the postero-anterior and right and left anterior oblique positions from three normal individuals with different habitus have been chosen. The effects of enlargement of each cardiac chamber are illustrated on these "normal" silhouettes. This method of representation illustrates the effects of varying habitus on roentgenographic interpretation, but it must be emphasized that orientation of the heart is only one of many sources of variation.

LEFT VENTRICULAR ENLARGEMENT

The principal sign of left ventricular dilatation is elongation of the outflow tract, which is most clearly visualized in the postero-anterior position (Fig. 11). The longitudinal axis of the heart tends to elongate, displacing the apex downward and to the left. Since the diaphragm limits the amount of the caudal expansion, the longitudinal axis of the heart tends to rotate toward the horizontal. The great vessels retain their normal position. For this reason the cardiovascular angle becomes more acute (see Fig. 8). As the left ventricle elongates, the apex of the cardiovascular angle (point of opposite pulsation) is generally located above the midpoint on the left border of the silhouette. The ventricles may also rotate around the longitudinal axis of the heart, but this has little effect on the cardiac configuration.

In patients with asthenic habitus and vertically oriented hearts, rather severe degrees of left ventricular enlargement must develop before these changes are beyond the range observed among normal individuals with average body build.

Since the left ventricle appears enlarged in the normal sthenic individual, even slight degrees of further elongation may displace the apex well beyond the midclavicular line. The normally prominent cardiovascular angle generally becomes accentuated.

In the left anterior oblique position, the posterior margin of the cardiac silhouette is displaced backward and overrides the spine to a greater extent than normal. During fluoroscopy, the patient is fre-

LEFT VENTRICULAR ENLARGEMENT

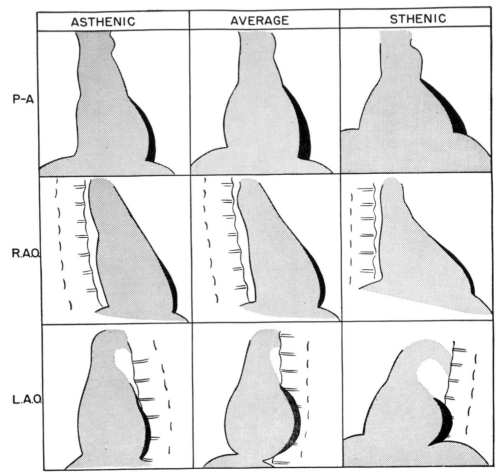

FIGURE 11.   The most common type of left ventricular enlargement is an elongation of the chamber which displaces the apex downward and to the left. This change is most easily observed in the posteroanterior projection, but is often difficult to detect in asthenic patients and may be exaggerated in sthenic patients. In the left anterior oblique position, an enlarged left ventricle extends posteriorly beyond the vertebral spine to an abnormal degree. Severe left ventricular enlargement may produce a bulge on the lower portion of the sternal margin of the silhouette in the right anterior oblique position.

quently rotated until the left ventricular border clears the spinal shadow. According to Wilson *et al.*,[26] the amount of rotation required may be expressed in degrees (the angle of clearance) as an indication of left ventricular enlargement.

Concentric Hypertrophy of the Left Ventricle

An increased pressure load on the left ventricle results from aortic valvular stenosis or systemic arterial hypertension. From the heart size in patients with es-

sential hypertension,[27] the response of the left ventricle is extremely variable. In some cases, marked cardiac enlargement was present for 10 years or more with little functional limitation. In others, the heart remained normal in size despite congestive heart failure. In some patients with hypertension, hypertrophy of the ventricular wall may completely compensate for the load without cardiac dilatation. Under these circumstances, the ventricular border of the heart becomes rounded, a condition called concentric hypertrophy (Fig. 12). Superficially, the ventricle appears to have assumed a more spherical shape, as viewed in the postero-anterior position. The cardiovascular angle is more acute, but the apex of the heart is not displaced downward or to the left. Concentric hypertrophy has little effect on the cardiac silhouette in the oblique views.

LEFT ATRIAL DILATATION

No portion of the main left atrial chamber appears on the border of the cardiac silhouette in the postero-anterior position.

Enlargement of the left atrium extends posteriorly and toward the right, as indicated by the dotted lines in Figure 13. Massive dilatation of the left atrium may extend so far toward the right that a double shadow is observed along the right border. This double shadow is composed of the right atrial margin superimposed upon the dilated left atrial chamber.

Early dilatation of the left atrium may be detected in the right anterior oblique position. Displacement of the dilated left atrial wall encroaches upon the retro-cardiac space in the midportion of the

CONCENTRIC HYPERTROPHY OF THE LEFT VENTRICLE

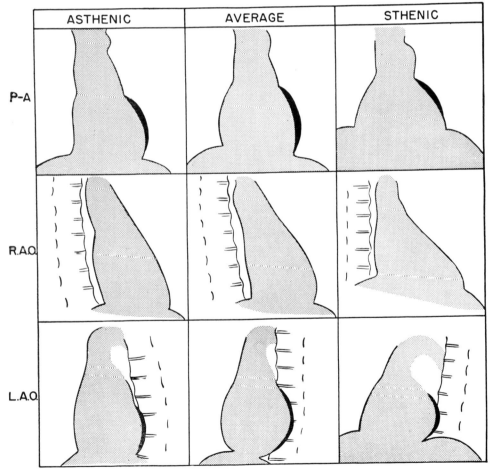

FIGURE 12.   When exposed to a chronic pressure load, the left ventricle may become more spherical with little or no enlargement of the heart shadow. This *concentric hypertrophy* produces a rounding of the cardiac silhouette in the frontal view. However, this change is frequently no greater than that encountered among normal individuals and is difficult to demonstrate with confidence.

LEFT ATRIAL ENLARGEMENT

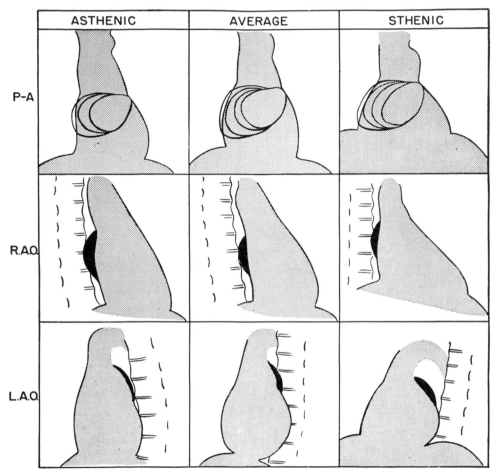

FIGURE 13. The left atrium is situated on the posterior aspect of the heart. Dilatation of this chamber produces displacement toward the right around the back of the heart. For this reason, rather extreme left atrial enlargement may be completely invisible in the postero-anterior projection. On the other hand, the first sign of left atrial dilatation can be observed in the left anterior oblique view where the expanding chamber encroaches upon the retrocardiac space. In the left anterior oblique position, extreme left atrial enlargement may be observed, particularly if it produces upward displacement of the left main bronchus.

cardiac silhouette. The barium-filled esophagus may be displaced posteriorly and toward the right by the distending atrial chamber. In early mitral stenosis, left atrial dilatation of this type may be the only objective evidence of organic heart disease.

In the left anterior oblique position, the left atrium is frequently difficult to visualize. Enlargement of the left atrium is not observed in this view at an early stage. Massive left atrial enlargement

may elevate and compress the left main bronchus, producing a dry, hacking cough.

RIGHT VENTRICULAR ENLARGEMENT

Since the right ventricle is on the anterior surface of the heart, it does not appear on the heart border in the frontal view. When the right ventricular chamber enlarges, it protrudes anteriorly toward the sternum. As a consequence of this forward bulging of the right ventricular wall, the pulmonary artery is displaced beyond the normal left border, tending to obscure the cardiovascular angle.[28, 29] Thus, the left border of the cardiac silhouette becomes straightened or even convex (Fig. 14).

In the left anterior oblique position, forward projection of the dilated right ventricular chamber produces a sharper angulation at its junction with the root of the aorta (Fig. 14). In the right anterior oblique position, the distance between the outflow tract of the right ventricle and the sternal shadow is reduced.

DILATATION OF THE PULMONARY ARTERY

In certain types of congenital malformations of the heart the pulmonary artery becomes markedly dilated. Such patients generally have an abnormally voluminous pulmonary blood flow. The dilated pulmonary artery appears as a local prominent bulge just above the

RIGHT VENTRICULAR ENLARGEMENT

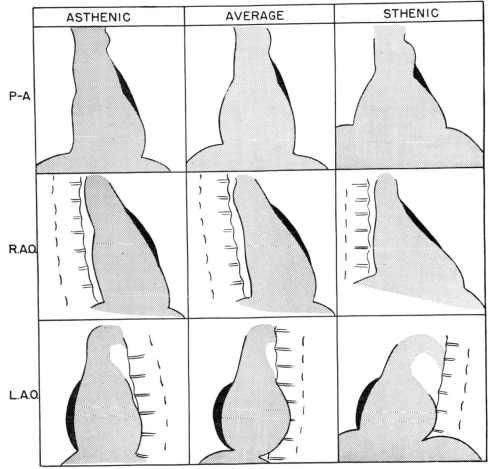

FIGURE 14.   When the right ventricle becomes enlarged, the outflow tract and the pulmonary artery are displaced upward and to the left so that the cardiovascular angle becomes straightened or convex. This is the only sign which can be observed in the postero-anterior view. The anterior protrusion of the chamber is best observed in the left anterior oblique position, and to a lesser extent in the right anterior oblique view. Right ventricular enlargement is most commonly encountered in children with congenital heart disease or rheumatic mitral valvular disease.

DILATATION OF PULMONARY ARTERY

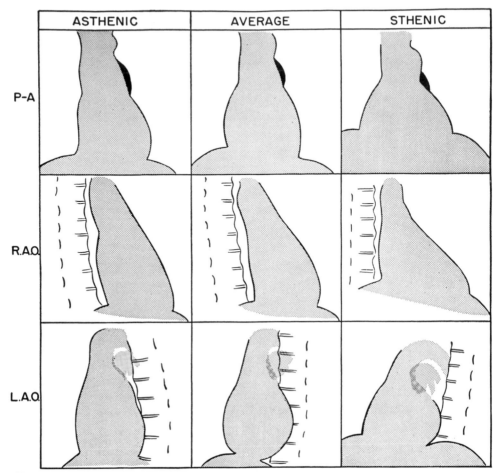

FIGURE 15.   A dilated pulmonary artery appears on the left border of the mediastinal shadow in the frontal view. It can be confirmed in some patients in the right anterior oblique view, but is invisible in the left anterior oblique position.

cardiovascular angle (Fig. 15). This alteration in the cardiac silhouette is usually associated with a marked increase in the density of the pulmonary vascular markings, particularly in the peripheral lung field. Pulmonary valvular stenosis with dilatation of the pulmonary artery above the obstruction is a prominent exception to this rule (see Chap. 12).

It is not considered appropriate here to delve deeply into roentgenographic interpretation. Additional information concerning the finer details may be obtained from standard textbooks on the subject.[30-32]

REFERENCES

1. HAYCRAFT, J. B. The movements of the heart within the chest cavity and the cardiogram. *J. Physiol.*, 12:438–474, 1891.
2. BURCHELL, H. B., and VISSCHER, M. B. The changes in the form of the beating mammalian heart, as demonstrated by high-speed photography. *Amer. Heart J.*, 22:794–803 1941.
3. MAJOR, R. H. *Physical Diagnosis.* 4th ed. Philadelphia, W. B. Saunders Co., 1951, 446 pp.
4. REYNOLDS, R. J. Cineradiography. *Brit. J. Radiol.*, 7:415–424, 1934.
5. JANKER, R. Roentgen cinematography. *Amer. J. Roentgenol.*, 36:384–390, 1936.
6. STEWART, W. H., HOFFMAN, W. J., and GHISELIN, F. H. Cinefluorography. *Amer. J. Roentgenol.*, 38:465–469, 1937.

7. RUSHMER, R. F. Circulatory effects of three modifications of the Valsalva experiment. *Amer. Heart J.*, 34:399–418, 1947.

8. BARCLAY, A. E., FRANKLIN, K. J., and PRICHARD, M. M. L. X-ray cinematography in research. *Brit. J. Radiol.*, 13:227–234, 1940.

9. DE CASTRO, J. M. Fundamental principles in the application of cineroentgenography as an auxiliary method to roentgen diagnosis. *Amer. J. Roentgenol.*, 57:103–114, 1947.

10. RAMSEY, G. H. S., WATSON, J. S., Jr., STEINHAUSEN, T. B., THOMPSON, J. J., DREISINGER, F., and WEINBERG, S. Cinefluorography: a progress report on technical problems, dosage factors and clinical impressions. *Radiology*, 52:684–690, 1949.

11. RUSHMER, R. F., BARK, R. S., and HENDRON, J. A. Clinical cinefluorography. *Radiology*, 55:588–592, 1950.

12. MORGAN, R. H., and STURM, R. E. Roentgen-ray motion pictures by means of screen intensification. *Amer. J. Roentgenol.*, 70:136–140, 1953.

13. UNGERLEIDER, H. E., and CLARK, C. P. A study of the transverse diameter of the heart silhouette with prediction table based on the teleoroentgenogram. *Amer. Heart J.*, 17:92–102, 1939

14. UNGERLEIDER, H. E., and GUBNER, R. Evaluation of heart size measurements. *Amer. Heart J.*, 24:494–510, 1942.

15. DOTTER, C. T., and JACKSON, F. S. Death following angiocardiography. *Radiology*, 54:527–533, 1950.

16. DOTTER, C. T., and STEINBERG, I. Angiocardiography. *Circulation*, 4:123-138, 1951.

17. DOTTER, C. T., and STEINBERG, I. Advances in angiocardiography. *Med. Clin. N. Amer.*, 34:745–756, 1950.

18. TEMPLE, H. L., STEINBERG, I., and DOTTER, C. T. Angiocardiography utilizing photoroentgen apparatus with rapid film changer, *Amer. J. Roentgenol.*, 60:646–649, 1948.

19. KEYS, A., and FRIEDELL, H. L.: Measurement of the stroke volume of the human heart from roentgenograms: simultaneous roentgenkymographic and acetylene-rebreathing experiments. *Amer. J. Physiol.*, 126:741–752, 1939.

20. DACK, S., PALEY, D. H., and SUSSMAN, M. L. A comparison of electrokymography and roentgenkymography in the study of myocardial infarction. *Circulation*, 1:551–563, 1950.

21. HENNY, G. C., BOONE, B. R., and CHAMBERLAIN, W. E. Electrokymograph for recording heart motion, improved type. *Amer. J. Roentgenol.*, 57:409–416, 1947.

22. HENNY, G. C., and BOONE, B. R. Electro kymograph for recording heart motion utilizing the roentgenoscope. *Amer. J. Roentgenol.*, 54:217–229, 1945.

23. BOONE, B. R., GILLICK, F. G., MORGAN, R. H., and OPPENHEIMER, M. J. (Eds.) *Proceeding· of the First Conference on Electrokymography.* (Public Health Service Publication No. 59.) Washington, D. C., U. S. Govt. Printing Office, 1951.

24. ZINSSER, H. F., JR., KAY, C. F. and BENJAMIN, J. M., JR. The electrokymograph: studies in recording fidelity. *Circulation*, 2:197–204, 1950.

25. MORGAN, R. H., and STURM, R. E. The quantitative electrokymograph. *Circulation*, 4:604–612, 1951.

26. WILSON, M. G., EPSTEIN, N., HELPER, H. N., and HAIN, K. Evaluation of routine serial fluoroscopic examinations of the heart in the postero-anterior and oblique views at specific degrees of rotation. *Circulation*, 8:879–882, 1953.

27. KLEINFELD, M., and REDISH, J. The size of the heart during the course of essential hypertension. *Circulation*, 5:74–80, 1952.

28. GRISHMAN, A., SUSSMAN, M. L., and STEINBERG, M. F. Angiocardiographic analysis of cardiac configuration in rheumatic mitral disease. *Amer. J. Roentgenol.*, 51:33–43, 1944.

29. DOTTER, C. T., and STEINBERG, I. Angiocardiographic study of the pulmonary artery. *J.A.M.A.*, 139:566–572, 1949.

30. RITVO, M. *Chest X-ray Diagnosis.* Philadelphia, Lea & Febiger, 1951, 558 pp.

31. STORCH, C. B. *Fundamentals of Clinical Fluoroscopy, with essentials of roentgen interpretation.* New York, Grune & Stratton, 1951, 196 pp.

32 UNGERLEIDER, H. E., and GUBNER, R. S. Roentgenology of the heart and great vessels. Pp. 1689–1798 in *Diagnosis and Treatment of Cardiovascular Disease*, vol. 2, 4th ed., W. D. Stroud, ed. Philadelphia, F. A. Davis Co., 1950.

Chapter 14

EMBRYOLOGIC DEVELOPMENT AND

CONGENITAL MALFORMATIONS OF THE HEART

Malformation of the heart during embryologic development was primarily of academic interest so long as no specific therapy was available. During the past 20 years, surgical techniques have been devised to alleviate or eliminate most of the cardiac defects. The consequent necessity for identifying cases suitable for surgical therapy has resulted in a widespread effort to develop and improve the techniques for differential diagnosis of all these conditions. The origin and nature of the various types of developmental defects can best be visualized as aberrations of normal embryologic processes. For this reason, the salient features of the normal development of the heart are presented. Many of the illustrations in this chapter have been derived from a series of motion picture films[1] dealing with the origin, functional effects and diagnostic signs of congenital malformations of the heart.

I. Embryological Development of the Heart

THE DEVELOPMENT OF THE NORMAL HEART

During embryologic development, the various tissues and organs rapidly pass through stages representing the evolutionary development of the species. For this reason, the extensive investigation of embryology in the chick is generally applicable to human embryos, but there is one important difference: the chick embyro is attached to the surface of an abundant yolk.

The heart develops from a pair of primordial tubes derived from clusters of endothelial cells which proliferate, become organized into strands of cells and acquire a lumen. The paired endocardial primordia are located near the margin of the anterior intestinal portal and are brought closer together by the infolding process which produces the foregut. These primitive tubes meet in the midline and fuse into a single elongated chamber which will ultimately develop into the ventricles. From the simple cardiac tube, the endocardial primordia proliferate toward the head to form the aortic arch system. The caudal extensions of the primordial tubes become the omphalomesenteric veins. As the formation of gut proceeds caudally, fusion of the primordial tubes continues, forming the primitive atrium and finally the sinus venosus.

390

EMBRYOLOGIC DEVELOPMENT OF THE HEART

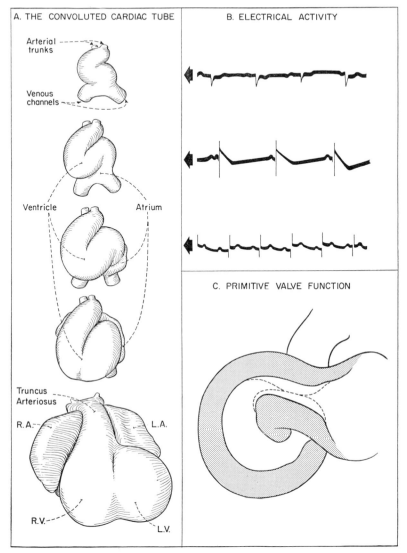

FIGURE 1.   *A,* The initial stage in the development of the heart is the formation of a single cardiac tube which will ultimately evolve into the ventricular portion of the heart. At this very early stage, contractions occur repetitively at a slow rate. Being anchored above by the developing arterial trunks and below by extensive venous channels, the cardiac tube, growing rapidly in length, is bent into a loop to the right of the midline. By progressive fusion of the cardiac primordia, the primitive atrium is formed, and remains relatively fixed in position as the cardiac loop grows longer and swings back to the midline to cover the expanding atrial chambers. In this process the ventricle assumes a position anterior and caudal to the atria.

B, Electrical activity can be recorded from the heart of the chick embryo at the very early stages of development, indicated by the first three drawings in Figure 1*A.* As the cardiac tube becomes convoluted, the electrocardiographic patterns produced by this electrical activity begin to resemble the patterns observed in fully developed hearts. (After Hoff *et al.*[5])

C, Contraction of the cardiac tube is persistaltic in character, beginning in the atrial region and progressing toward the truncus arteriosus. During contraction at the atrioventricular junction, the endocardial surfaces come into apposition to prevent retrograde flow of blood. A similar valve action may be observed at the root of the truncus arteriosus. (After Patten *et al.*[4])

Convolution of the Cardiac Tube

The primitive cardiac tube grows longer more rapidly than either the investing pericardium or the surrounding somatic structures. It is anchored above by the arterial trunks and below by developing venous channels. Since the tube is fixed at both ends, its rapid elongation causes flexion, initially toward the right side of the embryo. As elongation continues, the cardiac tube becomes more tortuous (Fig. 1A). At the same time, constrictions develop which indicate the ultimate division of this single convoluted tube into atria and ventricles. As the ventricular region progressively expands and grows longer, it swings back toward the midline to cover the atrial region, which remains relatively fixed in position. In this process, the primitive atrium and arterial trunks, which were originally on opposite ends of the cardiac tube, are brought into apposition. Thus, the inflow tract and outflow tract are adjacent and all four valve rings ultimately merge into a single fibrous skeleton (see Fig. 3, Chap. 2). The developing atria expand laterally to form two extensive sacculations, the primitive right and left atria. These sacculations ultimately become the right and left auricles, while the main atrial chambers develop by progressive incorporation of the venous channels into the posterior wall.

The Initial Cardiac Contraction

According to Patten,[2] the first signs of contraction of the heart in chick embryos appear while it is represented by only the ventricular portion of the cardiac tube (Fig. 1). Localized slow contractions usually are noted first on the right margin near the root of the primitive arterial trunks. However, the site and spread of these earliest undulations vary considerably. The initial contractions in the embryonic rat heart occur a few hours before the elaboration of fibrillae or cross striations.[3] About an hour after the first fibrillar contraction appears, the entire primitive ventricle contracts regularly and synchronously, but slowly. The nature of the contraction changes a few hours later as the atrium is formed. At this time, contractions originate in the atrial region and sweep over the ventricle like a peristaltic wave. The atrium assumes the role of pacemaker because its inherent rate of impulse formation is higher than that of the ventricle (see Fig. 2, Chap. 3). The sinus venosus has an even faster inherent rhythm and assumes control as soon as it is formed. The sinus venosus ultimately forms the sinoatrial node, the normal pacemaker of the fully developed heart.

By the time the atrium and sinus venosus are formed, this primitive tubular heart is actively pumping blood through the developing circulatory system. During the peristaltic type of cardiac contraction, retrograde flow of blood is prevented by developing mounds of endocardial tissue which project into the lumen at the junction of the primitive atria and ventricles.[4] During each contraction these endocardial cushions meet each other, completely blocking the channel (Fig. 1C). Thus, simple but effective atrioventricular valves are formed at this very early stage of development. Similar endocardial cushions develop in the outflow tract near the ventricular conus. This region ultimately becomes the conus of the right ventricle.

The Development of the Electrocardiogram

According to Hoff et al.,[5] electrical activity can be consistently recorded from chick embryos at the stage of development illustrated in Figure 1A. A few hours later a sharp downward deflection appears, which is interpreted as equivalent to a QRS complex. In the next three or four hours the atrium has become differentiated and the sinus venosus is formed. At about this time, downward deflections (P waves) can be recorded just preceding the QRS. As the primitive cardiac tube becomes convoluted, the electrocardiogram assumes a configuration similar to that of the adult (Fig. 1B).

Partitioning of the Atrioventricular Canal

At six weeks of age, the major components of the human heart can be readily identified (Fig. 1A). A shallow, interventricular groove forms a line of demarcation between the future right and left ventricles.

In spite of the apparent separation of the atria from the ventricles at the atrioventricular junction (Fig. 2A, arrow), the heart actually consists of a common atrioventricular canal with empties into a single arterial trunk. A four-chambered heart is developed from this convoluted, dilated tube by the formation of three partitions separating the atria, the ventricles and the two main arteries.

The first step in the separation of the

PARTITIONING OF THE HEART

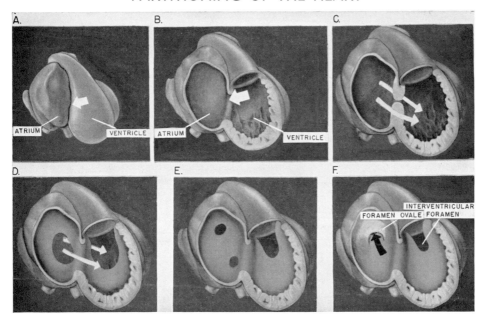

FIGURE 2. *A*, When the cardiac tube illustrated in Figure 1*A* is observed in a lateral view, the atrium and ventricles appear to be divided by a deep atrioventricular invagination.

B, Actually, this groove is merely a constriction at the atrioventricular junction. The embryonic heart at this stage is still a simple tube which has become convoluted and expanded into primitive chambers. A four-chambered heart with corresponding arterial trunks is formed by the elaboration of three septa dividing the atria, ventricles and truncus arteriosus.

C, First, the atrioventricular channel is divided at its waist by proliferating endocardial cushions which fuse into a column.

D, Septa dividing the atrium and ventricle grow simultaneously toward the atrioventricular grooves. If either of these partitions fails to form, the fully developed heart has only a single atrium or a single ventricle.

E, An aperture in the developing atrial septum persists near its junction with the endocardial cushions (the foramen primum). Before foramen primum is closed, a new aperture appears high on the interventricular septum (foramen secundum). These two embryonic apertures are the most common sites of interatrial septal defects.

F, The foramen secundum is covered by the developing septum secundum which grows down over the aperture. Its advancing edge becomes thickened to produce the foramen ovale, which acts as a unidirectional flutter valve. Closure of the interventricular foramen awaits the development of a complex spiral septum dividing the truncus arteriosus and conus region of the primitive ventricle (see Fig. 3).

PARTITIONING OF THE ARTERIAL TRUNKS

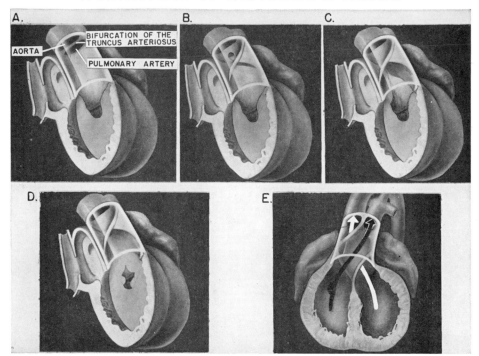

FIGURE 3.   A, The truncus arteriosus is illustrated as a transparent cylinder with the heart viewed in the right anterior oblique position.

B, A pair of spiral ridges develop in the internal surface of the truncus arteriosus, beginning at the bifurcation of the truncus arteriosus into the fourth and sixth aortic arches. Retaining their positions on opposite sides of the cylinder, the ridges pursue a spiral course toward the ventricles.

C, The ridges grow into the lumen and fuse to produce a spiral septum which extends into the conus region of the ventricles where they swing into line with the upper margin of the interventricular septum.

D, The interventricular foramen is normally obliterated by masses of endocardial tissue growing from the ventricular septum, the endocardial cushions and the spiral aortic pulmonary septum. This mass of endocardial tissue thins out to form the membranous portion of the interventricular septum just below the origin of the aorta and pulmonary artery. This is the most common site of interventricular septal defects.

E, The significance of the spiral aortic septum is more readily appreciated in a frontal view of the heart. The aortic pulmonary septum executes a spiral of about 180 degrees and swings into line with the superior margin of the interventricular septum. This process accounts for the manner in which the aortic and pulmonary trunks are entwined in the fully developed heart. Blood from the left ventricle enters the aorta, which passes to the right behind the pulmonary artery. The pulmonary artery passes in front of the aorta and turns posteriorly on the left side of the mediastinum.

atrial and ventricular chambers begins with the growth of endocardial cushions from the dorsal and ventral portions of the atrioventricular groove. These masses of endocardial tissue later fuse to form a column which splits the stream of blood flowing from atrium to ventricle (Fig. 2C). At the same time a muscular septum develops from the interventricular groove toward the base of the heart, separating the right and left ventricles.

In the atrium, a crescentic ridge (septum primum) appears on the dorsocephalic part of the atrium and rapidly grows down toward the ventricle. As this septum grows across the common atrial chamber, the aperture between the right and left atria (foramen primum) is progressively constricted (Fig. 2D). However, before the foramen primum is completely closed, a new opening (foramen secundum) appears high on septum primum (Fig. 2E).

The timely development of the foramen secundum prevents interruption in the shunting of blood from the right atrium into the left.

Another septum (secundum) develops just to the right of the septum primum and extends like a curtain down over the aperture in the septum primum (Fig. 2F). The septum secundum grows beside the septum primum to become a second atrial partition which is complete except for a persistent aperture adjacent to the foramen secundum. The thickened edge of this aperture forms the margin of the foramen ovale. Thus are formed two parallel partitions having apertures which are adjacent but not superimposed. The septum secundum eventually becomes fused to the septum primum except at the foramen ovale. Here the thin septum primum acts as a unidirectional flutter valve, permitting blood to flow only from the right atrium into the left. Blood cannot flow in the opposite direction because pressure in that direction presses the valvula (septum primum) against the orifice. The functional significance of this unidirectional valve is considered below in relation to circulatory adjustments after birth. Closure of the interventricular foramen awaits the partitioning of the conus and truncus arteriosus.

The Spiral Aortic Pulmonary Septum

The truncus arteriosus resembles a cylinder (Fig. 3A), extending from the conus region just above the partially divided ventricular chambers to its bifurcation into the aorta and pulmonary arteries. A pair of ridges appearing at the bifurcation and on opposite sides of the truncus arteriosus pursue a spiral course toward the ventricles (Fig. 3B). These ridges grow toward the axis of the cylinder and fuse to form a continuous spiral septum which twists 180 degrees and swings into line with the advancing edge of the interventricular septum (Fig. 3C). The spiral form of the aortic pulmonary

septum accounts for the manner in which the pulmonary artery and aorta intertwine in the fully developed heart (Fig. 3E).

The remaining interventricular foramen is closed by developing endocardial tissue from the atrioventricular cushions, the interventricular septum, and the spiral aortic pulmonary septum (Fig. 3D). The connective tissue which occludes the interventricular foramen gradually thins out to form the membranous portion of the interventricular septum.

The Formation of Cardiac Valves

The semilunar valves begin to form during the division of the truncus arteriosus into the aorta and pulmonary artery (Fig. 4A). At the junction of the ventricular conus and the truncus arteriosus, the spiral ridges on opposite sides of the channel develop localized pads of embryonic connective tissue (Fig. 4B). As the spiral ridges grow across the lumen, these endocardial cushions form two projections into each vessel and a third pad of tissue grows into each vessel from a point opposite the line of fusion of the spiral septum (Fig. 4B). In this way, three pads of connective tissue project into the lumens of the vessels and are gradually excavated and molded into valve cusps forming semilunar valves (Fig. 4C). The formation of the atrioventricular valves cannot be visualized so easily. Thick flaps of tissue proliferate from the region of the atrioventricular junction down into the ventricular chamber. The exact mechanism by which these crude flaps are converted into beautifully formed valve cusps, intricately guyed by chordae tendineae arising from the appropriate papillary muscles, is not clear.

The Ductus Arteriosus

Both the pulmonary arteries and the ductus arteriosus are remnants of the sixth pair of aortic arches. Like all the other pairs of aortic arches, the sixth connects

FORMATION OF SEMILUNAR VALVES

A. SPIRAL RIDGES

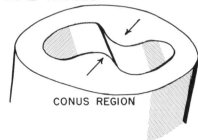

CONUS REGION

B. SECONDARY MOUNDS

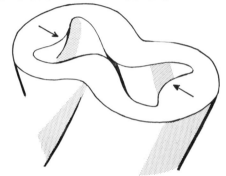

C. SEMILUNAR VALVES

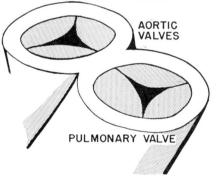

AORTIC VALVES

PULMONARY VALVE

FIGURE 4. *A*, The semilunar valves develop during the separation of the truncus arteriosus by the spiral aortic pulmonary septum (see Fig. 3).

B, Pads of endocardial tissue develop at the site of the valves. These pads originate from the spiral aortic pulmonary septum and as secondary mounds on opposite sides of the channel.

C, When partitioning of the truncus arteriosus is complete, three pads of endocardial tissue appear in the aorta and in the pulmonary artery. These pads are shaped and thinned out to produce the semilunar aortic and pulmonary valves.

THE ORIGIN OF THE DUCTUS ARTERIOSUS

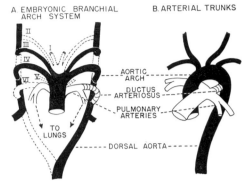

A EMBRYONIC BRANCHIAL ARCH SYSTEM   B. ARTERIAL TRUNKS

AORTIC ARCH
DUCTUS ARTERIOSUS
PULMONARY ARTERIES
TO LUNGS
DORSAL AORTA

FIGURE 5. *A*, The major arterial trunks originate by expansion and resorption of the various portions of the embryonic branchial arch system. The aortic arch develops from the left branch of arch IV, and right arch IV ultimately continues as the right subclavian artery. The pulmonary arteries to the right lung develop from right arch VI, and the right dorsal aorta normally disappears.

B, The connection between arch VI and the aorta on the left persists as the ductus arteriosus. The main pulmonary artery is divided from the ascending aorta by the spiral aortic pulmonary septum as indicated in Figure 3.

the ventral and the dorsal aorta and corresponds to the gill arches in fishes. Branching vessels arise from both the right and left limbs of the sixth aortic arch to supply the developing lungs. As the pulmonary branches from the right aortic arch develop, communication with the dorsal aorta regresses and ultimately disappears. The remnant of the sixth aortic arch between the pulmonary artery and the left aortic arch persists as the ductus arteriosus (Fig. 5). During fetal life, blood ejected by the right ventricle can bypass the pulmonary circuit and enter the descending aorta. The functional significance of this short circuit is more clearly visualized in relation to the fetal circulation as a whole.

CIRCULATORY CHANGES AT BIRTH

The early embryologic development of the circulatory system is characterized by the formation and regression of various channels to accommodate the growth patterns of the developing structures. By the eleventh week, the heart of a human embryo has been formed into a four-chambered organ with the corresponding arterial trunks. The circulatory pattern established at this time persists throughout the remainder of fetal development.

The Fetal Circulation

While the fetus remains in the uterus, the basic functions of respiration, digestion and elimination of waste products are carried out by the mother. The circulatory system must perform its logistic function during this parasitic type of existence and yet be capable of rapid accommodation to independent existence immediately after the fetus is delivered to the external world. Since the most critical commodity in both the fetus and the newborn infant is oxygen, the mechanisms required for independent respiratory activity have great importance.

In the fetus, the lungs are collapsed and have no respiratory function. The resistance to the flow of blood through the vessels of atelectatic lung tissue is extremely great. Before birth, the vascular resistance is so much greater in the pulmonary vasculature than in the systemic circulation that most of the flow is diverted around the lungs. The foramen ovale and ductus arteriosus act as bypasses permitting blood from the systemic veins to enter the systemic circulation without passing through the lungs.

If there is no orifice in the interatrial septum, left ventricular output is restricted to the quantity of blood flowing through the lungs. Under these conditions, the left ventricle pumps abnormally small amounts and may not develop normally. For example, Patten[6] illustrated the heart from an infant in whom the foramen ovale was sealed prematurely; the left ventricular cavity was very small and the wall was poorly developed. The fetal circulatory pattern can be viewed in terms of the mechanisms by which the output of the two ventricles can remain comparable in the face of greatly retarded pulmonary flow (Fig. 6A).

The flow of blood through the circulatory systems of human fetuses delivered by legal abortion has been studied angiocardiographically by Lind and Wegelius.[7] Blood returning from the placenta flows through the umbilical vein and enters the ductus venosus and vascular networks of the liver. This blood carries oxygen and nutrient materials delivered by the maternal blood in the placenta. Entering the vena cava, this partially oxygenated blood merges with systemic venous blood from the caudal portions of the fetus. Much of the blood flowing from the inferior vena cava into the right atrium streams across the chamber and passes through the foramen ovale into the left atrium. According to Windle and Becker,[8] all or nearly all of the blood from the inferior vena cava passes through the foramen ovale, while blood from the superior vena cava streams through the right atrium into the right ventricle with little mixing of the two streams. On the other hand, Everett and Johnson,[9] who used more sensitive radioisotope techniques, reported that about one-fourth of the blood from each of the vena caval streams becomes mixed.

Since the pulmonary venous return is relatively sparse, most of the oxygenated blood from the placenta flows directly into the left side of the heart to be pumped into the ascending aorta. Thus, the first branches of the aorta receive blood with maximal oxygen content for delivery to the heart and the rapidly developing brain (Fig. 6A). This mechanism is probably very important, considering the fact that at least one orifice is normally present in the atrial septum at all stages of fetal development. The blood flow through the pulmonary circulation probably increases as the lungs develop, but never even approaches the flow through

CIRCULATORY ADJUSTMENTS AT BIRTH

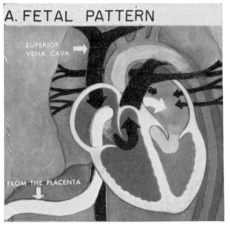
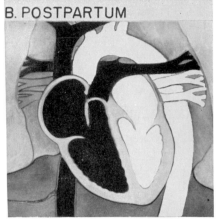

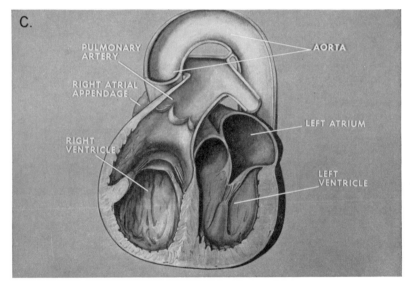

FIGURE 6.   *A,* The fetal circulatory pattern is adapted for intra-uterine existence. Venous blood from the superior vena cava flows into the right atrium and predominantly into the right ventricle. This unsaturated blood is ejected into the pulmonary artery where a major portion continues through the ductus arteriosus into the descending aorta. Resistance to flow through the collapsed lung is so great that only a small quantity of blood enters the pulmonary arteries. A correspondingly small amount of blood returns to the left atrium through the pulmonary veins. Oxygenated blood from the placenta joins the blood flowing through the inferior vena cava and tends to stream across the right atrium through the foramen ovale into the left atrium. This flow of oxygenated blood into the left atrium supplements the scanty venous return from the lungs. The mixture of oxygenated and unsaturated blood enters the left ventricle and is pumped into the aorta, from which the carotid arteries arise to supply the brain. In the descending aorta, this blood is joined by unsaturated blood flowing through the ductus and the mixture is distributed to the lower portions of the body.

B, Very shortly after birth, the flow of oxygenated blood from the placenta is interrupted. Respiratory function of the lungs must be promptly initiated if the infant is to survive. Pulmonary expansion greatly diminishes pulmonary resistance and the pulmonary blood flow is greatly increased. Constriction of the ductus arteriosus diverts the entire right ventricular outflow into the pulmonary circuit. When the increased pulmonary flow elevates left atrial pressure sufficiently to close the foramen ovale, the adaptation to extra-uterine existence is complete.

C, The components of the fully developed heart are illustrated as viewed from the left anterior oblique position for comparison with drawings portraying various developmental defects.

the systemic circuit. The output of the right and left ventricles is balanced by variations in the quantity of blood bypassing the lungs through the ductus arteriosus and through the orifices which persist in the interatrial septum (Fig. 2). The flow of blood from the right into the left atrium and from the pulmonary artery into the aorta provides a functional demonstration of the fact that pressures in the right atri m, right ventricle and pulmonary artery exceed the pressures in the corresponding channels on the left. This condition is the reverse of that seen shortly after birth.

Postpartum Circulation

Cardiorespiratory Adjustments after Delivery. When the umbilical cord is severed after delivery, the infant's only source of oxygen is eliminated pending the establishment of effective respiratory exchange in the lungs. Not only must air enter the lungs promptly, but blood flow through the pulmonary channels must be quickly augmented as well. Ardran *et al.*[10] demonstrated that the initial inflation of the lungs in fetal lambs was promptly followed by a precipitous fall in pressure in both the aorta and the pulmonary arteries (as much as 30 per cent of the initial pressure). This change was accompanied by a marked acceleration of flow through the pulmonary vascular tree, as would be expected from a reduced resistance to the flow of blood. Tying the umbilical cord caused both pressures to rise together toward or above their initial level. However, as the ductus arteriosus closed, pressures in the pulmonary artery progressively fell below that in the aorta.

Closure of the Ductus Arteriosus. In the fetus, the tunica media of the ductus arteriosus is loose in structure, and composed of elastic fibers and smooth muscle.[11] This histologic pattern is quite different from the compact tunica media of the other arterial trunks. Very shortly after respiratory activity is initiated, the

ductus arteriosus closes down. The prompt functional closure of the ductus arteriosus is probably due to contraction of smooth muscle within its walls.[12] Barclay *et al.*[13] reported angiocardiographic studies indicating that the ductus arteriosus is functionally closed 5 or 7 minutes after respiration begins, although the contrast medium was observed to flow through the channel intermittently for a considerable period. However, Everett and Johnson,[14] employing sensitive radioisotope techniques, found some reduction in ductus arteriosus flow 1 to 2 hours after birth, but a greater reduction after 9 hours. A small slitlike lumen in the ductus persisted from about the twelfth hour post partum until the eighteenth day, when anatomic obliteration was usually complete. Eldridge *et al.*[15] demonstrated that the oxygen content of "arterialized" blood from the hand and from the feet are different immediately after delivery. This difference persisted during observations lasting 3 hours and was still observable in some infants after 3 days. The lower oxygen content of blood from the feet was attributed to shunting of venous blood through the ductus arteriosus into the aorta. The oxygen content of arterialized blood in the upper and lower extremities apparently becomes equal when the ductus arteriosus is closed or the direction of flow through this channel has reversed because pressure in the pulmonary artery was lower than that in the aorta.

It is entirely possible that functional closure of the ductus arteriosus in human infants requires a period longer than the times observed during controlled experiments in animals. Hamilton *et al.*[16] stated that the ductus arteriosus in both dog and rabbit contains valvelike structures which prevent flow from the aorta into the pulmonary artery. This conclusion is not universally accepted. Similarly, reports concerning the time required to complete anatomic obliteration of the channel vary widely. According to Scammon and Norris,[17] the ductus arteriosus is obliterated by connective tissue proliferation during the first three months after delivery. The persistent patency of the ductus arteriosus in a small proportion of patients is one of the simplest forms of congenital heart disease, and will be considered in a subsequent section.

Closure of the Foramen Ovale. Soon after birth, the blood flow through the pulmonary circuit increases greatly because of the reduced resistance which follows inflation of the lungs. Functional closure of the ductus arteriosus diverts the entire right ventricular output through the lungs. These factors greatly increase the pulmonary venous flow into the left atrium. As soon as the left atrial pressure exceeds right atrial pressure, the valvula is pressed against the margin of the foramen ovale and partitioning of the heart is finally complete. Anatomic obliteration of the potential aperture of the foramen ovale requires many weeks or years. In fact, about 20 per cent of all adults have at least probe patency of this orifice,[18] a phenomenon without functional significance unless pressure in the right atrium becomes higher than that in the left. The interatrial communication will then be restored and may even enlarge until significant quantities of venous blood are shunted into the left atrium.

Changes in Arterial Pressure after Birth. The pulmonary arterial pressure immediately before birth probably ranges around 60/40 mg. Hg and slightly exceeds systemic arterial pressure. As pulmonary resistance falls and system arterial resistance rises, the pressures in the pulmonary artery and aorta diverge progressively. Ultimately, they reach the values typical of adults: systemic arterial pressures 120/80 and pulmonary arterial pressure 25/8. By this time, the pressures in the left atrium, left ventricle and aorta exceed the corresponding pressures on the right side of the heart. Judging from certain clinical observations, the systemic and pulmonary pressures diverge slowly in the human infant. For example, many infants with defective partitions in the heart or great vessels have no audible murmurs at birth and for weeks or months thereafter. The signs and symptoms of congenital deformities are usually not at all characteristic during the first few months of life. One explanation for these observations is that the pulmonary and systemic pressures remain fairly similar so that little or no blood flows through communicating channels between the systems. The typical signs do not appear until the pressure differences become sufficient to propel large quantities of blood through the abnormal apertures.

II. Congenital Malformations of the Heart

SIMPLE SHUNTS

The most common developmental defects in the heart and great vessels are incomplete partitioning of the pulmonary from the systemic circulation. During the development of the septa dividing the heart and truncus arteriosus, apertures may persist leaving orifices at various sites in the walls separating the atria, ventricles and arterial trunks, as indicated in Figures 2 and 3. The foramen ovale and the ductus arteriosus normally remain functional until after delivery, and incomplete closure of these shunts is among the most common developmental defects. The functional effects of the different simple shunts are remarkably similar whenever they occur as isolated lesions, uncomplicated by other developmental or acquired pathologic changes. The principal effect of any of these communications between the systemic and pulmonary circuits is the recirculation of oxygenated blood through the lungs, producing abnormally large pulmonary blood flow. The factors determining the direction of blood flow through simple shunts form the basis for any logical approach to the diagnosis of congenital malformations of the heart.

The Direction of Flow Through Simple Shunts

In the normal person, the pressures in the right atrium, right ventricle and pulmonary artery are lower than the corresponding pressures in the left atrium, ventricle and aorta. As indicated in Figure 23, Chapter 1, the very slight resistance to flow through the vascular system in the lungs is the fundamental reason for the low pressures in the pulmonary artery and right ventricle. The pressure in the right atrium is lower than that in the left because the thin-walled right ventricle is more easily distended during diastolic filling. So long as the pulmonary resistance remains low in relation to systemic resistance, and the right ventricular chamber remains normally distensible, the pressures in all the channels leading to the lungs are lower than those in corresponding channels leading to the systemic vascular tree.

Under these conditions, the pressure differences promote the flow of blood from the systemic to the pulmonary circuit through any communication between them as illustrated schematically in Figure 7. The quantity of blood passing through such simple shunts depends upon

FLOW THROUGH SHUNTS

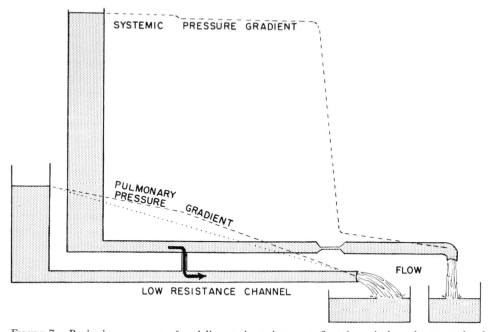

FIGURE 7. Beginning very soon after delivery, the resistance to flow through the pulmonary circuit becomes very low while the total peripheral resistance in the systemic circuit rises. The pressures in the left ventricle and aorta greatly exceed corresponding pressures in the right ventricle and pulmonary artery so long as the pulmonary vascular bed remains a low-resistance channel. These large pressure differences propel oxygenated blood through communicating channels from the systemic system into the pulmonary circuit. So long as pulmonary resistance remains low, pulmonary blood flow can be greatly increased with little change in pulmonary arterial pressure. The flow through abnormal channels connecting the pulmonary and systemic channels depends upon the size of the orifice and the magnitude of the pressure difference.

INTERATRIAL SEPTAL DEFECTS

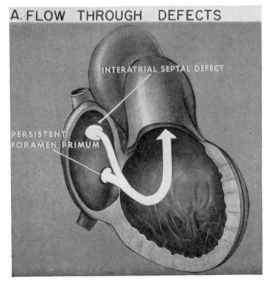
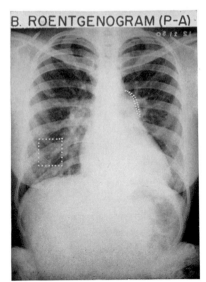

FIGURE 8.   *A*, Interatrial septal defects most commonly occur in the region of the foramen ovale. Occasionally the foramen primum fails to close (see Fig. 2). In either case, oxygenated blood surges from the left atrium into the right atrium and ventricle to be recirculated through the lungs along with the venous return from the systemic circulation.

B, The increased total pulmonary blood flow produces dilatation of the pulmonary artery, which appears as a vigorously pulsating bulge on the left side of the mediastinum. The pulmonary vascular markings are more prominent than normal. Increased pulsation of the smaller branches of the pulmonary artery is observed by fluoroscopic examination of small areas in the peripheral lung field (e.g., dotted square). Right ventricular enlargement can usually be demonstrated fluoroscopically when the patient is rotated into the oblique positions (see Fig. 13, Chap. 13) and on electrocardiograms (see Fig. 32, Chap. 10). Dilatation of the right atrium is generally indicated by tall, peaked P waves, particularly in lead II (see Fig. 33, Chap. 10), even when roentgenographic evidence is unconvincing

the pressure difference across the shunt and the resistance to flow through it. The resistance to flow is determined primarily by the caliber of the aperture or channel. The principles governing the flow through shunts are the same as those applying to valve orifices (Fig. 9, Chap. 12). The applicability of these concepts to various types of shunts will become apparent during the following discussion.

Defects in the Interatrial Septum

The most common congenital malformation of the heart is a functionally significant aperture in some part of the interatrial septum. The large proportion of individuals (20 per cent of the general population) with probe patency of the foramen ovale are not included in this group. Most interatrial defects are located at some distance from the tricuspid valves, in the general region of the foramen secundum or foramen ovale (Fig. 8*A*). Another fairly common site is in the vicinity of the foramen primum (see Fig. 2*E*). These defects range from simple apertures less than 1 cm. in diameter through multiple defects of varying size to virtual absence of the interatrial septum.

Functional Effects of Atrial Septal Defects.   As indicated in the preceding section, the pressure in the left atrium generally exceeds right atrial pressure so long as the right ventricle is more distensible than the left. For this reason, the predominant flow through atrial septal defects is from the left atrium into the right. The pressure difference between atria connected by an interatrial septal defect has been measured directly both in man[19] and in experimental animals.[20] Left atrial pressure exceeded right atrial pressure at all times except for transient reversal of the pressure gradient, usually at the beginning of atrial systole. Since the right atrial wall is excited first, pressure may build up faster in the right atrium than in the left. This mechanism could account for brief periods of reversed flow through the shunt during each cycle producing very slight unsaturation of the arterial blood. During rapid ventricular filling, the atrial pressure difference diminishes or disappears.[19]

The maximal recorded pressure differences between the right and left atria ordinarily range up to 6 or 8 mm. Hg, but the differences remain considerably below these levels during most of each cycle. These pressures do not sound particularly impressive until it is recalled that the pressure gradient along a 1 or 2 cm. stretch of the aorta or vena cava is imperceptible even when recorded by extremely sensitive apparatus. Yet, these minute pressure gradients propel the whole cardiac output along the main vascular trunks. Thus, a pressure gradient of 3 or 4 mm. Hg produces a voluminous flow through apertures of similar dimensions in the interatrial septum. The oxygenated blood that flows through the defect enters the right atrium and mingles with the returning systemic venous blood flowing to the lung (Fig. 8). Thus, the blood flowing through the shunt recirculates through the lung, increasing the total flow through the lung. The quantity of oxygenated blood flowing into the left ventricle and pumped through the systemic arteries to the tissues is approximately normal, being controlled by complex neural and humoral mechanisms indicated in Chapters 3 and 4.

Hickam[21] measured pulmonary blood flows of 15 to 20 l. per minute in resting patients with simple atrial septal defects. Thus, the right ventricular output was three or four times greater than left ventricular output. These large volumes were propelled through the lungs by a pressure difference of only 12 or 13 mm. Hg from the pulmonary artery to the left atrium. In one patient, blood flow of 15 l. per minute was maintained through the pulmonary circuit by a pressure gradient of only 4 mm. Hg. Such tremendous flow produced by a small pressure gradient signifies that the pulmonary resistance remains very low.

Diagnostic Signs of Atrial Septal Defects. Clinical evidence of atrial septal defects stems primarily from the functional effects of greatly increased pulmonary blood flow and its secondary effects.

Auscultation. A loud systolic murmur in the pulmonary area on the precordium is usually the first clue to the presence of heart disease in patients with defects in the interatrial septum. These murmurs are usually absent at birth, and may not become audible for months or years. Immediately after birth, the right ventricle has a relatively thick wall and functions under a pressure load similar to that of the left ventricle since the pressures in the pulmonary and systemic arterial systems are similar. Thus, there is little or no pressure gradient between the chambers, and insignificant quantities of blood pass through the interatrial shunts. As the pulmonary arterial resistance falls and systemic peripheral resistance rises, the pressure differences between the two systems become greater. The left ventricle becomes thick-walled and the right ventricle becomes more distensible as its pressure load diminishes. Flow through interatrial communications then increases greatly in response to the steeper pressure gradients across the interatrial partition. The intensity of the murmur appears to bear some relation to the volume flow through the interatrial defect. However, the sounds are actually due to the rush of abnormally large quantities of blood through the pulmonary conus. Thus, this systolic murmur is produced by the same mechanism that causes "functional" murmurs (see Fig. 15, Chap. 11). This fact was graphically demonstrated by phonocardiograms recorded directly from the surface of a dog's heart in which an interatrial septal defect had been produced surgically. Although a very distinct systolic murmur promptly appeared over the pulmonary conus and pulmonary artery, no murmur was recorded over either the right or the left atrium.[22] In patients, the murmur often attains such intensity that it is widely transmitted over the precordium and is associated with a thrill palpated in the pulmonary area. Diastolic murmurs in the pulmonary area may result from dilatation of the pulmonary artery, producing incompetence of the pulmonary valve.

Fluoroscopy. In most patients with functionally significant defects in the interatrial septum, the pulmonary artery is dilated. During fluoroscopic examinations of such patients in the postero-anterior position (see Fig. 8*B*), a prominent bulge can be observed on the left border of the heart just above the cardiovascular angle. Generally, abnormally great pulsation of this dilated arterial trunk can also be observed. Since it may be difficult to differentiate between simple displacement of the artery and expansile pulsation, the peripheral lung fields should be carefully examined for increased pulsation of the smaller ramifications of the pulmonary arterial tree. During this portion of the examination, the x-ray beam is restricted to a small area in the peripheral lung fields (dotted square in Fig. 8*B*), and the vascular markings are watched carefully for signs of increased pulsation. Expansile pulsation of the pulmonary artery and its branches may be increased by either increased blood flow or increased pulse pressure. Frequently both factors are present in patients with interatrial septal defects or other types of simple shunts.

Roentgenography. In most patients with interatrial defects, the right ventricle becomes enlarged because of the increased volume load (increased pulmonary blood flow), often supplemented by an increased pressure load (pulmonary hypertension). Roentgenographic evidence of anterior protrusion of the enlarged right ventricle is more easily observed when the patient is in the left anterior oblique position (see Fig. 14, Chap. 13). Usually the right atrium is also enlarged, but this is often difficult to demonstrate roentgenographically. Angiocardiography is not generally recommended as a helpful diagnostic procedure in patients with simple septal defects. However, Lind and Wegelius[23] have reported surprisingly good results using simultaneous biplanar exposures taken at rates of 10 to 12 per second.

Electrocardiography. In patients with atrial septal defects, the right atrium usually becomes somewhat enlarged and the P waves in leads I and II are tall and peaked (see Fig. 33, Chap. 10). The P waves on precordial leads are also affected by right atrial dilatation.[24] Electrocardiographic signs of right ventricular hypertrophy are generally present but are usually somewhat obscured by atypical QRS complexes. The sequence of ventricular excitation is apparently altered by an interventricular conduction disturbance. For example, the R and S waves usually have almost equal amplitude in the precordial leads from V_2 to V_6, so the normal transitional zone is not apparent. A deep S wave in lead I is often accompanied by a deep Q wave in lead III and the QRS complexes are frequently multiphasic. The QRS interval is generally at or above the upper limits of normal for the age of the patients. Such changes in QRS complexes may be associated with defects in either the interatrial or the interventricular septa, and are not very useful in distinguishing individual types of cardiac deformities.

However, they occur with sufficient regularity that they may lead to a suspicion of a congenital malformation even in young infants.

Since all the simple shunts are characterized by abnormally increased pulmonary blood flow, they share many of the same clinical signs. Although it is frequently possible to recognize the presence of an abnormal channel between the pulmonary and systemic circuits, its exact location often requires more direct demonstration by means of cardiac catheterization (see *Differential Diagnosis of Simple Shunts*). An accurate diagnosis of the exact site and nature of the lesion before corrective surgery is attempted is very important because certain types of defects are more amenable to current surgical techniques. Thus, various methods are being developed[25-29] for closure of atrial septal defects, but aberrant right pulmonary veins, which produce an identical clinical picture, present an entirely different surgical problem.

Aberrant Right Pulmonary Veins

The veins draining the right lung normally empty into the left atrium very near the interatrial septum. It is not surprising that as a result of defective development, the right pulmonary veins occasionally empty into the right atrium. Aberrant right pulmonary veins drain fully oxygenated blood from the right lung into the right atrium. This has precisely the same functional effects as the shunting of the same quantity of oxygenated blood through an interatrial septal defect. For this reason, the clinical signs symptoms of the two conditions are identical.[30] Furthermore, an interatrial septal defect and aberrant pulmonary veins are frequently seen in the same patient, with functional effects corresponding to those of a very large atrial septal defect. In this regard, a symposium on anomalous pulmonary venous connection and drainage is well worth reading.[31] Rarely, all the pulmonary veins drain into the right atrium, a condition producing a quite different set of symptoms and signs which will not be considered here.

The presence of right pulmonary veins emptying into the right atrium can often be demonstrated by inserting the tip of a cardiac catheter, under direct fluoroscopic control, into such a vein and withdrawing fully oxygenated blood from the channel (see Fig. 11B).

Ventricular Septal Defects

During the last stages of partitioning in the heart, an aperture in the interventricular septum persists (Fig. 2F). Endocardial cushion tissue proliferates into this aperture and later thins out to form the membranous portion of the interventricular septum just below the origin of the aorta and pulmonary arteries. Incomplete closure of this opening is the most common defect in the interventricular septum although apertures in the muscular portion of the septum are occasionally reported. For example, Konar and Sen Gupta[32] described an isolated defect in the muscular interventricular septum near the apex of the heart.

Functional Effects of Interventricular Septal Defects. Through an aperture connecting the two ventricular cavities, oxygenated blood is propelled from the left ventricle into the right by pressure differences which can be very large during systole (e.g., 100 mm. Hg) and relatively small during diastole (0 to 10 mm. Hg). Extremely large flows through the shunt must result unless the ventricular septal defects are small or the pressure difference is greatly reduced.

Interventricular defects are usually small and produce no functional disturbance of any kind. The heart is normal in size and configuration, the pulmonary vascular markings are normal (Fig. 9B) and exercise is well tolerated. The presence of such small interventricular shunts

INTERVENTRICULAR SEPTAL DEFECT

A. TYPICAL SITE OF SHUNT

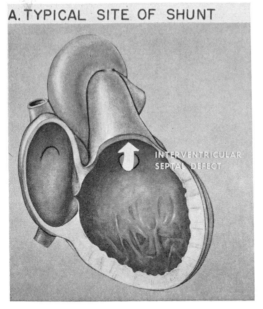

B. ROENTGENOGRAMS

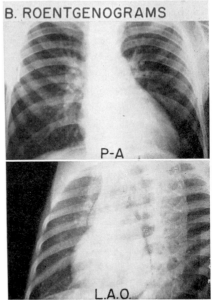

FIGURE 9.   *A*, Defects in the interventricular septum most frequently occur in the membranous septum just below the roots of the aorta and pulmonary artery. This region corresponds to the interventricular foramen, which is the last portion of the septum to be filled in (see Fig. 3). Oxygenated blood surges through this orifice from the left ventricle at high velocity during systole because the difference in pressure between the ventricular cavities is very large. Loud coarse systolic murmurs are produced by the rush of blood through the restricted orifice. They are widely transmitted over the precordium, but have maximum intensity in the third or fourth intercostal spaces along the left sternal border. Diastolic murmurs are not generally audible.

B, Usually the interventricular defect is small and is not accompanied by symptoms of any kind. The cardiac silhouette is normal in size and configuration, and the principal sign is the loud systolic murmur. This picture conforms to the classic descriptions of Roger's disease. However, if the defect is large enough to be functionally significant, frontal roentgenograms often resemble those observed in patients with atrial septal defects. The dilated, pulsating pulmonary artery is accompanied by increased pulmonary vascular markings. Left ventricular enlargement may be demonstrable in the postero-anterior view, and signs of both right and left ventricular enlargement may appear in the left anterior oblique view (see also Fig. 14).

is heralded by an extremely loud systolic murmur, transmitted widely over the precordium but with greatest intensity in the third intercostal space at the left sternal border. In most patients of this type, minor ventricular conduction disturbances are observed electrocardiographically. The P waves are usually normal in size and shape. In contrast to the small shunts, large interventricular septal defects profoundly affect the pulmonary circulation and will be considered along with other large simple shunts in subsequent sections (see *Simple Shunts with*

Pulmonary Hypertension and *Acquired Cyanosis*).

Patent Ductus Arteriosus

If the ductus arteriosus fails to close, part of the oxygenated blood ejected by the left ventricle surges through this shunt into the pulmonary artery, and merges with venous blood passing out to the lungs. The pressure difference across the ductus arteriosus can be extremely large, ranging as high as 100 mm. Hg during systole and around 70 mm. Hg during diastole. The signs and symptoms of a small persistent ductus arteriosus are distinctly different from those resulting when this channel has large caliber, just as in the case of interventricular septal defects (see *Simple Shunts with Pulmonary Hypertension* and *Acquired Cyanosis*).

Functional Effects of Patent Ductus Arteriosus. The ductus arteriosus serves as a low-resistance channel through which blood gushes out of the systemic arterial system. The volume of flow through the shunt is usually greatest during systole, diminishing during diastole in response to the variations in pressure difference. The high-velocity flow of blood through the restricted channel into the larger pulmonary artery produces turbulence (see Figs. 14 and 16, Chap. 11). Such turbulence is responsible for the vibrations, audible during both systole and diastole.

Escape of blood from the systemic arterial system tends to depress the diastolic pressure. Since the oxygenated blood flowing through the ductus does not contribute to perfusion of the tissues, left ventricular stroke volume is augmented to compensate for the shunted blood (Fig. 10*A*). However, the systolic pressure in the systemic arteries is not usually elevated in patients with patent ductus arteriosus.

Clinical Signs of Patent Ductus Arteriosus. The volume of flow through a *small* ductus arteriosus is not sufficient to require any compensatory mechanism to maintain normal blood flow through the systemic circulation. Left ventricular output is readily increased to provide normal systemic flow plus the small quantity of blood which escapes through the shunt. The slight increase in left ventricular dimensions is often not apparent from roentgenographic examination (Figs. 10*B*, *C*), the electrocardiogram is within normal limits, the arterial blood pressure remains normal and the only obvious sign is the characteristic murmur (Fig. 10*D*).

Auscultation. The most distinctive sign of patent ductus arteriosus is the "continuous" murmur. The pressure difference between the aorta and the pulmonary artery persists throughout the cardiac cycle but is greatest during systole. Thus, the velocity of flow, the degree of turbulence and the intensity of the resulting murmur reach a maximum during late systole and progressively diminish during diastole. In contrast to the systolic and diastolic murmurs associated with semilunar valvular disease (Figs. 6 and 7, Chap. 12), there is neither an interruption of the murmur nor a change in quality of the sound at the transition between systole and diastole. For this reason, the continuous quality of the murmur is quite distinctive. Furthermore, the murmur is best heard high on the left precordium, usually in the left infraclavicular area. In a large proportion of patients, the characteristic murmur is the only definite sign of the lesion. In about 10 per cent of patients, the diastolic component of the murmur is either inaudible or absent. This usually signifies elevated pulmonary pressure, retarding the flow of blood through the ductus during the diastolic interval.

Roentgenography. If the ductus arteriosus is narrow, the size and configuration of the cardiac silhouette are usually normal except for a bulge on the left border which signifies dilatation of the pulmonary artery. The dilated pulmonary trunk and the peripheral vascular markings often exhibit expansile pulsation to an abnormal degree as in other types of simple shunts. Even though the left ventricular stroke volume must increase to compensate for the shunting of blood from the systemic arterial system, left ventricular enlargement is usually not great enough to be readily distinguished roentgenographically.

Systemic Arterial Blood Pressure. A *small* ductus arteriosus produces some reduc-

PATENT DUCTUS ARTERIOSUS

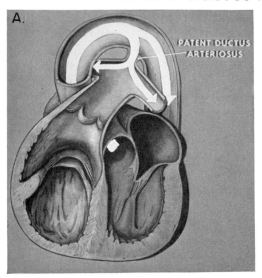

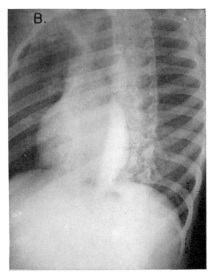

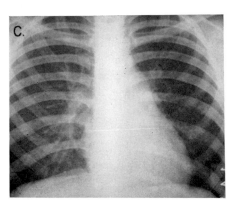

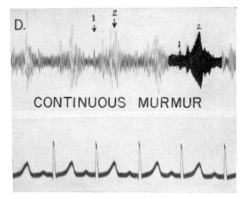

FIGURE 10.   *A*, If the ductus arteriosus remains patent, the high pressure in the aorta forces oxygenated blood into the pulmonary artery, increasing pulmonary blood flow.

B, The configuration of the cardiac silhouette in the left anterior oblique position conforms to the outline of the schematic drawing in *A*. If the ductus arteriosus is small, the cardiac silhouette may remain within normal limits when viewed from this angle. Since left ventricular stroke volume is generally increased, the movements of the left ventricular wall are somewhat exaggerated, a sign which may be distinguished during fluoroscopy.

C, In many patients the size and configuration of the cardiac silhouette are entirely normal. Dilatation of the pulmonary artery with normal or increased pulmonary vascular markings can often be demonstrated in the postero-anterior view. Left ventricular enlargement is indicated by elongation of the heart (see Fig. 11, Chap. 13). Definite evidence of cardiac enlargement generally signifies that the ductus arteriosus is large (see also Fig. 14).

D, The most characteristic sign of patent ductus arteriosus is a "continuous" murmur which begins shortly after the first heart sound gains intensity during late systole and diminishes during diastole This murmur has maximal intensity in the left intraclavicular region. The electrocardiogram is usually within normal limits.

tion in total peripheral resistance, similar to the effects of vasodilatation in peripheral vascular beds. The systemic arterial blood pressure remains within normal limits during both systole and diastole. A *large* ductus arteriosus allows blood to escape from the arterial system so rapidly that the diastolic pressure may be depressed to levels of 50 to 60 mm. Hg.

Surgical Transection of Patent Ductus Arteriosus.

During the past 20 years, techniques of intrathoracic surgery have developed to the point that in most cases the ductus arteriosus can be ligated and transected with remarkably little hazard to the patient. On rare occasions, the ductus arteriosus is so large and friable that the surgeon feels obliged to withdraw without attempting to close the vessel. Although many patients with small shunts develop normally and have a normal life span, it is quite clear that patency of the ductus arteriosus usually reduces the life expectancy and produces signs and symptoms from the abnormal load either during childhood or in adult life. Thus, patients, particularly children and young adults, whose growth is retarded or who suffer excessive fatigue or signs of heart failure from this cause are candidates for corrective surgery. Subacute bacterial endocarditis is an indication for surgery after the infection has been treated optimally by antibiotics. Appropriate therapy in patients who show no evidence of disability must be decided on the basis of the specific situation. The advisability of prophylactic ligation of the ductus arteriosus must be decided by weighing the hazard of the operation against the probability of future disability and reduced life expectancy. This problem has been discussed in detail by Gross and Longino.[38]

Aortic Septal Defect

Although the clinical signs and symptoms of patent ductus arteriosus appear distinctive, this lesion cannot be differentiated from a functionally identical communication between the pulmonary artery and the aorta. During the partitioning of the truncus arteriosus by the proliferating spiral aortic pulmonary septum (see Fig. 3), incomplete fusion may leave a residual aperture just above the semilunar valves. Fortunately, from a diagnostic point of view, this aortic septal defect is rare. When it occurs, blood from the aorta surges through into the pulmonary artery during both systole and diastole. The resulting continuous murmur is just like that heard in a patient with patent ductus arteriosus. It is frequently stated that the greatest intensity is heard lower on the precordium (e.g., in the third intercostal space to the left of the sternum) when the murmur results from an aortic septal defect. This point of distinction has not prevented its being mistaken for a ductus arteriosus.[34-36] Gross[37] has reported surgical closure of an aortic septal defect unexpectedly encountered in a patient presumed to have a patent ductus arteriosus.

Differential Diagnosis of Simple Shunts

Because of the pressure differences between the systemic and pulmonary channels, simple communications between these systems characteristically result in abnormally large blood flow through the lungs. Thus, dilatation and abnormal pulsations of the pulmonary artery and of the peripheral vascular markings in the lungs can occur in each type of defect described above. Certain characteristic features, however, permit differentiation by routine clinical methods in "typical" patients. For example, whenever a characteristic continuous murmur is heard on the upper left precordium of a patient with evidence of increased pulmonary blood flow, he probably has a shunt between the aorta and pulmonary artery. As pointed out above, this murmur is common to both a patent ductus arteriosus

DIFFERENTIAL DIAGNOSIS OF SMALL SHUNTS

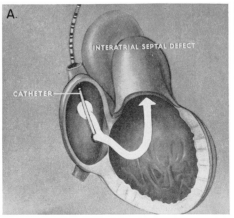
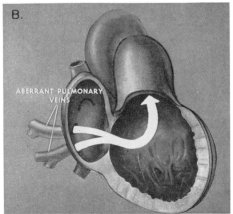
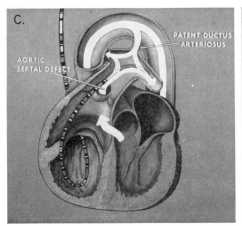
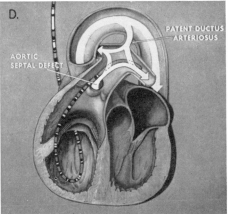

FIGURE 11.   *A,* The oxygen content of blood samples withdrawn from a catheter in the right atrium is higher than that of blood from the venae cavae if an interatrial septal defect is present.

B, If right pulmonary veins empty into the right atrium, the oxygen content of blood in this chamber is elevated just as with an atrial septal defect. The only convincing method of distinguishing between these two conditions consists of inserting the tip of the catheter into the pulmonary vein or into the atrial septal defect under fluoroscopic control. This feat can be accomplished in a fairly large proportion of patients.

C, The functional similarities of an interventricular septal defect, aortic septal defect and patent ductus arteriosus are indicated in this schematic representation. Defects in the interventricular septum are generally characterized by loud systolic murmurs over the lower precordium, without audible diastolic murmurs. The shunts between the aorta and pulmonary artery generally cause "continuous murmurs" (see Fig. 10), and may also diminish systemic arterial diastolic pressure and widen the pulse pressure.

D, Patent ductus arteriosus and aortic septal defects are functionally identical and may not be distinguished by cardiac catheterization, since the shunts are in the same region. The principal point of distinction is the fact that patent ductus arteriosus is much more common than aortic septal defects.

and an aortic septal defect which generally cannot be distinguished by routine clinical methods. If the continuous murmur has maximum intensity in the third intercostal space just to the left of the sternum, the lesion is more apt to be an aortic septal defect. Cardiac catheterization often fails to distinguish these two lesions (see Fig. 11). Angiocardiography should give more definitive information, but is rarely employed because an aortic septal defect is usually not considered.

The usual descriptions of interventricular septal defects apply only to small shunts. The heart remains normal in size and configuration because the flow through the small aperture is not sufficient to impose a load on either ventricle. In such patients, the only sign is a loud systolic murmur. However, large defects in the interventricular septum produce signs and symptoms much like those associated with other simple shunts. The pulmonary artery may become dilated, pulmonary vascular markings are accentuated and pulsate vigorously, and both right and left ventricles may become enlarged to different degrees.

Interatrial septal defects and aberrant right pulmonary veins are functionally identical and usually cannot be distinguished by routine clinical methods. Small interatrial septal defects probably produce no clinical sign whatever (not even a significant murmur).

In view of the functional similarity of the various simple shunts, a definitive diagnosis often requires cardiac catheterization. The presence of a left to right shunt can be detected by inserting the catheter into the pulmonary artery and then withdrawing blood samples through the catheter as its tip is moved under fluoroscopic control into different positions in the pulmonary arteries, right ventricle, right atrium and venae cavae. The flow of oxygenated blood through a shunt elevates the oxygen saturation both near the orifice and beyond it.

Changes in blood oxygen saturation serve to localize the shunts to arterial trunks, ventricles or atria, but fail to distinguish between patent ductus arteriosus and aortic septal defects, or between interatrial septal defects and aberrant right pulmonary veins. These shunts can be more accurately localized by inserting the catheter through the orifice or channel (Fig. 11).

Additional valuable information concerning the site and magnitude of shunts is now being obtained by means of indicator dilution curves. If a dye is injected into a peripheral vein and the changes in its concentration in a peripheral artery are continuously registered, a curve of increasing and decreasing concentration of the dye can be recorded. The configuration of this dye concentration curve is altered by the presence of shunts. By injecting the dye through a catheter with its tip at various locations in the pulmonary arteries, right ventricle, right atrium and venae cavae, the changes in the contour of the recorded curves can be interpreted to provide information concerning the location of the aperture and the amount and direction of flow through the abnormal channels. If the dye is injected distal to the site of a defect, the blood traverses normal pathways and a normal pattern is recorded. If material is injected proximal to a defect, some of the dye will either be shunted through the defect or diluted by blood traversing the shunt in the opposite direction through the abnormal channel. This technique is particularly valuable for detecting shunts through which blood flows only from the right side of the heart into the systemic circulation.[38] In such patients, oxygen saturation within the right chambers and the pulmonary artery is not affected.

In the presence of interatrial septal defects or aberrant right pulmonary veins, the curves produced by injecting the dye first into the left pulmonary artery and then into the right are different because flow into the right atrium is predominantly from the right lung rather than from the left.[39] For additional information on this subject, the reader is referred to original publications of Wood and his associates.[38-41]

In most patients with significantly increased pulmonary blood flow, the systolic pressures in the pulmonary artery and right ventricle are elevated. The pressures may be in the upper range of normal or far above normal levels. Generally, normal pressures are recorded from catheters wedged in peripheral pulmonary arterial branches. This indicates that the principal cause of the pulmonary hypertension is increased resistance to the flow of blood through the pulmonary arterial system. Since increased pulmonary resistance may grossly affect the signs and symptoms generally found with simple uncomplicated shunts, the hemodynamic alterations associated with pulmonary hypertension deserve consideration.

SIMPLE SHUNTS WITH PULMONARY HYPERTENSION

The classic signs and symptoms of the various shunts described in preceding sections actually apply only to small or moderate-sized communications. The quantity of blood flowing through such shunts constitutes no immediate threat to survival. However, large defects, particularly those between the ventricles and arterial trunks, can transmit such large portions of the total left ventricular output into the pulmonary circuit that the patients cannot long survive unless flow through the lungs is severely restricted.

Normally, the pulmonary resistance is so slight that an arteriovenous pressure gradient of 4 to 6 mm. Hg is sufficient to propel not only the normal resting flow through the lungs (4 to 5 l. per minute) but as much as three times this amount with no increase in pulmonary arterial pressure.[42] In the systemic circulation, the same volume flow is propelled from the aorta to the venae cavae by a mean arteriovenous pressure difference of some 90 mm. Hg or more. Thus, the normal resistance to flow through the systemic circuit must be some 10 to 15 times greater than pulmonary vascular resistance.

The significance of this fact becomes apparent in considering a heart with a very large interventricular septal defect.

THE SIGNIFICANCE OF PULMONARY HYPERTENSION

A. EXCESSIVE PULMONARY FLOW

B. EQUALIZED PULMONARY AND SYSTEMIC FLOW

PULMONARY RESISTANCE < SYSTEMIC RESISTANCE

PULMONARY RESISTANCE = SYSTEMIC RESISTANCE

FIGURE 12. *A*, The pulmonary vascular resistance is greatly increased when there are large shunts in the partitions of the heart. The functional importance of the response is illustrated by an extreme example in which the interventricular septum failed to form (see Fig. 2*C*). Blood ejected from the single ventricle would tend to flow predominantly into the pulmonary artery, since this circuit offers less resistance. If the pulmonary resistance were only one-tenth that of the systemic circuit, a correspondingly small fraction of the total ventricular ejection would enter the aorta to perfuse the tissues. Usually, pulmonary blood flow exceeds systemic flow by only three- or fourfold, indicating that pulmonary resistance is much higher than normal.

B, The flow through the systemic and pulmonary circuits can be the same only if the pulmonary resistance equals systemic arterial resistance.

In such a case, the right and left ventricles function more or less like a single ventricular chamber. Since the blood ejected from this chamber can go into either the pulmonary artery or the aorta, the quantity entering each vessel is determined by the relative resistance to flow through the two vascular systems. Clearly, the preponderant flow would pass through the low-resistance pulmonary circuit (Fig. 12*A*). If the pulmonary resistance diminished and the systemic resistance increased normally in an infant with this condition, the systemic resistance might well exceed pulmonary resistance by tenfold. The systemic blood flow would be only one-tenth the pulmonary blood flow. Thus, normal perfusion of the tissues would require a total ventricular output about ten times normal. Such tremendous output is beyond the capacity of the ventricles and the infant would not survive. However, pulmonary resistance at birth is approximately equal to systemic resistance. If a balance between pulmonary and systemic resistance were maintained, the systemic and pulmonary flow would be equalized even with a large defect in the partitions of the heart (Fig. 12B). Since the systemic resistance always progressively increases after birth, the maintenance of abnormally high pulmonary resistance is essential for survival in the presence of large apertures between the ventricles and arterial trunks.

Causes of Pulmonary Hypertension

In the fetus, the walls of the pulmonary arteries have thick muscular coats (which normally thin out during early childhood). The pulmonary resistance actually exceeds systemic resistance and pulmonary blood flow is much less than systemic flow. Thus, even large shunts produce little circulatory disability in the fetus. Immediately after birth, pulmonary resistance normally diminishes progressively and systemic resistance rises. During this adjustment many infants expire. For example, of 1000 live infants with congenital malformations of the heart, nearly half died within the first month.[43] Presumably, many patients die because the heart cannot sustain either the required volume or the required pressure load abruptly imposed during the conversion from the fetal type of circulation. The high pulmonary resistance may persist longer than normal in infants surviving with large shunts, and flow through the shunts may be absent or in the reverse direction from that observed in older individuals. The causes of high pulmonary resistance must be sought among the factors which produce pulmonary constriction.[44-46]

Histologic changes in the walls of pulmonary arterial branches are generally demonstrable in patients with persistent severe pulmonary hypertension. Edwards and his associates[47-49] have repeatedly reported finding extensive hypertrophy of the media in the muscular arteries within the lungs of patients with large shunts between the ventricles or arterial trunks. This hypertrophy was often accompanied by fibrosis of the intima. They have emphasized the similarity between the pulmonary arteries in such patients and in the normal fetus, suggesting that the former may represent a carry-over from fetal life. However, many such patients fail to develop evidence of severe pulmonary hypertension until later in life, often after reaching maturity.

Paul Wood[50] was impressed with the fact that the incidence of pulmonary hypertension ranged around 20 per cent in his series of patients with different cardiac disorders including atrial septal defects, ventricular septal defects, patent ductus arteriosus and mitral stenosis. On this basis he proposed that approximately 20 per cent of such persons react to pulmonary congestion or increased pulmonary blood flow in a vigorous and vicious manner, developing pulmonary hypertension, while others tend to decrease pulmonary resistance in response to increased pulmonary flow. The incidence of pulmonary hypertension is not uniform in different series reported. For example, Swan et al.[51] reported mean pulmonary arterial pressures in excess of 40 mm. Hg in only 1 of 24 patients with atrial septal defects, 14 of 20 patients with ventricular septal defects, and 10 of 24 patients with patent ductus arteriosus. Significantly, they observed that the pulmonary blood flow was similar in the three groups. Thus, the degree of pulmonary hypertension appears to reflect an increase in pulmonary resistance sufficient to restrict the total output of the ventricles to a level within their capacity.

If the pulmonary arterial resistance exceeds total systemic resistance, flow through the shunt is reversed, forcing unsaturated blood from the pulmonary circuit into the systemic circulation. This circulatory pattern resembles that observed in the normal fetus (Fig. 6). Flow of unsaturated blood through simple shunts into the systemic circulation has been most frequently reported in patients suffering from patency of the ductus arteriosus.[52-56] However, similar effects also result from other large simple shunts such as large interventricular septal defects (see above) and interatrial septal defects.[57, 58] If sufficient quantities of unsaturated blood returning from the systemic veins are shunted into the systemic arterial system, a bluish discoloration of the skin, mucous membranes and nailbeds, called cyanosis, becomes visible.

ACQUIRED CYANOSIS

Normally, 100 ml. of blood contains about 15 gm. of hemoglobin, which is almost completely saturated with oxygen when it leaves the lungs. While the oxygenated blood flows through the systemic capillary networks, some oxygen diffuses into the tissues, part of the oxyhemoglobin being converted to reduced hemoglobin. Typical venous blood contains about 5 mg. of reduced hemoglobin per 100 ml., which is responsible for its bluish color. Because of the voluminous blood flow through the skin, so little oxygen is extracted that the amount of reduced hemoglobin within the cutaneous capillaries is only slightly larger than that in arterial blood. In the normal person, the red oxyhemoglobin in cutaneous capillaries and venules is responsible for pink flesh tones, particularly where dense vascular networks are near the surface (e.g., lips, mucous membranes, nailbeds, cheeks). If the quantity of reduced hemoglobin in these cutaneous vessels rises above 5 gm. per 100 ml. of blood, the bluish color characteristic of venous blood

replaces the pinkish hue in these areas. This bluish tinge, or cyanosis, must be explained in terms of the factors which increase the quantity of reduced hemoglobin in the small cutaneous vessels.

If arterial unsaturation with cyanosis persists for long periods, a bulbous enlargement of the terminal phalanges on the fingers and toes develops. In this condition, called clubbing, the configuration of the distal phalanges changes from a roughly cylindrical to a more spherical shape. The nails develop a pronounced longitudinal curvature. The cause of clubbing is not known.

Etiology of Cyanosis

The quantity of reduced hemoglobin in the venous blood from any particular tissue depends upon four factors: (a) the total hemoglobin concentration in the blood, (b) the quantity of reduced hemoglobin in the arterial blood, (c) the rate of blood flow through the tissue and (d) the rate of oxygen utilization by the tissue. For reasons pointed out above, blood in the cutaneous vessels usually contains very little reduced hemoglobin (about 1 or 2 gm. per 100 ml.) (see Fig. 2, Chap. 4). The concentration of reduced hemoglobin in these vessels can increase as a result of either retarded blood flow or abnormally high levels of reduced hemoglobin in the arterial blood. If arterial blood contains reduced hemoglobin in excess of 3 to 4 gm. per 100 ml., the normal oxygen uptake in the skin may well increase the total quantity of reduced hemoglobin in cutaneous vessels above the critical level of 5 gm. per 100 ml. of blood. Whenever cyanosis occurs during rapid cutaneous blood flow, the arterial blood must contain abnormally large quantities of reduced hemoglobin. In patients with developmental defects in the heart, cyanosis results primarily from the flow of unsaturated venous blood through the defect to mix with the arterial blood.

The amount of venous admixture required to produce cyanosis is related to the quantity of blood being oxygenated by the lungs. Under some conditions, the entire systemic venous return mixes with the blood returning from the lungs without producing cyanosis. As an oversimplified example, consider a patient in whom the interventricular septum failed to develop (Fig. 13). Blood returning from the systemic veins and from the lungs mixes within a single ventricular chamber and is then ejected into both the pulmonary artery and theaorta. In such cases, it is rather common for the pulmonary blood flow to be three times as large as systemic flow. If 5 liters of systemic venous blood (6.7 gm. of reduced hemoglobin per 100 ml.) were completely

ETIOLOGY OF CYANOSIS

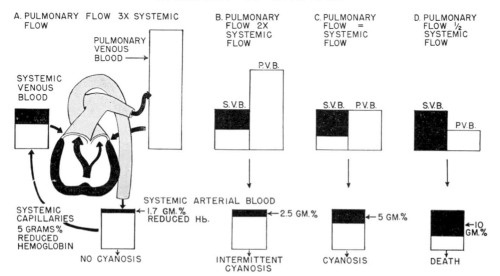

FIGURE 13. Cyanosis becomes visible when the blood in superficial vessels of the skin contains approximately 5 gm. of reduced hemoglobin per 100 ml. The conditions under which cyanosis would appear when the systemic and pulmonary venous blood is completely mixed in a single chamber can be evaluated by making certain assumptions which are not always applicable. First, let us assume that during flow through the skin, 2 gm. of oxyhemoglobin per 100 ml. of blood is converted to reduced hemoglobin by oxygen extraction in the skin capillaries. Under these conditions, the arterial content of reduced hemoglobin must be increased to 3 gm. per 100 ml. to produce a total of 5 gm. per 100 ml. in the skin. If oxygen consumption and the volume flow through the systemic vessels are normal,[59] the mixed systemic venous blood should contain 5 gm. more of reduced hemoglobin per 100 ml. than the arterial blood. To simplify discussion, assume that pulmonary venous blood is fully oxygenated and contains no reduced hemoglobin.

A, Under the conditions outlined above, if the pulmonary blood flow is three times the normal systemic flow, the mixture in the arterial blood would contain 1.7 gm. of reduced hemoglobin per 100 ml. The additional 2 gm. of reduced hemoglobin per 100 ml. acquired in the skin brings the level to 3.7 gm. of reduced hemoglobin per 100 ml., a quantity insufficient to produce cyanosis.

B, If pulmonary blood flow were only twice the systemic flow, the skin vessels would contain about 4.5 gm. per 100 ml. of reduced hemoglobin so that an increase in oxygen consumption (e.g., exercise) or retardation of blood flow (crying) could produce visible cyanosis.

C, Equal flow through the systemic and pulmonary circuits (see Fig. 12) would result in an arterial content of reduced hemoglobin of more than 5 gm. per 100 ml. of blood, which should produce a cyanosis at rest that would become more severe under various conditions. Note that the mixed venous content of oxygen is greatly depressed, indicating that the oxygen tensions in the tissues are probably greatly depressed.

D, If pulmonary resistance increased so much that pulmonary flow was reduced to one-half the systemic flow, the arterial blood would contain 10 gm. of reduced hemoglobin (only 5 gm. of oxyhemoglobin) per 100 ml. and mixed venous blood would be completely unsaturated. Obviously, this situation could not be survived.

mixed with 15 liters of fully oxygenated blood from the lungs, the arterial blood would contain only 1.7 gm. of reduced hemoglobin per 100 ml. During flow through the cutaneous vessels, extraction of 1 or 2 gm. more of hemoglobin per 100 ml. of blood would be insufficient to produce cyanosis (see Fig. 13*A*). Although the quantity of reduced hemoglobin in mixed venous blood from the systemic veins is higher than normal (6.7 gm. per 100 ml.), there would be no cyanosis because this blood is mixed with such a large volume of fully oxygenated blood from the lungs. Similarly, if pulmonary blood flow were just twice systemic flow (Fig. 13*B*), the mixed blood leaving the single ventricle would contain only 2.5 gm. of reduced hemoglobin per 100 ml. Although a patient with this degree of arterial unsaturation might not display cyanosis under resting conditions, he would develop cyanosis more easily during retarded blood flow in the skin (crying) or during greater oxygen consumption and unsaturation of the systemic venous blood (e.g., exercise). Furthermore, cyanosis would be more readily visible if the cutaneous vessels were engorged with blood. If pulmonary and systemic flows were equal (pulmonary resistance = systemic resistance), the mixed blood in the arteries would contain 5 gm. of reduced hemoglobin per 100 ml. and cyanosis would surely result (Fig. 13*C*). If pulmonary blood flow were diminished to one-half of the systemic flow, the arterial and venous blood would contain 10 and 15 gm. of reduced hemoglobin per 100 ml., respectively (Fig. 13*D*). In other words, the arterial blood would contain little oxygen and venous blood would contain none, a condition which would not support life unless cardiac output and the oxygen carrying capacity of the blood were greatly increased.

Cyanosis also develops in patients with large shunts through which blood flows from systemic veins into the left atrium, left ventricle or aorta. Under these conditions, unsaturated blood, which would otherwise pass through the lungs for oxygenation, escapes through the shunt and mixes with the systemic arterial blood. In other words, the systemic flow is augmented at the expense of pulmonary blood flow. If the oxygen consumption and total systemic blood flow remain normal, cyanosis would appear when some 2 liters of blood returning from systemic veins with 8.5 gm. of reduced hemoglobin per 100 ml. is mixed with 5 liters of arterial blood per minute. Under these conditions, systemic flow greatly exceeds pulmonary flow. Smaller volumes passing from right to left through the shunt would produce cyanosis only if oxygen consumption increased (more reduced hemoglobin in mixed venous blood) or systemic blood flow were diminished.

Although these examples are oversimplified, their interpretation leads to two important generalizations: (*a*) If pulmonary blood flow exceeds normal systemic flow by twofold or more, cyanosis is not likely even with complete mixing of the total systemic and pulmonary venous return. (*b*) Cyanosis develops in patients with large unidirectional right to left shunts when pulmonary blood flow is significantly below systemic blood flow. In the presence of a large shunt between the ventricles or arterial trunks, pulmonary flow is less than systemic flow only when pulmonary resistance exceeds systemic resistance. Thus, the factors which lead to pulmonary hypertension (increased pulmonary resistance) also promote the development of cyanosis if the pulmonary vascular changes become excessive.

In addition to the factors considered above, the total concentration of hemoglobin in the blood affects the development of cyanosis. For example, a patient with severe anemia is less apt to develop cyanosis since a much greater proportion of the hemoglobin must be relieved of oxygen to produce 5 gm. of reduced hemoglobin per 100 ml. of blood. In this process the oxygen tension in the blood would be lowered to an extreme degree. This unfavorable condition is avoided by acceleration of systemic blood flow (increased cardiac output). Conversely, many patients with arterial unsaturation and cyanosis develop polycythemia. The total hemoglobin concentration in the blood is increased to abnormally high levels. Although polycythemia increases the oxygen capacity of the blood, a smaller drop in blood oxygen tension produces 5 gm. of reduced hemoglobin per 100 ml., and cyanosis is more apt to develop.

Differential Diagnosis of Shunts with Acquired Cyanosis

Since cyanosis in congenital malformations of the heart means that unsaturated blood from the systemic veins is entering the systemic arterial system, the direction of flow through the defects must be reversed. This means that the pressures in the channels leading to the lungs must exceed the corresponding pressures on the systemic side of the circulation. Most patients who acquire cyanosis as a result of large shunts with compensatory pulmonary hypertension have a history of transient or intermittent cyanosis extending over months or years during the time that the pulmonary resistance has built up. In some patients, intermittent cyanosis is present from birth, indicating that the pulmonary resistance did not fall in the normal fashion after respiratory activity was initiated.

Atrial Septal Defects

Even large defects in the interatrial septum are fairly well tolerated. Indeed, complete absence of the septum may give rise to remarkably slight cyanosis. The increased volume flow through the lungs imposes a volume load on the right ventricle, which is well tolerated. However, if pulmonary blood flow is excessive, pulmonary resistance increases and pulmonary hypertension develops. The right ventricle hypertrophies to compensate for the pressure load and its distensibility is reduced. If the diastolic pressure of the thick-walled right ventricle rises, right atrial pressure also increases. The right and left atrial pressures become equalized and the flow through the shunt diminishes or even reverses. Under these circumstances, the systemic arterial blood contains some shunted venous blood and exhibits slight unsaturation. Catheterization may fail to demonstrate any significant shunt in either direction across the septal defect. Pressures in the pulmonary artery and right ventricle tend to be elevated but not to very high levels. At this stage, systemic and pulmonary blood flows are often roughly equal. Thus, the circulatory compensation for a large interatrial septal defect tends to eliminate the characteristic signs of this condition. The quantity of venous blood passing into the left atrium is frequently increased by exertion and during certain phases of the respiratory cycle. If advantage is taken of these facts, the presence of atrial defects may be more easily demonstrated during cardiac catheterization.

Atrial Septal Defect with Pulmonary Stenosis

Defects in the interatrial septum often accompany stenosis of the pulmonary valve (see Fig. 15). In this condition, increased right ventricular systolic pressure is required to force the normal complement of blood through the stenotic orifice. Thus, the valvular stenosis places a pressure load on the right ventricle corresponding to the increased resistance which may develop in peripheral pulmonary arterial branches due to atrial septal defects alone. If hypertrophy diminishes

LARGE SHUNTS PRODUCING PULMONARY HYPERTENSION AND ACQUIRED CYANOSIS

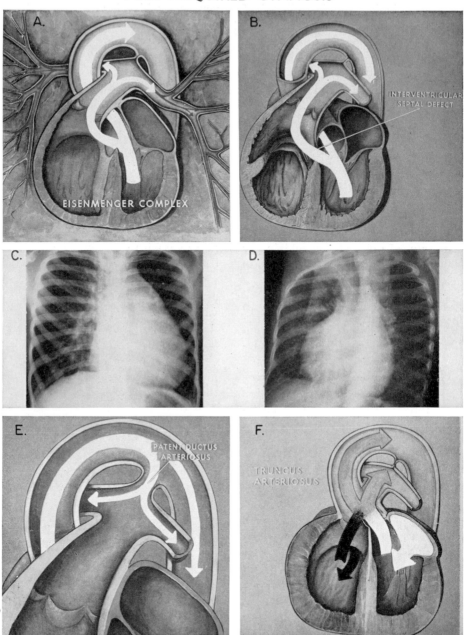

FIGURE 14. *A*, The Eisenmenger complex is essentially a large interventricular septal defect accompanied by an apparent displacement of the aorta toward the right so that its orifice lies over the defect. So long as pulmonary resistance remains lower than total systemic resistance, oxygenated blood from the left ventricle joins the systemic venous blood in the right ventricle and recirculates through the lung. The right ventricle becomes hypertrophied to compensate for the sustained pressure load. In response to the greatly increased pulmonary blood flow, pulmonary resistance rises as indicated in Figure 12. The left ventricle must eject an abnormally large stroke volume and must dilate to compensate for the volume load. In many such patients, pulmonary resistance ultimately exceeds systemic resistance, so the shunt is reversed and unsaturated blood enters the aorta to produce cyanosis (see text).

right ventricular distensibility, the right atrial pressure may increase enough to reverse the normal pressure gradient and force unsaturated blood into the left atrium. From a functional point of view there is no significant difference between localized valvular stenosis and generalized peripheral increase in pulmonary arterial resistance, and these two conditions can often be distinguished only by catheterization. A sharp pressure drop across the pulmonary valve region indicates local stenosis in this region (see Fig. 15). Angiocardiography in the right anterior oblique position often reveals a constricted region near the pulmonary valve if pulmonary stenosis is present. Post-stenotic dilatation, abnormally low pulmonary flow and diminished pulmonary vascular markings are frequently observed.

Large Defects in the Interventricular Septum

As indicated in the preceding discussion of pulmonary hypertension, free communication between the right and left ventricles through a large defect in the ventricular septum can be survived only if the pulmonary resistance remains high. The systolic pressure in the right ventricle and in the pulmonary artery are characteristically identical with systolic pressure in the systemic arteries even during changes in cardiac output (e.g., exercise). Although left ventricular output may have been grossly increased in the earlier stages, by the time the pres-

sures become equalized, its ejection is probably normal. Right ventricular hypertrophy and right atrial dilatation remain the predominant electrocardiographic signs. Roentgenographic evidence of right ventricular hypertrophy, pulmonary arterial dilatation and pulsation, and increased pulmonary vascular markings is comparable to that in other types of acquired cyanosis with large simple shunts (Fig. 14).

Eisenmenger's complex has been the traditional example of acquired cyanosis. It consists of right ventricular hypertrophy, interventricular septal defect with orifice of the aorta situated above the interventricular septum (overriding or dextroposed aorta), and cyanosis, usually developing around the time of puberty. The ready access of blood from the right ventricle into an overriding aorta has been erroneously ascribed a role in the development of cyanosis in these patients. Actually, blood ejected by the right ventricle follows the path of least resistance and enters the aorta in significant quantities only if the pulmonary resistance is as high as or higher than the systemic resistance. The presence of an overriding aorta is not easily distinguished even during pathologic examination because a probe can be easily passed from the right ventricle into the aorta through any large ventricular septal defect. For these reasons, there seems little justification for making a distinction between the Eisenmenger complex and any other large interventricular septal defect with cy-

B, A large interventricular septal defect is functionally identical with the Eisenmenger complex.

C, Massive dilatation of the pulmonary artery, greatly increased pulmonary vascular markings, and enlargement of both right and left ventricles occur whenever a large shunt exists between either the ventricles or the arterial trunks.

D, Right and left ventricular enlargements are easily demonstrated in the left anterior oblique view. Roentgenographic changes illustrated in *C* and *D* could occur in patients with any of the large shunts illustrated in this figure.

E, If the ductus arteriosus attains a caliber approaching or exceeding that of the aorta, pulmonary hypertension must develop to prevent siphoning off of most of the total systemic flow. When aortic and pulmonary arterial pressures are approximately equal, blood flow through the shunt is diminished or absent during certain phases of each cyle. The characteristic "continuous" murmur is often replaced by either systolic or diastolic murmurs (see text).

F, A truncus arteriosus with a large pulmonary artery is fundamentally a very large aortic septal defect and has the same functional effects as a large ductus arteriosus.

anosis due to vascular changes in the lungs.

Persistent Truncus Arteriosus

Complete absence of the spiral aortic pulmonary septum is merely an exaggerated form of aortic septal defect. The functional effects are exactly the same as those of a large interventricular septal defect so long as a large pulmonary artery arises from the common trunk to supply the lungs. Here again, the pulmonary resistance must be greatly elevated to provide a degree of balance between systemic and pulmonary flow which is compatible with life. The systolic pressures in the right and left ventricles, truncus arteriosus, and aortic and pulmonary arteries are equal. This lesion does not characteristically produce cyanosis until pulmonary blood flow is diminished below aortic flow, indicating that venous admixture has occurred. The pressures and blood oxygen saturation determined from catheters in the truncus arteriosus are often indistinguishable from those encountered with either a large interventricular septal defect or a large patent ductus arteriosus.

Patent Ductus Arteriosus

The signs and symptoms of a *large* patent ductus arteriosus complicated by severe pulmonary hypertension differ greatly from those produced by small aortic-pulmonary shunts. The distinctive "continuous" murmur is generally absent, being replaced by a blowing diastolic murmur along the left border, a systolic murmur of varying intensity, or even no audible murmurs at all.[55] The systemic arterial pressure is normal. The heart is enlarged, usually from expansion of both the right and left ventricles. Electrocardiograms may indicate either right or left ventricular preponderance. However, another fairly characteristic sign has been described as useful.[46, 55] Unsaturated blood passing through the ductus arteriosus from the pulmonary artery enters the aorta at a point just beyond the origin of the innominate artery and opposite or beyond the origin of the left subclavian and left carotid arteries. For this reason, the degree of unsaturation of arterial blood is often demonstrably greater in the lower extremities than in the right arm or head. If there is no demonstrable difference between arterial oxygen saturations in the upper and lower extremities under ordinary circumstances, it may be induced if the patient breathes gas mixtures with low oxygen tensions. The resulting increase in pulmonary resistance fosters larger flow of unsaturated blood from the pulmonary artery into the descending aorta. Because of the variable relationship between the ductus arteriosus and the vessels springing from the aortic arch, the exact peripheral distribution of unsaturated arterial blood cannot be accurately predicted.[46] If dyes are injected into the peripheral vein or through a catheter into the right side of the heart, the dye entering directly into the aorta from the pulmonary artery can be distinguished in the femoral artery and occasionally in progressively diminishing quantities in arteries more proximal on the aortic arch.

STENOSIS OF THE PULMONARY VALVE

Three main types of congenital pulmonary stenosis are found: valvular stenosis, infundibular stenosis, and a combination of the two[60] (Fig. 15). In the first type, the pulmonary valvular cusps are fused during embryologic development into a diaphragm or conical membrane with a small central orifice. Infundibular stenosis sometimes develops as a long narrow muscular channel replacing the normally capacious outflow tract of the right ventricle. More commonly, there is a narrow constriction at some level below the pulmonary valve. As an isolated lesion, valvular stenosis is much more common than infundibular stenosis; occasionally they occur together. In contrast, infundibular stenosis is a much more common cause of pulmonary obstruction in the tetralogy of Fallot (see below).

The mainstem of the pulmonary artery is often grossly dilated just beyond the valvular stenosis, and even the right and left branches may be larger than normal in spite of diminished pulmonary blood flow. This post-stenotic dilatation is a typical response to many kinds of local obstruction in the vascular system.

Functional Effects of Pulmonary Stenosis

Constriction of the outflow tract of the right ventricle imposes a requirement for a greater systolic ventricular pressure to

PULMONARY STENOSIS

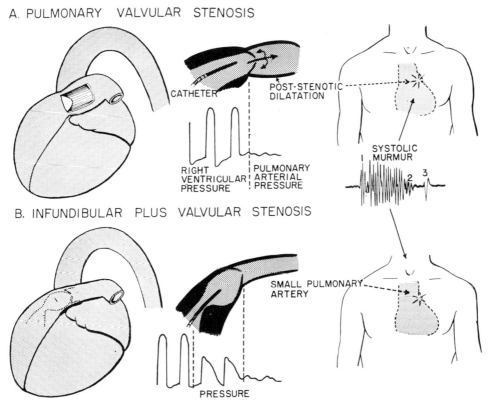

A. PULMONARY VALVULAR STENOSIS

CATHETER

POST-STENOTIC DILATATION

RIGHT VENTRICULAR PRESSURE

PULMONARY ARTERIAL PRESSURE

SYSTOLIC MURMUR

B. INFUNDIBULAR PLUS VALVULAR STENOSIS

SMALL PULMONARY ARTERY

PRESSURE

FIGURE 15. *A*, Occasionally, congenital stenosis of the pulmonary valve is an isolated lesion, but it is usually accompanied by defects in either the atrial or the ventricular septum. The pulmonary valve consists of a conical diaphragm with a small aperture at the apex, and the pulmonary artery beyond the valve is usually dilated (post-stenotic dilatation). To overcome the high resistance to flow through the restricted valvular orifice, the right ventricular systolic pressure becomes greatly elevated. The mean pulmonary arterial pressure beyond the constriction is normal or diminished but the pulse pressure is greatly reduced. Turbulent flow of blood through the small orifice produces a systolic murmur which is widely transmitted over the precordium, but has maximal intensity in the pulmonary area. Post-stenotic dilatation of the pulmonary artery produces a prominent bulge on the left border of the mediastinal shadows in the postero-anterior position. Right ventricular hypertrophy is more easily detected with the patient in the left anterior oblique position (see drawing on the left).

B, A combination of infundibular and valvular stenosis produces signs and symptoms similar to those of isolated pulmonary valvular stenosis. In this condition, the pulmonary artery is generally hypoplastic rather than dilated. Pressure records obtained during slow withdrawal of a catheter usually demonstrate a stepwise change in pressure rather than the abrupt change in pressure patterns observed with isolated pulmonary valvular stenosis.

eject the normal complement of blood into the pulmonary artery. Obviously, the magnitude of the pressure gradient between the right ventricle and the pulmonary artery depends upon the resistance to outflow (caliber of channel) and the velocity of blood flow. The basic problem is the same as that presented by aortic stenosis. In a case of infundibular stenosis, cinefluorographic angiocardiograms indicated that the caliber of the narrowed channel was greatly diminished during systole, apparently by constriction of the surrounding myocardium. Such constriction serves to augment impedance to right ventricular outflow during systolic ejection. The systolic pressure in the right ventricle ranges from high normal values to levels exceeding 200 mm. Hg.[60] The normal right ventricle is ill prepared to develop such high intraventricular pressure. As has been repeatedly mentioned, a long-continued right ventricular pressure load causes the right ventricle to assume many of the characteristics of the left ventricle. This is particularly true in congenital malformations where the load is present at least from birth. The right ventricular wall is very thick (often exceeding 1 cm.). The chamber is more rounded in contour instead of having a crescentic cross section. So long as myocardial hypertrophy is an adequate compensatory mechanism, right ventricular dilatation is not functionally significant. The rush of blood through the constricted pulmonary outflow tract produces intense turbulence, with loud systolic murmurs occupying most of the systolic interval but often exhibiting maximal intensity in mid-systole (such as occurs with aortic stenosis).

Symptoms of Pulmonary Stenosis

Many patients with isolated pulmonary stenosis have no symptoms whatever. Their growth, appearance, exercise tolerance and subjective feeling of well-being are deceptively normal. When the con-dition is more severe, mild or moderate dyspnea on exertion and occasional palpitation are noted, even when the right ventricular systolic pressure is as high as 170 mm. Hg.[61] If the orifice is small, the principal effect is limitation in the maximum cardiac output which can be maintained by the right ventricle. Very high pressures may be required to provide high-velocity flow through restricted apertures. Right ventricular failure is the principal hazard in these patients.

Diagnostic Signs of Isolated Pulmonary Stenosis

The murmur of pulmonary stenosis is widely transmitted over the precordium, but usually is loudest in the pulmonary area, the third intercostal space at the left sternal margin. It is important to recall that in some patients the murmur of aortic stenosis may also have maximal intensity in that area. Evidence of right ventricular hypertrophy is best observed roentgenographically in the left anterior oblique position. Electrocardiograms usually provide confirmatory evidence of right ventricular preponderance. Valvular stenosis with post-stenotic dilatation usually can be identified in the antero-posterior position by the local bulge on the left of the mediastinum in the presence of diminished vascular markings in the lung fields (Fig. 15). In patients with infundibular stenosis, the mid-portion of the left border of the cardiac silhouette is normal or concave (Fig. 16). Fluoroscopic examination is useful for demonstrating diminished pulsations of the pulmonary vessels.

During cardiac catheterization, a definitive diagnosis of pulmonary stenosis can be obtained if systolic pressures in the right ventricle are elevated and accompanied by a sharp drop in pressure in the pulmonary artery (Fig. 15). The constriction in the outflow tract of the right ventricle can often be demonstrated by angiocardiography, particularly with the patient in the right anterior oblique position.

DEVELOPMENTAL DEFECTS WITH INTRINSIC CYANOSIS

Cyanosis is such an obvious clinical sign that congenital malformations of the heart are usually divided into a cyanotic and a noncyanotic group. However, under certain conditions, cyanosis develops in patients with simple shunts which are generally classified as noncyanotic (see *Acquired Cyanosis*). To this extent, the common classification of these lesions causes unnecessary confusion. Nevertheless, cyanosis accompanies certain types of developmental defects with sufficient regularity that they can be grouped in the cyanotic category if it is recognized that even these lesions do not always produce cyanosis in all cases or at all times. For example, some patients with these lesions develop cyanosis immediately after birth while others do not exhibit this sign for some months after delivery. The widely diversified lesions which characteristically produce cyanosis have two features in common: (*a*) defects in the partitions of the heart and (*b*) anatomic obstruction to the flow of systemic venous blood into or through the lungs. The differential diagnosis of these defects is facilitated by always considering the site of the shunt and the nature and location of the obstruction to flow of venous blood into the lungs. Variations in these two factors produces a bewildering array of malformations, many of which are extremely rare. For this reason, a few of the more common examples will serve to illustrate the basic approach to their diagnosis.

Tetralogy of Fallot

The most familiar congenital defect typically accompanied by cyanosis is the tetralogy of Fallot, so named because four main items were included in the original description: (*a*) a defect in the membranous portion of the interventricular septum, (*b*) an overriding aorta in which the aortic orifice lies over the interventricular septum, (*c*) pulmonary stenosis (valvular or infundibular) and (*d*) right ventricular hypertrophy. Two of these four features are redundant. An overriding aorta cannot occur without an interventricular septal defect, and pulmonary stenosis regularly causes right ventricular hypertrophy. Excluding the superfluous descriptive features, the basic defects are interventricular septal defect and pulmonary stenosis, which acts to obstruct the flow of unsaturated systemic venous blood into the lungs.

Although the exact embryologic origin of this type of defect is not established, its location suggests abnormal partitioning of the conus region by the spiral aortic-pulmonary septum (see Fig. 16*A*). If the ridges which ultimately form this spiral septum deviated toward the right during their original development, the caliber of the outflow tract from the right ventricle would be reduced and the aortic orifice would be relatively large. The spiral aortic septum could not fuse with the proliferating interventricular septum, and an interventricular septal defect would be left directly below the origin of the aorta (an overriding aorta). This explanation is probably oversimplified, but it gives some insight into the possible mechanisms underlying this defect. It seems significant that most patients with tetralogy of Fallot have an infundibular type of stenosis rather than a valvular stenosis, although the latter does occur. Valvular stenosis also could result from a deviation of the spiral septum to the right, producing an asymmetric division of the endocardial cushions which ultimately form the pulmonary valves (see Fig. 4).

Functional Effects of Tetralogy of Fallot. The pulmonary stenosis impedes the flow of blood into the pulmonary artery. To provide a steeper pressure gradient across the restricted pulmonary orifice, right

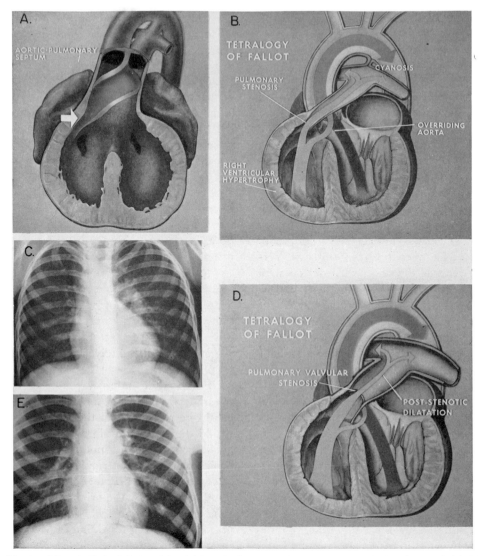

FIGURE 16. *A*, If the lower portion of the spiral aortic-pulmonary septum deviated toward the right during its development, the infundibular portion of the right ventricle would be constricted and the aorta would override the interventricular septum. This schematic diagram is probably oversimplified, but it illustrates a mechanism by which the tetralogy of Fallot could develop.

B, The tetralogy of Fallot is characterized by an infundibular type of pulmonary stenosis, overriding of the aorta, a large interventricular septal defect, and right ventricular hypertrophy. Because of the increased resistance to flow past the infundibular obstruction into the lungs, cyanosis generally develops during the first weeks or months of life.

C, The outflow tract of the right ventricle and the pulmonary trunk are usually diminished in size, so the left border of the cardiac silhouette is concave in the frontal view. The vascular markings in the peripheral lung fields are greatly reduced. The hilar shadows are often quite prominent but appear disorganized, probably owing to the presence of dilated bronchial arteries which serve to supplement pulmonary blood flow (see text). Right ventricular hypertrophy can be demonstrated by rotating the patient into the left anterior oblique view (see *B* above).

D, In a small proportion of patients with tetralogy of Fallot, the pulmonary valve is stenotic, with or without an accompanying infundibular type of stenosis. Valvular stenosis may also result from unequal partitioning of the truncus arteriosus by deviation of the spiral aortic pulmonary septum (see Fig. 4). The functional effects of valvular and infundibular stenosis are the same, so the clinical pictures are correspondingly similar.

E, Pulmonary valvular stenosis is often accompanied by post-stenotic dilatation of the pulmonary artery which appears as a prominent bulge on the left side of the mediastinum.

424

ventricular pressure must reach abnormally high levels. Because of the large interventricular septal defect, the right ventricular systolic pressure equals left ventricular pressure. If resistance to flow through the stenotic region into the pulmonary artery is sufficiently great, unsaturated blood from the right ventricle joins the oxygenated blood from the left ventricle, entering the aorta for distribution throughout the systemic circulation. The arterial blood therefore contains increased quantities of reduced hemoglobin, producing visible cyanosis.

An important factor contributing to the development of cyanosis is the reduction in pulmonary blood flow. Since systemic venous blood is shunted away from the pulmonary circuit into the aorta, pulmonary blood flow is less than systemic flow. Mechanisms increasing pulmonary flow are beneficial under these conditions. For example, children may not have visible cyanosis for months or years after birth; closure of the ductus arteriosus is frequently delayed. However, as the ductus arteriosus finally closes, the degree of cyanosis and severity of the patient's clinical condition usually become worse. Thus, the equalizing effect of a patent ductus arteriosus on pulmonary and systemic flow is beneficial even though the arterial blood passing into the pulmonary artery is only slightly unsaturated and can take up only limited quantities of oxygen during passage through the lungs. This is the functional basis for one approach to therapy of tetralogy of Fallot and related lesions (see Fig. 17). Many patients improve to varying degrees between 5 and 9 years of age, presumably because bronchial flow through the alveolar membranes increases by a mechanism similar to that operative when pulmonary flow is obstructed by an embolus. The dilated bronchial arteries serve to supplement pulmonary blood flow just like a patent ductus arteriosus or an artificial shunt (see Fig. 17).

Clinical Signs of Tetralogy of Fallot. The typical roentgenographic changes in patients with tetralogy of Fallot include diminished pulmonary vascular markings in the peripheral lung fields on teleroentgenograms and during fluoroscopy. The shadows in the hilar region may be prominent but are disorganized, apparently because the bronchial arteries are dilated (Fig. 16C). Infundibular stenosis is generally associated with a small pulmonary artery which leaves a prominent convexity in the mid-portion of the left border of the cardiac silhouette. Right ventricular hypertrophy tends to elevate the apex of the heart. The resulting cardiac silhouette is shaped like a wooden shoe, the *cor en sabot*. However, right ventricular hypertrophy is more easily demonstrated with the patient in the left anterior oblique position. The enlarged right ventricle protrudes anteriorly toward the sternum and increases the angulation at the junction of the right ventricle and the ascending aorta. The space enclosed within the aortic arch—the aortic window—is abnormally clear if the pulmonary artery and its main branches are smaller than normal. A small proportion of patients with tetralogy of Fallot have pulmonary valvular stenosis instead of infundibular stenosis. In this disorder, the peripheral lung fields are clearer than normal, but the pulmonary arterial trunk is distended by the post-stenotic dilatation, which appears as a prominent bulge on the left border of the cardiac silhouette viewed in the postero-anterior position (Fig. 16E).

Right ventricular hypertrophy produces the characteristic changes in the electrocardiographic pattern, but this may be somewhat obscured by the ventricular conduction disturbance which commonly accompanies defects in the ventricular septum. The P waves are generally tall and peaked in leads I and II, indicating right atrial enlargement. Loud coarse systolic murmurs are widely

SURGICAL THERAPY OF INSUFFICIENT PULMONARY FLOW

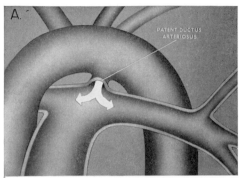

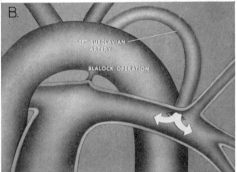

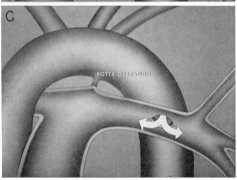

FIGURE 17. *A*, In patients with tetralogy of Fallot or other congenital deformities including obstruction of flow into the pulmonary artery, the pulmonary blood flow is supplemented by blood flowing through a patent ductus arteriosus. When the ductus arteriosus closes spontaneously, total pulmonary blood flow is diminished, cyanosis becomes worse and exercise tolerance is further reduced.

B, By joining a subclavian artery to a branch of the pulmonary artery, Blalock produced an artificial ductus arteriosus to supplement pulmonary blood flow.

C, A direct anastomosis of the aorta to the pulmonary artery was developed by Potts as an alternative method for producing an artificial ductus arteriosus.

These surgical procedures often produce dra-

transmitted over the precordium, but have maximum intensity in the third left intercostal space. Unfortunately, these murmurs are not sufficiently distinctive to permit tetralogy of Fallot to be distinguished from other congenital or acquired lesions on the basis of auscultatory findings. A definitive diagnosis can be made by cardiac catheterization in which a catheter is passed through the interventricular septal defect into the aorta. Pulmonary stenosis is indicated by a marked pressure drop between the right ventricle and the pulmonary artery (see Fig. 15).

Treatment of Tetralogy of Fallot. The beneficial effects of a patent ductus arteriosus on patients with tetralogy of Fallot led to the development of the Blalock-Taussig operation. Anastomosing a subclavian artery to a pulmonary artery produces an artificial ductus arteriosus and increased pulmonary blood flow (Fig. 17*B*). Potts' modification of this procedure involves a direct anastomosis between the pulmonary artery and descending aorta (Fig. 17*C*). Definite improvement followed these procedures because pulmonary blood flow was supplemented even though the artificial shunts carried partially oxygenated blood from the systemic system. In other words, pulmonary flow more nearly approaches systemic flow if these procedures are successful. From a functional point of view, it is far more important to remove the obstruction to the flow of systemic venous blood from the right ventricle into the pulmonary artery. A direct attack on the pulmonary stenosis with infundibular resection or valvulotomy is more physiologic than an artificial shunt.

Tricuspid Atresia

If the tricuspid orifice is blocked during embryologic development, the right ven-

matic improvement in the condition of patients with scanty pulmonary blood flow, even though systemic arterial blood is used to supplement pulmonary flow.

tricle fails to develop normally and persists as a small rudimentary chamber. Since venous blood from the systemic circuit cannot enter the right ventricle directly, it must flow through a defect in the interatrial septum (Fig. 18*A*). In the left atrium this unsaturated blood mixes with the oxygenated blood returning from the lungs. The mixed blood then enters a large left ventricular cavity. Blood ejected from this functionally single ventricle flows readily into the aorta, but must pass through an interventricular septal defect into the rudimentary right ventricle and then into the pulmonary artery (Fig. 18*B*). As if this were not enough, most of

TRICUSPID ATRESIA

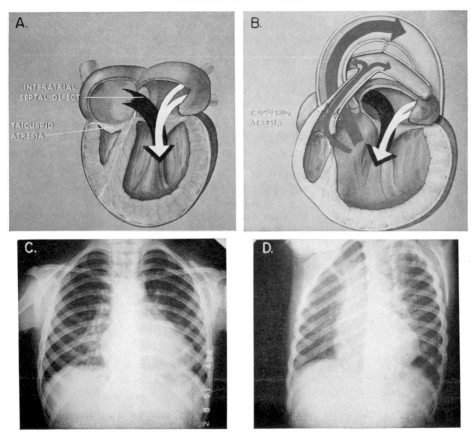

FIGURE 18.   *A,* Tricuspid atresia blocks the channel between the right atrium and right ventricle so the entire systemic venous return must pass through an atrial septal defect and mix with pulmonary venous blood in the left atrium.

B, The mixed blood enters the left ventricle. Blood ejected from this single chamber flows readily into the aorta, but must pass through an interventricular septal defect into a rudimentary right ventricular chamber. Flow into the pulmonary artery is usually restricted by either infundibular or pulmonary valvular stenosis, so pulmonary blood flow is less than systemic flow. This condition often leads to severe cyanosis, as indicated in Figure 13. However, if the channel to the lungs offers slight resistance and pulmonary flow exceeds systemic flow, cyanosis can be slight.

C, In the frontal view, the cardiac silhouette has a concave left border similar to tetralogy of Fallot (Fig. 16). The pulmonary vascular markings are usually diminished and disorganized.

D, In the left anterior oblique view, the anterior margin is flattened because of the diminutive right ventricle. In some patients, presystolic pulsation of the right atrium can be observed on the anterior border of the heart because this chamber is not hidden behind the right ventricle. The left ventricle projects posteriorly over the spine, and left ventricular preponderance is demonstrated electrocardiographically.

these patients have pulmonary stenosis either in the form of a long, narrow infundibular channel or a valvular diaphragm with a small central perforation. The high resistance to flow past these obstructions restricts pulmonary blood flow and results in cyanosis, as indicated in Figure 13C.

The severity of the cyanosis and diminished exercise tolerance is related to the degree of resistance to flow into the pulmonary artery. Most patients have severe pulmonary stenosis and correspondingly severe cyanosis. However, I have seen a 17 year old girl with this lesion who had moderate cyanosis and prominent clubbing of the fingers, and yet was quite athletic, indulging in sports such as swimming. The pulmonary vascular markings indicated unusually good pulmonary blood flow. Theoretically, if the pulmonary resistance is slight and pulmonary blood flow is greater than systemic flow, arterial unsaturation need not be sufficient to produce visible cyanosis although the blood from the lungs and systemic veins is mixed in the single ventricle (see Fig. 13).

Diagnosis of Tricuspid Atresia.   Because of the small pulmonary outflow tract and pulmonary artery, the left border of the heart is concave, closely resembling tetralogy of Fallot in the frontal projection. The pulmonary vascular markings are diminished in the peripheral lung fields, and the hilar shadows generally appear disorganized from dilatation of the bronchial vessels (Fig. 18C). Viewed in the left anterior oblique position, the cardiac silhouette is usually flattened anteriorly (Fig. 18D). Owing to the hypoplastic condition of the right ventricle, the right atrium may be prominent on the sternal border and presystolic movement of this portion of the silhouette constitutes a fluoroscopic sign of tricuspid atresia. Evidence of left ventricular enlargement appears on both roentgenograms and electrocardiograms. Thus, cyanosis associated with diminished pulmonary blood flow and left ventricular enlargement are the characteristic features of this condition.

Truncus Arteriosus

A persistent truncus arteriosus with a large pulmonary artery branching off was considered in the section on large shunts with pulmonary hypertension and acquired cyanosis. If the truncus arteriosus persists because the pulmonary artery is absent, the lungs are served only by dilated bronchial arteries (Fig. 19A). Under these conditions, pulmonary blood flow is extremely sparse and cyanosis is severe immediately after birth. Most patients with this type of lesion expire during the first few weeks of life. No surgical therapy for the condition has been devised. Since the pulmonary artery is missing, the cardiac silhouette has a concave left border in the frontal view (Fig. 19B). The ventricular shadow often appears rounded and the mediastinal shadow is often narrow. In the left anterior oblique position, the heart shadow is reminiscent of a large apple suspended on a stem, the truncus arteriosus (Fig. 19A).

Complete Transposition of the Arterial Trunks

If the truncus arteriosus is divided by a straight septum rather than the normal spiral septum, the right ventricle pumps systemic venous blood into the aorta and the left ventricle ejects oxygenated blood back through the pulmonary artery (Fig. 20A, C). When the arterial trunks are transposed in this manner (Fig. 20B), all the normal partitions dividing the heart act to obstruct the flow of systemic venous blood into the lungs. If no defects in the partitions remain, none of the oxygenated blood from the lungs can be distributed to the tissues of the body and the patient promptly expires (Fig. 20C). On the other hand, any patient with a large atrial septal defect and a large patent ductus arteriosus has a chance of surviving at least for some years (Fig. 20D). If only one shunt persists between the pulmonary and systemic circuits, flow through the shunt must periodically reverse its direction. This means that the pressures on the two sides of the communication must fluctuate in opposite directions. One such patient survived for 11 months with extremely severe cyanosis from birth. Her venous blood was extremely viscous and nearly as black as tar. Postmortem examination disclosed that the only communications between the systemic and pulmonary systems consisted of three small interatrial septal defects, none of which was larger than a match head. The ductus arteriosus was obliterated. That patients can survive with such low oxygen tensions in the blood and tissues seems incredible.

The pressures in the systemic and pulmonary circuits are approximately equal when flow is periodically reversed through shunts between them. Under these conditions, pulmonary vascular pressures are greatly elevated and the lungs are congested. For this reason, the pulmonary vascular markings are accentuated and pulsate vigorously. This is the only congenital malformation with severe cyanosis from birth with evidence of increased pulmonary blood flow. In most patients, the size of the cardiac silhouette increases progressively to reach a massive degree of enlargement in the first few months of life (Fig. 21). This cardiac enlargement has been ascribed to a deficient oxygen supply to the myocardium. Such an explanation may be particularly applicable to those patients in whom the coronary arteries arise from the aorta and are per-

TRUNCUS ARTERIOSUS

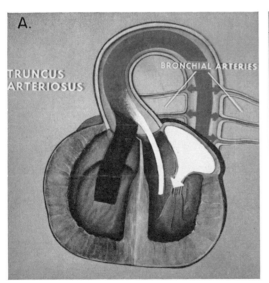 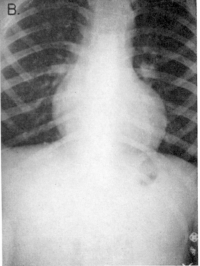

FIGURE 19. A, If the pulmonary arteries fail to develop, the truncus arteriosus persists and the lungs are served solely by dilated bronchial arteries (see Fig. 24, Chap. 1). The blood flow through the lungs is scanty, so the oxygenated blood is mixed with larger volumes of highly unsaturated systemic venous blood and cyanosis is very intense. Most patients with this condition usually succumb during the first few weeks of life.

B, On roentgenograms exposed in the postero-anterior position the left border of the cardiac silhouette is concave and the mediastinum is very narrow because the pulmonary artery is missing. The lung fields are abnormally clear and the pulmonary vascular shadows are spotty and lack continuity. In the left anterior oblique view, the heart shadow resembles an apple suspended from a curved stem, as suggested by the contours of the schematic drawing in A. The right ventricle forms an angle of almost 90 degrees with the ascending aorta, a condition known as shelving.

COMPLETE TRANSPOSITION OF THE ARTERIAL TRUNKS

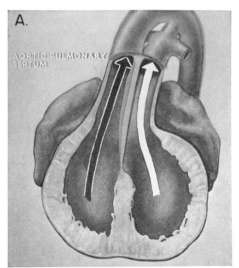

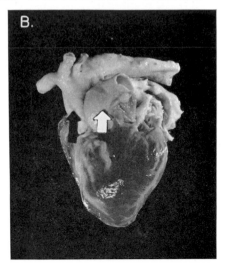

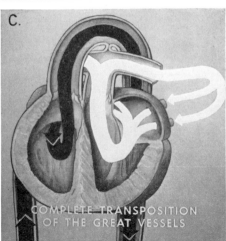

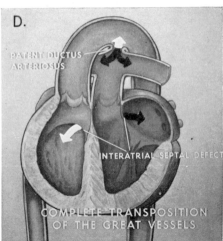

FIGURE 20.   *A,* The spiral form of the aortic pulmonary septum accounts for the manner in which the aorta and the pulmonary arteries are entwined in the fully developed heart (see Fig. 3). If the aortic pulmonary septum were straight, the arterial trunks would be parallel and the right ventricle would empty into the aorta and the pulmonary artery would arise from the left ventricle.

B, A specimen from a patient with complete transposition of the great vessels demonstrates the parallel courses of the aorta and pulmonary artery suggested in *A.* Furthermore, the arterial trunks arise from the wrong ventricles.

C, When the arterial trunks are completely transposed, systemic venous blood enters the right ventricle and is pumped directly back into the aorta. Oxygenated blood from the pulmonary veins enters the left ventricle and is recirculated right back through the lungs. All the partitions of the heart serve to obstruct the flow of systemic venous blood to the lungs.

D, Complete transposition of the great vessels would be fatal immediately after birth unless there are communications between these two independent circulatory systems. Through defects in the atrial or ventricular septa or through a patent ductus arteriosus sufficient exchange of blood may occur to support life. In this case, larger defects in the partitions of the heart are most advantageous, and on occasion have been induced surgically.

fused with systemic venous blood with its very low oxygen tension. Currently the only treatment consists of producing or expanding shunts between the systemic and pulmonary circuits. An artificial ductus arteriosus (Fig. 17) or a surgically induced interatrial septal defect augments the exchange between the two independent systems. With the development of the mechanical heart-lung apparatus to take over cardiopulmonary function during surgery, it may be possible to correct this condition by reversing the origins of the arterial trunks. This technique also has important potential applications in direct surgical correction of many of the congenital malformations of the heart.

SUMMARY

The embryologic development of the heart is so complex that one may marvel that congenital malformations are not common. Most of the developmental defects are due to incomplete development of partitions which divide a single convoluted tube into four chambers and corresponding arterial trunks. Since the pulmonary resistance normally becomes much less than systemic resistance after delivery into the external world, the pressures in the left atrium, left ventricle and aorta are much higher than those in the corresponding channels carrying systemic venous blood to the lungs. For this reason, oxygenated blood returning from the lungs is diverted through the shunts into the right chambers or pulmonary artery to be recirculated back through the lungs. Therefore, all the simple shunts have common features, representing compensation to increased pulmonary flow.

Large shunts between the left and right ventricles and between the aorta and pulmonary artery theoretically could divert virtually all the output of both ventricles through the lungs, leaving insufficient flow through the systemic arteries to support life. This contingency is prevented by a greatly increased pulmonary resistance, which approaches or even exceeds systemic resistance. Under these conditions, the systemic and pulmonary blood flows are roughly balanced. Excessive pulmonary resistance sometimes develops, which

ROENTGENOGRAMS IN COMPLETE TRANSPOSITION

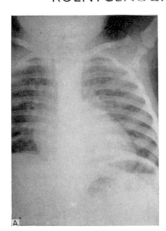 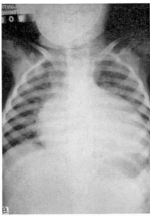 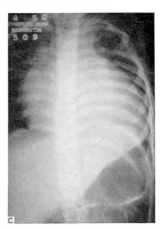

FIGURE 21.   *A*, Complete transposition of the great vessels is the only condition producing severe cyanosis from birth in the presence of pulmonary congestion. Since the pulmonary artery lies behind the ascending aorta, the mediastinal shadow is narrow in the frontal view and the left border of the heart is concave. This roentgenogram was taken on a patient at 4 months of age.

B, At the age of 28 months, the cardiac silhouette was greatly enlarged. This is a characteristic feature of complete transposition of the great vessels, and frequently obscures the narrow mediastinal shadow.

C, By 34 months, the heart had become tremendous, virtually filling the thoracic cavity.

diverts unsaturated blood returning from the systemic veins into the systemic arteries to produce "acquired" cyanosis. Certain common congenital malformations characteristically cause cyanosis because anatomic arrangements impede or restrict the flow of systemic venous blood into the lungs. In each type of lesion it is important to consider the location of the septal defects and the site and nature of the obstruction to flow of unsaturated systemic blood into or through the pulmonary circuit.

REFERENCES

1. RUSHMER, R. F., and BLANDAU, R. J. Congenital malformations of the heart. Part I. Development of the normal heart. Part II. Acyanotic congenital heart disease. Part III. Cyanotic heart disease. (Motion picture. Abstract descriptions in *J.A.M.A.*, 150:241, 1952; 154:703, 1954.)

2. PATTEN, B. M. The first heart beats and the beginning of the embryonic circulation. *Amer. Scien.*, 39:225–243, 1951.

3. GOSS, C. M. First contractions of the heart without cytological differentiation. *Anat. Rec.*, 76:19–27, 1940.

4. PATTEN, B. M., KRAMER, T. C., and BARRY, A. Valvular action in the embryonic chick heart by localized apposition of endocardial masses. *Anat. Rec.*, 102:299–311, 1948.

5. HOFF, E. C., KRAMER, T. C., DuBOIS, D., and PATTEN, B. M. The development of the electrocardiogram of the embryonic heart. *Amer. Heart J.*, 17:470–488, 1939.

6. PATTEN, B. M. *Human Embryology.* Philadelphia, The Blakiston Co., 1948.

7. LIND, J., and WEGELIUS, C. Angiocardiographic studies on the human fetal circulation. A preliminary report. *Pediatrics*, 4:391–400, 1949.

8. WINDLE, W. F., and BECKER, R. J. The course of the blood through the fetal heart: an experimental study in the cat and guinea pig. *Anat. Rec.*, 77:417–426, 1940.

9. EVERETT, N. B., and JOHNSON, R. J. Use of radioactive phosphorus in studies of fetal circulation. *Amer. J. Physiol.*, 162:147–152, 1950.

10. ARDRAN, G. M., DAWES, G. S., PRICHARD, M. M. L., REYNOLDS, S. M. R., and WYATT, D. G. The effect of ventilation of the foetal lungs upon the pulmonary circulation. *J. Physiol.*, 118:12–22, 1952.

11. JAGER, B. V., and WOLLENMAN, O. J., JR. An anatomical study of the closure of the ductus arteriosus. *Amer. J. Path.*, 18:595–613, 1942.

12. KENNEDY, J. A., and CLARK, S. L. Observations on the ductus arteriosus of the guinea pig in relation to its method of closure. *Anat. Rec.*, 79:349–371, 1941.

13. BARCLAY, A. E., BARCROFT, J., BARRON, D. H., FRANKLIN, K. J., and PRICHARD, M. M. L. Studies of the foetal circulation and of certain changes that take place after birth. *Amer. J. Anat.*, 69:383–406, 1941.

14. EVERETT, N. B., and JOHNSON, R. J. A physiological and anatomical study of the closure of the ductus arteriosus in the dog. *Anat. Rec.*, 110:103–112, 1951.

15. ELDRIDGE, F. L., HULTGREN, H. N., and WIGMORE, M. E. The physiological closure of the ductus arteriosus in newborn infants: a preliminary report. *Science*, 119:731–732, 1954.

16. HAMILTON, W. F., WOODBURY, R. A., and WOODS, E. B. The relation between systemic and pulmonary blood pressures in the fetus. *Amer. J. Physiol.*, 119:206–212, 1937.

17. SCAMMON, R. E., and NORRIS, E. H. On the time of the post-natal obliteration of the fetal blood passages (foramen ovale, ductus arteriosus, ductus venosus). *Anat. Rec.*, 15:165–180, 1918.

18. PATTEN, B. M. The changes in circulation following birth. *Amer. Heart J.*, 6:192–205, 1930.

19. SHAFFER, A. B., SILBER, E. N., and KATZ, L. N. Observations on the interatrial pressure gradients in man. *Circulation*, 10:527–535, 1954.

20. LITTLE, R. C., OPDYKE, D. F., and HAWLEY, J. G. Dynamics of experimental atrial septal defects. *Amer. J. Physiol.*, 158:241–250, 1949.

21. HICKAM, J. B. Atrial septal defect. A study of intracardiac shunts, ventricular outputs and pulmonary pressure gradient. *Amer. Heart J.*, 38:801–812, 1949.

22. SCHUELER, L. A. JR. The mechanisms of origin and transmission of heart sounds and murmurs. Medical thesis. University of Washington School of Medicine, 1952.

23. LIND, J., and WEGELIUS, C. Atrial septal defects in children. An angiocardiographic study. *Circulation*, 7:819–829, 1953.

24. THOMAS, P., and DEJONG, D. The P wave in the electrocardiogram in the diagnosis of heart disease. *Brit. Heart J.*, 16:241–254, 1954.

25. GROSS, R. E., WATKINS, E., JR., POMERANZ, A. A., and GOLDSMITH, E. I. A method for surgical closure of interauricular septal defects. *Surg. Gynec. Obstet.*, 96:1–23, 1953.

26. MURRAY, G. Closure of defects in cardiac septa. *Ann. Surg.*, 128:843–853, 1948.

27. BLOUNT, S. G., JR., SWAN, H., GENSINI, G., and McCORD, M. C. Atrial septal defect. Clinical and physiologic response to complete closure in five patients. *Circulation*, 9: 801–812, 1954.

28. BAILEY, C. P., DOWNING, D. F., GECKELER,

G. D., LIKOFF, W., GOLDBERG, H., SCOTT, J. C., JANTON, O., and REDONDO-RAMIREZ, H. P. Congenital interatrial communications: clinical and surgical considerations with a description of a new surgical technic: atrio-septo-pexy. *Ann. Intern. Med.*, 37:888–920, 1952.

29. BAILEY, C. P., BOLTON, H. E., JAMISON, W. L., and NEPTUNE, W. B. Atrio-septo-pexy for interatrial septal defects. *J. Thorac. Surg.*, 26:184–219, 1953.

30. SNELLEN, H. A., and ALBERS, F. H. The clinical diagnosis of anomalous pulmonary venous drainage. *Circulation*, 6:801–816, 1952.

31. EDWARDS, J. E., SWAN, H. J. C., BURCHELL, H. B., WOOD, E. H., MANKIN, H. T., GERACI, J. E., KIRKLIN, J. W., and BRUWER, A. Symposium on anomalous pulmonary venous connection (drainage). The pathologic and developmental considerations in anomalous pulmonary venous connection. *Proc. Staff Meet. Mayo Clin.*, 28:441–452, 1953.

32. KONAR, N. R., and SEN GUPTA, A. N. Ventricular septal defect at an unusual site with other congenital anomalies. *Brit. Heart J.*, 16:224–226, 1954.

33. GROSS, R. E., and LONGINO, L. A. The patent ductus arteriosus. Observations from 412 surgically treated cases. *Circulation*, 3:125–137, 1951.

34. DOWNING, D. F. Congenital aortic septal defect. *Amer. Heart J.*, 40:285–292, 1950.

35. SPENCER, H., and DWORKEN, H. J. Congenital aortic septal defect with communication between aorta and pulmonary artery. Case report and review of literature. *Circulation*, 2:880–885, 1950.

36. DAMMANN, J. F., JR., and SELL, C. G. R. Patent ductus arteriosus in the absence of a continuous murmur. *Circulation*, 6:110–124, 1952.

37. GROSS, R. E. Surgical closure of an aortic septal defect. *Circulation*, 5:858–863, 1952.

38. SWAN, H. J. C. Diagnostic applications of indicator dilution curves in heart disease. *Minnesota Med.*, 37:123–130, 1954.

39. SWAN, H. J. C., BURCHELL, H. B., and WOOD, E. H. Differential diagnosis at cardiac catheterization of anomalous pulmonary venous drainage related to atrial septal defects or abnormal venous connections. *Proc. Staff Meet. Mayo Clin.*, 28:452–462, 1953.

40. BROADBENT, J. C., and WOOD, E. H. Indicator-dilution curves in acyanotic congenital heart disease. *Circulation*, 9:890–902, 1954.

41. SWAN, H. J. C., and WOOD, E. H. Localization of cardiac defects by dye-dilution curves recorded after injection of T-1824 at multiple sites in the heart and great vessels during cardiac catheterization. *Proc. Staff Meet. Mayo Clin.*, 28:95–100, 1953.

42. RILEY, R. L., HIMMELSTEIN, A., MOTLEY, H. L., WEINER, H. M., and COURNAND, A. Studies of the pulmonary circulation at rest and during exercise in normal individuals and in patients with chronic pulmonary disease. *Amer. J. Physiol.*, 152:372–382, 1948.

43. MACMAHON, B., MCKEOWN, T., and RECORD, R. G. The incidence and life expectation of children with congenital heart disease. *Brit. Heart J.*, 15:121–129, 1953.

44. KAUNITZ, V. H., and ANDERSON, M. N. An experimental study of the effect of parasympathetic denervation of the lung on pulmonary artery pressure. *J. Thorac. Surg.*, 27:55–63, 1954.

45. WESTCOTT, R. N., FOWLER, N. O., SCOTT, R. C., HAUENSTEIN, V. D., and MCGUIRE, J. Anoxia and human pulmonary vascular resistance. *J. Clin. Invest.*, 30:957–970, 1951.

46. BURCHELL, H. B., SWAN, H. J. C., and WOOD, E. H. Demonstration of differential effects on pulmonary and systemic arterial pressure by variation in oxygen content of inspired air in patients with patent ductus arteriosus and pulmonary hypertension. *Circulation*, 8:681–694, 1953.

47. EDWARDS, J. E., DOUGLAS, J. M., BURCHELL, H. B., and CHRISTENSEN, N. A. Pathology of the intrapulmonary arteries and arterioles in coarctation of the aorta associated with patent ductus arteriosus. *Amer. Heart J.*, 38:205–233, 1949.

48. EDWARDS, J. E., and CHAMBERLIN, W. B., JR. Pathology of the pulmonary vascular tree. III. The structure of the intrapulmonary arteries in cor triloculare biatriatum with subaortic stenosis. *Circulation*, 3:524–530, 1951.

49. CIVIN, W. H., and EDWARDS, J. E. Pathology of the pulmonary vascular tree. I. A comparison of the intrapulmonary arteries in the Eisenmenger complex and in stenosis of ostium infundibuli associated with biventricular origin of the aorta. *Circulation*, 2:545–552, 1950.

50. WOOD, P. Pulmonary hypertension. *Brit. Med. Bull.*, 8:348–353, 1952.

51. SWAN, H. J. C., ZAPATA-DIAZ, J., BURCHELL, H. B., and WOOD, E. H. Pulmonary hypertension in congenital heart disease. *Amer. J. Med.*, 16:12–22, 1954.

52. JOHNSON, R. E., WERMER, P., KUSCHNER, M., and COURNAND, A. Intermittent reversal of flow in a case of patent ductus arteriosus. A physiologic study with autopsy findings. *Circulation*, 1:1293–1301, 1950.

53. MYERS, G. S., SCANNELL, J. G., WYMAN, S. M., DIMOND, E. G., and HURST, J. W. Atypical patent ductus arteriosus with absence of the usual aortic-pulmonary pressure gradient and of the characteristic murmur. *Amer. Heart J.*, 41:819–833, 1951.

54. DAMMANN, J. F., BERTHRONG, M., and BING, R. J. Reverse ductus. A presentation of the syndrome of patency of the ductus arteriosus with pulmonary hypertension and a shunt-

ing of blood flow from the pulmonary artery to aorta. *Johns Hopkins Hosp. Bull.*, 92:128–150, 1953.

55. HULTGREN, H., SELZER, A., PURDY, A., HOLMAN, E., and GERBODE, F. The syndrome of patent ductus arteriosus with pulmonary hypertension. *Circulation*, 8:15–35, 1953.

56. SMITH, G. Patent ductus arteriosus with pulmonary hypertension and reversed shunt. *Brit. Heart J.*, 16:233–240, 1954.

57. COSBY, R. S., GRIFFITH, G. C., ZINN, W. J., LEVINSON, D. C., DIMITROFF, S. P., OBLATH, R. W., and JACOBSON, G. Cardiac catheterization in interatrial septal defect. *Amer. J. Med.*, 14:4–13, 1953.

58. DENOLIN, H., LEQUIME, J., WYBAUW, M., and BOLLAERT, A. Communication interauriculaire avec hypertension pulmonaire et veine pulmonaire aberrante. *Acta cardiol.*, 8:64–75, 1953.

59 BURCHELL, H. B., TAYLOR, B. E., KNUTSON, J. R. B., and WOOD, E. H. Circulatory adjustments to the hypoxemia of congenital heart disease of the cyanotic type. *Circulation*, 1:404–414, 1950.

60. KIRKLIN, J. W., CONNOLLY, D. C., ELLIS, F. H., JR., BURCHELL, H. B., EDWARDS, J. E., and WOOD, E. H. Problems in the diagnosis and surgical treatment of pulmonic stenosis with intact ventricular septum. *Circulation*, 8:849–863, 1953.

61. MANNHEIMER, E., LARSSON, Y., MÖLLER, T., LAGERLÖF, M. H., and WERKÖ, L. Congenital isolated pulmonary stenosis. A clinical study of seven cases diagnosed by heart catheterization. *Acta paediat.*, Stockh., 38 484–500, 1949.

Chapter 15

THE CARDIAC RESERVE

AND COMPENSATED HEART DISEASE

The cardiovascular system is designed to meet the widely varying metabolic requirements of the body, shifting blood flow patterns to favor one set of tissues or another as they serve various bodily activities. However, the total sustained blood flow through the system is limited. When an individual develops heart disease, the maximal cardiac output he can sustain is usually curtailed, because reserve capacity of his cardiovascular system is being utilized to make up the deficit imposed by disease even during routine activity. Thus, the attributes of the various components of the cardiovascular reserve are very important in understanding the functional response to heart disease.

The cardiac reserve will be considered in terms of six factors: (a) the venous oxygen reserve, (b) the maximum effective heart rate, (c) the stroke volume reserve, (d) the work of the heart, (e) the coronary vascular reserve and (f) cardiac enlargement. Particular attention will be directed to the limitations in each factor.

I. The Cardiovascular Reserve Capacity

The reserve capacity of the cardiovascular system is most sorely taxed during physical exercise. The severity of the exercise that can be performed over any extended period of time apparently is limited by the maximal capacity of the cardiovascular system to deliver oxygen to the tissues because it is this substance which is stored in the least quantity in relation to its utilization rate. The quantity of oxygen consumed by the tissues is limited by the cardiac output and the amount of oxygen extracted from each increment of blood. In other words, the oxygen available to the tissues depends upon the cardiac output (blood flow per unit time) and magnitude of the arteriovenous oxygen difference.

The manner in which these factors are related can be represented by a mechanical pumping system (Fig. 1A). Under basal conditions, the quantity of fluid pumped through the system is determined by the stroke volume and the number of strokes per minute (rate). If the stroke volume can be doubled and the cycle rate can be increased about two-and-a-half times, the maximum capacity of pump is about five times the basal level (Fig. 1B). The total quantity delivered from the exchanger is determined by the relationship between the flow each min-

435

PUMPING EFFICIENCY AND RESERVE

A. MECHANICAL EFFICIENCY

B. CARDIOVASCULAR RESERVE

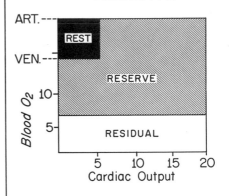

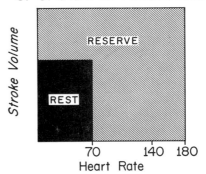

FIGURE 1.   *A,* The useful mechanical work of a pump in a hydraulic system takes the form of propelling fluid onward against a pressure head. The efficiency is determined by the useful work per unit of fuel consumption.

B, The oxygen delivery to the tissues at rest is determined by the product of the A-V oxygen difference and the cardiac output (black area). The maximum oxygen delivery is achieved by greater oxygen extraction and increased cardiac output (hatched area), corresponding to the cardiovascular reserve for oxygen delivery. Residual oxygen remains in the mixed venous blood even at maximal levels of oxygen transport.

C, Cardiac reserve refers to the extent to which cardiac output can be increased by greater stroke volume and acceleration of the heart rate (hatched area). Note that the heart rate is increased to greater extent than the stroke volume (see Fig. 2).

ute and the amount extracted from each unit of blood. The oxygen delivery to the tissues at rest is represented by a rectangular area, which is the product of the blood flow (cardiac output) and the oxygen extracted from each increment of blood. Thus, 250 cc. of oxygen would be delivered by a systemic flow of 5 liters of blood with each liter giving up 50 cc. of oxygen. This is equivalent to an arteriovenous oxygen difference of 5 cc. per 100

cc. of blood or 5 volumes per cent (Fig. 1*C*). Theoretically, extraction of a large quantity of oxygen from the blood and a simultaneous five-fold increase in the cardiac output can increase the maximum oxygen delivery by as much as ten-fold.

In traditional concepts, the increased oxygen consumption during strenuous exercise was attributed to almost equal contributions by each of the three major mechanisms: stroke volume, heart rate and oxygen extraction. However, in dogs exercising on a treadmill, only a slight change in stroke volume was indicated by direct recordings of left ventricular length, circumference or diameter (see Fig. 10, Chap. 8). This observation led to a re-examination of the relative contributions of these three factors,[1,2] effected by compiling data collected during various levels of exercise by normal human subjects participating in ten series of experiments conducted by different investigators (Fig. 2). (Since some of them reported observed oxygen consumption and others

corrected their data for body surface area, two separate scales have been used on the abscissa in Figure 2.)

The stroke volume was surprisingly uniform over wide ranges of exertion and oxygen consumption. In general, the values from erect subjects were lower at rest and slightly higher at maximal levels of exertion (see also Fig. 12, Chap. 8). The stroke volume did not increase progressively with an increase in oxygen consumption. The heart rate increased progressively to a level between 160 and 200 beats per minute and stabilized there.

UTILIZATION OF CARDIOVASCULAR RESERVE DURING EXERTION

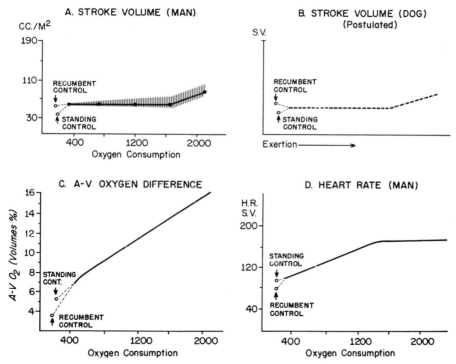

FIGURE 2. *A*, In normal human subjects, the mean values for stroke volume remain remarkably constant over a very wide range of exertion, from marking time to running on a treadmill. In some series the stroke volume appears to remain constant over an extended range of exertion and, in others, the stroke volume increases on the average about 10 per cent. Included in these data are individuals whose stroke volume actually diminished as exercise became more severe. At maximum levels of exertion the stroke volume unquestionably tends to increase as the heart rate levels off.

B, Available evidence suggests that the stroke volume increases little or not at all in dogs over wide ranges of exertion. It is postulated that stroke volume increases at the maximum levels of exertion as in man.

C, The oxygen extraction increases progressively during exertion up to the maximum that can be sustained for even brief periods (i.e., $2\frac{1}{2}$ minutes).

D, The heart accelerates progressively up to about 180/min. where it tends to level off as the oxygen consumption continues to rise.

The arteriovenous oxygen difference apparently increased progressively over the full range of oxygen consumption. Among most recumbent subjects the stroke volume changed very little. In general, the control values for erect subjects revealed a faster heart rate and a smaller stroke volume than were seen in the recumbent subjects (see also Fig. 13, Chap. 8). Even at relatively slight degrees of exercise, the stroke volume of erect subjects increased to about the level typical of recumbent subjects.

The relationships displayed in Figure 2 are applicable to average normal persons. Among patients in whom the increase in heart rate is limited during exertion, the stroke volume unquestionably contributes more to the greater cardiac output during exercise. Thus, patients with abnormal conduction and atrioventricular block have a slow, constant heart rate and unquestionably achieve a greater cardiac output by greater stroke volume. When Warner et al.[3] controlled the heart rate of exercising dogs, the cardiac output was increased to a normal degree by increased stroke volume. Many trained athletes have slow heart rates at rest (as low as 50 to 60 beats a minute) and display much less tachycardia during exertion than do untrained individuals under the same conditions. This bradycardia is more commonly associated with training for long distance events than that for sprints, and appears to be a response to long-sustained demands for increased cardiac output. In the same way, increased stroke volume is the typical response to sustained volume loads induced by various disease states (see below).

In the ventricular response to exertion by average normal persons and dogs, the contribution to oxygen delivery by stroke volume is relatively slight or even absent. The progressive increase in cardiac output is achieved primarily by tachycardia. The oxygen extraction from the blood becomes progressively greater as the exertion becomes more strenuous and oxygen consumption rises. Mitchell, Sproule and Chapman[4] measured oxygen consumption as the work load was progressively increased until the oxygen consumption reached a maximal level. At a later date, indicator dilution techniques were employed to measure the cardiac output and to compute the arteriovenous oxygen differences. The oxygen extraction increased progressively with greater work loads and at maximal levels of exertion some 75 per cent of the oxygen was removed from the blood passing through the systemic capillaries. The venous oxygen reserve can be depleted this completely only if oxygen extraction increases in both active and inactive tissues.

Venous Oxygen Reserve

It was pointed out in Chapter 1 that delivery of oxygen from the blood to the tissues depends upon a diffusion gradient determined by the differences in the partial pressures of oxygen in the blood and in the cell. If the cells become more active and take up oxygen at a more rapid rate, the lower end of this diffusion gradient will fall, the transfer of oxygen to the cells will be accelerated and more oxygen will be removed from the blood.

Each 100 cc. of arterial blood entering the capillary networks contains approximately 19 cc. of oxygen. Different tissues extract different amounts of oxygen from the capillary blood. The amount of oxygen extracted from each increment of blood during its passage through the capillary networks is determined by the relation between the oxygen consumption of a particular tissue and the volume flow of blood.

The oxygen consumption and blood flow in cerebral vessels is normally quite constant, so the oxygen extraction remains relatively fixed. The blood flow through the kidneys, skin and inactive muscle is so great in relation to oxygen consumption that large quantities of oxygen remain in the venous blood leaving these tissues. Indeed, most inactive tissues extract relatively little of the oxygen available in the arterial blood. In contrast, active skeletal muscle and the myocardium extract more than 75 per cent of the oxygen from the capillary blood. Vasoconstriction in inactive tissues would tend to shunt blood through the dilated capillary networks in the active muscles. During muscular exertion, blood flow may be diverted into active muscles from the skin, kidneys, gastrointestinal tract, spleen, etc. These tissues then uti-

lize more oxygen from the remaining blood flow at the expense of a moderate reduction in the oxygen tensions within the tissues. Thus, increased oxygen consumption characteristically causes an increased arteriovenous oxygen difference in both active and inactive tissues. In normal subjects an increase in oxygen consumption by 100 per cent produces an average increase in cardiac output of only about 70 per cent.[5] The difference between these values is made up by increased extraction of oxygen from the blood and a widened arteriovenous oxygen difference.

VENTRICULAR VOLUMES UNDER VARIOUS CONDITIONS

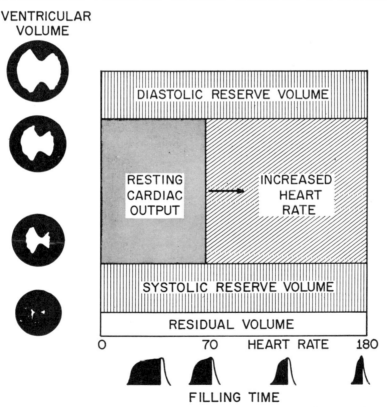

FIGURE 3.   The normal resting cardiac output, about 5 liters per minute (dark stippled area) is the product of stroke volume (about 70 cc.) and heart rate (about 70 beats per minute). The cardiac output can increase maximally to about six times the resting value (total cross-hatched area) if heart rate and stroke volume increase simultaneously. Heart rate can increase to about 180 beats per minute, which would increase cardiac output two and a half times if the reduced filling time did not diminish stroke volume. Stroke volume can also increase through utilization of the systolic reserve and diastolic reserve volumes. The residual volume is the quantity of blood remaining in the ventricle after a maximal systolic ejection.

RESERVE CARDIAC OUTPUT

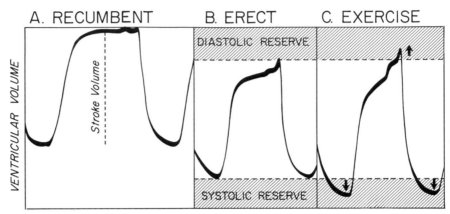

FIGURE 4.   Changes in ventricular volume are represented schematically. In the supine position, the diastolic volume is approximately maximal and the stroke volume is relatively large. On standing, diastolic ventricular volume and stroke volume diminish to provide potential diastolic and systolic reserve capacity. During exertion, any increase in stroke volume may be attained by either greater diastolic filling, more complete systolic ejection or both.

Maximum Effective Heart Rate

During sustained exercise, the heart responds to an increase in volume flow through the circulation with an acceleration of the heart rate, tachycardia. Tachycardia encroaches mainly upon the interval of diastasis during which little or no filling occurs (see Fig. 3). The maximal effective increase in heart rate is approximately two and a half times (i.e., from a resting rate of about 70 beats per minute to levels of 170 to 180 beats per minute).[6] At faster heart rates, the rapid filling period is curtailed and the stroke volume tends to diminish. Tachycardia is very effective in rapidly increasing cardiac output in response to increased systemic blood flow, but it involves a sacrifice of efficiency in both ventricular contraction and the diastolic filling. Further, an increase in cardiac output by extreme tachycardia interferes with coronary blood flow.

Stroke Volume Reserve

The stroke volume during maximum exertion does not necessarily exceed that which is to be found in normal subjects who are relaxed in recumbent positions. The left ventricle functions at or near its maximal dimensions in relaxed, reclining dogs and the stroke volume, as judged from the systolic deflections on the dimensional records, also approaches maximal levels under these conditions (see Fig. 11, Chap. 7). However, in the change from the recumbent to the standing position, the ventricular dimensions diminish and the stroke deflection is also smaller (Fig. 4). Under these conditions, an increase in stroke volume can theoretically be achieved by an increase in diastolic distention, by greater systolic ejection or by augmentation of both.[7] In other words, the extent to which the ventricles can distend farther represents a diastolic reserve capacity. The ability to increase the degree of ejection constitutes a systolic reserve capacity. These two reserves may be utilized to varying degrees in different animals or in the same animal on various occasions. Examples can be easily distinguished among the illustrations in Chapter 8.

At rest in the erect position, a stroke volume of about 80 cc. at a heart rate of 70 beats a minute will provide a cardiac output of 5600 cc. per minute. The heart rate may increase to about 180 beats a minute and the stroke volume can increase by utilizing the diastolic and systolic reserve capacities. By these mechanisms, the cardiac output can be increased by five or six fold.

Systolic Reserve Volume. At the end of normal systolic ejections, considerable quantities of blood remain within the cardiac chambers. Attainment of increased stroke volume by utilization of the systolic reserve volume ordinarily implies an increased "contractility" of the myocardium.

Diastolic Reserve Volume. The magnitude of the diastolic filling is determined by the effective filling pressure in relation to the resistance to distention offered by the ventricular walls. Ventricular contraction beginning at a large diastolic size is favorably influenced by (a) a greater energy release (Starling's law), (b) the large volume of blood ejected per unit of myocardial shortening and (c) reduced internal friction (viscosity) within the myocardium. On the other hand, the radius of the circles described by the myocardial fibers is increased and much greater myocardial tension is required to produce equivalent elevation of intraventricular pressure during ejection (according to the formula $P = T/R$). (The factors which determine the extent of diastolic distention have been discussed in detail in Chapter 3.) The heart appears to function with greater efficiency at a larger diastolic (and systolic) size. However, the question of efficiency must be considered in terms of the quantity of useful work performed in relation to the quantity of fuel consumed by the myocardium (oxygen utilization).

The Work of the Heart

In a mechanical pump, the useful work performed can be easily visualized in terms of the energy expended in propelling fluid through pipes (see Fig. 1A). It is common knowledge that only part of the energy released in a combustion engine is delivered as useful work. The remainder is wasted as heat, which is dissipated in many different ways. Thus, we speak of the efficiency of such an engine in terms of the relation between the energy supplied (fuel burned) and the useful external work accomplished. In such a hydraulic analogue, the work produced by the pump is directly limited by the rate at which fuel is supplied to the engine. Certain features of such a mechanical device are applicable to the functioning of the heart as a pump.

Energy produced by the oxidation of organic fuels such as glucose, glycogen or lactic acid is partly converted to mechanical energy during myocardial contraction. For purposes of discussion, the avenues of energy dissipation will be divided into two main categories: (a) useful work, expressed as the energy expended for ejection of blood under pressure into the arterial trunks, and (b) wasted energy, including all other avenues of energy dissipation.

Useful Work of the Heart. This work occurs during active ejection of blood from the ventricular chambers. No work is accomplished during isometric contraction, isometric relaxation or diastole. During the ejection phase of ventricular contraction, blood is propelled into the root of the aorta. A major portion of the potential energy is stored as tension in the arterial walls. According to Prec et al.,[8] the potential energy developed by the left ventricle is more than 98 per cent of the total useful work; kinetic energy amounts to only about 0.25 to 2.0 per cent. Since the stroke volume and velocity of flow for the two ventricles are approximately equal, equal quantities of kinetic energy are transferred to the blood by the two ventricles. The kinetic energy is a greater proportion of the total useful work of the right ventricle (about 2.4 to 12.5 per cent) because the potential en-

THE TOTAL WORK OF THE HEART

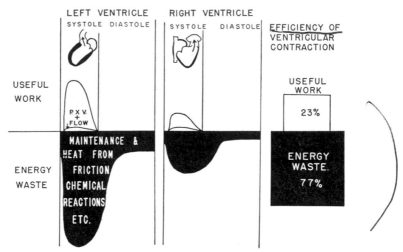

FIGURE 5.   The useful work of the heart is the potential and kinetic energy imparted to the blood during the ejection phase of systole. The quantity of wasted energy exceeds the useful work by about fourfold, and is probably dissipated largely during systole. However, the exact time relations of this energy waste have never been described. The efficiency of myocardial contraction (useful work/total energy release) varies widely, but averages about 23 per cent.

ergy is much less than in the left ventricle. The distinction between potential and kinetic energy is somewhat artificial because most of the potential energy is converted to kinetic energy in producing flow through the vascular elements. In other words, the arterial blood pressure produces flow through the circulatory bed, so the potential energy is converted into kinetic energy and then into heat due to friction. The total quantity of useful work accomplished by the heart is ultimately dissipated by frictional losses as the blood flows through the circulation except for the potential energy at the point of venous inflow into the next ventricle in the circuit. This energy is utilized to distend the ventricle during diastole.

Energy Waste During Ventricular Contraction.   Such waste takes many forms. The metabolic activity required to maintain and repair the myocardial cells is essential for myocardial integrity, but does not contribute to the circulation of the blood. The energy expended in the wave of excitation is in a similar category. However, these two processes dissi-

pate negligible amounts of energy in comparison to other forms of energy waste associated with chemical reactions, myocardial viscosity, turbulence in the blood and energy stored as interfascicular tension (Chap. 3). A major portion of both useful work and energy waste occurs during ventricular systole, illustrated schematically in Figure 5. As the useful work of the heart increases, the amount of energy waste usually increases simultaneously. Since the useful work of the heart is the only external evidence of energy dissipation, the large quantities of wasted energy are frequently overlooked, although they have considerable functional importance. The myocardium must release energy equal to both the "wasted energy" and the useful work. Enough oxygen must be delivered to the heart through coronary blood flow to meet this total energy expenditure. Some disease processes interfere with oxygen delivery to the myocardium (diseases of the coronary arteries, ventricular hypertrophy). Other types of heart disease reduce the efficiency with which the myocardium converts chemical energy into the mechanical energy of contraction.

Efficiency of Ventricular Energy Release. The efficiency of the ventricular myocardium may be defined as the relation of the quantity of useful work performed to the total energy expended. The total energy release can be estimated from the oxygen consumption of the myocardium by assuming that 2 kg.-m. of work are performed in the process of utilizing 1 cc. of oxygen. Coronary sinus catheterization is providing information on the efficiency of the left ventricular myocardium.[9-11] Measurements of coronary blood flow, myocardial oxygen consumption and useful work of the left ventricle provide the necessary data for computing the efficiency of the left ventricular myocardium as indicated by the formula:

$$\text{Mechanical efficiency (per cent)} = \frac{\text{work of left ventricle (kg.-m./min.)}}{\text{aerobic energy uptake of left ventricle (kg.-m./min.)}}$$

The efficiency of the normal left ventricle may improve during exercise when the increase in its useful work is more than the increase in myocardial oxygen consumption. On the other hand, in patients with congestive heart failure, the efficiency of left ventricular energy conversion is reduced at rest[9] and declines even further during exercise.[12]

Energy Restoration in the Heart. Since cardiac activity cannot be interrupted for long intervals, the delivery of oxygen and metabolic fuels must be continuously maintained at levels commensurate with the energy released by the myocardium. The total energy released during systole must be restored during the succeeding diastolic interval. Oxygen and metabolic fuels are delivered to the myocardium by the coronary blood flow. After passing through the capillaries of the coronary system, the coronary venous blood of normal humans contains only about 3.9 to 6.9 cc. of oxygen per 100 cc. of blood. Such complete extraction of oxygen from coronary blood signifies that oxygen tension in the myocardial fibers is very low. In other words, the myocardium continuously operates in an environment with a very low partial pressure of oxygen. During exercise and other forms of stress, the oxygen extraction is even more complete, so the oxygen tension immediately around the myocardial cells must be extremely low. Since the oxygen extraction from blood in the coronary vessels is so complete, the myocardium has little coronary venous oxygen reserve and must depend primarily upon an increase in coronary blood flow to supply increased demands. In this sense, the maximum sustained cardiac output is limited by the cardiac efficiency and the coronary blood supply.

Coronary Reserve Capacity

The total quantity of oxygen presented to the myocardium can be represented as a rectangular figure obtained as the product of coronary flow per unit time and the oxygen content of the arterial blood. The oxygen extraction at rest is the product of the coronary flow per unit time and the arteriovenous oxygen difference (black area in Fig. 6). An increase in oxygen delivery to the myocardium is attained

CORONARY RESERVE CAPACITY

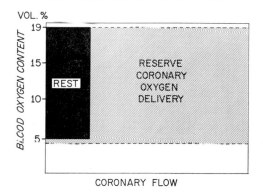

FIGURE 6. Oxygen transport to the myocardium depends upon the coronary flow and the oxygen extraction from coronary blood (A-V oxygen difference). The coronary venous blood contains very little residual oxygen and increased oxygen delivery must be attained in direct proportion to the increase in coronary flow.

primarily by greater coronary blood flow with little contribution by the venous oxygen reserve (see Fig. 6). Although an increase in coronary flow without a corresponding increase in oxygen extraction from the blood has been demonstrated in a human subject,[12] the maximum coronary flow or coronary oxygen delivery to the myocardium during most strenuous exertion has not been determined.

As in other tissues of the body, blood flow through the coronary vessels is increased primarily by reducing the resistance to flow through the small vessels. Diminished oxygen tension has a very powerful dilatory effect on the coronary vessels, which may automatically adjust coronary flow in relation to requirements. Other factors influencing coronary flow are presented in Chapter 4 (Figs. 13 and 15) and in Chapter 9.

Acute changes in metabolism are accompanied by greater cardiac output, cardiac work and coronary oxygen delivery through the mechanisms indicated in Figures 1, 3, 5 and 6. Various disease states impose chronic loads on the heart for which the characteristic compensations are changes in the size of the ventricular chambers and the thickness of their walls.

Cardiac Enlargement

As indicated in Chapter 2, the architecture of the right and left ventricles reflects the nature of the normal load which they sustain. The left ventricle is a roughly cylindrical cavity enclosed by a thick wall of myocardium, encircling the ventricle like a clenched fist. Such a chamber is ideally suited to develop high pressure for ejecting blood against high outflow pressure. In contrast, the right ventricular cavity is a relatively narrow crescentic space between two broad surfaces—the free wall and the interventricular septum. This chamber has a very large surface area which would necessitate great myocardial tension to develop high intra-

VENTRICULAR RESPONSES TO LOADS

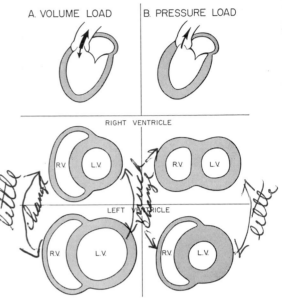

FIGURE 7.   *A*, The right ventricle is such an efficient volume pump that it can accommodate to an abnormal volume load with little change in chamber size or wall thickness, so long as the outflow pressure remains low. In contrast, the left ventricle accommodates to an increased volume load by distending to greater diastolic and systolic ventricular dimensions.

B, In response to a chronic pressure load, the right ventricle develops thick walls and a rounded contour; it assumes some of the characteristics of the normal left ventricle as it becomes a pressure pump. The left ventricle adjusts to a chronic pressure load by greater wall thickness, usually without much increase in diastolic ventricular volume.

ventricular pressures but which can readily eject large volumes of blood against low outflow resistance. In the course of various disease processes, the right or left ventricle may be individually taxed by having to overcome higher outflow pressure or resistance (increased pressure load) or to pump larger volumes of blood continuously (increased volume load). Compensation to such chronic loads involves gross changes in the size and shape of the ventricles (Fig. 7).

Ventricular Response to Volume Loads. The volume ejected by the ventricles dueing each systolic contraction is increasrP over long periods of time by many kinds of systemic disease. For example, increased activity of the thyroid gland (hyperthyroidism) so elevates the resting metabolic rate of the whole body including the heart that cardiac output is increased. Since anemia reduces the oxygen-carrying capacity of the blood, cardiac output must be increased to deliver the normal quantity of oxygen. Abnormal communicating channels between the arteries and veins (A-V shunts) syphon off some of the systemic flow and the cardiac output must be correspondingly increased. Deformities of the cardiac valves may prevent complete closure so that blood regurgitates through them. For example, incomplete closure of the aortic valve (aortic insufficiency) permits blood to flow from the aorta back into the left ventricle during diastole. The net forward flow through the systemic circulation is maintained at normal levels primarily by an increase in stroke volume equal in amount to the quantity regurgitating through the valves. Thus, the effective cardiac output and heart rate are normal. Since the normal left ventricle is not an effective volume pump, the chamber dilates to a much larger size (Fig. 7) so that the larger stroke volume can be ejected with less myocardial shortening (see also Figs. 7 and 8, Chap. 3). By this mechanism, the loss of tension due to excessive shortening is avoided (see Fig. 6, Chap. 3). The dilated left ventricle has a large internal surface area and functions more as a volume pump. In short, this chamber assumes some of the characteristics of the normal right ventricle. The mean arterial pressure remains about normal, so the myocardium of the dilated ventricle must develop increased tension.

If progressive dilatation occurs over a long period of time, the ventricular volume may become very large without a significant rise in filling pressure. The effective filling pressure of a dilated left ventricle may remain normal for years so long as the heart remains competent.

Chronic ventricular dilatation is probably not simple stretching of the wall; the myocardial fibers probably grow longer so that the blood vessels, connective tissue stroma, and pericardial sac must also expand by elaboration of new tissue structure.

Chronic left ventricular dilatation is almost invariably associated with some degree of myocardial hypertrophy. Not only is the weight of the ventricular walls increased by an increased mass of tissue, but the myocardial fibers generally have increased diameter. Ventricular dilatation increases the radius of the circles described by the constituent myocardial fibers, so their tension must be correspondingly increased to develop the same intraventricular pressure according to the law of Laplace ($P = T/R$). Thus, pure dilatation of a chamber without some degree of myocardial hypertrophy rarely occurs. If the volume load on the left ventricle can be relieved (by ligation of a patent ductus or excision of an arteriovenous aneurism), the dilated chamber reverts toward normal dimensions, often to an amazing degree. This change indicates that the adaptive mechanisms of the ventricle are reversible.

According to Grant,[13] dilatation of the left ventricular wall is not accompanied by a similar dilatation of the mitral valve ring. However, the papillary muscles, chordae tendineae and mitral valve leaflets become longer. In spite of very different morphologic characteristics, these structures participate almost equally in adapting to the new dimensions of the chamber. If such a change in length did not occur, the traction on the valves by a massively dilated chamber would probably prevent complete closure of the mitral valves during systole. Although mitral regurgitation may result from this mechanism in acute left ventricular dilatation, gradual dilatation apparently does not produce valvular insufficiency.

The normal right ventricle is particularly suited for the pumping of large volumes of blood against low outflow resistance with minimal myocardial shortening. Because of the large surface area per unit volume in the normal right ventricle, a relatively small degree of dilatation can accommodate greatly increased diastolic and stroke volumes. Under these circumstances, a chronic volume load can be well sustained without dilatation. For example, a defect in the interatrial septum allows recirculation of blood through the lungs so that the right ventricle may pump two or three times as much blood as the left. Patients with such a defect may have a good exercise tolerance without significant right ventricular dilatation so long as the pulmonary resistance remains low. However, a sustained increase in pulmonary blood flow often leads to an increased resistance to the flow of blood through the lungs and pulmonary hypertension. The right ventricle adjusts to this pressure load by hypertrophy, by thickening of the wall and rounding of the chamber; in short, by assuming some of the characteristics of the normal left ventricle.

Ventricular Hypertrophy. Myocardial hypertrophy is the typical response to a chronic pressure load, as exemplified by arterial hypertension (see Chap. 6) or semilunar valvular stenosis (see Chap. 12). Under these conditions, the intraventricular pressure must be abnormally high during each cycle to eject the normal increment of blood into the arterial trunk. Dilatation of the ventricular chamber would require an even greater myocardial tension in accordance with the law of Laplace ($P = T/R$). Greater contractile force can be attained by the elaboration of additional contractile units. Although the myocardial fibers do not multiply in number, their diameter increases as they become packed with more contractile elements. In patients with a chronic pressure load (essential hypertension), no direct relationship has been established between

the duration and degree of hypertension and the size of the heart.[14] Many patients may endure severe hypertension for years and progress to serious heart failure without demonstrable cardiac enlargement. Under these conditions, the principal compensation to the increased pressure load is myocardial hypertrophy. The power of the ventricular contraction is enhanced by the greater number of contractile units and the volume of the chamber remains relatively small (Fig. 7), avoiding the increased myocardial tension required by an expansion to larger systolic and diastolic volumes.

Thus, the usual response to a chronic pressure load is myocardial hypertrophy with various degrees of ventricular dilatation unless heart failure should supervene. The thickened ventricular walls probably have diminished distensibility, requiring a greater effective filling pressure to attain a particular diastolic volume. In other words, the myocardial hypertrophy tends to permit utilization of the systolic reserve capacity with some sacrifice of distensibility. On the other hand, ventricular dilatation involves an encroachment on the diastolic reserve capacity, apparently with some sacrifice of the contractility, since these distended ventricles fail to empty as completely during systole as the normal. Ventricular dilatation probably places some restriction on oxygen delivery to the myocardium, owing to lengthening of the coronary capillaries (Fig. 8). Myocardial hypertrophy impairs oxygen delivery to an even greater extent by increasing the diffusion distance from the capillaries to the center of the enlarged myocardial fibers.

Oxygen Delivery to Hypertrophied Myocardial Fibers. Normal myocardial fibers range from 13 to 16 μ in diameter. Hypertrophied myocardial fibers may reach 25 to 32 μ in diameter, but rarely exceed that value. The apparent limitation on hypertrophy of myocardial fibers has been attributed to retardation of oxygen delivery because of the greater diffusion distance to the center of the fibers. The relation between the rate of oxygenation and the diameter of nerve fibers was discussed by Hill[15] (see Fig. 2, Chap. 1).

The rate of diffusion through tissues varies as the square of the distance, which accounts for the prolongation of the time required for saturation of fibers with larger diameters. Harrison[16] reasoned that slower diffusion of oxygen to the center of hypertrophied myocardial fiber would prolong the recovery time required for the fiber to fully regain its energy-rich state. On this basis, the heart rate should be much slower when the ventricle is hypertrophied than when it is in the normal state. However, the heart rates in such patients are either normal or elevated, so the hypertrophic myocardium is probably suffering some degree of oxygen deficiency. This type of analysis indicates that the diameter of myocardial fibers rarely exceeds a value of 32 μ because the

central core of larger myocardial fibers would not receive adequate oxygen.

Jones[17] weighed the right and left ventricular walls and interventricular septum from a large number of patients with systemic arterial hypertension. He concluded that, "(a) only the left ventricle hypertrophies in hypertensive individuals without congestive failure; (b) with the advent of congestive failure, the right ventricle hypertrophies progressively with the duration of failure, both auricles hypertrophy and the left ventricle also continues to increase in weight; (c) after failure has existed for over three years, the two chambers diminish in weight; the reduction in weight may be more marked in the left ventricle. . . . It is possible that the cases with cardiac failure represent a group separated from the other on the basis of a more marked hypertrophy which has 'outstripped the capillary bed.' " At every turn we encounter examples which indicate that the rate of

EFFECTS OF VENTRICULAR DILATATION AND HYPERTROPHY ON CORONARY SUPPLY

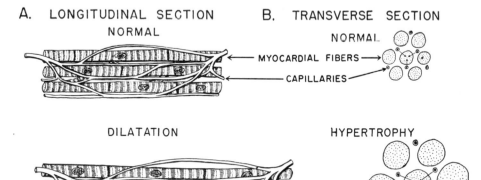

FIGURE 8.   A, Chronic ventricular dilatation involves elongation of both the myocardial fibers and the coronary capillaries. The mass of myocardial contractile units being supplied is greater and the distance traversed by the blood is increased. A greater proportion of oxygen in the blood is probably extracted under these conditions.

B, Ventricular hypertrophy is accomplished by proliferation of contractile units within the individual myocardial fibers. The distance of diffusion from the capillaries to the center of adjacent fibers is increased, retarding the exchange of various substances, particularly oxygen. The diameter of myocardial fibers rarely exceeds 32 μ even in extreme degrees of hypertrophy.

oxygen delivery to the myocardium limits the cardiac output while the maximum cardiac output limits the amount of physical exertion which can be sustained.

Summary

In the normal individual, the cardiovascular reserve mechanism provides a prompt and effective response to widely varying demands for blood flow to provide oxygen and metabolic fuels, to dissipate heat, for digestion of food, for proper function of glands and excretory organs, and for other essential functions. The maximum oxygen delivery to tissues depends upon four principal components of cardiovascular reserve: the venous oxygen reserve, the maximum cardiac output which can be sustained, the efficiency of myocardial energy release and the oxygen delivery to the myocardium. Depletion of any one of these components diminishes the total reserve, deleteriously affecting all other reserve factors. The various types of cardiac disease affect total cardiovascular reserve in different ways, but the end result is always some reduction in the total oxygen delivery to tissues which can be sustained during physical exertion. Thus, diminished exercise tolerance is a common denominator of cardiac disease.

II. Compensated Heart Disease

Many patients with various forms of heart disease continue to lead relatively normal, moderately active lives for many years. Often individuals with functionally significant valvular disease live a normal life span. Their exercise tolerance may be reduced, but the average person rarely utilizes his maximal exertion capacity. Thus, patients can frequently live fairly normal lives in spite of restrictive forms of heart disease so long as they retain cardiovascular reserve capacity at rest. Under these conditions they can increase their level of activity by utilizing whatever reserve remains for them. Although a particular form of heart disease may directly deplete only one form of the cardiovascular reserve capacity, other reserve factors are generally affected to some degree. For this reason, all portions of the cardiovascular reserve should be kept in mind in evaluating the status of any patient with heart disease (see Fig. 9). These can be summarized as follows.

Maximum Oxygen Transport

The total oxygen delivery to the tissues of the body is determined by the average quantity of oxygen extracted from each increment of blood (mean ateriovenous oxygen difference) and the systemic blood flow (cardiac output). Thus, the total oxygen delivery can be represented by an area determined by the product of the cardiac output and the average oxygen extraction from the blood (Fig. 9A). The total oxygen delivery at rest amounts to about 250 cc. per minute (5 liters of blood per minute times 50 cc. of oxygen per liter). Tissues may be supplied with increased oxygen by greater cardiac output or by greater oxygen extraction from the blood. Since a number of vital tissues must be supplied with blood even though their oxygen extraction is relatively slight (kidneys, central nervous system, etc.), the mixed venous oxygen content rarely falls below some critical value. Thus, there is a minimal residual oxygen content of blood which is rarely encroached upon except in certain persons with severe cyanosis from congenital malformations of the heart (see Chap. 14). In such instances the tissues apparently accommodate to existence in an environment of very low oxygen tensions.

Cardiac Output

The cardiac output is determined by the product of the stroke volume and the heart rate. At rest, a heart rate of slightly more than 70 beats per minute and a stroke volume of about 70 cc. of blood accounts for a cardiac output of about 5 liters per minute. The stroke volume may be increased by greater diastolic distention or by more complete systolic ejection (Figs. 3 and 9).

Efficiency of the Heart as a Pump

The cardiac output represents only about 20 per cent of the total energy release, the remainder of the energy being wasted in the form of friction, lost in chemical reactions, etc. (Figs. 5 and 9). When cardiac output increases, the energy waste is also greater and may reach very large values during maximal effort.

Myocardial contraction represents the conversion of chemical energy into mechanical energy. During each cardiac cycle the contractile mechanisms must be restored to the high-energy, resting state. Obviously the total energy restoration must equal the total energy release over a period of time. In these circumstances the rate at which oxygen reaches the contractile units is a limiting factor in the process of attaining the high energy state.

Total Oxygen Delivery to the Myocardium

The oxygen delivery to the myocardium depends upon the same factors which determine oxygen delivery to the other tissues of the body, namely, the blood flow and the average quantity of oxygen removed from each increment of blood. The oxygen extraction from coronary blood is so great that little oxygen remains after the blood passes through the capillaries. For this reason, the principal mechanism for increasing oxygen delivery to the heart is increased coronary flow.

Compensation for Chronic Volume and Pressure Loads

In response to a *chronic volume load*, the amounts of oxygen in the arterial and venous blood are normal, indicating that the venous oxygen reserve is not utilized at rest so long as heart remains capable of fully compensating for the increased demands placed upon it (Fig. 9B). The quantity of blood ejected each minute is increased, so the cardiac reserve capacity is utilized to some extent at rest. The heart rate is normal at rest indicating that the stroke volume at rest is greater than normal. In many cases, the discrepancy becomes larger with exercise. The increased stroke volume is associated with a distention of the heart such that the diastolic volume is larger than normal. The systolic ejection is greater and there is a larger residual volume which cannot be utilized as a systolic reserve capacity. In this manner, a significant portion of the cardiac reserve is utilized at rest, but the ability to increase cardiac output through tachycardia tends to remain as a reserve to be employed during exertion.

In a purely physical sense, the quantity of blood being moved by the ventricle is increased so the useful work is augmented. From a functional point of view, the normal quantity of oxygen is delivered by an increased quantity of cardiac work. In this sense the efficiency of the cardiovascular system is diminished and the oxygen requirements of the myocardium are increased at rest and at all levels of exercise. The coronary oxygen delivery at rest must be increased to support this greater energy release. The coronary flow must be greater than normal at all times: thus, the coronary flow reserve capacity must be diminished. In this example, the reserve capacity of all components are adversely affected by the chronic volume load. The cardiovascular system cannot support the normal maximal oxygen de-

EFFECTS OF LOADS ON THE COMPONENTS
OF CARDIOVASCULAR RESERVE

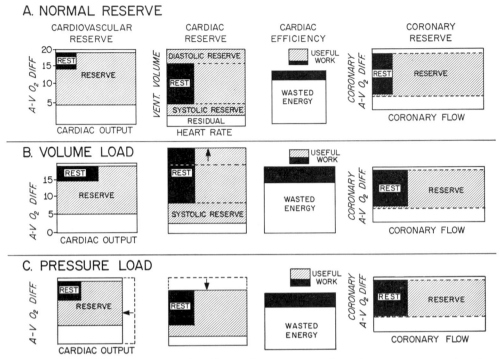

FIGURE 9.   *A*, The components of cardiovascular reserve are dependent upon one another since cardiac reserve affects cardiovascular reserve. Cardiac efficiency and coronary reserve influence cardiac reserve.

B, In response to a volume load, the cardiac output at rest is increased leading to diminished efficiency. The coronary flow at rest is greater than normal so the reserve is reduced.

C, A pressure load ultimately tends to diminish the maximum cardiac output and stroke volume reserve. The work is increased without a corresponding increase in oxygen delivery. The coronary flow is increased to deliver the greater oxygen requirements.

livery and the exercise tolerance is less than normal.

Under the influence of a *chronic pressure load* (e.g., systemic arterial hypertension or aortic stenosis), cardiac output and the over-all arteriovenous oxygen difference are both normal at rest. Superficially, the cardiac reserve appears to be entirely normal (Fig. 9*C*). However, the myocardium must develop a great deal more systolic tension to raise the intraventricular pressure to eject the normal complement of blood into the aorta. On this basis, the useful work of the heart is greatly increased at rest and the total energy expenditure much greater than

normal at all levels of exercise. The mass of myocardial fibers is increased, so the oxygen delivery by coronary flow must be accelerated. Since the coronary flow reserve is partially utilized at rest, some decrease in exercise tolerance might well be expected. In the early stages of hypertension, the left ventricular cavity is not greatly enlarged so long as the coronary oxygen delivery is adequate to maintain function. In more advanced stages of hypertension, the left ventricle tends to distend and the myocardial fibers display patchy degeneration[18] as though the coronary supply were inadequate. Coronary insufficiency is probably the major facto

r

in converting a fully compensated ventricle into a failing ventricle as described in Chapter 16.

Some Conditions Which Limit Maximal Oxygen Transport

A few specific clinical conditions have been selected to illustrate the relations between these various components of cardiovascular reserve. The primary effects are schematically illustrated in Figure 10 by altering the configuration of the graphs in Figure 9.

Anemia. If the hemoglobin concentration of the blood is diminished, the oxygen content of blood may be reduced from 20 volumes per cent to 12 volumes per cent. In the systemic capillaries, a smaller amount of oxygen is extracted from each 100 ml. increment of

EFFECTS OF DISEASE ON CARDIOVASCULAR RESERVE

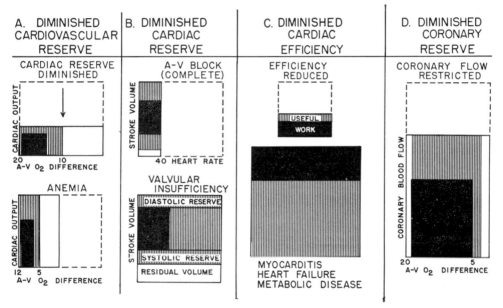

FIGURE 10.   The effects of various cardiac abnormalities on the cardiovascular reserve are schematically illustrated by appropriate modifications of Figure 9.

A, Diminished cardiac reserve limits the maximal amount of oxygen which can be delivered to the tissues. More complete utilization of venous oxygen reserve and restricted tolerance to exertion are obvious sequelae to this condition. Most forms of heart disease diminish cardiac reserve in one way or another. The cardiovascular reserve is also depleted by conditions which interfere with the transport of oxygen by the blood, such as occur in anemia. Some of the cardiac reserve capacity is used at rest and a smaller increment is therefore available during increased activity.

B, Cardiac reserve can be diminished in many ways. However, complete A-V block with the heart rate fixed at 40 beats per minute is a rather pure form of restriction of the heart rate response. Under these conditions, cardiac output can be increased only through augmented stroke volume. Valvular insufficiency is a common source of diminished stroke volume reserve. The affected ventricle must pump a quantity of blood equal to flow through the vessels plus the amount which regurgitates through the valve. The stroke volume is greatly increased and the reserve is depleted. Constrictive pericarditis tends to limit stroke volume in a very direct way.

C, The conditions which deleteriously affect mechanical efficiency of the heart have not been completely tabulated. It seems clear that myocarditis, heart failure and certain metabolic diseases may diminish all the other components of cardiovascular reserve by reducing cardiac efficiency. This places an added load on the coronary oxygen delivery as well as restricting the maximal stroke volume and oxygen transport.

D, Restricted coronary flow limits oxygen delivery to the myocardium. In this way it diminishes total energy release by the ventricles and reduces reserve cardiac output and the maximal sustained oxygen transport by the blood.

blood since the mixed venous oxygen content is not decreased below some critical value. Thus, the principal adjustment to a reduced arteriovenous oxygen difference caused by anemia is an increase in the cardiac output (Fig. 10*A*). Since the cardiac output is increased at rest, the reserve is diminished and the maximal sustained increase in cardiac output is less than normal. The increased systemic flow is not as effective as normal oxygen extraction in supplying the tissue because of the reduced oxygen capacity of the blood. The arterial blood entering the coronary capillaries also carries a reduced quantity of oxygen, impairing the oxygenation of the myocardium. Further, cardiac acceleration is more pronounced with moderate exercise than normal. Thus, significant anemia deleteriously affects a number of components of cardiovascular reserve: oxygen transport, total energy release, and total oxygen delivery to the myocardium.

Complete Atrioventricular Block. When the atrioventricular node blocks all impulses of atrial origin, a site in the ventricle usually assumes the role of pacemaker. It emits impulses at a slow but fairly constant rate of about 40 to 50 per minute even during exertion. Thus, the cardiac reserve is limited because the normal cardio-acceleration does not occur in response to increased requirements for greater peripheral blood flow (Fig. 10*B*). As the heart rate is slower than normal, the stroke volume is excessive even with normal resting cardiac output. Thus, the stroke volume reserve is diminished and compensatory acceleration is abolished. With such extreme limitation in cardiac reserve, compensation to exertion must produce an abnormally increased arteriovenous oxygen difference in the peripheral blood. If the atrioventricular block persists, the ventricles often dilate because increased stroke volume is constantly required. Dilatation produces elongation of the coronary capillaries and

may produce extraction of more oxygen from the coronary blood. Unfortunately, atrioventricular block is commonly caused by coronary insufficiency or occlusion. Impeded oxygen delivery to the myocardium may well limit the energy restoration and here, again, several components of cardiac reserve may be affected.

Adhesive Pericarditis. Diastolic distention of the ventricles may be seriously restricted by the thickened, adherent pericardium produced by chronic pericarditis. Under these conditions, the diastolic reserve volume is extremely limited and the principal mechanism for increasing stroke volume is greater contractility. The effective filling pressure is markedly elevated in most instances, even though this is of little avail. Marked venous congestion is a characteristic sign of the condition. Furthermore, the stroke volume reserve is so depleted that the principal adjustment in cardiac output is cardio-acceleration. Thus, the heart rate is very labile, reflecting every change in output Tachycardia interferes with coronary flow and oxygen delivery to the myocardium. Since cardiac efficiency is considerably reduced when a particular level of cardiac output is attained, predominately by tachycardia, the energy waste is greater and the total energy expenditure must be increased.

Reduced Cardiac Efficiency. Although the normal heart may operate with 20 per cent efficiency, certain disease processes reduce the efficiency of cardiac contraction by means other than the effects of tachycardia mentioned above. This means that energy wastage and total energy expenditure must be greater, that the energy restoration and oxygen delivery in the myocardium must be accelerated, and that the cardiac reserve is curtailed (Fig. 10*C*). For example, some young patients with apparently normal hearts may develop myocarditis and, in a short space of time, develop the classic signs and symptoms of heart failure, including severe cardiac enlargement, venous congestion and edema. Patients with serious degrees of heart disease may compensate for long periods of time before signs of heart failure appear. One alteration which may precipitate an attack of heart failure is a reduction in the efficiency of cardiac contraction, as has been indicated in direct measurements of myocardial oxygen utilization in relation to the work of the heart.

Diminished Coronary Oxygen Delivery. Obstruction or occlusion of the coronary arteries impedes blood flow to the myocardium and restricts the quantity of oxygen which can reach the contractile units (Fig. 10D). In addition to direct mechanical interference with coronary flow, oxygen delivery may be retarded by a number of other circumstances, such as hypertrophy of the myocardial fibers, diminished pressure gradient along the coronary arteries (aortic stenosis and aortic insufficiency), myocarditis with interstitial edema and tachycardia. Indeed, inadequate myocardial oxygenation may be the prime limitation on the cardiac output in many pathologic conditions of the heart and circulation.

REFERENCES

1. RUSHMER, R. F. Constancy of stroke volume in ventricular responses to exertion. *Amer. J. Physiol.*, 196:745–750, 1959.
2. RUSHMER, R. F. Postural effects of the baselines of ventricular performance. *Circulation*, 20:897–905, 1959.
3. WARNER, H. R., and TORONTO, A. F. Regulation of cardiac output through stroke volume. *Circulat. Res.*, 8:549–552, 1960.
4. MITCHELL, J. H., SPROULE, B. J., and CHAPMAN, C. B. The physiological meaning of the maximal oxygen intake test. *J. Clin. Invest.*, 37:538–547, 1958.
5. BROWN, H. R., JR., and PEARSON, R. Demonstration of a positive relationship between cardiac output and oxygen consumption. *Proc. Soc. Exp. Biol., N.Y.*, 65:307–309, 1947.
6. REMINGTON, J. W. Relation between length of diastole and stroke index in intact dog. *Amer. J. Physiol.*, 162:273–279, 1950.
7. RUSHMER, R. F. Work of the heart. *Mod. Conc. Cardiov. Dis.*, 27:473–477, 1958.
8. PREC, O., KATZ, L. N., SENNETT, L., ROSENMAN, R. H., FISHMAN, A. P., and HWANG, H. Determination of kinetic energy of the heart in man. *Amer. J. Physiol.*, 159:483–491, 1949.
9. BING, R. J., HAMMOND, M. M., HANDELSMAN, J. C., POWERS, S. R., SPENCER, F. C., ECKENHOFF, J. E., GOODALE, W. T., HAFKENSCHIEL, J. H., and KETY, S. S. The measurement of coronary blood flow, oxygen consumption, and efficiency of the left ventricle in man. *Amer. Heart J.*, 38:1–24, 1949.
10. SPENCER, F. C., MERRILL, D. L., POWERS, S. R., and BING, R. J. Coronary blood flow and cardiac oxygen consumption in unanesthetized dogs. *Amer. J. Physiol.*, 160:149–162, 1950
11. CULBERTSON, J. W., HALPERIN, M. H., and WILKINS, R. W. Catheterization of the coronary sinus in man. *Amer. Heart J.*, 37:942–951, 1949.
12. LOMBARDO, T. A., ROSE, L., TAESCHLER, M., TULUY, S., and BING, R. J. The effect of exercise on coronary blood flow, myocardial oxygen consumption and cardiac efficiency in man. *Circulation*, 7:71–78, 1953.
13. GRANT, R. P. Architectonics of the heart. *Amer. Heart J.*, 46:405–431, 1953.
14. KLEINFELD, M., and REDISH, J. The size of the heart during the course of essential hypertension. *Circulation*, 5:74–80, 1952.
15. HILL, A. V. The diffusion of oxygen and lactic acid through tissues. *Proc. Roy. Soc. Lond.*, B104:39–96, 1928.
16. HARRISON, T. R. *Failure of the Circulation.* Baltimore, Williams & Wilkins Co., 1939, 502 pp.
17. JONES, R. S. The weight of the heart and its chambers in hypertensive cardiovascular disease with and without failure. *Circulation*, 7:357–369, 1953.
18. BUSCH, V. W. Neue Ergebnisse der Messung und Wägung der Herzkammern bei den verschieden Hypertrophieformen mit besonderer Berücksichtigung der Histologie. *Arch. Kreislaufforsch*, 22:267–288, 1955.

Chapter 16

BLOOD VOLUME AND

DISTRIBUTION; CONGESTIVE HEART FAILURE

I. Control of Total Volume and Distribution

In spite of wide variations in environmental conditions of food and fluid intake, the body weight of the average adult remains remarkably constant over extended intervals of time. Under these conditions the consumption of food and fluids must precisely balance their utilization and excretion. Since about 70 per cent of the body weight consists of water, the total water content of the body must be well controlled and relatively constant in spite of changes in levels of activity, dietary habits and seasonal variations in environmental conditions. The fluids of the body are generally considered in terms of three compartments, separated by two types of membranes. In an average adult, about 35 liters of water are enclosed within cell membranes. This intracellular fluid contains relatively high concentrations of potassium and magnesium as the principal cations and phosphate and protein as the anions (Fig. 1A). The composition of the intracellular fluid is quite different from that of the extracellular fluids which are located in the interstitial spaces and within the blood vascular system. The predominant ions in these extracellular fluids are sodium, chloride and bicarbonate. Thus, the cell membranes of the body serve as partitions separating two dissimilar solutions, the

454

differences being maintained by active transport of particles against steep concentration gradients. The capillary membranes are quite freely permeable to all constituents of the blood and interstitial fluid except the cells and proteins. Thus, the extracellular fluid volume is divided into two compartments by the capillary endothelial barriers. The composition of the interstitial fluid differs slightly from that of the plasma because of the difference in protein concentration and the resulting Donnan equilibrium (Fig. 1A).

All the cell and capillary membranes are freely permeable to water (except perhaps those of the distal tubules and collecting ducts in the kidney). Movement of water rapidly erases any differences in osmotic concentration within and between the various fluid compartments. In fact, the very large potential osmotic pressures of body fluids (Figure 14, Chap. 1) assures that all fluids within the body will be in osmotic equilibrium. The volume and composition in one of the three compartments cannot be altered without affecting the others. For this reason, the blood volume must always be considered in relation to the total body fluids in all the compartments. The maintenance of a constant blood volume and constant total of body fluids despite the many pathways of intake and elimination of water, electrolytes, nutrient materials and waste products is accomplished by some extremely complex interactions indicated in Figure 1.

WATER BALANCE

In the course of a day, an average healthy man drinks about 1500 ml. of water, imbibes 1200 ml. in food and receives an additional 300 ml. from oxidation during the metabolism of foodstuffs. This average total intake of 2500 ml. of water is normally eliminated in the same period as water vapor in air exhaled from the lungs (500 ml.), insensible perspiration from the skin (500 ml.), water content of feces (100 ml.) and urine (1500 ml.). Such a precise balance seems quite reasonable and proper until one considers the magnitude of fluid exchange in the body which would tremendously influence water losses through any one of these pathways. For example, increased environmental temperature coupled with high humidity induces overt sweating up to 14,000 cc. per day. This water loss must be made up by drinking equally large quantities of water, supplemented by electrolytes to replace lost ions.

Some 8000 ml. of fluid are secreted into the gastrointestinal tract and reabsorbed almost completely each day. Increased gastrointestinal motility may propel these fluids through the gut so rapidly that reabsorption is incomplete (diarrhea) and large volumes of fluid, isotonic with the blood, are lost within a single day. In the kidneys a volume (170,000 ml.), equal to more than three times the total volume of body fluid, is filtered in the glomeruli and virtually all of it is re-

WATER AND ELECTROLYTE BALANCE

A. ELECTROLYTE BALANCE

B. WATER BALANCE

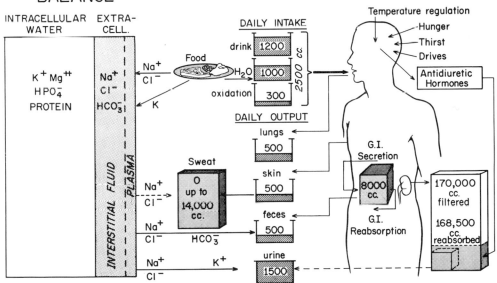

FIGURE 1. *A*, The fluids of the body can be considered as three compartments: intracellular, interstitial and intravascular. These three compartments are separated by cell membranes and capillary membranes respectively. The fluids and electrolytes that enter or leave the cells must pass through interstitial fluid and the blood plasma.

B, The quantities of water entering and leaving the body tend to remain in balance in spite of wide variability in the quantities of fluid being ingested and being lost by way of the skin, gastrointestinal tract and kidneys.

absorbed along with electrolytes and small organic molecules. The maximum daily urine volume reaches 20 to 30 liters a day (diabetes insipidus) and the minimum volume about 300 to 500 ml. a day during water deprivation. The urinary output of fluids can be varied within this extremely wide range. Since urinary output can be controlled over such a tremendous range, it is tempting to assume that the intake of fluid is ample and that urinary output is adjusted to eliminate the excess, whatever that may be. As a matter of fact, both the intake and output of water appear to be controlled.

Control of Fluid Intake

Adolph[1, 2] deprived dogs of water for varied periods of time, recording the quantity of the deficit. When he presented these animals with an unlimited supply of water they drank, within 2 or 3 minutes, a quantity of it which precisely made up the deficit. They then became disinterested in drinking. Thus, enough fluid was taken in to restore the fluid content of the body before any significant portion could have been absorbed from the gastrointestinal tract. A series of animals was prepared with esophageal fistulas so that all the water taken in by mouth escaped to the ground before reaching the stomach. The quantity of water drunk by these dogs was also closely related to the size of the water deficit and the rate of drinking was approximately proportional to the magnitude of the water deficit. Bellows[3] reported that the temporary satisfaction from the passage of water through the mouth and pharynx is superseded by a delayed and more prolonged satisfaction when the fluid reaches the lower portions of the gut.

Maire[4] implanted stimulating electrodes in the diencephalon of rats. Immediately after weak stimuli were applied to certain sites the rats would go straight to the water and drink. Stimulation in slightly different areas consistently evoked eating reactions. The neural mechanisms which are involved in such experiments may play some role in the cerebral aspects of hunger and thirst "drives." Richter[5] reviewed a wide variety of evidence that animals, infants, children and adult humans would selectively vary their intake of specific material in a manner which was appropriate to counter alterations in the internal environment due to endocrine or nutritional factors. For example, Bare[6] demonstrated that adrenalectomized rats selectively imbibed greater quantities of salt than normal rats and thereby improved their survival rates.

Interchanges Between Compartments

Although water enters and leaves the body by way of the blood, all three body fluid compartments tend to participate in any total water loss or gain. For example, profuse sweating may produce a loss of several liters in a day. The plasma volume is supported by movement of water from the cells into the intersitial fluids and from the interstitial fluids into the blood vascular system. Similarly a large water intake is distributed throughout all the fluid compartments illustrated in Figure 1A. Thus, the large fluid volumes within and between cells tend to cushion the effects of severe imbalance between intake and output of fluid volume and lend immediate support to blood volume through changes in fluid balance across the capillary membranes (see Fig. 15, Chap. 1). So long as the plasma osmotic pressure, capillary pressures and capillary permeability are within normal limits, the plasma volume is about one-fourth of the total extracellular volume. After a severe hemorrhage, reduction in arterial pressure is countered by intense peripheral vasoconstriction, which lowers capillary pressure so that fluid is reabsorbed from interstitial spaces to swell the circulating plasma volumes. In some forms of edema and following administration of adrenal cortical hormones, the blood volume is expanded at the expense of the interstitial fluid volumes. An increase in blood volume is commonly accompanied by collection of fluid in the interstitial spaces in the form of edema fluid. Thus, the state of the fluids in the interstitial spaces is of particular importance.

The Interstitial Spaces. In all tissues, the interstitial spaces are occupied by some form of connective tissue stroma which is traversed by the terminal branches and capillary networks of the vascular system (see Fig. 1, Chap. 4). The nature and extent of this connective tissue varies from one organ to another. In some tissues, the cells are very tightly packed (e.g., skeletal muscle; see Fig. 11). In other regions, the cells are widely distributed throughout loose areolar connective tissue (e.g., subcutaneous tissue). It is now becoming clear that the spaces between cells are not occupied by "tissue fluid" in the usual sense, but rather by a gelatinous matrix composed of long-chain polysaccharid-protein combinations (hyaluronates) organized into a latticework.[7, 11] The water which is dispersed through such a gel does not flow as a free fluid in response to pressure gradients; it does not gravitate to dependent parts; and it cannot be withdrawn through a hypodermic needle thrust into the tissue spaces. Water or physiologic saline injected into loose connective tissue becomes localized as an edematous tumor. On the other hand, substances such as alcohol, chloroform or xylol disperse readily and do not accumulate around the point of injection.[12] Water is held by hydrophilic properties of the gel in the connective tissue matrix. Even when the subcutaneous tissues are waterlogged by massive edema, incision of the skin exposes a pearly gray surface from which water does not flow spontaneously, but a blotting paper placed in contact with this fully hydrated gel rapidly becomes soaked. The physical characteristics of such a gel can influence the water content of tissues. According to Lloyd and Phillips,[13] the molecules of an organized protein can approach as closely as the length of their side chains permits. At the isoelectric point, the molecules tend to be drawn together by electrostatic attraction, a condition which will favor the greatest degree of packing and hence the lowest degree of hydration. On either side of the isoelectric point, adjacent protein molecules mutually repel each other. By this means, the spaces between the molecules in an organized protein are increased, leading to an increase in the amount of water which can enter freely between the individual molecules.

The gelatinous "ground substance" gradually polymerizes, beginning shortly after birth, and tends to become progressively dehydrated with advancing age. However, many factors may acutely alter the viscosity and hydrophilic character of this gel. For example, enzyme systems (hyaluronidase) liquefy the gel by dissociating the long chain molecules. These have been called "spreading factors" because they accelerate the dispersion of dyes or saline solutions injected into the subcutaneous connective tissues.[14] The gelatinous state of interstitial spaces may have direct bearing on the exchange of fluid between tissues and capillaries.

It has been shown that connective tissues swell when exposed to a 0.125 molar solution of sodium chloride, and that the degree of swelling increases greatly if the concentration is increased to 0.25 molar (1.46 per cent).[15] These values lie on either side of a solution which is isotonic with the cells of the body. Theoretically, edema would be promoted and increased by salt concentration in the interstitial gels of the body.

Control of Water Excretion

Regulation of the water excretion to maintain normal water balance requires at least one sensing mechanism, some integrating system and an effector. Our information regarding the control over water balance is very incomplete, but the kidney is quite clearly the principal effector organ through which the control of water and electrolyte elimination is exercised. The kidney functions primarily by the filtration of very large volumes of cell-free and protein-free glomerular fluid, resembling plasma in its composition. Practically all of this fluid and its solutes are reabsorbed in the kidney tubules, so the quantity of water or salt excreted is determined by the amount that is not returned to the blood within the kidney parenchyma. In general, the urine volume can be increased by two mechanisms, (a) the excretion of increased quantities of osmotically active particles which are diluted by water (osmotic diuresis) and (b) the excretion of increased amounts of osmotically free water (water diuresis).

The excretion of osmotically free water in the urine is controlled primarily by the antidiuretic hormone excreted from the posterior lobe of the pituitary gland. This antidiuretic hormone (ADH) apparently acts by increasing the permeability of distal tubules or collecting ducts, permitting water to escape from the tubular lumen to the interstitial fluid of the medullary region, which is strongly hypertonic. The normal hypertonicity of urine is an expression of the more or less continuous action of antidiuretic hormone. The release of ADH by the pituitary gland is apparently influenced by at least two mechanisms, (a) osmoreceptors in the diencephalon and (b) left atrial distention receptors.

Osmoreceptors. Injection of hypertonic saline solution into the carotid arteries of animals results in an obvious reduction in urine formation. Verney[16] postulated that cells responsive to changes in the osmotic pressure of surrounding fluids are located in the diencephalon

CONTROL OF WATER AND ELECTROLYTE EXCRETION

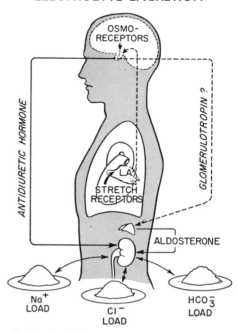

FIGURE 2.   The quantity of water excreted by the kidney is controlled in part by the antidiuretic hormone excreted from the posterior lobe of the pituitary gland in response to changes in the osmolarity of the plasma. No direct control over the electrolyte excretion by the pituitary gland has been demonstrated although for this purpose a hormone has been postulated (glomerulotropin). In addition to these factors, the kidney tends to excrete ions in response to the load of these materials presented to the kidney tubules. This occurs in the absence of known external regulatory mechanisms. The excretion of large quantities of electrolytes is accompanied by increased water loss in the form of osmotic diuresis. This diagram emphasizes how limited our knowledge is regarding the regulation of water and electrolyte excretion.

(Fig. 2). These osmoreceptors are believed to be an important mechanism by which ADH is released to regulate the free water excretion by the kidney as a compensation for changes in the osmolar concentration of the blood and interstitial fluids. Since the osmoreceptors can sense only the osmotic concentration of fluid near them, this mechanism cannot serve as a monitor of fluid volumes. An infusion of isotonic saline would theoretically have no influence on these receptors. Some other mechanisms must be involved in the regulation of total fluid volume.

Volume Receptors. In a stimulating review, Smith[17] pointed out that, despite a general consensus that an increase in the volume of the blood, plasma or extracellular fluid can induce diuresis and a decrease can induce antidiuresis, there is no consensus on where the receptors are located. A wide variety of receptors or mechanisms based on hemodynamic changes has been proposed, involving renal venous pressure, pressure in the great veins, arterial distention, interstitial fluids in the legs, or intravascular or interstitial fluids of the head or cephalic portion of the body. Gauer *et al.*[18] demonstrated that breathing against a negative pressure produced an increase in urine formation in dogs, and Sieker *et al.*[19] demonstrated that the same procedure caused an increase in urine production in man. Evidence was presented that stretch receptors in the left atrium and in the portions of the pulmonary veins within the pericardium respond to distention and reflexly induce diuresis.[20] This effect is presumably accomplished by impulses passing by way of the vagus nerve to the diencephalon to inhibit the release of ADH from the pituitary gland (Fig. 2). The atrial receptors represent the only "volume" sensing system influencing urinary excretion for which substantial evidence has been brought forth. Tentative acceptance of this mechanism does not preclude the possibility that other unidentified volume receptors may serve a similar function.[17] This hypothesis would appear to explain antidiuresis induced by orthostasis (sitting as compared with supine position), or by experimental distention of veins in the legs because these procedures would be expected to diminish the distention of the central veins and left atrium. On the contrary, diuresis would be favored by conditions causing distention of the left atrium, such as infusion of saline, isotonic saline, albu-

min solutions and, possibly, infusion of the whole blood.

If the osmotic pressure of the body fluids is controlled within relatively narrow limits, the electrolyte content must have considerable importance in determining the volume of the body fluids. Since sodium appears to be the predominant ion in plasma and interstitial tissues, the factors which regulate its intake and excretion have received a great deal of attention. For reasons which are not all clear, the quantities of sodium, chloride, potassium and bicarbonate which are excreted in the urine are influenced by the quantities which pass into the tubular lumen per unit time (filtered load). This is a basic mechanism influencing renal function. The mechanism functions in denervated or isolated kidneys and is not dependent upon external regulation. It has long been known that the adrenal glands have something to do with renal conservation of sodium. According to Smith,[17] some 14,598 papers regarding the adrenal glands were published in 1951, 1952 and 1953, and we still do not know much about their role in electrolyte balance except that they somehow promote tubular reabsorption of some fraction of the filtered sodium and that, in their absence, excessive loss of sodium in the urine leads to depletion of the extracellular fluid. Sodium excretion is excessive following abrupt expansion of body fluids with saline infusion in prehydrated normal subjects, hypertensive patients and subjects who have received cortisone. Aldosterone, excreted by the adrenal gland, facilitates the conservation of sodium and the excretion of potassium. The release of this hormone is not apparently dependent upon trophic hormones from the anterior pituitary (ACTH), but may involve another postulated hormone, glomerulotropin (Fig. 2). Even though the importance of aldosterone in electrolyte balances is recognized, the factors that regulate its release into the blood remain mysterious. Logical arguments can be advanced for the necessity for a volume receptor mechanism for the control of sodium balance, but the presence or location of such receptors remains to be demonstrated.

Control of the Composition of Total Body Fluids

If the total quantity of body fluids remains fairly constant and the concentration of each substance in the various compartments remains unchanged, then the total quantity of each of the constituents of the body fluids must remain about the same. If the balance between the intake and the output of these substances is maintained by individual control systems, sensing mechanisms, or receptors, the integrating mechanisms and their relation to the effector systems must be acting on each species—electrolytes, small organic molecules, proteins, cells, etc. Most of these control mechanisms remain completely unexplored.

CONTROL OF BLOOD DISTRIBUTION

The arterial system is well distended with blood at normal pressures. Consequently, the addition of an increment of blood during each ventricular stroke produces a large increase in pressure. Thus, the capacity of the arterial system is quite constant unless large changes in pressure occur. The systemic venous system, on the contrary, is clearly not fully distended because the pressure is low and the veins above the heart collapse when the body is erect. Furthermore, the capacity of the venous system is subject to very large changes with very little change in pressure. For example, about 10 per cent of the total blood volume can be removed with little functional evidence of any hemodynamic change.

The venous side of the circulation can be represented by a series of channels with variable blood content (Fig. 3). The capacity of the pulmonary vascular sys-

VENOUS VOLUME RESERVOIRS

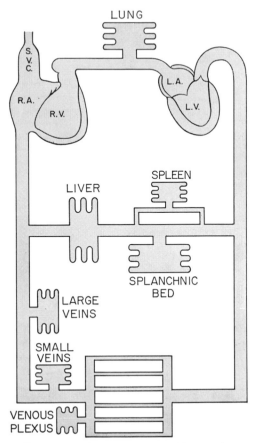

FIGURE 3. Changes in total blood volume are accompanied by variations in the capacity of numerous distensible reservoirs distributed widely throughout the vascular system. Note that the capacity of the pulmonary reservoir is small in relation to that of the systemic circulation. The distribution of blood in these various sites is subject to change as a result of gravitational forces (i.e., changes in posture). However, the capacity of the total systemic venous system is normally adjusted so that the level at which the systemic venous pressure equals extravascular pressure occurs within the thorax a few centimeters above the right atrium. When the cardiovascular system functions normally, the cardiac output can change rapidly over wide ranges with very little shift of blood from one reservoir to another (see Fig. 4).

tem is small compared with the very large capacity of the splanchnic bed, including the spleen and liver. Indeed, it is estimated that a major portion of the entire blood volume could be accommodated within the splanchnic reservoirs. In addition, the large and small veins are invested with smooth muscle under neural and hormonal control and can constrict to extremely small caliber under appropriate conditions (e.g., mechanical stimulation). Venous plexuses, like the one under the skin, can adapt to contain large or small volumes as the occasion demands (e.g., for temperature regulation).

At some point in the circulation, pressure should remain essentially unchanged regardless of the orientation of the body (i.e., during rotation around all three axes in space). In spite of the differences in the capacities of the venous system above and below the heart level, the point at which pressure remains unchanged during three-dimensional rotation is apparently within the right venticle.[21] In fact, the venous pressure at or near heart level remains about normal during exposure of animals to centrifugal forces as great as five times the force of gravity, directed toward either the head or tail.[22] These observations suggest that the distribution of the blood volume is so adjusted that an expansion in the capacity of the venous system in one part of the body is quite precisely compensated by a reduction in capacity elsewhere. For example, Kjellberg *et al.*[23] reported that changes in the pulmonary blood content vary inversely with blood content of the lower extremities. The cardiac chambers also serve as variable capacity reservoirs, and the heart volume apparently changes with pulmonary vascular volume.

As techniques for the direct measurement of volumes on the venous side of the circulation have not been developed, precise descriptions of actual capacity and variability in blood content of the various reservoirs are largely unavailable. It is generally recognized that, during the change from the supine to the erect position, the quantity of blood in the legs increases by 0.5 to 1.0 liter of blood, which must have come from some other site. The pulmonary vascular bed and the cardiac chambers contribute a considerable proportion of this blood and some of it undoubtedly comes from the partially collapsed veins above heart level.

During cardiovascular adjustments, displacement of blood from one part of the circulation is implicit in the concept of increasing venous return. On this basis, the onset of exercise is generally believed to be accompanied by displacement of blood from the periphery and the splanchnic bed by muscular and respiratory pumping action. For example, Wade *et al.*[24] reported that splanchnic blood volume was reduced by 300 to 700 ml. (mean 400 ml.) during exercise in the recumbent position. Alexander[25] stressed the importance of "venomotor tone" in hemorrhage and shock.

The concept that volumes shift from one portion of the vascular system is one that is widely held. If this were the case, the onset of exercise should be accompanied by shift of blood toward the heart, with a resulting rise in effective ventricular diastolic filling pressure; the ventricles should become distended; and the volume should diminish in other reservoirs such as the splanchnic bed, liver or spleen. The "venous return" should first affect the amount of blood entering the right ventricle, so that increased inflow into the right ventricle should precede increased outflow from the left ventricle by a time correponding to circulation time through the lungs. Direct measurements of inferior vena caval flow and aortic flow have failed to demonstrate clearly that increased venous return to the right atrium preceded increased outflow from the left ventricle.[26] Furthermore, simultaneous measurements of pulmonary arterial and aortic flow demonstrated that the right and left ventricular outputs were remarkably in phase. Contrary to expectation, virtually every time the stroke in one ventricle increased, the stroke output of the other also increased (Fig. 4). Marshall *et al.*[27] found that the volume

EVIDENCE AGAINST SHIFTS OF BLOOD DURING EXERTION

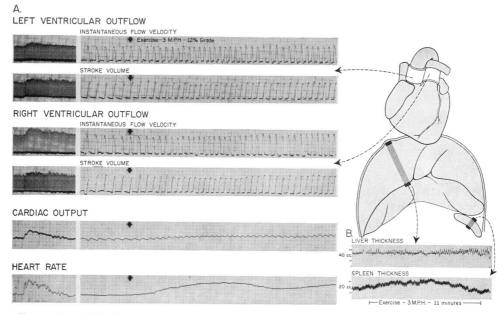

FIGURE 4.   *A,* Simultaneous measurements of the instantaneous and integrated flow (stroke volume) through the pulmonary artery and aorta at the onset of exercise disclose that the stroke volume ejected by the right and left ventricles changes in the same direction during virtually every beat during the increase in cardiac output at the onset of exercise. This observation suggests that the flow through systemic and pulmonary circuit increases concurrently so no shift of blood would be required.

B, Direct measurements of dimensions of the liver and spleen in active healthy dogs do not indicate any consistent reduction in the size of these organs at the onset of exertion. Thus, these two organs need not serve as reservoirs, giving up blood at the onset of exercise. (These records are presented through the courtesy of Dr. Warren Guntheroth, Department of Pediatrics, University of Washington.)

of blood in the lungs and the left heart chambers increased not at all in some subjects during severe exercise and by 20 per cent in the most extreme instances. They concluded that any increase in pulmonary blood volume in dog or man during exercise would be small or insignificant. In addition, Guntheroth[28] directly recorded the dimensions of the liver and spleen during spontaneous activity in intact dogs. No consistent or significant changes in these dimensions were recorded during spontaneous activity, including treadmill exercise. Except for the displacement of blood into dependent extremities accompanying changes in posture, the evidence for shifts of blood from one part of the circulation to another is somewhat tenuous. It seems quite possible that the postulated redistribution of blood

volume under normal conditions has been greatly exaggerated. On the other hand, disease of the left ventricle may produce an imbalance in the reserve capacity of the two ventricles, leading to displacement of blood from the systemic reservoirs into the lungs at the onset of exercise and producing the cardinal signs of the left ventricular failure (see below).

SUMMARY

The blood volume is but a small fraction of the total body fluid volume for which it serves to maintain states of equilibrium in relation to the composition, temperature, pH, etc. In this way the cellular environment is maintained within fairly constant ranges. Complex control mechanisms are required to maintain both total blood volume and total body fluid volume within a relatively narrow range over long periods in spite of wide variations in food and fluid intake and in excretions and losses of water through various routes. The osmotic pressure in body fluids is also regulated by mechanisms which involve the electrolyte balance. The mechanisms which regulate these exchanges must be very extensive, but they are poorly understood. For example, neural receptors in the left atrium have been described as monitoring the total blood volume and influencing the pituitary gland to excrete varying amounts of antidiuretic hormone to control the output of urine. Osmoreceptors in the diencephalon are believed to adjust urine flow by the same mechanism in response to changes in osmolarity in the body fluids. These are the only mechanisms for control of water balance which appear to have substantial experimental support. In view of the complexity of the problem, these mechanisms constitute only a small step toward an understanding of the whole system that regulates the intake of food, water, and electrolytes and the output of these substances as required to maintain the quantity and composition of the blood and other body fluids. The regulation of blood volume is one part of this total picture, but our understanding of this process is also very sketchy.

Since the venous sides of the systemic and pulmonary systems are capable of changes in capacity, the distribution of blood within these vascular beds may change from one group of venous reservoirs to another. Such a redistribution of blood volume occurs when one stands up; blood accumulates independent extremities, having been displaced from elsewhere in the system. According to traditional concepts, changes in the blood flow through various organs or changes in cardiac output characteristically involve some shift of blood from one part of the circulation to another. The onset of exercise should be an extreme example of the so-called "increased venous return." Recently, direct measurements have failed to confirm an increase in pulmonary blood volume or a reduction in the dimensions of the liver and spleen at the onset of exercise. These observations suggest that blood flow may accelerate in all divisions of the cardiovascular system more or less simultaneously without the need for shifts in blood distribution under normal conditions. However, the pulmonary congestion developing during exertion in patients with left ventricular "failure" suggests that blood from the systemic circulation pumped into the pulmonary vascular bed may be an important factor when left ventricular output is restricted by disease.

II. Congestive Heart Failure

Patients with heart disease may have neither symptoms nor external signs of it during routine activity so long as they remain "compensated." This term actually means that the cardiovascular reserve capacity is sufficient for the range of activity usually encountered by a particular patient. The diminished cardiac reserves become manifest during more intense exertion by the appearance of breathlessness, perceptibly forceful heart beat and fatigue at levels of exercise which could previously be tolerated with ease. As the cardiovascular reserves become further depleted, the maximal sustained cardiac output is seriously curtailed and a greater proportion of oxygen transport is attained by oxygen extraction which widens the arteriovenous oxygen difference. The final stages are reached when the cardiac output is barely adequate for the metabolic requirements at rest. As various components of the cardiac reserve are progressively depleted, diminished exercise tolerance is the most obvious symptom. In many patients with advanced heart disease, the heart remains compensated for a long time and the signs and symptoms of congestive heart failure appear abruptly without any obvious precipitating cause. Some patients with moderately advanced heart disease may display severe signs of congestive heart failure while other individuals with apparently more serious cardiac impairment remain compensated.

The factors involved in the transition from compensation to decompensation have not been clearly elucidated. The failing ventricle has been described[29] as having a slower pressure rise during isometric contraction, a lower systolic peak pressure, a larger diastolic size, a higher filling pressure and diminished efficiency. This description is consistent with a reduction in "contractility" as defined previously (Chap. 3). The reduction in the mechanical efficiency of myocardial contraction is an important factor in heart failure. A failing heart does not fully use the energy derived from the breakdown of glucose. Detailed investigation of the changes in myocardial metabolism should clarify the nature and significance of ventricular failure.

LEFT VENTRICULAR FAILURE

Depletion of the left ventricular reserve capacity should curtail the maximum sustained cardiac output in accordance with the principles discussed in Chapter 15. This fact has been clearly established by several studies utilizing cardiac catheterization to measure cardiac output in normal individuals and in patients with heart disease.

Hickam, Cargill and Golden[30] studied the cardiovascular responses of patients with heart disease and normal subjects, and arrived at the following conclusions: "(1) In normal persons during exercise there is an increase in both cardiac output and arteriovenous oxygen difference but the increase in cardiac output predominates; (2) in persons with congestive heart failure, there is little or no increase in the cardiac output during exercise, but there is a large increase in arteriovenous oxygen difference . . . (3) in frank chronic congestive heart failure the resting output is the greatest that can be consistently maintained, but even at rest this output may not be great enough to supply the tissues with blood at a rate normally commensurate with their metabolic needs." Briggs et al.[31] measured many variables including cardiac output, blood volume, thiocyanate space, and filling pressures of the heart. They found that the oxygen saturation of mixed venous blood correlates best with the clinical status in compensated and uncompensated patients.

Oxygen Extraction in Patients with Heart Failure

As cardiac function is impaired by disease, the maximum sustained increase in cardiac output is curtailed. Under these conditions, increased oxygen needs are met by a more complete oxygen extraction than normal. In patients with seriously limited cardiac performance, the resting cardiac output may be significantly diminished even though the oxygen uptake remains normal. For example, a normal resting subject with a mean cardiac ouput of 4290 cc. per minute and an oxygen consumption of 217 cc. per minute has an average arteriovenous oxygen difference of 4.7 volumes per cent (Fig. 5A). Patients with heart failure have about the same resting oxygen uptake (214 cc. per minute) even though the cardiac output is significantly diminished (2860 cc. per minute), but the arteriovenous oxygen difference is increased (7.3 volumes per cent) (Fig. 5B). The increased oxygen extraction in the various tissues is accomplished by reduced blood flow through the skin, kidney, gastrointestinal tract, skeletal muscle and even through the brain. When patients with such advanced heart disease exert themselves even mildly, the oxygen consumption increases largely by further reduction in venous oxygen content from various tissues. However, a further diminution in blood flow through the cerebral circula-tion, kidneys and splanchnic bed is not well tolerated and unpleasant symptoms discourage any form of physical exertion.

A greatly increased oxygen consumption can theoretically be attained solely through utilization of the venous reserve oxygen without any increase in cardiac output. If the blood flow and oxygen ex-

THE UTILIZATION OF VENOUS OXYGEN RESERVE

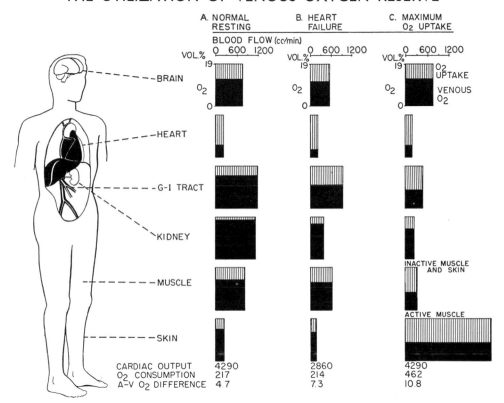

	A. NORMAL RESTING	B. HEART FAILURE	C. MAXIMUM O2 UPTAKE
CARDIAC OUTPUT	4290	2860	4290
O2 CONSUMPTION	217	214	462
A-V O2 DIFFERENCE	4.7	7.3	10.8

FIGURE 5.   The rectangular area, delimited by plotting oxygen content against blood flow, represents the quantity of oxygen per minute delivered to each tissue by the arterial blood. The area covered by vertical lines indicates the quantity of oxygen extracted by each tissue. The black areas represent the venous oxygen reserve, the quantity of oxygen remaining in the blood when it leaves the tissue.

A, The normal distribution of blood flow and oxygen extraction is the same as in Figure 2, Chapter 4.

B, In patients with advanced congestive heart failure, the resting cardiac output may be abnormally low (2860 cc. per minute). A greater proportion of the venous oxygen reserve is utilized because flow is diminished and greater oxygen extraction occurs in all the tissues except the myocardium. Even cerebral blood flow is diminished.

C, A normal individual with an average resting cardiac output (4290 cc. per minute) could theoretically double his oxygen consumption by maximal utilization of the venous oxygen reserve. If the cerebral and coronary flow remain normal, the oxygen extraction from the blood in the splanchnic bed, skin and inactive muscle could be increased to about 12 volumes per cent and in the kidney to 5.5 volumes per cent. These are the maximal arteriovenous oxygen differences reported in the literature. If blood flow is conserved by this means, one-half of the cardiac output can be diverted to active muscles, greatly augmenting their supply of oxygen without an increase in cardiac output. Neither the normal individual nor the patient with acquired heart disease utilizes venous oxygen reserve to this extent. (Data compiled from the literature[30-34] and organized in this form by Dr. Loren D. Carlson, University of Kentucky.)

ETIOLOGY OF PULMONARY CONGESTION

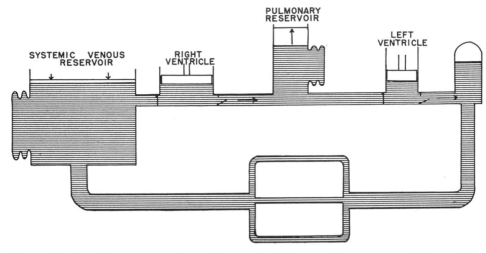

FIGURE 6.   According to current theory, the capacity of the systemic venous reservoir is much larger than that of the pulmonary venous reservoir. Under these conditions, transfer of small quantities of blood from the systemic circulation would produce a relatively large increase in pulmonary vascular volume and pressure. Very slight imbalance between the output of the right ventricular chamber (volume pump) and the left ventricle (pressure pump) could theoretically produce significant pulmonary congestion. A sustained increase in left ventricular filling pressure could theoretically produce chronic pulmonary congestion without appreciable increase in total blood volume.

traction in the brain and heart remained normal and if the maximum tolerable oxygen extraction in splanchnic bed, skin and muscle was 12 volumes per cent and in the kidney was 5.5 volumes per cent, the total oxygen consumption could be doubled without any change in total systemic blood flow (Fig. 5C). Note the tremendous potential increase in oxygen delivery to active muscle by more complete utilization of venous oxygen reserve through redistribution of blood flow. Neither normal individuals nor patients with advanced heart disease utilize these mechanisms to the fullest extent. Such a marked reduction in renal blood flow could probably be tolerated only briefly before it interfered with renal function. Indeed, such an extreme reduction in renal blood flow is rarely encountered even in patients with advanced congestive failure and extensive edema. Reduced renal blood flow resulting from restricted cardiac output may produce serious impairment of kidney function.

Pulmonary Congestion

The reservoir capacity of the pulmonary vascular tree is generally believed to be smaller than that of the systemic venous system (see Fig. 3). Cournand[33] estimated that the lungs normally contain only about 5 per cent of the total blood volume while the systemic veins contain about 55 per cent. Accordingly, he concluded that pulmonary congestion could be caused by a transfer of blood from the systemic venous system into the pulmonary vascular tree (Fig. 6). If right ventricular output exceeds left ventricular output, a large quantity of blood would be quickly transferred to the lungs from the systemic venous reservoirs. The right ventricle is so well adapted as a volume pump that transient imbalance between right and left ventricular output could produce some degree of pulmonary congestion under many circumstances. Accumulation of blood within the pulmonary vascular tree is probably more extensive in patients having increased total blood volume (i.e., right ventricular failure). Congestion of the lungs could also result from any factor that displaced blood from the systemic to the pulmonary vascular bed. One such mechanism would be a generalized constriction of veins in the systemic circulation. Shuman et al.[35] found that blockade of the sympathetic nervous system reduced the elevated venous pressure in patients with congestive heart failure. Such changes have been ascribed to redistribution of blood volume by the release of constrictor reflexes that may produce the increased venous and atrial pressures in patients with congestive heart failure.[36, 37] Under these conditions, a reduction in constrictor tone in veins may provide symptomatic relief without any alteration in cardiac function.

Pulmonary edema can be produced by a wide variety of experimental procedures

PULMONARY CONGESTION FROM LEFT VENTRICULAR FAILURE

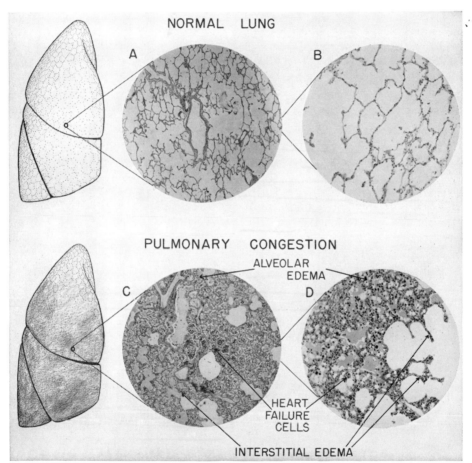

FIGURE 7.   A, The normal lung is partitioned by delicate alveolar membranes into microscopic air sacs. This structural organization provides a tremendous surface area for gas exchange.

B, The alveolar membranes are exceedingly thin and blood in capillaries coursing through them comes into almost direct contact with the alveolar air.

C, Pulmonary congestion and edema seriously impede aeration of the alveolar sacs and gas exchange between alveolar air and blood. The presence of edema fluid in alveolar sacs renders them almost functionless and the foaming effect of the fluid impedes respiratory gas movement.

D, Accumulation of fluid within the alveolar walls (interstitial edema) produces an increase in the distance of diffusion, so that gas exchange between alveolar air and blood is slowed even in alveoli which contain no fluid. (Microscopic slides were obtained through courtesy of Dr. Theodore Thorson.)

PULMONARY HYPERTENSION FROM LEFT VENTRICULAR FAILURE

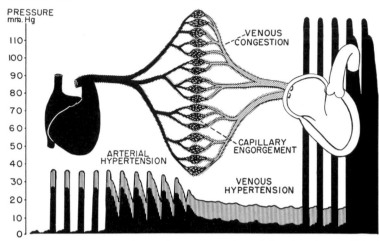

FIGURE 8.   The pressure gradient from pulmonary arteries to left atrium is very slight (about 6 mm. Hg), so any increase in left ventricular filling pressure is immediately reflected throughout the pulmonary vascular tree. Increased pressure in distensible pulmonary veins and capillaries produces marked distention and engorgement. Thus, pulmonary venous and capillary hypertension produces pulmonary congestion and pulmonary edema if the pressures reach sufficient height.

involving the central nervous system: increasing the intracranial pressure,[38] injecting fibrinogen[39] or veratrine[40] intracisternally, or making discrete lesions in the preoptic region of the hypothalamus.[41] The mechanisms by which these neural factors become expressed as pulmonary congestion and edema have not been clarified. Paine *et al.*[42, 43] demonstrated elevated pulmonary vascular pressures in pulmonary edema precipitated by embolism of cerebral vessels; similar hemodynamic effects presumably occur when other cerebral factors result in the same functional disturbances.

Normal lungs are delicate, spongy, crepitant and resilient. Their color is uniformly salmon pink in young individuals, but with advancing age, accumulation of carbonaceous substances produces a tinge of slate gray. Microscopic sections of inflated pulmonary parenchyma show the delicate alveolar membranes partitioning the alveolar ducts and air sacs (Fig. 7A). The blood in the alveolar capillaries comes very close to the alveolar air, so the distance of diffusion for gaseous exchange is extremely short (Fig. 7B).

The lungs of patients who have died after chronic left ventricular failure are engorged with blood and are heavy, discolored, tough and indurated. The normal resilience is diminished because connective tissue has proliferated within the parenchyma. The alveolar membranes are thickened and edematous, increasing the distance between the alveolar air and capillary blood (Fig. 7C). Many alveoli are partially or completely filled with edema fluid, which would seriously impair respiratory exchange. Scattered throughout the alveolar spaces are phagocytes containing a yellow brown pigment (hemosiderin) derived from erythrocytes extravasated into the alveolar spaces. The caliber of the small bronchial airways may be diminished by congestion and edema of the mucosa, and by increased excretion of mucus. Thus, gas exchange in the lungs of patients with chronic left ventricular failure is impeded in three ways: (a) by increased resistance to the flow of air in and out of the alveoli, (b) by alveolar flooding with edema fluid, and (c) by retarded diffusion of gases from alveolar air to capillary blood by interstitial edema (Fig. 7D).

Accumulation of blood within the pulmonary vessels is associated with increased pressure in these channels. Since the lungs function as a blood reservoir, the pulmonary vasculature, particularly capillaries and veins, is highly distensible. The pressure in the capillaries and veins must exceed the diastolic pressure in the left ventricle, which is the point of outflow from the pulmonary vessels. The pressure gradient from pulmonary artery to left ventricle is so shallow (6 mm. Hg) that any increase in left ventricular filling pressure produces a generalized increase in pulmonary vascular pressures (Fig. 8).

Symptoms from Pulmonary Congestion. The most common presenting symptom of left ventricular insufficiency is dyspnea on exertion. This shortness of breath is characterized by rapid, shallow respiration in contrast to the deep, full inspiration which is the normal respiratory response to exercise. After varying periods of time, the amount of exercise required to induce dyspnea progressively decreases. Eventually the individual may develop respiratory distress when he lies down (orthopnea). Then the patient can breathe comfortably only with his head and trunk erect, even during sleep. For unknown reasons, orthopnea is the initial symptom in many patients with left ventricular insufficiency, particularly that caused by hypertension or coronary insufficiency. Such patients are apt to develop attacks of respiratory distress, similar to asthma, with forced inspiratory and expiratory movements (cardiac asthma), and associated with coughing or choking and expectoration of blood-tinged sputum. Thus, the fundamental symptoms of left ventricular failure are those of respiratory dysfunction associated with pulmonary congestion.

Effects of Pulmonary Congestion on Gas Exchange. Blood in the pulmonary capillaries can become oxygenated only if oxygen can diffuse rapidly from the alveolar spaces through the intervening membranes to reach the blood. Rapid diffusion of dissolved gases occurs over very short distances in response to steep concentration gradients. An increased distance of diffusion across the alveolar walls theoretically retards the rate of oxygen transfer. For this reason, relatively thin layers of extravascular fluid interposed between the capillaries and the alveolar air should seriously reduce the efficiency with which the blood is oxygenated (Fig. 8C). Pulmonary edema results from excessive filtration of fluid through the pulmonary capillaries in accordance with Starling's hypothesis of capillary fluid balance. Flooding of alveolar spaces interferes with aeration of both the alveolar air cells and the blood.

Interference with gas exchange between the alveolar air and the pulmonary capillary blood may well contribute to cyanosis appearing in the terminal stages of left ventricular failure. Since cyanosis is neither a common nor a prominent feature of pulmonary congestion, the extreme degrees of pulmonary edema found at postmortem examination (Fig. 7C) may not necessarily be typical of most cardiac patients during life.

The presence of fluid in the airways of the lungs is detected clinically by auscultation of the chest. The presence and distribution of rales is generally considered a reliable indication that pulmonary edema is present. However, Vitale et al.[44] found a poor correlation between the auscultatory signs of pulmonary edema and the arterial oxygen saturation. For example, in some patients with minimal signs over the base of the lungs the oxygen tension was low while in seven of twelve patients with acute pulmonary edema and bubbling rales over all lung fields the arterial saturation was above 93 per cent.

Dyspnea. In the past, dyspnea was attributed to diminished oxygen and increased carbon dioxide content of the arterial blood reaching the respiratory centers. There is no doubt that inhalation

WORK OF BREATHING

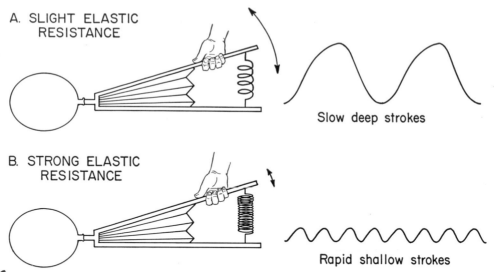

A. SLIGHT ELASTIC RESISTANCE

Slow deep strokes

B. STRONG ELASTIC RESISTANCE

Rapid shallow strokes

FIGURE 9.   To pump equal volumes of air per unit time, a spring loaded bellows should be operated with short rapid strokes to achieve greatest efficiency and reduce the total work. Congested lungs tend to resist inspiratory distention with greater force than normal so that rapid shallow breathing tends to reduce the work of breathing, particularly when respiratory minute volume must be greatly increased as during exertion. This observation suggests that the dyspnea observed in patients with congestive heart failure may actually diminish the excess work of breathing imposed by the rigidity of the lungs. *tachypnea in CHF*

of gas mixtures with either low oxygen tension or increased carbon dioxide concentration results in stimulated respiratory activity. However, under these conditions, increased pulmonary ventilation is accomplished by deep inspiratory excursions rather than by rapid shallow breathing, which typifies dyspnea. Further, dyspnea occurs in patients with left ventricular decompensation without any evidence of pulmonary edema and with normal arterial oxygen and carbon dioxide levels. Thus, dyspnea cannot be ascribed solely to interference with the primary function of the pulmonary circulation, namely, gaseous exchange between the blood and the alveolar air.

Harrison et al.[45, 46] demonstrated that artificially induced pulmonary congestion in dogs produced rapid shallow breathing which disappeared after section of the vagi. They postulated that such dyspnea resulted from reflex stimulation of respiratory activity initiated by stretch receptors responding to distention of vascular channels within the thorax. Mechanical factors may also be invoked to explain the rapid shallow breathing in response to pulmonary congestion. For example, Drinker et al.[47] described the turgidity of the lungs produced by artificial pulmonary congestion. The lungs resembled erectile tissue in that they became rigid and inelastic when engorged with blood. Further, the lungs of patients with chronic pulmonary congestion often become indurated by a proliferation of supporting connective tissue. While the fibrotic reaction may supply additional external support to the pulmonary vessels, it also tends to reduce the mobility and elasticity of the lungs. Under these conditions, increased effort is required to inflate and deflate the lungs.

The underlying connection between congestion of the lungs and the rapid shallow breathing typical of dyspnea in such patients is illustrated in Figure 9.

Relatively little muscular tension is required to expand a normal lung, and it might be compared with a bellows with a weak spring, as in Figure 9A. In contrast, much more muscle tension is needed to overcome the resistance to expansion of the congested lung, because it has stiffened. Greater expansion involves even greater tension, and, in general, the congested lung resembles a bellows with a stiff spring (Fig. 9B). To pump equal volumes rapidly, the bellows with the weak spring functions most effectively by increasing both rate and stroke volume. Because the work involved in increasing distention and compression is relatively great, the bellows with the stiff spring functions most effectively with rapid shallow strokes. Similarly, the work of breathing is minimized in patients with congested lungs by increasing the respiratory minute volume through rapid shallow breaths. Asked to breathe in and out as rapidly and deeply as possible for some 15 seconds (maximal breathing capacity), patients with left ventricular failure manifest a reduced ability to increase their respiratory minute volume.

Orthopnea. When the body is erect, blood tends to accumulate in the dependent extremities. The veins are distended by the high hydrostatic pressures. During the day, fluid filters from the capillaries into the tissue spaces in the dependent parts in response to the high intravascular pressures. When a person lies down, the pressure in these vessels diminishes and the excess fluid is reabsorbed, expanding the blood volume at night. At the same time, the blood which had distended the peripheral veins is redistributed and much of it accumulates in the pulmonary tree. In normal individuals, this shift of blood into the lungs produces no disturbance. However, in patients with antecedent pulmonary congestion due to left ventricular failure, the added load induces dyspnea in the reclining position. The patients prop themselves up in bed to avoid the unpleasant consequences of reclining.

Symptoms from Bronchial Congestion. The pulmonary and bronchial arteries serve independent capillary networks except at the respiratory bronchioles and alveolar ducts. However, all the alveolar capillaries and most of the bronchial capillaries drain into the pulmonary veins. Elevation of the left ventricular diastolic pressure and the pulmonary venous pressure is accompanied by congestion in those bronchial vessels which drain by this route. Engorgement of the mucous membranes produces edema and encroachment on the airways. These events tend to impede movement of air in and out of the lungs (Fig. 10). Greater muscular effort is required for respiratory ventilation and the maximum breathing capacity may be impaired. The result may be a contribution to the shortness of breath closely resembling the asthma produced by allergic reactions.

A productive cough is a prominent symptom in congestive heart failure. The increased production of mucus by congested bronchial mucosa is a logical explanation for this complaint. Although coughing is not a particularly effective mechanism for removing fluid from the alveoli, edema fluid transported to bronchial airways may be eliminated by this mechanism. Blood-tinged sputum is frequently noted and was formerly explained on the basis of extravasation of erythrocytes into the alveolar sacs. Hemoptysis is now more frequently attributed to small hemorrhages from the congested bronchial mucosa.

Symptoms from Restricted Cardiac Output. Although the classic symptoms of left ventricular failure result from pulmonary dysfunction, restricted cardiac output reserve is an essential feature of this condition. When the resting cardiac output is diminished, the blood flow through nearly all regions of the body is curtailed to some extent and the oxygen

ETIOLOGY OF RESPIRATORY SYMPTOMS FROM PULMONARY HYPERTENSION

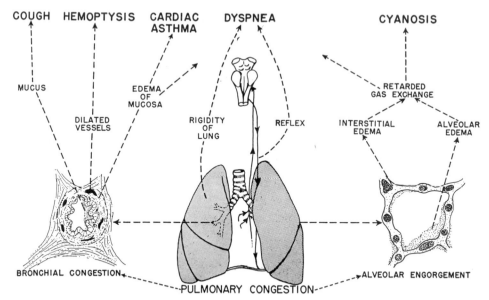

FIGURE 10.   Since most bronchial capillaries drain by way of the pulmonary veins, congestion develops simultaneously in alveolar and bronchial vascular networks. Bronchial congestion tends to stimulate production of mucus, leading to a productive cough. The distended bronchial capillaries may rupture so the patient coughs up blood-tinged sputum (hemoptysis). Edema of the bronchial mucosa increases resistance to air flow, producing respiratory distress similar to asthma. Dyspnea results primarily from reflexes initiated by vascular distention, but may be supplemented by increased rigidity of the lungs and by impaired gas exchange resulting from interstitial edema and accumulation of fluid in alveolar sacs (see Fig. 7). Cyanosis is not consistently observed even in patients with severe pulmonary edema (see text).

extraction is correspondingly increased (see Fig. 5). Such depletion of the venous oxygen reserve means that the oxygen tension in these tissues must be subnormal. One would certainly expect evidences of dysfunction to result from such a state. For example, restricted blood flow through skeletal muscle should lead to weakness and fatigability. Richards[48] directed attention to the fact that patients' exercise tolerance may be limited by fatigue or exhaustion as well as by the accompanying dyspnea, from which it must be distinguished. Fatigue is difficult to define or describe, and is very easily prevented by voluntary restriction in activity to avoid the unpleasant sensation. For this reason, relief from weakness or fatigability is most readily recognized by patients whose cardiac condition has been

rather suddenly improved, e.g., by mitral valvulotomy. The sensation of fatigue subjectively stems directly from exercising muscle, and is generally ascribed to oxygen debt and local deficiency in blood flow.

Diminished blood flow through the splanchnic bed might also interfere with gastrointestinal activity. Actually, indigestion is a fairly common complaint in older patients with heart disease, but it is neither distinctive nor consistently observed. Most older patients with advanced heart disease might well have similar gastrointestinal complaints without any heart disease.

The kidney is one tissue where the blood flow always remains very large in relation to the oxygen extraction. It seems significant that the renal arteriovenous oxygen difference rarely exceeds 3 to 4 cc. per 100 cc. of blood, even in patients with full-blown congestive heart failure (Fig. 5). Although renal dysfunction leads to retention of salt and water and the production of generalized venous congestion and peripheral edema, the cause is probably not insufficient oxygenation of the tissue since the kidney must actually work excessively during abnormally great reabsorption of salt and water (see *Peripheral Edema*, below).

RIGHT VENTRICULAR FAILURE

The right ventricular chamber is so well adapted as a volume pump that it rarely fails as a result of a pure volume load. Certain congenital anomalies produce recirculation of blood through the lungs so that the right ventricular output consistently remains two or three times that of the left ventricle. Such patients may have an essentially normal exercise tolerance and, in them, right heart failure is brought about by the pulmonary hypertension which frequently develops in response to excessive pulmonary blood flow (see Chap. 14). Thus, the principal cause of right ventricular failure is a chronic pressure load which may result from a number of conditions, including (*a*) left ventricular failure with pulmonary congestion and hypertension, (*b*) mitral stenosis, (*c*) primary disease of the lung with pulmonary hypertension and (*d*) pulmonary valvular stenosis.

Pathologic Evidence of Right Ventricular Failure

In contrast to left ventricular incompetence, right ventricular failure is manifested in external signs rather than in subjective symptoms. Fully developed right ventricular failure can be recognized from evidence of generalized systemic venous congestion and the development of peripheral edema.

Venous Congestion. Since blood tends to accumulate in those portions of the sys-temic venous system with the greatest distensibility in relation to the venous pressure, the most obvious engorgement occurs in the systemic venous reservoirs: the liver, spleen, splanchnic bed, skin, and the central and peripheral venous channels.

The liver characteristically enlarges in right ventricular failure. It extends well below the right costal border and may descend below the level of the umbilicus. Often the engorged liver is tender on palpation and occasionally is the site of spontaneous abdominal pain. The periportal sinusoids of the liver are engorged with blood. The degree of congestion tends to diminish from the periphery of the lobules toward the hepatic veins (Fig. 11). Chronic hepatic congestion may produce proliferation of the connective tissue stroma with a reduction in the size of the liver. The organization of the liver may be seriously disrupted by diffuse necrosis and scarring, which produce the pathologic picture of cirrhosis. It is often difficult to distinguish from cirrhosis with another cause. Chronic congestion of the liver is occasionally associated with evidence of dysfunction in the form of increased bilirubin in the blood or even perceptible jaundice. Bromsulphalein may not be as rapidly extracted from the blood under these conditions. A seriously engorged liver may contain such large quantities of blood that pressure over the organ may significantly distend the superficial cervical veins even when the patient is semi-erect.

The spleen tends to become enlarged during the development of hepatomegaly, presumably because both organs have a reservoir function and a common venous drainage system. However, an enlarged spleen is not as obvious as an enlarged liver.

The kidneys are enlarged, firm and dark red. The capillaries in the glomeruli and around the tubules tend to be engorged (Fig. 11). Histologic demonstration of such engorgement is difficult be-

THE EFFECTS OF RIGHT VENTRICULAR FAILURE

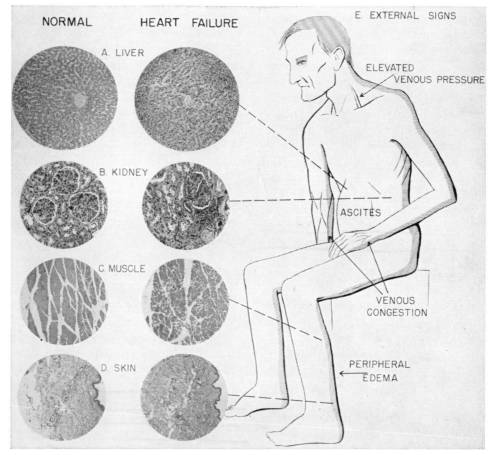

FIGURE 11.   Microscopic sections from a patient who died during an attack of congestive heart failure are compared with those from a young adult killed in an automobile accident.

A, The liver is engorged with blood, distending the liver sinusoids in the periportal regions (around the periphery of the photomicrograph).

B, The congested kidney is characterized by engorgement of both the glomerular and the peritubular capillaries.

C, Normally, the skeletal muscle fibers are packed so tightly that the cell borders cannot be readily distinguished with low power magnification. Edema fluid may force the fibers apart so they stand out individually.

D, Edematous skin becomes greatly thickened and waterlogged. The organization of the connective tissue appears to be disrupted.

E, External signs of advanced congestive heart failure are obvious on superficial inspection. Elevated venous pressure is evidenced by distention of the jugular vein in the erect position and prominence of peripheral veins. Ascites produces increased abdominal girth. Pitting edema tends to be localized in dependent parts. (The slides for this illustration were obtained through the courtesy of Dr. Theodore Thorson and Dr. E. C. Roosen-Runge.)

cause the kidney frequently becomes congested at the time of death from many causes.

The capacious splanchnic bed tends to become engorged in association with hepatomegaly and splenomegaly because blood from the mesenteric veins passes through the liver. Such splanchnic engorgement generally produces neither symptoms nor external signs.

Distention of the superficial veins is an early sign of venous congestion. Since the level of zero effective venous pressure is normally within the thorax, the cervical veins are collapsed when the individual is erect. Generalized engorgement of the venous channels is accompanied by elevated central venous pressure, so the level of zero effective venous pressure is higher. Under these circumstances, the jugular vein remains distended even when the patient is erect. The earliest sign of central engorgement may be elicited by gradually elevating the patient from the supine to the sitting position and observing the level of the transition between collapse and distention of the jugular vein above the sternal notch. Alternatively, the hand can be held dependent until the dorsal veins are distended, then elevated gradually so that the level at which the veins become emptied can be observed. Abnormal distention of veins may be detected before there is any obvious liver enlargement or peripheral edema.

These procedures provide a rather crude measure of venous pressure. It is preferable to measure venous pressure directly. The normal venous pressure in the median basilic vein of normal adult males ranges from 5 to 14 cm. of water with the average being 9.7 cm.[49] In any particular subject, venous pressure varies under many conditions including age, muscular activity, respiration, time of day, administration of fluids, etc. A single determination of venous pressure under standard conditions is often meaningless in assessing the presence or degree of congestive heart failure. However, serial measurements have value in revealing the course of the development and regression of heart failure. Changes in venous pressure occur much more promptly than other pathologic signs and symptoms of congestive heart failure, so the correlations among them may be somewhat obscured. In other words, elevated venous pressure often occurs well in advance of external signs of venous congestion or peripheral edema. During recovery, it may return to

the normal range before the other manifestations have completely disappeared. An authoritative discussion of venous pressure measurement and interpretation has been presented by Burch.[49]

Cyanosis. Cyanosis is severe in certain patients and imperceptible in others for no obvious reason. Since the skin is a major venous reservoir, its blood flow may be curtailed as part of the general conservation of flow, particularly if the cardiac output is diminished. Slow cutaneous flow produces the so-called "stagnant" anoxia, with more complete oxygen extraction and diminished oxygen content of the venous blood. If the quantity of reduced hemoglobin in cutaneous vessels exceeds 5 gm. per 100 cc. of blood, cyanosis becomes perceptible. An increased quantity of blood in the skin (congestion) probably emphasizes cyanosis which might otherwise be overlooked. Further, left ventricular failure with pulmonary congestion and edema may interfere with the oxygenation of arterial blood.[44] If the arterial blood entering the capillaries has a diminished oxygen content, the quantity of reduced hemoglobin in venous blood is more apt to reach levels above 5 gm. per 100 cc. of blood. For these reasons, cyanosis would be anticipated in patients with advanced cardiac failure involving both right and left ventricles, but this prediction is not consistently verified.

Peripheral Edema. Swelling of the ankles appearing during the day and subsiding during the night is a characteristic feature of right ventricular decompensation. A considerable quantity of fluid must accumulate in the interstitial spaces before it becomes manifest as edema. The edema accompanying congestive heart failure is generally most severe in dependent regions, particularly the lower extremities. Digital pressure over such edematous regions displaces fluid and leaves a depression which persists for a few minutes (pitting edema). The skin becomes thickened and waterlogged, as illustrated by a specimen from a patient who died with severe congestive heart failure (Fig. 11). The soft tissues of the genitalia are particularly prone to develop edema. Skeletal muscle fibers which are normally packed closely together are forced apart by the accumulation of edema fluid in the connective tissue stroma (Fig. 11). In bedridden patients with advanced right ventricular failure, edema is often most prominent over the sacrum, which is the most dependent region in the supine position.

Effusion into Serous Cavities.   Advanced stages of right ventricular failure in some patients are associated with the accumulation of fluid within the peritoneal cavity (ascites), within the pleural cavity (hydrothorax) and within the pericardium (hydropericardium).

Ascites may produce no signs or symptoms other than an increased abdominal girth, and may pass unnoticed. The extent of ascites apparently correlates more with the pressures in the portal circulation than with the cardiac status. A large proportion of patients with severe heart disease develop peripheral edema without demonstrable peritoneal effusion. In contrast, patients with stenosis of the tricuspid valve or constrictive pericarditis often have severe ascites and mild peripheral edema. No satisfactory explanation has been offered for the poor correlation between the severity of edema and of ascites. Perhaps the mechanisms underlying the two conditions are different, since subcutaneous edema fluid usually contains less than 0.5 per cent protein while ascitic fluid contains protein in concentrations approaching that of plasma (5 to 6 per cent). The etiology of ascites has been reviewed recently by Hyatt and Smith.[50] Extensive ascites is frequently associated with cirrhosis of the liver. On this basis, ascites has been attributed to the escape of liver lymph into the peritoneal cavity, but reasons for such a

phenomenon have never been clearly expressed.

Pleural effusion occurs most commonly in patients with combined right and left ventricular failure. Bedford and Lovibond[51] cited cases with isolated left ventricular failure and pleural effusion to support their concept that the transudation comes from the capillaries in the visceral pleura which drain into the pulmonary veins. They expressed their belief that elevated pressure in pulmonary veins is a major cause of hydrothorax in such patients. The observation that hydrothorax occurs more frequently in the right pleural space than in the left has never been satisfactorily explained.

Pericardial effusion from congestive heart failure is rarely extensive or significant.

Peripheral edema and effusion into serous cavities represent the accumulation of extravascular fluid, which has previously been attributed to a number of factors, including: (a) increased effective capillary pressure, associated with elevated venous pressure, (b) reduced effective colloid osmotic pressure of the blood from abnormally increased capillary permeability, (c) interference with lymphatic drainage and (d) selective retention of water and electrolytes by the kidneys. Theories based on each of these factors have been discarded or criticized. For example, capillary and venous pressures normally become greatly elevated in dependent extremities without edema formation, evidence for increased capillary permeability has not been convincing, causes of impaired lymphatic drainage have not been elucidated and mechanisms underlying renal retention of salt and water have been controversial. A most unfortunate controversy has existed between proponents of two theories concerning the development of congestive heart failure: the backward failure and forward failure theories. Mention of these two concepts has been studiously avoided on the basis that they have channeled thought and investigative effort along relatively fruitless lines. This controversy is comparable to a debate among police officers concerning the relative seriousness of embezzlement and burglary, sustained to the point that effective investigation of suspects is neglected.

The Concept of Backward Failure

According to the backward failure theory, the failing ventricle becomes distended and loses contractile power. To maintain the required cardiac output the diastolic filling pressure rises, increasing the stroke volume in accordance with Starling's law of the heart. If the ventricular distention exceeds some critical value, further increase in ventricular filling pressure reduces ventricular output. The increased diastolic pressure in the left ventricle elevates the pressures throughout the venous and capillary channels upstream from the failing chamber. The increased venous pressure is attained by venous engorgement as though the blood were dammed up behind an obstruction in a flowing stream. This idea is sometimes expressed as "the ventricle is unable to eject the quantity of blood which comes to it," although it is not clear what that phrase means in a closed circuit. The generalized increase in venous and capillary pressures augments filtration through the capillary walls so that fluid tends to collect in the interstitial spaces. Fluid lost into the interstitial spaces is replaced by increased fluid intake or by adjustment in renal output so edema and effusion continue until a new equilibrium is established. In response to recent emphasis on the importance of renal retention of salt and water, proponents of this idea have presented evidence that elevation of renal venous pressure produces a diminution in urine output.

Both the strength and the weakness of this concept lie in the fact that it is a functional interpretation of the pathologic changes in patients dying from heart failure. Certainly, the pathologic picture of congestion "looks" like the result of a damming of blood behind a failing chamber. However, a number of discordant factors can be marshalled against this concept.

If blood is dammed up behind the right ventricle, where does all this blood come from? From reference to the hydraulic model in Figure 6, it seems clear that a failure of the pump on the left would accumulate fluid in the large reservoir upstream only by evacuating the blood from the smaller (pulmonary) reservoir. Generalized systemic and pulmonary congestion implies a marked increase in total blood volume (renal retention of fluids). If increased renal venous pressure produces renal retention of salt and water, how did the renal venous pressure become elevated in the first place?

Burch and Ray[52] reviewed some of the observations which are incompatible with the backward failure theory. For example, venous hypertension is known to exist in clinical states with little or no edema, e.g., therapeutic ligation of the inferior vena cava.[53] The capillary pressures in the dependent extremities of normal individuals are much higher than the elevated central venous pressure during congestive heart failure. Systemic venous congestion and edema do not appear even after destruction of practically all the right ventricular musculature either in experimental animals[54, 55] or in patients with extensive right ventricular infarction.[56]

Therapeutic procedures, such as a low salt diet or the administration of mercurial diuretics, promote disappearance of edema, decline in venous pressure and reduction in the size of the liver, but have no known direct effect on the heart. A syndrome very similar to congestive heart failure can be produced by excessive administration of desoxycorticosterone acetate, which is not supposed to affect the heart significantly. A similar syndrome occurs when large amounts of water and electrolytes are administered to patients with anuria due to renal disease. Recognition of such deficiencies has led many investigators to favor the forward failure theory.

The Concept of Forward Failure

Advocates of this theory attribute the formation of edema to diminished cardiac output. The forward failure theory antedated the backward failure theory but was not widely accepted for many years. Originally, the diminished cardiac output was believed to produce peripheral constriction and anoxia, which increased capillary permeability and thus produced transudation of fluid into the tissue spaces. However, the capillary endothelium is in direct contact with the blood. If these cells are sufficiently anoxic to increase capillary permeability, what must be the state of the cells at some distance from the capillaries? Neither venous congestion nor edema is characteristically produced by severe anoxia resulting from pulmonary disease, cyanotic congenital heart disease or living at high altitude. However, more recently cardiac catheterization has provided direct evidence of abnormally low cardiac output in many patients with advanced heart failure. Reduction in the renal blood flow of such patients has also been demonstrated. Thus, the diminished cardiac output is now supposed to lead to a diminished renal blood flow and the retention of salt and water. Particularly damaging arguments result from observations that urinary output does not correlate well with renal blood flow, and that control of urine volume is vested primarily in the extent of tubular reabsorption. The kidney actually expends more energy in reabsorbing salt and water than in excreting large urine volumes with a specific gravity of about 1.010. The connection between cardiac output and renal tubular function has not been established.

For these reasons, I would like to see both the forward and the backward failure theories discarded to avoid the semantics and the emotional connotations involved.

Renal Retention of Salt and Water

One common omission from discussions of edema is a suggestion of the source of the accumulated extracellular fluid. Patients developing congestive failure and peripheral edema gain weight because the amount of body fluid increases. Similarly, a generalized systemic venous congestion implies an increased total blood volume. This additional fluid in the form of blood, edema and effusion must accumulate as a result of either greater fluid intake or incomplete excretion. Ample evidence now indicates changes in the control of blood and fluid volumes of the body which are very important in promoting this condition.

As Elkington and Squires[57] have stated: "The absolute level of cardiac output does not correlate with the degree of edema, and cannot explain it on either a 'backward' or 'forward failure' theory. An output of the heart which is inadequate in relation to metabolic demands would appear to be a primary factor leading to secondary changes in circulatory dynamics in several regions of the body. Renal retention of salt and water results from more than circulatory disturbance causing a diminished glomerular filtration; tubular transfers are involved and these are conditioned by humoral and cellular, as well as by circulatory factors. . . . In short, the homeostatic mechanisms which control body fluid volume unknown in part, may be functioning in an abnormal way in congestive failure."

Clearly the causes of the increase in blood volume and total body fluids constituting the principal signs of heart failure cannot be understood until clarification of the basic mechanisms of normal control discussed in the first section of this chapter. Comparing the complexity of water intake and output in Figure 1 with the simplicity of the proposed control mechanisms illustrated in Figure 2 provides a clue regarding the disparity between the magnitude of the problem and progress towards its solution.

SUMMARY

Left ventricular failure is characterized by symptoms resulting from pulmonary congestion induced by elevated pressures in the pulmonary vascular bed. The most prominent symptom is dyspnea, which apparently results from increased respiratory effort due to rigidity of a congested and indurated pulmonary parenchyma, perhaps supplemented by reflexes associated with distention of pulmonary veins and the left atrium. Congestion of the bronchial mucosa is associated with pulmonary congestion because the capillary networks of both systems drain by way of the pulmonary veins. Congestion and edema of the membranous lining of the airways increases the resistance to the airflow in and out of the alveoli. Secretion of mucus causes a productive cough. Extravasation of blood from the bronchial capillaries, and possibly into alveolar sacs, may produce blood-tinged sputum (hemoptysis). Vague symptoms such as fatigue, gastrointestinal disturbance and renal dysfunction may be attributed in part to restricted cardiac output.

Right ventricular failure produces generalized systemic venous congestion associated with increased central venous pressure. Peripheral edema consists of accumulation of fluid in the interstitial spaces, first appearing in dependent extremities (ankles) and later advancing up the legs and frequently involving the genitalia. Such subcutaneous fluid contains protein in concentrations less than 0.5 per cent. Effusions in the serous cavities (ascites, pleural and pericardial effusions) represent extravasation of fluid containing protein in considerable quantities (3 to 6 per cent). Generalized venous congestion, peripheral edema and effusion into serous cavities cannot occur unless the total quantity of body fluids increases. In this sense, the renal retention of salt and water must play an important role in the development of congestive failure.

In the past, two concepts have been employed to explain the origin of congestive failure. Advocates of the backward failure theory suggest that blood is dammed up behind the failing ventricle, elevating venous pressure, promoting venous congestion and producing peripheral edema through elevated capillary pressure. The same changes were originally attributed to diminished cardiac output (forward failure), anoxia of peripheral vessels, increased capillary permeability and escape of fluids into the tissues. More recently restricted cardiac output has been assigned a role in causing abnormal retention of salt and water which expands blood volume as well as promoting edema. Serious discrepancies are apparent in both theories. It would seem profitable to investigate the normal mechanisms for monitoring and controlling both the total blood volume and total body fluids. On this basis the aberrations produced by cardiac disease might be more clearly understood.

REFERENCES

1. ADOLPH, E. F. *Physiological Regulations.* Lancaster, Pennsylvania, The Jaques Cattell Press, 1943.
2. ADOLPH, E. F. Measurements of water drinking in dogs. *Amer. J. Physiol.,* 125:75–86, 1939.
3. BELLOWS, R. T. Time factors in water drinking in dogs. *Amer. J. Physiol.,* 125:87–97, 1939.
4. MAIRE, F. W. Eating and drinking responses elicited by diencephalic stimulation in unanesthetized rats. *Fed. Proc.,* 15:124, 1956.
5. RICHTER, C. P. Total self regulatory functions in animal and human beings. *Harvey Lect.,* 38:63–103, 1942.
6. BARE, J. K. The specific hunger for sodium chloride in normal and adrenalectomized white rats. *J. Comp. Physiol. Psychol.,* 42:242–253, 1949.

7. MEYER, K. The biological significance of hyaluronic acid and hyaluronidase. *Physiol. Rev.*, 27:335–359, 1947.

8. DURAN-REYNALS, F. Tissue permeability and the spreading factors in infection. A contribution to the host:parasite problem. *Bact. Rev.*, 6:197–252, 1942.

9. BENSLEY, S. H. On the presence, properties and distribution of the intercellular ground substance of loose connective tissue. *Anat. Rec.*, 60:93–109, 1934.

10. ROPES, M. W., ROBERTSON, W. V. B., ROSSMEISL, E. C., PEABODY, R. B., and BAUER, W. Synovial fluid mucin. *Acta med. scand.*, 128, Suppl. 196:700–744, 1947.

11. DAY, T. D. The nature and significance of the cementing substance in interstitial connective tissue. *J. Path. Bact.*, 59:567–573, 1947.

12. DAY, T. D. The spread of fluids in connective tissue. *J. Path. Bact.*, 60:150–151, 1948.

13. LLOYD, D. J., and PHILLIPS, H. Protein structure and protein dehydration. *Trans. Faraday Soc.*, 29:132–148, 1933.

14. ELSTER, S. K., FREEMAN, M. E., and DORFMAN, A. Effect of hyaluronidase on the passage of fluid and of T-1824 through the capillary wall. *Amer. J. Physiol.*, 156:429–432, 1949.

15. DAY, T. D. The mode of reaction of interstitial connective tissue with water. *J. Physiol.*, 109: 380–391, 1 pl., 1949.

16. VERNEY, E. B. The anti-diuretic hormone and the factors which determine its release. (Croonian Lecture.) *Proc. Roy. Soc. Lond.*, B135:25–106, 1947.

17. SMITH, H. W. Salt and water volume receptors: an exercise in physiologic apologetics. *Amer. J. Med.* 23:623–652, 1957.

18 GAUER, O. H., HENRY, J. P., SIEKER, H. O., and WENDT, W. E.: The effect of negative pressure breathing on urine flow. *J. Clin. Invest.*, 33:287–296, 1954.

19 SIEKER, H. O., GAUER, O. H., and HENRY, J. P. The effect of continuous negative pressure breathing on water and electrolyte excretion by the human kidney. *J. Clin. Invest.*, 33:572–577, 1954.

20. HENRY, J. P., GAUER, O. H., and REEVES, J. L. Evidence of the atrial location of receptors influencing urine flow. *Circulat. Res.*, 4:85–90, 1956.

21. GUYTON, A. C., and GREGANTI, F. P. A physiologic reference point for measuring circulatory pressure in the dog—particularly venous pressure. *Amer. J. Physiol.*, 185:137–141, 1956.

22. RUSHMER, R. F., BECKMAN, E. L., and LEE, D. Protection of the cerebral circulation by the cerebrospinal fluid under the influence of radial acceleration. *Amer. J. Physiol.*, 151: 355–365, 1947.

23 KJELLBERG, S. R., RUDHE, U., and SJÖSTRAND, T. The relationship between the pulmonary blood content, the heart volume and the filling rate of the left ventricle. *Acta physiol. scand.*, 24:49–60, 1951.

24. WADE, O. L., COMBES, B., CHILDS, A. W., WHEELER, H. O., COURNAND, A., and BRADLEY, S. E. The effect of exercise on the splanchnic blood flow and splanchnic blood volume in normal man. *Clin. Sci.*, 15:457–463, 1956.

25. ALEXANDER, R. S. Venomotor tone in hemorrhage and shock. *Circulat. Res.*, 3:181–190, 1955.

26. RUSHMER, R. F., BAKER, D., and VAN CITTERS, R. L. Evaluation of "venous return" initiating increased cardiac output. *Fed. Proc.*, 19:107, 1960.

27. MARSHALL, R. J., WANG, Y., SEMLER, H. J., and SHEPHEARD, J. T. Flow pressure and volume relationship in the pulmonary circulation during exercise in normal dogs and dogs with divided left pulmonary artery. (In press.)

28. GUNTHEROTH, W. G. Function of the liver and spleen as venous reservoirs. *Fed. Proc.*, 17:63, 1953.

29. WIGGERS, C. J. Dynamics of ventricular contraction under abnormal conditions. (The Henry Jackson Memorial Lecture.) *Circulation*, 5:321–348, 1952.

30. HICKAM, J. B., CARGILL, W. H., and GOLDEN, A. Cardiovascular reactions to emotional stimuli. Effect on the cardiac output, arteriovenous oxygen difference, arterial pressure, and peripheral resistance. *J. Clin. Invest.*, 27:290–298, 1948.

31. BRIGGS, A. P., FOWELL, D. M., HAMILTON, W. F., REMINGTON, J. W., WHEELER, N. C., and WINSLOW, J. A. Renal and circulatory factors in the edema formation of congestive heart failure. *J. Clin. Invest.*, 27:810–817, 1948.

32. CASE, R. B., BERGLUND, E., and SARNOFF, S. J. Ventricular function. II. Quantitative relationship between coronary flow and ventricular function with observations on unilateral failure. *Circulat. Res.*, 2:319–325, 1954.

33. COURNAND, A. Some aspects of the pulmonary circulation in normal man and in chronic cardiopulmonary diseases. (The Fourth Walter Wile Hamburger Memorial Lecture, Institute of Medicine of Chicago.) *Circulation*, 2:641–657, 1950.

34. CAMERON, G. R. Pulmonary œdema. *Brit. Med. J.*, 1:965–972, 1948.

35. SHUMAN, C. R., LEARNER, N., and DOANE, J. H., JR. The effect of ganglion blocking agents in congestive heart failure. *Amer. Heart J.*, 47:737–744, 1954.

36. FEJFAR, S., and BROD, J. The mechanism of general haemodynamic changes in heart failure. *Acta med. scand.*, 148:247–272, 1954.

37. BURCH, G. E. Evidence for increased venous tone in chronic congestive heart failure. *Arch. Int. Med.*, 98:750–766, 1956.

38. CAMPBELL, G. S., and VISSCHER, M. B

Pulmonary lesions in guinea pigs with increased intracranial pressure and the effect of bilateral cervical vagotomy. *Amer. J. Physiol.*, 157:130–134, 1949.

39. CAMERON, G. R., and DE, S. N. Experimental pulmonary œdema of nervous origin. *J. Path. Bact.*, 61:375–387, pl. 86, 1949.

40. JARISCH, A., RICHTER, H., and THOMA, H. Zentrogenes Lungenödem. *Klin. Wchnschr.*, 18:1440–1443, 1939.

41. GAMBLE, J. E., and PATTON, H. D. Pulmonary edema and hemorrhage from preoptic lesions in rats. *Amer. J. Physiol.*, 172:623–631, 1953.

42. PAINE, R., SMITH, J. R., BUTCHER, H. R., and HOWARD, F. A. Heart failure and pulmonary edema produced by certain neurologic stimuli. *Circulation*, 5:759–765, 1952.

43. PAINE, R., BUTCHER, H. R., HOWARD, F. A., and SMITH, J. R. Observations on mechanisms of edema formation in the lungs. *J. Lab. Clin. Med.*, 34:1544–1553, 1949.

44. VITALE, A., DUMKE, P. R., and COMROE, J. R., JR. Lack of correlation between rales and arterial oxygen saturation in patients with pulmonary congestion and edema. *Circulation*, 10:81–83, 1954.

45 HARRISON, T. R., CALHOUN, J. A., CULLEN, G E., WILKINS, W. E., and PILCHER, C. Studies in congestive heart failure. XV. Reflex versus chemical factors in the production of rapid breathing. *J. Clin. Invest.*, 11:133–154, 1932.

46. HARRISON, W. G., JR., CALHOUN, J. A., MARSH, J. P., and HARRISON, T. R. Congestive heart failure. XIX. Reflex stimulation of respiration as the cause of evening dyspnea. *Arch. Intern. Med.*, 53:724–740, 1934.

47. DRINKER, C. K., PEABODY, F. W., and BLUMGART, H. L. The effect of pulmonary congestion on the ventilation of the lungs. *J. Exp. Med.*, 35:77–95, 1922.

48. RICHARDS, D. W. The nature of cardiac and of pulmonary dyspnea. (The Lewis A. Conner Memorial Lecture.) *Circulation*, 7:15–29 1953.

49. BURCH, G. E. *A Primer of Venous Pressure.* Philadelphia, Lea & Febiger, 1950.

50. HYATT, R. E., and SMITH, J. R. The mechanism of ascites. A physiologic appraisal. *Amer. J. Med.*, 16:434–448, 1954.

51. BEDFORD, D. E., and LOVIBOND, J. L. Hydrothorax in heart failure. *Brit. Heart J.*, 3:93–111, 1941.

52. BURCH, G. E., and RAY, C. T. A consideration of the mechanism of congestive heart failure. *Amer. Heart J.*, 41:918–946, 1951.

53. RAY, C. T., and BURCH, G. E. Vascular responses in man to ligation of the inferior vena cava. *Arch. Intern. Med.*, 80:587–601, 1947.

54. STARR, I., JEFFERS, W. A., and MEADE, R. H., JR. The absence of conspicuous increments of venous pressure after severe damage to the right ventricle of the dog, with a discussion lof the relation between clinical congestive failure and heart disease. *Amer. Heart J.*, 26:291–301, 1943.

55. BAKOS, A. C. P. The question of the function of the right ventricuar myocardium: an experimental study. *Circulation*, 1:724–732, 1950.

56. ZAUS, E. A., and KEARNS, W. M., JR. Massive infarction of the right ventricle and atrium. Report of a case. *Circulation*, 6:593–598, 1952.

57. ELKINTON, J. R., and SQUIRES, R. D. The distribution of body fluids in congestive heart failure. I. Theoretic considerations. *Circulation*, 4:679–696, 1951.

Index